# Teacher's Guide
# CONCEPTS AND CHALLENGES IN
# Earth Science
## SECOND EDITION

LEONARD BERNSTEIN

MARTIN SCHACHTER

ALAN WINKLER

STANLEY WOLFE

**STANLEY WOLFE**
*Project Coordinator*

**Globe Book Company, Inc.**
A CEBCO BOOK
New York/Cleveland/Toronto

# INTRODUCTION

This teacher's guide has been designed to help you use *Concepts and Challenges in Earth Science* with your classes. This text is part of the *Concepts and Challenges in Science (CCS) Series*. The goal of the CCS Series is to provide students with an east-to-read, hightly motivating textbook containing science material suited to their grade, but with a reading level 3 to 4 grades lower.

Each module of a CCS text is complete on two facing pages. The concepts are presented on the left-hand page; the challenges, on the facing page. While studying, pupils need not move from page to page, but may concentrate on the complete concept before them.

We suggest that you use one module of CCS for each classroom period. For classes that meet four or five times per week, this allows one or two periods per week for laboratory work. Sufficient material is provided for a full year of science work.

The title of each module is phrased so that it may be used as the aim of a day's lesson. The demonstrations or other illustrative activities in the lesson may be done by the teacher or may be assigned to pupils to perform. Additional or alternate activites are suggested in this guide.

Following each paragraph or short text section in each module there is a reading comprehension question. These questions may be answered in class after the reading of the paragraph and the teaching of the concept. Alternatively, they may be assigned as homework to serve as reinforcement of the day's learnings.

It is important to point out to the students that the answer to the reading comprehension is explicitly stated in the passage. If at first the student is unable to answer the question, he should be able to find the answer by reading the passage again. The gratification of successfully answering these comprehension questions not only reinforces learning, but also acts as motivation to read each text section carefully, and to reread it when necessary until it is understood.

Further reinforcement of the concepts of each module is provided by the following elements:

*What You Learned* — A clearly stated summary.

*Science Words* — A review of the new vocabulary of the module.

*Answer These* — Designed as homework questions.

The second page of the module usually contains one or more of the following additional features:

*Now Try This* — Follow-up questions of a more challenging nature than those in "Answer These," and in a different format. Puzzles are frequently included under this heading.

*Finding Out More* or *What's Happening* — An enrichment section offering additional information related to the module.

*Do This at Home* — Pupil activities that may be carried out with readily available materials. They may be offered as optional work to be done at home and reported on, or they may be performed in school as part of the lesson.

*People in Science* — Short biographies of scientists whose work is related to the content of the module.

Students should be made aware of the cumulative glossary beginning on page 359, which lists all "Science Words" alphabetically, gives brief defintions, and provides a cross-reference to the module in which the term is explained. Discuss with the class how the glossary can be used to recall the meaning of a word when it is encountered in a later module, refering to the example in the paragraph on page 359.

Students should also be encouraged to use the index, which has been carefully constructed to fit the needs of young people with limited reading ability and little familiarity with the structure and function of index entries. Experience with the index in this book can help develop an important learning skill.

As you begin to use CCS with your classes, we hope that you will find, as many have already, that for the first time your pupils are able to *read* and *understand* science material. We believe that as pupils succeed with materials appropriate to their grade level, their intrinsic motivation will increase and that further success will follow.

We will welcome your comments and suggestions concerning the text or the teacher's guide.

*The Authors*

ISBN 0-87065-463-2

Printed in the United States of America

9 8 7 6 5 4 3

# METRIC SYSTEM

## 1. Why do we measure?

During the current period of transition to the use of metric units in the United States, students will vary in their experience with the metric system and their facility in using it. But even if a class has had considerable exposure to metric units, it will be worthwhile to use these two modules to review the basic ideas of the system. The desired outcomes of these lessons are an understanding of the need for units of measurement, the names of the fundamental units, and the scheme of prefixes to obtain units of more convenient size for large and small measurements. The students should be encouraged to "think metric" by acquiring a mental image of the size of quantities expressed in metric units, without recourse to conversion to English units.

A good way to begin this lesson is to distribute standard masses marked in grams. Have the students handle these masses to acquire a "feel" for the weight associated with each. Then challenge them to estimate the masses of common objects by hefting them. Point out that the weight of an object is a force — the force of gravity acting on it, while the mass of an object is the amount of matter in it. The mass of an object is always the same, but its weight can change if it is taken to a place where gravity is weaker (for example, to the moon). Emphasize that the gram is a unit of mass. However, since the weight of an object depends on its mass, we often measure weights in grams, too. Scientists use a separate unit, called the newton, for measuring weight and other forces. The newton is introduced in Unit 10, Module 8.

To introduce the use of prefixes with metric units, ask the students to estimate their masses (or weights) in grams. Then have them refer to the table of prefixes to choose one (kilo-) that can be combined with "gram" to make the numbers smaller and thus easier to deal with. Point out that larger units are used to make the numbers smaller, and smaller units to make the numbers larger.

Show the need for a unit smaller than a gram. On a sensitive balance, weigh any lightweight object, such as a small scrap of paper, a feather, a piece of pencil lead, etc. Pupils will see that by using the milligram, they can avoid using fractions of a unit or decimals less than one. At this point, you may wish to discuss the selection of the proper size unit for the object being measured. The second should now be introduced as the universal unit of time. Other units such as the minute, hour, day, etc. should be defined. It is important to note that the only units common to the metric and English systems are the second and its multiples.

*Answer These*
1. microgram, milligram, centigram, gram, hectogram, kilogram
2. microsecond . . . one one-millionth of a second
   millisecond . . . one one-thousandth of a second
   megaton . . . one million tons

*Now Try These*
1. Seconds in a century:
   60 sec/min × 60 min/hour × 24 hours/day × 365¼ days/year × 100 years/century = 3,155,760,000 seconds/century
   or 3,155.76 megaseconds/century
2. 500 megabucks = 500 million dollars

*Finding Out More*
If the standard mass were to be scratched, some of the metal alloy might be removed. This would cause the mass of the standard to be decreased.

## 2. How do we measure size?

The use of models will help make the concepts of area and volume more concrete and easy to understand. These models are usually available in the mathematics department.

First, establish the centimeter and the meter as units of length. Have pupils estimate the length of common objects in metric units and check their results using rulers. Among the measurements made should be the pupils' heights. Next, introduce the square centimeter and the square meter as units of area. Construct a model of a square meter, using meter sticks. Then, have pupils use matchsticks and glue to construct models of square centimeters. Another good activity is measuring the area of the hand, using graph paper with 1-cm squares. If such paper is not available, it can easily be prepared and run off on a spirit duplicating machine. Have pupils trace the outline of their hand on the squared paper. By counting the whole squares and those squares with more than half their area inside the outline of the hand, a good estimate of the area of the hand can be made. Those squares with less than half their area inside the outline should be ignored.

Teach volume by having each pupil make his or her own cubic decimeter. Refer to the drawing on page 5 as a model. Using the 1-cm graph paper, have pupils cut, fold, and paste to make a cubic decimeter.

Display a one-liter flask and explain that its volume is the same as 1000 cubic centimeters. Refer to the prefixes and point out that 1/1000 of a liter is a milliliter, and that this is the same as one cubic centimeter. Tape 12 meter sticks together to produce a cube with a volume of one cubic meter. The model will need some support. Taping it in the corner of an open box or in the corner of the room will provide the needed support. Collect all the cubic decimeter models made by the class. Place them together to show larger volumes. Arrange the cubes in different configurations to make the point that shape and volume are not related. Show pupils how to calculate the volume of rectangular solids.

*Answer These*
1. a
2. c
3. c

## 3. How do we determine density?

This lesson could be conducted as a laboratory exercise. It will give the pupils experience in making metric measurements and using scientific equipment such as a balance.

Motivate the lesson by displaying various rectangular blocks of wood of similar volumes. Maple, oak, basswood, pine and balsa are available at various hobby shops and lumber yards. Have the pupils try to determine which woods are the heaviest by hefting. Define density and determine the density of some of the samples.

Demonstrate the relationship of size to density by comparing a smaller rectangular block of lead to a larger block of wood of the same mass.

Review how metric measurements are made and how volume is calculated. Review the operation of the triple beam balance. Stress the importance of accurate measurements with the metric ruler and the balance. Allow the pupils to determine the density of several rectangular objects. (Density kits can be obtained from scientific supply houses.) Have the pupils compare their results to the chart on page 7 and identify what materials their blocks are made of.

## MEASURING: REVIEW

**Matching**
Group A
  1. 1000 milligrams = 1 g
  2. 1,000 grams = 10 kg
  3. 0.1 gram = 100 mg
  4. 0.1 kilogram = 100 g
  5. .01 gram = 10 mg

Group B
  6. 10 centimeters = 100 mm
  7. 1000 centimeters = 10 m
  8. 1000 millimeters = 100 cm
  9. 0.1 kilometer = 100 m
10. 1000 meters = 1 km

**Multiple Choice**
1. a   2. b   3. b   4. a   5. c

# UNIT 1. STUDYING THE EARTH

## 1. How does a scientist study the earth?

This lesson introduces the pupil to the techniques of science. Develop the idea that the study of earth sciences, as well as all sciences, utilizes the scientific method in reaching conclusions. Stress the fact that interpretations are based upon observations and experimentation. Guide the class to see that this method leads to the construction of hypotheses, followed by further experimentation and observations before drawing of conclusions.

Direct the pupils' attention to the photograph of the surface of Mars. Ask them to speculate on the nature of the Martian landscape. Have pupils describe the surface and atmospheric conditions. Next, have them compare the Martian environment to the environments at different locations on earth. Point out that they are using their sense of sight to make observations about conditions on the planet Mars.

Prior to the lesson place a small object, such as a wooden block, spool, or ball into a cardboard shoe box. Challenge pupils to describe what is in the box without opening it up. Have them suggest ways of making observations. Allow some pupils to shake the box and others to reach inside the box and touch the object without looking at it. Elicit from the pupils the fact that they are using their senses of touch and hearing to make their observations. Establish with the class the idea that senses allow us to make observations.

Ask a pupil to describe an object in the room. Then have members of the class try to name the object. Point out the difference between describing an object and naming it.

Have the following drawing on the board before the class arrives:

Make the lefthand line 30 cm long and the righthand line 32 cm. Ask for opinions as to which line is longer. There is likely to be considerable doubt and disagreement. Some pupils may say they know about that trick — that both are the same. Let the students measure the lines with a meter stick. Elicit that the senses are undependable for making accurate measurements, and that is why we use measuring instruments. Use a thermometer and balance to illustrate how other instruments are used to make accurate measurements.

Demonstrate how the stethoscope and microscope aid the senses. Have the pupils tell which sense is aided by each instrument.

Guide the pupils to see that a hypothesis is an educated guess. Compare the job of a scientist to that of a detective and lead pupils to see how each follows a similar procedure. They each make observations, propose a hypothesis, and gather evidence before coming to a conclusion.

Module 1 may be divided into two lessons. The first, showing that observations are made by the senses, can be developed as a laboratory exercise. Set boxes at various locations around the room. Each box should be designed for study and observation, using only one of the five senses.

Relate the experiments of Pasteur, Redi, Koch, and Salk to illustrate how a hypothesis is tested before a conclusion is reached. Discuss how the scientific method is used to check different consumer products.

*Answer These*
1. a
2. b
3. c
4. b
5. a

*Now Try These*
1. sight, hearing, taste, smell, touch
2.

|  | **Rock** | **River** |
|---|---|---|
| **sight** | size, shape, color presence of minerals | size, color of water, speed of flow |
| **hearing** | solidity (use hammer) | current flow |
| **taste** | salty, earthy, metallic | fresh, salty, brackish |
| **smell** | earthy, organic | fresh, marshy |
| **touch** | texture, shape | temperature, wetness |

3. Answers will vary. Some possible instruments include: telescope, microscope, binoculars, magnifying glass, eyeglasses.

## 2. What are the parts of the earth?

The earth includes everything from the outermost layers of the atmosphere to the center of the earth. Use a globe, a basketball, and other spheres to illustrate the earth's shape. Discuss events that showed that the earth is curved (Magellan's circumnavigation, altitude of the North Star, a ship appearing or disappearing on the horizon, earth's shadow in eclipse of the moon).

Note that the hydrosphere includes all surface and subsurface water.

Use a map to show that the continents are part of the lithosphere. Point out that the ocean floor is also part of the lithosphere, but is covered by the hydrosphere. Develop the concept that the hydrosphere, lithosphere, and atmosphere together make up the earth.

Refer to the photograph on page 12 to identify the parts of the earth. The center of this photograph is just east of the southern tip of Africa. The Arabian peninsula can be seen at the top and Antarctica at the bottom. Ask whether the atmosphere can be seen in this picture. (Yes; the clouds are part of the atmosphere.)

*Answer These*
1. Atmosphere, hydrosphere, lithosphere.
2. About ¾ of the surface.
3. Lithosphere.

## 3. What is the inside of the earth like?

To illustrate the layers of the earth, prepare a small ball of clay of one color. Wrap a second color of clay around the small ball to form another layer. Make another layer with a third color. Cut this ball in half and describe the different zones. An overhead projector with overlays of different colors can also be used.

Measure the thickness of an eggshell and the diameter of an egg to determine how good a comparison this is with the relative thickness of the earth's crust. A satisfactory way to measure the shell thickness is to hold a shell fragment edgewise, with tweezers, against a millimeter scale and observe it with a 10X magnifier. Typical results are: shell thickness, 0.3 mm; egg radius (½ diameter), 16 mm. The eggshell is relatively about twice as thick as the earth's crust at its thickest (40 miles).

Assign reports on Project Mohole. Show a film or filmstrip on Project Mohole.

*Answer These*
1. Inner and outer core.
2. Crust.
3. Mantle.
4. a
5. b
6. two (mantle and crust)

*Now Try This*
1. crust
2. mantle
3. core

## 4. What is a globe?

Display a globe and review the fact that the earth is a sphere. Direct pupils' attention to the photograph of the earth taken from a distance of 35,000 km out in space. Show the class a photograph and a scale model of a plane, car or train. Elicit the idea that a model or photograph represents some real object. Develop the concept that models enable us to study and learn more about objects that are too large (the earth) or too small (atoms) to be observed directly. Point out that when an object cannot be observed directly, a photograph or model of the object is the next best thing.

Using the globe, develop the concept that such a model shows a true picture of the earth's actual shape. Guide the pupils to see how directions are shown correctly on the globe. Using the scale model (plane, train, or car), develop and discuss the meaning of scale. Next, discuss the scale of the globe and guide pupils to see how distances on the globe's surface are related to distances on the earth's surface.

Have the pupils suggest some of the shortcomings of the globe in studying the earth. They should note how little detail can be shown on the globe. Point out the inconvenience of carrying a globe back and forth to class, or trying to get a globe in the glove compartment of the family car.

Display a wall map of the world and point out that it, too, is a model of the earth. Guide the pupils to see how the map eliminates some of the globe's shortcomings.

Display a hollow sphere, such as a rubber ball, ping pong ball, or papier-mache sphere. Challenge members of the class to transform the sphere into a flat surface without tearing it or stretching it out of shape.

Guide pupils to see that a map drawn on a globe cannot be transferred onto a flat surface without having some distortion of the surface. One way to do this is to distribute navel oranges to groups of students. Have each group draw "continents and oceans" on the surface of its orange with a felt-tip pen. Then ask the pupils to peel their oranges carefully and to arrange the peels on a flat surface. Have pupils discuss how the flattening process changes their "continents and oceans."

Refer to the Finding Out More section and ask pupils to bring various types of maps to class. Make a bulletin board display of these maps. Have members of the class draw several different kinds of maps.

*Answer These*
1. b
2. c
3. b
4. b

*Now Try These*
1. model
2. globe

## 5. What is a map projection?

The object of this lesson is to help the pupils to understand how a globe can be projected onto a flat surface. They should not be expected to learn all the projections and their uses.

From the previous lesson review the fact that a globe cannot be flattened without distorting it in some way. Following the directions in this lesson, demonstrate how a projection is formed. A slide projector can be used as the light source. Move the plastic hemisphere back and forth until a sharp image forms on the screen. Have a pupil trace the image on a piece of paper.

Demonstrate how cylindrical and conic projections are made. Map projection models can be purchased from any of several scientific supply companies.

Display a Mercator (cylindrical) projection together with a globe and guide pupils to see how this projection is distorted at the higher latitudes. Show the relative sizes of different land masses on the globe to their counterparts on the Mercator projection. Display other projections and guide the pupils to see how each is useful for certain purposes and how each is distorted.

*Answer These*
1. c
2. a
3. a

*Now Try This*
DOWN
1. hemisphere
3. screen
4. globe
5. rips

ACROSS
2. map
6. projection

## 6. How do we find places on maps?

Display a large map of the world. Point out the lines of latitude and longitude on the map. Demonstrate how latitude and longitude help locate positions on the map. Give the pupils some practice finding locations and directions on the map.

Use a large globe to illustrate that the altitude of Polaris is equal to the latitude of an observer in the Northern Hemisphere. Place a protractor at the North Pole of the globe. Guide the class to see that Polaris is directly overhead, at an angle of 90°. Next, place the protractor on the Equator, showing that Polaris is at an angle of 0° above the horizon. Place the protractor at some point between the Equator and the North Pole. Show that the latitude of that point is equal to the altitude of the North Star. A transparency of a globe and a clear plastic protractor can also be used to demonstrate this principle.

Have the pupils construct a device for determining the angle of an object above the horizon. Use a straw, protractor, string and paper clip, as shown in the figure below. Secure the straw and string to the protractor, and demonstrate how to read the angle.

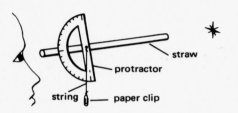

Allow the pupils to go outdoors to determine the angle between the horizon and the tops of tall buildings or trees. If you must work inside, see if you can meet in the gym or auditorium. Have the pupils gather at the rear of the room and observe objects near the ceiling at the front of the room.

*Answer These*
1. b  2. a  3. c  4. c  5. c

*Now Try This*
A. 60°N latitude, 120°W longitude
B. 0° latitude, 60°W longitude
C. 30°S latitude, 30°E longitude
D. 60°N latitude, 60°E longitude
E. 30°N latitude, 90°E longitude
F. 30°S latitude, 120°E longitude

## 7. How do you read a map?

The first part of this lesson can be conducted as a laboratory exercise in which the pupils help construct a compass face on the classroom floor. Have the following materials on hand when the class convenes: directional compass, string, file cards (8), masking tape, magic marker, and a class quantity of maps. The maps, which could be teacher-constructed, should show: the direction of north, the scale of the map, and several locations clearly labeled (A, B, C, etc.).

When pupils come in, have them arrange their desks so that the center of the room is clear. Show pupils which direction is north. Elicit from the class that the direction opposite from north is south. Using a length of string and tape, construct a north-south line on the classroom floor. Tape blank file cards at each end of the string and have a pupil mark one card with an N and the other with an S.

At this time you may wish to point out the fact that noontime shadows can be used to establish a fairly accurate north-south line. Everywhere in the United States, the noontime sun is to the south. Thus, at solar noon, shadows point to the north. If you stand with your back directly toward the sun, your shadow represents a north-south line, and you will be facing north.

Next have pupils explain how to determine east and west once the N-S line has been established. Construct an east-west line on the floor and have a pupil label the ends accordingly. Tape a blank card on the floor at a position halfway between north and east. Elicit that this direction is northeast. Have a pupil mark NE on the card. Then elicit the fact that the direction opposite from northeast is southwest. Construct a NE-SW line and have a pupil label the SW end. Repeat these steps to construct and label a NW-SE line. If practical, leave this "compass face" in place for the remainder of the period.

Once pupils have returned to their desks, display a large wall map and have pupils identify directions on the map. Point out two locations on the map and have pupils determine the direction from one location to the other. Repeat this exercise using several different locations.

One common mistake pupils often make in early dealings with map work is to think of the top of the map (usually North) as being "up" and the bottom as being "down." Toss an object in the air and elicit the definition of the word "up" as being *away* from the earth's center and "down" as being *toward* the earth's center. Stress the fact that these words have no directional connotation. Establish the fact that all rivers flow downward, from greater to lesser elevations. Point out on the map that rivers flow in all *directions*—north, south, etc.

Next call attention to the scale of the wall map. Review the concept of scale models from Module 4. Elicit the fact that the map is a scale model of that part of the earth's surface. Using a ruler or a strip of paper, demonstrate how the scale is used to determine distances on the map and how this information can be used to determine actual distances on the earth's surface.

Distribute maps to the pupils and ask them to complete the compass face, which has only N marked on it. Dictate two locations on the map and ask pupils to use the map scale to find the distance between the two locations. Also ask them to determine the direction from one location to the other. You may wish to prepare an assignment sheet for them to complete at home.

Have pupils study the table of map symbols found on page 23 of their texts. The symbols shown here should be sufficient for the pupils at this level. However, a more comprehensive table of topographic map symbols can be obtained free from the U.S. Geological Survey Distribution Section, 1200 South Eads Street, Arlington, Virginia 22202.

Once pupils have become familiar with the symbols, assign an exercise in which they are required to identify symbols on a prepared map, such as the one in the text, or on a topographic map showing many of the symbols.

*Answer These*
1. c
2. b
3. a
4. c

*Now Try These*
1. southeast
2. 4 kilometers
3. northwestern
4. 22 (students may overlook the building near the railroad tracks)

## 8. What are contour lines?

This lesson can be conducted as a laboratory exercise.

Display some aerial photographs showing various land features, such as towns, rivers, mountains, valleys, volcanic cones, deltas, etc. Index maps, bibliographies, and monographs on the use and interpretations of aerial photographs are available from the U.S. Geological Survey. Many scientific supply houses can also supply aerial stereophoto kits. Photographs are also available from the National Aeronautics and Space Administration, Washington, D.C. 20546.

Conduct a class discussion about the type and quality of information that can be gained by studying aerial photographs. Most of these photographs are accompanied by information about direction (north is usually at the top) and surface area encompassed by the photograph. Therefore, distances and directions can be determined fairly accurately. In addition, pupils should be able to get some idea of the nature of the land surface and features from studying the photographs. Stereo photographs provide some additional "feel" for the relief of the surface. Pupils should agree, however, that elevation cannot be determined from the photographs.

Divide the class into several groups. Have each group construct a contour "map" using a contour model kit. These kits can be purchased from any of several scientific supply houses. If you prefer, a contour model kit can be made from a clear plastic box, a deep bowl (or model of a mountain), a crayon, and a heavy piece of clear plastic. Instruct pupils to follow the directions outlined on pages 24 and 25 of the text. Have plenty of paper towels available as there is usually some spillage during this exercise. (This activity appears as Lab Challenge 4 in the Laboratory Program for this text.)

Allow the pupils a few minutes to study the plastic contour maps they have constructed. Elicit the fact that the contour lines join points of equal height above the level of the water. Establish that the contour interval (height between successive contour lines) is one centimeter.

*Answer These*
1. c
2. a
3. b

## 9. What is a topographic map?

Review the exercise from Module 8 in which a contour map of a bowl was constructed. Remind pupils that the lines drawn to show elevation are called contour lines. Elicit the fact that a contour line connects all points that have the same elevation.

Define topography as being the physical features of the earth's surface. Ask pupils what is meant by "physical features." Responses should include mountains, valleys, lakes, rivers, beaches, glaciers, etc. Remind pupils that land maps, even aerial photographs, do not provide much, if any, information about the elevation of the surface.

Have pupils read the definition of a topographic map as given on page 26 of the text. Inform them that topographic maps are also called contour maps. Have pupils study the topographic maps at the top and bottom of page 26. Point out how the spacing between consecutive contour lines shows the relative steepness of slope. Also point out the use of scale, direction, and symbols on the maps. Elicit that the map at the bottom of the page shows two buildings (probably dwellings) and a church near the shore.

If possible, U.S. Geological Survey topographic maps should be available for the pupils to study. Preferably, maps showing your community should be available. Information pertaining to the purchase of maps can be obtained from U.S. Geological Survey

Distribution Section, 1200 South Eads St., Arlington, VA 22202. Information concerning aerial photographs can be obtained from the National Cartographic Information Center, 507 National Center, Reston, VA 22092.

Discuss the use of color to indicate elevation. Most geopolitical maps will use some degree of color. If available, display and discuss a wall map which uses color to show physical relief.

*Answer These*
1. c
2. b
3. c
4. a

*Now Try These*
1. Elevations in the western half of North America are generally greater than in the eastern half.
2. On topographic maps of mountainous regions, large contour intervals are used so that the contour lines will not fall on top of one another.

## UNIT 1: REVIEW

**Matching**
1. model
2. sphere
3. elevation
4. mantle
5. atmosphere
6. map projection
7. parallel
8. hemisphere
9. distorted
10. core

**Multiple Choice**
1. b    2. c    3. a    4. c
5. c    6. a    7. b    8. c

## UNIT 2. MINERALS OF THE EARTH

### 1. What are elements?

Display samples of elements such as iron, copper, carbon sulfur, zinc, lead, and mercury. Also display tubes filled with such gases as argon, oxygen and nitrogen. Elicit from the pupils that, at room temperature, some elements are solids, some are liquids, and some are gases. Note that the number of observed elements increases from time to time as atoms of higher numbers are synthesized in high energy machines.

The illustration for the electrolysis of water on page 30 is intended to be schematic. A demonstration is best performed with a Hoffman apparatus or its equivalent. Pure water will not conduct enough current to produce noticeable results. A solution of sulfuric acid is usually used to provide ions for conduction. The solution can be prepared by adding concentrated sulfuric acid (36N) to water in the proportion of 1 part acid to 15 parts water. ALWAYS ADD THE ACID TO THE WATER. DO NOT ADD WATER TO CONCENTRATED ACID. A 6-volt or 12-volt storage battery should be used as a source of energy.

Point out to the class that an electric current is breaking down water into its constituent gases, hydrogen and oxygen. *Note*: Start the decomposition early in the period. It will take between 5 and 10 minutes to collect about 25 ml of hydrogen and half that much oxygen.

To demonstrate the chemical tests by which hydrogen and oxygen are identified, hold the test tube of hydrogen mouth downward and bring a lighted splint to the mouth. A slight explosion or pop will be observed. Test the second tube by inserting a glowing splint (one that has been ignited and then blown out). The reignition of the splint indicates the presence of oxygen.

The decomposition of water can be a lesson by itself. Remember that the purpose of this demonstration is to illustrate that some substances, like water, are made up of more than one element.

*Answer These*
1. b
2. b
3. a
4. a
5. b

## 2. What are chemical symbols?

Briefly review the meanings of the term element. Elicit the fact that an element is the simplest kind of substance.

Two reasons given in the text (page 32) for using chemical symbols are savings in time and space. Add to this the fact that the "language" of chemistry, when written in symbols (and formulas), is a universal one. That is, the same chemical symbols are used and understood all over the world. Thus, while the word for a given element, such as gold, is different in different languages, the *symbol* for that element (Au for gold) is the same everywhere. This makes it possible for scientists to communicate in this special "language."

Have the pupils study the lists of elements and symbols found in this lesson. One exercise you may wish to use to help pupils learn some of the symbols is the use of flash cards. Use file cards on which the name of an element is written on one side and its symbol on the other. Hold up the card with the element name facing the class and have someone give the symbol for that element. Later, you may vary this by showing the symbol and asking pupils to give the name of the element.

An exercise pupils often find interesting is to find the derivations of the symbols of elements. Some are derived from the Latin or Greek word for the element, some from the names of famous scientists, and some from the places where they were discovered.

*Answer These*
1. c
2. b
3. a. W    metal wire in light bulbs
   b. H    flammable, explosive gas
   c. Br   used in photography, medicine and insecticides
   d. Al   light metal used in airplanes
   e. Ne   gas that lights up red
   f. U    metal used in nuclear reactions
   g. Ca   metal found in bones and teeth
   h. Cu   metal used in electric wire
   i. Pb   metal used in automobile batteries
   j. Ag   used in tableware

ACROSS
1. aluminum
5. tin
8. oxygen
9. sodium

DOWN
2. lead
3. mercury
4. nitrogen
6. neon
7. gold

## 3. What is a compound?

Display some paper clips, nails, pins, tacks and a magnet. Elicit that these items are made of iron. Challenge pupils to suggest a method of identifying them as iron. Have the pupils suggest and identify other materials around the room that are also iron.

Show the class sulfur. Elicit that sulfur is yellow, and can be ground to a fine powder. Sulfur burns emitting an irritating poisonous gas. DO NOT BURN SULFUR! ITS FUMES ARE POISONOUS!

Display a piece of pyrite. Tell the class that it is composed of iron and sulfur. Try to attract the pyrite to a magnet and then try to burn it. Point out that the iron is combined with the sulfur to form iron sulfide. It is no longer magnetic. The sulfur is combined with the iron and it will not burn. The properties of the compound can differ from the properties of the elements that make it up.

Have the pupils recall that the elements oxygen and hydrogen come from water. Guide them to see that water must be a compound.

Ask the class for the chemical name of table salt. Display some sodium and demonstrate how it can be cut with a knife. *CAUTION!!* KEEP SODIUM AWAY FROM WATER. Show them the clean shiny metal. Tell the pupils that chlorine is used in some bleaches. Point out that each of these elements is extremely dangerous, but when combined in the compound sodium chloride, they take on new properties.

*Answer These*
1. a
2. c
3. c
4. b
5. b
6. b
7. c

*Now Try This*

| Element | Compound |
|---|---|
| 1. aluminum | 2. water |
| 4. carbon | 3. salt |
| 5. oxygen | 6. sugar |
| 7. hydrogen | 10. pyrite |
| 8. chlorine | |
| 9. mercury | |
| 11. bromine | |
| 12. gold | |

## 4. What are chemical formulas?

Once pupils understand that compounds are combinations of elements, they should have no trouble grasping the idea that chemical formulas for compounds consist partially of the symbols of the elements in that compound. Spend some time making sure the pupils understand what the subscripts are used for. If you conducted the decomposition of water demonstration for Module 1, remind pupils that twice as much hydrogen gas was produced as oxygen gas. Thus the reason for the subscript 2 in the formula $H_2O$. However, this relationship holds only for gaseous elements. A chemical formula does not generally refer to "amounts" of the elements either by volume or by weight. It tells only the number of atoms in a molecule of that compound.

*Answer These*
1. c
2. b
3. a

*Now Try This*
Names of Elements
1. carbon and oxygen
2. calcium, carbon, oxygen
3. mercury, sulfur
4. magnesium, chlorine
5. aluminum, sulfur

Relative Number of Atoms
1 carbon, 2 oxygen
1 calcium, 1 carbon, 3 oxygen
1 mercury, 1 sulfur
1 magnesium, 2 chlorine
2 aluminum, 3 sulfur

## 5. What materials make up the crust of the earth?

Have pupils examine samples of rocky soil and describe what they see. Have the pupils note that the small pieces of rock are not all alike. Then display large samples of quartz, mica, and feldspar (these specimens are available from many scientific supply houses). Hand out smaller specimens of the same minerals and add the rock granite. Have the pupils use a hand lens to find the minerals in the rock granite. Point out that a mineral is a non-living substance found in nature and having definite chemical and physical characteristics.

Review elements, compounds, and chemical symbols from Modules 1 through 4 of this unit.

*Answer These*
1. "Minerals" is a satisfactory response. Some students may name the eight elements in the bar graph.
2. Gold, silver, copper.
3. Quartz, calcite, halite, galena, pyrite.

*Now Try This*
DOWN
1. eight
3. oxygen

ACROSS
2. geologist
4. elements

## 6. How can you identify a mineral?

Allow a student to describe some object in the classroom without naming it. Have the rest of the pupils try to identify the object. Illustrate the meaning of physical properties by listing the terms used in describing the object.

Show specimens of galena, pyrite, smoky quartz, rose quartz, milky quartz, and crystalline quartz for their property of color.

For luster, show specimens of the following:

| Mineral | Luster |
|---|---|
| pyrite | metallic |
| galena | metallic |
| calcite | dull, pearly, glassy |
| feldspar | pearly |

Allow the class to do the scratch hardness test using a glass plate, steel nail, and specimens. Mention the Mohs scale of hardness. Explain how it is used as an index.

*Answer These*
1. c
2. b
3. a

*Now Try This*
1. Diamond.
2. Quartz.
3. Calcite.
4. Quartz.

## 7. What else can help you identify minerals?

Show the class a piece of plaster board. Tell them it is made from the mineral gypsum. Demonstrate that gypsum also leaves a white streak. Allow pupils to do streak tests with a piece of bathroom tile and specimens of hematite, mica, pyrite, calcite, and gypsum.

Demonstrate density by using equal-sized specimens of galena and bauxite. Point out that galena contains lead and bauxite contains aluminum.

*Answer These*
1. Rub a mineral on a piece of bathroom tile. Look for the powder left by the mineral.
2. A mineral may have different colors, but its streak will always be the same color.
3. Minerals differ in densities, but the same mineral always has the same density.

*Now Try These*
Streak
Density

## 8. How does a mineral split or break?

If an old iron is not available, some toasters have sheets of mica. To show cleavage planes, use large samples of mica (1 plane), feldspar (2 planes), and galena (3 planes). Good cleavage planes can also be seen on calcite, halite, and pyrite. Note that cleavage depends upon molecular arrangement.

To show fracture, allow pupils to examine specimens of asbestos, obsidian, and flint. Point out that the specimens are smaller pieces that have broken away from larger chunks.

*Answer These*
1. In fracture, the mineral breaks into pieces with uneven surfaces; in cleavage the mineral breaks into pieces with some flat surfaces.
2. Mica.
3. Galena.

*Now Try This*
1. c     4. b
2. f     5. d
3. e     6. a

## 9. What are some special properties of minerals?

Show specimens of halite and quartz crystals. Assign reports on crystalline shape. Display and discuss gem stones. Have the pupils make reports on gems. Use 3-dimensional models and compare the shapes with the specimen crystals. Have the pupils make paper models of crystal shapes.

Make salt crystals. Suspend a string in a saturated salt water solution. Use a paper clip to weigh down the string. After about a week, cubic crystals of salt form on the string.

Always caution pupils when they are working with acids. Even dilute acid can affect sensitive skin.

*Answer These*
1. Each has a definite crystal shape.
2. Magnetite.

9

*Now Try This*
1. hard, crystal
2. magnetite
3. calcite

## 10. Why do we study minerals?

Have pupils identify objects in the room that are made of materials obtained from minerals (window glass, iron on desks, filament in light bulbs, copper pipes, demonstration table top). List the objects and their sources on the board. Discuss each of the minerals shown in the chart. Assign reports on each.

Display ore samples mentioned in the chart. In addition, show samples of cinnabar (mercury), cuprite (copper), magnetite (iron), and sphalerite (zinc). Use the photograph on page 44 to discuss how different minerals are mined. This is a photo of a copper mine in which the ore has been stripped from the surface along horizontal contours. Assign reports on other types of mining operations.

Obtain films from ore producing companies. These films show how the metals are extracted from the ore and refined.

*Answer These*

| 1. MINERAL | USE |
|---|---|
| quartz | glass, sandpaper |
| feldspar | china, dishes |
| mica | insulators, toasters |
| talc | talcum powder |
| calcite | cement, building materials |

2. a. Aluminum.
   b. Lead.
   c. Iron.
   d. Iron.

*Now Try This*

| ACROSS | DOWN |
|---|---|
| 1. hematite | 2. galena |
| 4. bauxite | 3. pyrite |

## 11. What are gems and precious stones?

Display pictures, slides or actual samples of gems. If practical, take a field trip to a museum or large jewelry shop where specimens of gems can be viewed. Some mineral and rock clubs lend out displays. A member of one of these clubs may be available to speak to the class and demonstrate how gemstones are cut and polished. Frequently these clubs have shows to display their collections. At these shows pupils are often able to purchase inexpensive stones and make jewelry out of them. Your school can start a small collection. Sometimes gemstones have a bad flaw which makes them quite inexpensive.

Children frequently question the monetary value of a sample stone. Guide them to see that the more difficult a stone is to find, or the more beautiful it looks, the more it is worth in terms of money.

Display a sample of corundum. Most hardness kits include a specimen of corundum. Larger samples can be purchased from scientific supply houses. Have the pupils describe the specimen. Display a sample or picture of a ruby and a sapphire. Point out that all are composed of aluminum and oxygen, however there are atoms of other elements present in sufficient amounts to produce different colors.

Exhibit samples of coal, graphite and diamonds. Point out that all of these minerals are composed of only the element carbon. Tell the pupils that each mineral is different because of the way the atoms are arranged in them.

Review the property of hardness in minerals. Ask the pupils to explain why rubies, sapphires and diamonds are so durable.

Assign reports on the various precious and semiprecious gems found in the chart listed in the chapter. Discuss the Finding Out More section and assign reports on man-made gems.

*Answer These*
1. b     3. b
2. c     4. c

## UNIT 2: REVIEW

**Fill In the Blank**
1. corundum
2. ore
3. shape
4. streak
5. physical property
6. minerals
7. subscript
8. compound
9. universal
10. hydrogen

**Multiple Choice**
1. c    2. a    3. b    4. c
5. a    6. b    7. a    8. b

## UNIT 3. ROCKS AND HOW THEY FORM

### 1. What kinds of rocks are in the earth's crust?

Obtain a large carton. Go around the classroom and have each student deposit one shoe into the box. Pick one pupil to remove the shoes and arrange them in some order. Have the rest of the class identify the method being used to arrange the shoes. Point out that the pupil is establishing a method of classification.

Have the class suggest how other things are classified. Use departments in supermarkets or large department stores as examples. Ask pupils to describe what would happen if items in the supermarket were not classified.

At this point introduce the classification of rocks and include a brief definition of each of the three main types.

*Answer These*
1. Classification is grouping things together that are alike in some way.
2. Igneous, sedimentary, metamorphic.

*Now Try These*
1. R + OCK + S (rocks)
2. IG + NE + OUS (igneous)
3. PA + ST (past)

### 2. How are igneous rocks formed?

The temperature rise of 1°C for every 30 meters applies only to the upper crust. The rise in temperature decreases as you go deeper. Point out that igneous rocks had to form deep within the earth to be melted.

It can be stated here that the first rocks that made up the earth were igneous, since the earth cooled from a molten state.

Use the diagram on page 56 to illustrate that pockets of magma are found within a solid crust.

At this point develop the concept of intrusive and extrusive igneous rocks, without using those terms. Igneous rocks can cool slowly and harden within the earth and become exposed later on (intrusive), or they can pour out onto the earth and can harden quickly (extrusive).

*Answer These*
1. From temperature readings in deep mines and the temperature of oil from deep wells.
2. Melted rocks and minerals inside the earth.
3. Magma that flows onto the earth's surface.

*Now Try This*
(from left to right) LAVA, HOT, MAGMA

## 3. How can you identify igneous rocks?

Perform this as a laboratory lesson.

Allow the pupils to examine specimens of granite, quartz, feldspar, and mica. Supply them with a hand lens and have them identify the minerals in granite. Tell them that the color of an igneous rock is determined by the minerals that make up the rock. Color can be used as a method of identifying igneous rocks.

Hand out specimens of basalt, obsidian, gabbro, rhyolite, and pumice. Have the pupils identify the texture of each. Obsidian is sometimes called volcanic glass.

Have the pupils arrange the igneous rocks in four classifications: light-colored with coarse texture; light-colored with fine texture; dark-colored with coarse texture; and dark-colored with fine texture.

*Answer These*
1. Coarse-textured, light-colored rock containing the minerals quartz, feldspar, and mica.
2. Fine-textured, light-colored rock containing the minerals quartz, feldspar, and mica.
3. An igneous rock that cools slowly will have larger crystals than one which cools faster. An igneous rock that cools very quickly will have no visible crystals.

## 4. How are sedimentary rocks formed?

Prepare some homemade sandstone or conglomerate by pouring white glue over a small pile of sand or pebbles. Allow it to stand for about 10 minutes. Meanwhile, refer to photographs of outcrops of sedimentary rocks and discuss the formation of layers of sediment. Point out that rock fragments are deposited in bodies of water.

Show the homemade sandstone. Tell the pupils that the cement for the formation of sedimentary rocks comes from minerals dissolved in the water. Break the homemade sandstone. Tell the class that the durability of the rock depends upon the cement. Display a piece of concrete and ask how it is made. Discuss the method by which sedimentary rocks form.

Evaporate the water from a salt water solution. Show the pupils the salt that was formed.

*Answer These*
1. b        4. c
2. a        5. a
3. b

*Now Try These*
a. sediment
b. concrete
c. sedimentary
d. evaporate

## 5. How are sedimentary rocks formed from living things?

Perform this as a laboratory lesson.

Allow the pupils to examine coquina. Ask them to tell how and where it was formed. Have them try to identify some of the shells.

Distribute specimens of shell limestone and have them test for the mineral calcite. Ask them to explain how this sedimentary rock was formed.

*Answer These*
1. Coquina was formed when the shells of dead sea animals piled up in layers and became cemented together.
2. Both were formed from shells.
3. In shell limestone you can't recognize the shells as you can with coquina, because the shells were broken into very small pieces.
4. When sea animals die, their shells pile up in layers to build up the beach.

*Now Try These*
1. shells
2. very small pieces
3. calcite

## 6. How can you identify sedimentary rocks?

Tell the pupils that the terms pebbles, gravel, sand, and clay all refer to broken rock, but with different particle sizes. Pebbles and gravel have large pieces of rock; sand has smaller pieces; and clay has very small pieces (mostly microscopic). (Silt is intermediate between sand and clay. The word "mud" as used here refers to silt, a term considered unnecessary for this lesson.) Particle size helps identify sedimentary rocks.

Treat this module as a laboratory lesson. Distribute specimens of conglomerate, sandstone, and shale. Allow the pupils to examine the specimens to determine particle size. Ask pupils to describe how each rock was formed.

Point out that the smaller the rock particles of the sedimentary rock, the more tightly packed the particles are. Demonstrate this with beads of different sizes.

*Answer These*
1. Conglomerate, sandstone, shale, limestone, halite, coquina, shell limestone.
2. Shale.
3. The particles in sandstone are larger than those that make up shale.
4. b
5. a
6. b

## 7. How are metamorphic rocks formed?

Have the pupils compare a piece of dried clay and a similar piece that has been fired in a kiln. (If a kiln is not available, heat the clay in a clay flower pot or crucible.) Have the pupils identify the dried clay as the sedimentary rock shale, and the fired clay as a metamorphic rock made from it.

Have the pupils recall that temperatures increase with depth. Discuss the fact that heat causes chemical changes. Point out that tremendous pressures deep within the earth also cause chemical changes.

Establish that metamorphic rocks form from sedimentary and igneous rocks deep within the earth.

*Answer These*
1. By heat, pressure, and chemical changes.
2. Heat inside the earth "bakes" the rocks and changes them. The heat also causes chemical reactions to form new minerals.
3. As you go deeper into the earth, it gets hotter.

*Now Try This*
1. CHEMICAL     3. MAGMA
2. IGNEOUS      4. METAMORPHIC
Secret word: HEAT

## 8. What do some metamorphic rocks look like?

The demonstration with the toothpicks illustrates foliation. Point out that under tremendous pressures, the crystals of many minerals in the rocks are forced to arrange themselves in parallel layers or bands.

In a laboratory lesson allow the pupils to examine specimens of gneiss, schist, slate, quartzite, and marble. Have them identify the foliated and unfoliated rocks. It is not necessary for the pupil to know the term *foliated*. The important thing is that he should be able to recognize banding as a method of identifying metamorphic rocks.

Use the chart on page 69 and allow the pupils to compare the metamorphic rock with the igneous or sedimentary rock that changed.

Test the marble with acid.

Spend some time with the rock cycle. Draw it on the board and allow the pupils to explain how all of the rocks are related.

*Answer These*
1. Great pressure causes the mineral crystals to flatten out into bands.
2. Slate.
3. Limestone.

*Now Try This*
1. METAMORPHIC
2. IGNEOUS
3. CRUST
4. ROCK
5. SHALE
Secret word: ROCKS

## UNIT 3: REVIEW

**Fill In the Blank**
1. marble
2. slate
3. igneous rocks
4. conglomerate
5. coquina
6. sediment
7. granite
8. lava
9. classification
10. quartzite

**Multiple Choice**
1. a   2. c   3. b   4. a
5. b   6. c   7. a   8. b

## UNIT 4: WEARING DOWN THE EARTH

### 1. What are physical and chemical changes?

Demonstrate the tasks described in the first section of this module. Elicit from the pupils that in each case, no new substance is produced, even though the substance is changed in form. Identify such changes as physical changes.

Burn a wooden splint; react acetic acid (vinegar) with baking soda. Elicit the fact that new substances are produced. Have pupils try to describe the new substances. Identify these changes as chemical changes.

Melt ice; boil water. Point out that these changes are changes in state. Elicit the fact that the substance remains the same and no new substances are formed. Thus only the physical properties of the substance (water) change. Identify such changes as physical changes.

Display samples of sandstone and sand. Guide the pupils to see that the sandstone was broken down into particles of sand. Elicit that this is a physical change.

Dissolve a small piece of halite in water. Guide pupils to see that this, too, is a physical change. Challenge the pupils to suggest how to get the salt back out of the solution.

Distribute pieces of wet shale and have the pupils note the odor of wet mud. Point out that shale can change physically into mud.

Display a rusty nail. Demonstrate how the rust crumbles. Guide the pupils to see that, in moist air, iron undergoes a chemical change to form rust (iron oxide). Show the class samples of hematite and limonite. Tell the pupils that these minerals contain iron oxide. Have the pupils note the rust color. Point out that iron in the rock went through a chemical change to become hematite (iron oxide).

*Answer These*
1. b
2. a
3. c
4. a

*Now Try This*
1. physical change
2. chemical change
3. chemical change
4. physical change
5. chemical change

### 2. What is mechanical weathering?

A field trip around the school building can best illustrate examples of weathering. Refer to pupils' own experiences, such as exploding soda cans or broken water pipes due to freezing. Cracked pavement from frost action or tree roots are other good illustrations. A study of tombstones also proves interesting.

Review physical changes and relate mechanical weathering to physical changes.

Wrap a piece of weathered rock in heavy cloth and crack it open with a hammer. Show the class the weathered and unweathered surfaces. Elicit that the surfaces show differences in color and texture. Challenge them to speculate as to the cause of these appearance differences.

*Answer These*
1. b
2. a

*Now Try These*
1. Water may fill small cracks in the sidewalks. In winter the

waterfreezes and expands. The expanding water cracks the sidewalks further.
2. As the roots grow, they can "pick up" or crack the water pipes.
3. Traffic causes cracks to form in the street. Water may fill these cracks. When it gets cold enough the water freezes and expands. The expanding water cracks the street further. Traffic causes small pieces to break off and the holes get wider and bigger.

## 3. What is chemical weathering?

Have the pupils recall that in a chemical change, a new substance is formed. Guide them to see that chemical weathering involves a chemical change of the substances in rocks and minerals. Three major kinds of chemical weathering are: oxidation, hydration and carbonation.

Oxidation can be demonstrated with some moistened steel wool. After several days show the class how the steel wool has rusted. Tell the pupils that rusting is a form of oxidation. Elicit that rocks and minerals containing iron undergo oxidation. On the board, write the equation for the oxidation of iron, $Fe + O_2 \longrightarrow Fe_2O_3$, which shows how iron combines with oxygen to form a new substance—iron oxide. Have pupils rub some hematite with their fingers. Ask them to speculate what the red stain might be.

Elicit that the bubbles in club soda are carbon dioxide. Use litmus paper to prove that club soda (carbonic acid, $H_2CO_3$) is acidic. Have the class recall how acid reacts with calcite, limestone and marble. Demonstrate the effect of carbonic acid on calcite by placing a small piece into some club soda. Have the pupils note the formation of small bubbles on the calcite as the acid reacts with it.

Point out that water not only chemically weathers rocks during hydration, but is also needed for oxidation and carbonation to occur.

*Answer These*
1. to prevent rusting
2. c
3. b
4. a
5. b

*Now Try This*
In mechanical weathering, except for size the small pieces of rock are the same as the original rock. In chemical weathering, a chemical change takes place to produce rocks with a different composition.

## 4. What factors affect the rate of weathering?

Motivate the lesson by displaying a piece of steel wool and asking what is needed to cause it to rust. Guide the pupils to see the importance of moisture in chemical weathering. Have them note how chemical weathering is speeded up in humid regions. Discuss the economic implication for people living in humid areas. Cars rust faster in these areas. Coatings must be applied to retard chemical weathering. Have the pupils note the importance of rainfall to carbonation and production of carbonic acid.

Discuss why frost action is not an important weathering agent in tropical and frigid regions. Elicit that frost action is not a dominant weathering agent in mid-winter in places where the temperature does not go below freezing.

Use a cube of sugar to illustrate the effect of surface area on the rate of weathering. Break the cube in half. Crush one half then both halves into separate beakers containing water. Stir both for a short time and have pupils note the speed at which each sample dissolved. Hold up another cube of sugar and have the pupils count the surfaces (6). Break the cube in half and draw attention to the two

new surfaces. Guide the class to see that, as you break the cube in smaller pieces, you expose more surfaces and thereby speed up the rate of dissolving. Compare this to weathering.

You might want to summarize this chapter by constructing a chart listing rocks and minerals and the rate at which they weather mechanically and chemically.

*Answer These*
1. a
2. b
3. a
4. b

## 5. What is soil?

Review weathering from the three previous lessons. Have the pupils explain if they consider weathering to be a constructive or destructive process. Guide them to see that soil production is a constructive result of weathering. Develop with the pupils the importance of soil.

Display several samples showing weathered and unweathered rock surfaces. Challenge pupils to explain what caused the samples to weather. Guide them to see that as soon as a surface becomes exposed, it begins to weather.

Break a rock into smaller pieces and show that the smaller pieces have a greater surface area than the original chunk. CAUTION: Wrap the sample while you smash it to prevent pieces from hitting you or the pupils. Shale is a good rock to use; it breaks easily and can be pulverized.

Distribute a small amount of soil to each pupil. Have them examine and describe what they see. Elicit from the pupils that soil is a mixture of different materials. Write a definition of soil on the board and develop with the pupils how soil forms.

Using a photograph or drawing of a soil profile, guide pupils through a step-by-step development of the formation of the profile.

*Answer These*
1. c
2. a
3. a
4. b

## 6. How may one soil differ from another?

Display large samples of limestone and granite along with samples of soil formed from each. Soil samples can be purchased from scientific supply houses. Establish with the pupils that different minerals form different kinds of soils. Review how a limestone-rich soil develops from a limestone bedrock. Point out that some soils form from the bedrock beneath them while other soils are transported from one place to another. Elicit that transported soil is usually different from the bedrock beneath it.

Distribute soil samples of different texture and allow pupils to examine each and describe the differences.

Demonstrate permeability (rate at which water moves through porous material) using three funnels. Fill one funnel with gravel, another with sand, and the third with clay. Set each on a stand and pour water in each. Have pupils time how long it takes the water to move through each material. This activity can be conducted as a laboratory exercise.

Demonstrate how compact soil slows the rate of movement of water through the soil. Set up two funnels with loam. Compact the soil in one. Time how long it takes the water to move through each soil sample.

*Answer These*
1. b  2. a  3. c  4. b

## 7. What is a soil profile?

The ideal way to present this lesson would be a field trip to a road cut. Have students locate and identify the different horizons. Direct them to measure the depth of each horizon and describe its appearance. Assign some students to remove sections of each horizon and place them on masonite, plywood, or heavy cardboard. Cover the section with plexiglass and secure it to the masonite with heavy tape. It is sometimes possible to obtain soil horizon samples with a bulb planter. Push the bulb planter down and remove plugs of soil. By joining them together you can probably obtain a topsoil and subsoil horizon sample.

In cases where a field trip is impractical, models of soil profiles can be constructed from collected materials that resemble the various horizons.

Review how soil is produced and discuss how each horizon is formed.

*Answer These*
1. a
2. b
3. b
4. b
5. c

*Now Try This*
DOWN
1. horizon
2. clay
4. humus

ACROSS
3. profile
5. subsoil
6. topsoil

## 8. How do soils differ in different climates?

Establish with the class that soils differ. Elicit that they may differ in color, texture, kinds and amounts of minerals, amounts of humus, and depth of topsoil. On the board, list the various regions in which soils may form. The text lists forests, deserts, grassland, prairie and tundra soils. Display a large variety of photos of each. Have the pupils describe each region briefly. Discuss how the climate (range of temperature, amount of rainfall) influences these regions. Discuss the development of each soil in each region.

Allow the pupils to examine samples of different kinds of soils. Have them describe the samples and then speculate which type they might be. Soil samples can be obtained from various state agriculture departments and agricultural schools. They can also be purchased from scientific supply houses.

It should be noted that climate is not the only agent of soil formation. Other agents include: (1) parent material, which is the residual or transported mineral matter in the region; (2) topography of the region (some soils are classified as mountain soils); (3) organic material (plants and animals that live in the soil); (4) length of time soil has had to form. You may want to mention these other factors.

Use the Now Try This and the map in this chapter to locate and describe the different soils found in the United States. Assign reports on crops, types of soils, and their locations around the country.

*Answer These*
1. b
2. c
3. b
4. b

*Now Try This*
1. forest soil
2. desert soil
3. grassland soil
4. tundra soil
5. grassland soil
6. tundra soil
7. forest soil
8. desert soil

## 9. What are some chemicals in the soil?

Display a green plant and elicit from the pupils that green plants need water, minerals, carbon dioxide, and sunlight to live. Write the formulas for carbon dioxide and water on the board. Call attention to the chart of elements needed by plants (page 88) and guide pupils to see that carbon and oxygen come from carbon dioxide in the air, and that water supplies the hydrogen and oxygen.

Place a colored gum ball in a funnel and pour water through the funnel. Catch the water in a beaker and direct pupils' attention to the color of the water. Elicit that the coloring on the gum ball dissolves in the water and is carried down the funnel into the beaker. Use this demonstration to explain how, in leaching, some minerals dissolve in soil water and are carried downward through the soil. Point out that leaching removes minerals from the soil, and elicit that fertilizers replace these minerals.

Display labels of gardens or house plant fertilizers and develop the ways in which natural processes and fertilizers help replace the elements taken out of the soil by plants and by leaching. Commercial fertilizers contain the elements that soils are most deficient in—nitrogen, phosphorus, and potassium (potash $K_2O$). The numbers on the labels (e.g. 5-10-5) refer to the percent of each element in the fertilizer.

*Answer These*
1. c
2. a
3. b
4. b
5. c

*Now Try This*
1. n + it + ro + gen (nitrogen)
2. p + hos + p + hor + us (phosphorus)
3. pot + ass + i + um (potassium)

## 10. What are basic and acidic soils?

Discuss the differences between basic and acidic soils. Samples can be obtained from county agricultural extension services, state agricultural colleges, or state departments of agriculture. Information on types of soil can be supplied from federal and state departments of agriculture and departments of conservation.

Demonstrate how soils are tested (or use this as a laboratory exercise). Soil test kits can be purchased from scientific supply houses or local nurseries. Have pupils collect samples of soil from different places. Include some from under evergreens and others from open grassy fields. Indicators such as chlorophenol red, litmus, phenol red and bromcresol green have different pH ranges and can be used in testing soils.

Some pupils may have tropical fish. Aquarium water is also measured for pH. Kits are sold to test the water. You might want to discuss the importance of testing for and maintaining a proper pH in aquarium water.

If time permits, have pupils recall that a great deal of leaching takes place in a forest soil, while lack of rainfall limits leaching in the desert. Have pupils identify which of these two soils is basic and which is acidic.

*Answer These*
1. a
2. b
3. b
4. a
5. c

*Now Try This*
1. neutral
2. acidic
3. acidic
4. neutral
5. acidic
6. acidic
7. basic
8. basic
9. acidic
10. basic

## 11. What life is found in the soil?

Distribute hand lenses and fresh soil samples to groups of pupils for examination. If possible take the class to an area where they can collect and examine soil samples. Supply pupils with plastic bags or jars to carry the samples back to class. Direct the pupils to moist rather than dry soil areas. A good sample should be about 6 centimeters on each side. Have the pupils note and count the different forms of life found in the sample. Ask pupils to sketch some of the things they see.

Prepare charts, photographs, and collections of various forms of animal life found in the soil. Have some insect field guides available for reference. Set up terrariums of animal life found in the samples. Keep it moist and well stocked with plant material.

Point out that most soil life is microscopic. Using charts or overhead transparencies, describe bacteria, protozoa, and fungi. Display cultures of bacteria and fungi that have been grown in sterilized Petri dishes. Mention the use of the control Petri dish. Allow pupils to examine several drops of prepared soil cultures under the microscope. Boil some plant material for 15 to 20 minutes. Cool the mixture and add several teaspoonfuls of soil. Cover the mixture and allow it to stand for several days in a warm place before viewing.

Show the pupils dead tree material. Look for masses of white threadlike mycelium in the wood and in the soil. Separate the moist rotting wood to expose these white strands. Point to the fact that fungi and bacteria cause decay. Describe humus and develop with the pupils how humus puts needed elements back into the soil.

Have the pupils examine the roots of leguminous plants to observe the nodules on the roots. Explain how the nitrogen-fixing bacteria in these nodules add nitrates to the soil. As an interesting project show how clover growing in a soil increases the nitrogen content of that soil. Use an inexpensive nitrate soil testing kit to check the soil before and after the planting of the clover. Using a large chart or transparency develop with the pupils an understanding of the nitrogen cycle.

Use audiovisual materials to show the various forms of animal life found in the soil. Have the pupils make reports on spiders, mites, slugs, etc. Set up terrariums in the classroom containing earthworms, slugs, etc. Discuss the role these animals play in the production of humus.

*Answer These*
1. b
2. c
3. c
4. a

## UNIT 4: REVIEW

**Modified T/F**
1. T
2. F, BASIC
3. T
4. F, DESERT
5. F, YOUNGER
6. T
7. F, UNDER
8. F, FASTER
9. T
10. T

**Multiple Chocie**
1. c    2. c    3. a    4. b
5. a    6. a    7. c    8. a

## UNIT 5. AGENTS OF EROSION

### 1. How does running water wear away the earth's surface?

A diagram of the water cycle should be shown to the class and discussed. Refer to pupils' experiences of water under pressure. Water from a hose or fire hydrant has enough pressure to move objects.

Make a stream table with a 3-foot-long rain gutter. Attach a piece of ⅛-in. wire mesh to one end of the gutter. Fill the gutter with gravel, sand, and clay. Place the gutter on a slight incline and pour water on the upper end. (A tin can with small holes at the bottom will allow the water to fall slowly). Have the pupils see how the running water produces grooves. Tell them that the grooves are called gullies, which in time become river valleys.

*Answer These*
1. From rain and other forms of precipitation.
2. The moving water causes pieces of sand and gravel to hit against each other.
3. The running water carries the pieces of sand and gravel away.

*Now Try These*
1. ABRASION
2. EROSION

### 2. How does a river move rocks?

Show pictures of different parts of a river. Challenge the pupils to identify the various parts of the river. Using the pictures, describe and compare the mouth and the source.

Develop with the pupils the fact that velocity determines the rate and amount of erosion done by a river. Demonstrate how the slope of the land influences a river's velocity. This concept may be developed as a laboratory exercise instead of a demonstration. With the same stream table used in Module 1, have pupils time the speed at which a cork floats down the rain gutter. Instruct them to place the gutter at different angles and time the speed of the cork at each angle. Elicit that the steeper the slope, the faster the flow.

Demonstrate how a greater amount of water will increase the rate of flow. This too can be done as a laboratory exercise. Instruct pupils to measure the speed of the cork when a small amount of water is poured into the rain gutter. Then have them increase the amount of water and time the cork's movement down the stream.

Both exercises are time consuming and should be planned for two separate lessons. Have plenty of paper towels available to clean up spilled water.

Elicit that material washed into a river makes it appear muddy. Guide pupils to see that the river's velocity will determine the size of the particles it will move. Point out that some large rocks are dragged or rolled along the bottom.

*Answer These*
1. c
2. b
3. b
4. a

*Now Try These*
1. The slope of a river bed is steeper at its head than it is at the mouth. Water flows fastest where slope is steepest.
2. During floods, more water runs off into rivers. The more water a river contains, the faster it flows.
3. The steeper the slope, the faster a river flows; the faster a river flows, the greater the amount of erosion.

## 3. What land shapes are produced by running water?

Using the rain gutter, demonstrate how a river valley forms. Have the pupils identify the beds and banks of a river. Have pupils recall that rapidly flowing rivers can drag large rocks along its bed. Guide the pupils to see how rapidly flowing water can cause erosion deep into a river bed to produce steep-sided valleys. Lead the pupils to see that a rapidly flowing river is engaged mainly in downcutting. Show pictures of the Grand Canyon, Royal Gorge, etc.

Show pictures of the Lower Falls and Canyon at Yellowstone National Park, Niagra Falls, and other falls. Using a diagram, lead the pupils to see how unequal erosion produces rapids and waterfalls. Challenge them to explain why waterfalls will disappear in time. Summarize this part of the lesson by listing the features of a quick-flowing river: steep-sided valley, straight flowing path, downcutting action, waterfalls and rapids. Have pupils recall that as the slope becomes gentler, the river slows down. Lower the angle of the stream table to slow down the flow of water.

A rock placed in the path of flow of the water in the stream table will cause the stream to meander. Show pictures of meandering rivers and, with the aid of a diagram or overhead transparency, show the pupils how meanders develop.

Using an overhead projector transparency, guide pupils to see that as the river erodes deeper and deeper, its slope gets gentler. This decreasing slope causes the river to slow down, thus reducing its ability to carry rock materials.

Demonstrate deposition with the stream table. Have pupils note the amount of sediment that forms at the bottom of the gutter. Also have them note the shape of the deposited sediments. Show pictures of deltas and alluvial fans. Discuss deposition in rivers.

A field trip to a nearby stream would be ideal at this time. After a rainfall, some features of erosion and deposition may be seen in areas where runoff flows over unprotected areas, such as road cuts, excavation pits, etc.

Topographic maps can also be used in this lesson to illustrate different river features.

*Answer These*
1. a
2. b
3. c
4. b
5. a

## 4. How does moving ice change the surface of the earth?

The use of motion pictures of glaciers will dramatically show the work of these moving rivers of ice and snow. Recall pupils' experiences of packing snow to make snowballs. As pressure is added, the snowball changes to ice. Check with local museums of natural history for areas that show evidence of glaciers.

Show pupils specimens or pictures of rocks with grooves, striations. Show pictures of crevasses, cirques, matterhorns, and erratics, and discuss how they were formed. Assign reports on icebergs and the Ice Age.

*Answer These*
1. Ice and snow.
2. Sand, gravel, and larger pieces of rock.
3. Moraine.

*Now Try These*
1. ice, snow
2. erode
3. rocks, sand, gravel
4. terminal

## 5. How can you tell the age of a river?

It is important that pupils understand that the terms youth, maturity, and old age do not have a chronological meaning. The important factor here is not time; it is the rate of flow of a river's water. The age of a river is determined by its rate of flow. A river in youth flows very quickly. As the rate of flow decreases the river reaches maturity then old age. Point out that if, for some reason, a river in the old age stage begins to flow faster, its age reverses itself.

Have pupils recall from previous chapters how erosion from a young fast-flowing river creates features such as steep V-shaped valleys, rapids, and waterfalls. Use visual aids such as color slides, photographs, and drawings to illustrate these features. Use similar visual aids to illustrate the features of maturity and old age.

Set up a stream table to demonstrate a river at various stages. A stream table can be constructed or purchased from a scientific supply house. Point out that a river can be young at its source, old at its mouth and mature in between all at the same time. The Mississippi river shows such characteristics. Use a map to locate the various rivers mentioned in this chapter.

*Answer These*

| | |
|---|---|
| 1. a | 11. a |
| 2. b | 12. b |
| 3. c | 13. a |
| 4. b | 14. a |
| 5. a | 15. b |
| 6. c | 16. c |
| 7. b | 17. a |
| 8. b | 18. c |
| 9. a | 19. b |
| 10. a | 20. c |

## 6. What is an ice age?

Have pupils recall from the previous lesson what a glacier is. Place a heavy weight on top of an ice cube and elicit that in 24 hours the ice cube will melt, the water will evaporate, and the weight will be sitting on the table. Call attention to the picture of an erratic on page 106. Tell the class that giant boulders such as these are found in many places, and that they are different from other rocks found in the same area. Challenge the pupils to explain how such large boulders got there.

If the reports suggested in Module 5 were assigned, allow several pupils to present their reports to the class. Discuss the conditions which led to the ice age. Point out that the climate must have gotten colder, and the increased weight of accumulated snow caused the glaciers to move further southward and cover more land. The question, "Will we again have another ice age?" can be used to initiate a lively class discussion. Use a large wall map to locate present continental glaciers.

Use an ice cube and modeling clay to demonstrate how a glacial lake forms. Gouge the surface of the clay with the ice cube and then allow the ice to melt. Direct pupils' attention to the steep sides and long narrow shape of the gorge that will fill with water when the ice melts. Display a map of the Great Lakes. Inform the class that at one time the lakes were river valleys and that the rivers became blocked at their northern ends by the glacier. As the glacier receded, the lakes took on their present shape and drainage moved northeast through the St. Lawrence River. Topographic maps of Glacier National Park can also be used to show features of glacial lakes.

Display pictures of drumlins, eskers, kames and kettle lakes. Discuss how each forms. Display a large map of the United States and trace the edge of the last ice age glacier through New York, New Jersey, Pennsylvania, Ohio, Indiana and Illinois. Use a topographic map that includes the terminal moraine left in these areas.

Use the *People in Science* section to lead a discussion of how Agassiz concluded that an ice age did exist.

*Answer These*
1. a
2. c
3. b
4. b

## 7. How do winds change the earth's surface?

Films and filmstrips showing desert scenes can be most useful with the topic of wind erosion. Where possible, a trip to a sandy beach will show dune formation. Snowdrifts also show characteristics of dune formation. Assign reports on arid regions, and have pupils collect pictures and make drawings of evidence of wind erosion. Assign reports on the "Dust Bowl."

Introduce the topic of conservation, and allow the pupils to research it and bring reports back to class.

*Answer These*
1. The wind.
2. The lower part of the rock, which is closest to the ground.
3. The gentle-sloped windward side and the steep leeward side.

*Now Try These*
1. To prevent the part closest to the ground from being eroded by the wind.
2. To help form sand dunes, which prevent the sand from being blown off the beaches on to the land behind the beaches.

## 8. How do waves erode the land?

A field trip to a lake or ocean area would best illustrate wave erosion. Films or filmstrips will also show important features. Refer to the diagram on page 110 for the parts of a wave. Use a long rope to show waves. Elicit features of wave action from pupils' experience at the beach. Duplicate a beach scene with sand and a fish tank. Demonstrate wave erosion in the tank. With the aid of a large diagram, explain the formation of breakers, surf, sandbars, lagoons, and offshore bars.

*Answer These*
1. b
2. b
3. c

*Now Try These*
1. c
2. e
3. d
4. a
5. f
6. b

## 9. What shoreline features are produced by wave erosion?

Review the previous chapter on wave erosion. Have pupils recall how the energy from moving water causes rocks to move and abrade other rocks. With the use of a clay model, show how the portion of the rocky shoreline in contact with the water is eroded by the waves. With this model, show how the higher protruding portions of the rock collapse and tumble down into the water. They in turn become tools for further abrasion.

Use charts or chalkboard drawings to reinforce the learning. Use photographs, slides and pictures to show these features. Assign pupils to bring in newspaper articles reporting storm damage that occurred along shorelines due to wave erosion.

If possible take a field trip to a shoreline and have the pupils identify the various features.

*Answer These*
1. c
2. a
3. b
4. b

## 10. What shoreline features are built by waves?

Have pupils recall their experience at the beach. Ask how many have experienced the water pulling the sand out from under their feet. Point out that this outward flow of water is called an undertow. Discuss how dangerous some undertows can be.

If a field trip to the shore cannot be arranged, use slides, photographs and drawings. Invite pupils to bring in their own photographs. Travel agents, airlines, and steamship companies can also supply you with abundant visual aids. Brochures from tourist agencies of various countries and coastal states are filled with excellent pictures.

Assign pupils (also ask colleagues) going on vacation to the seashore to bring in samples of beach material. Within a short time you will have enough materials to illustrate several types of beaches. Have pupils examine these samples and explain where and how each type of beach formed.

Use diagrams to explain how longshore currents form. Discuss the formation of sandbars, offshore bars, barrier beaches, lagoons, spits, hooks, and coral reefs. Use topographic maps of Brooklyn, New York, Sandy Hook, New Jersey, and Point Reyes, California to illustrate these shoreline features.

*Answer These*
1. Water from waves thrown onto the beach flows back to the ocean carrying sand off the land with it.
2. Energy from waves deposits weathered material onto the land.
3. Weathered quartz along the Atlantic coast produces white sands.
4. Pieces of shells produce beaches in Bermuda.
5. Weathered lava from volcanoes produces beaches in Hawaii.
6. Offshore bars, sandbars, barrier beaches.

*Now Try This*
ACROSS
1. shoreline
2. beach
4. undertow

DOWN
1. sandbar
3. lagoon
5. current

## 11. What happens to the eroded material from the land?

Display samples of tap water and sea water. Artificial sea water may be prepared by adding the following to 1000 ml of tap water:
  27   g sodium chloride
   3.5 g magnesium chloried
   1.8 g magnesium sulfate
   1.2 g calcium sulfate
   0.9 g potassium sulfate
Have students recall the salty taste of sea water. Recall pupils' experience with the stream table, showing that rocks and minerals are carried from the land to the sea.
Demonstrate the flame tests and discuss how the tests are used.

*Answer These*
1. b
2. c
3. a

*Now Try This*

| 1. water | (swimming) |
| (salt) | seasoning for food; raw material for chemicals |
| (clams) | food |
| plants, small animals, other |  |
| fish | (food for fish) |
| (iodine) | medicine; making chemicals |
| (copper) | electrical conductors; pipe; coins |
| seaweed | agar for preservative |
| shells | lime for mortar |
| oysters | pearls; food |

2. SO + DI + UM (sodium)

3. Star
  pAil
  baLl
  boaT (SALT)

## 12. What helps to prevent erosion?

Perform the demonstration as described in the first paragraph of the lesson. Ask pupils to explain how plants and trees help prevent the soil from being washed away from falling water.
Display pictures of gullies and describe how gullies are formed.
Use the stream table to demonstrate how vegetation helps prevent soil from being washed away by moving water. Pour water through loose soil and direct pupils to observe the sediment that collects at the bottom of the gutter. Replace the soil with pieces of grass-covered sod and repeat the demonstration. Again have pupils observe the amount of sediment formed at the bottom of the gutter. Have the class compare the amount collected in each experiment and explain the results. Permit pupils to examine the network of roots in the sod, and have one of the pupils pull some of the sod apart. Guide pupils to see how the roots hold the soil together.
Assign reports on forest conservation, flood control, soil conservation, contour farming, and terrace farming.
Show pictures of dams. Draw a diagram of a dam on the board and guide pupils to see how a dam slows down the velocity of a river. Have pupils explain how a dam helps prevent erosion during times of floods. Discuss how dams help in supplying water and electrical energy. Some governmental agencies will supply you with films and booklets on this subject. Write to the Department of the Interior for information.
Use pictures of a beach. Elicit from the pupils that beach grass can help stop sand erosion.

*Answer These*
1. a
2. b
3. c
4. c

*Now Try These*
1. GULLIES
2. DAM
3. BEACH

## UNIT 5: REVIEW

**Matching**
1. sea cliff
2. gully
3. glacier
4. crest
5. runoff
6. bed
7. bank
8. erratic
9. tributaries
10. meanders

**Multiple Choice**
1. b  2. a  3. b  4. c
5. a  6. c  7. a  8. b

# UNIT 6. BUILDING UP THE EARTH

## 1. How does the earth's crust move?

Review all the erosional processes that are wearing down the surface of the earth. Elicit from the pupils that if the erosional processes continued, all of the earth's surface would eventually be worn flat. Point out that other processes are constantly at work building up the earth's surface. These processes cause the crust to move. Sometimes this movement is so gradual that the movement cannot be noticed or measured by ordinary means. In other cases, the movement of the crust is rapid and violent, often causing great amounts of destruction.

Earthquakes are examples of this second type of movement. Use films, filmstrips, pictures, and newspaper articles with this topic. Have pupils make a list of some of the most destructive earthquakes. Have them report on the date, region, and amount of destruction. Use "Silly Putty" to demonstrate the nature of the mantle. Show the pupils that a force exerted slowly will cause the putty to stretch and change shape. Then pull the putty apart quickly. It snaps. Use this demonstration to discuss earthquakes.

Using painted shoe boxes or models made of wood, demonstrate faulting. Point out that a sudden movement caused by faulting is an earthquake.

Discuss evidence of earth movement, e.g., fossils on mountain tops, beach features high on mountain slopes, earthquakes, volcanoes, folded rock structures. Discuss folding, using the photograph on page 122. Demonstrate folding with sheets of different colored paper or use layers of clay of various colors.

*Answer These*
1. a
2. b
3. c

*Now Try These*
1. During an earthquake, the movement of the ground can cause buildings to collapse, possibly killing many people.
2. Slight movements of the ground.
3. The earth's crust breaks at a weak point called a fault.

## 2. What are earthquake waves?

Refer to the diagram on page 124 to show the locations of focus and epicenter. Find the location of the nearest fault in your community. Ask pupils if an earthquake could occur in your area. Have them research newspapers for the date and location of the most recent and closest earthquake.

Point out that earthquakes send out three types of shock waves. All are sent out at the same time, but each travels at a different speed and moves differently. Use a Slinky spring to demonstrate how longitudinal waves move. Have two pupils stretch the coil across the front of the room. Then direct one pupil to compress about 10 coils and then let them go. Direct the pupils to observe how the compressions move. Use the method mentioned in the text to demonstrate transverse waves. The surface waves resemble ocean waves.

Assign the construction of a seismograph. Discuss the operation of the instrument. Point out that the one described in the text measures vertical movements. Have pupils describe modifications that would allow the seismograph to measure horizontal earth movements. A homemade seismograph is sensitive enough to measure vibrations made by trailer trucks and low-flying jets, airplanes.

*Answer These*
1. b       3. a
2. a       4. c

## 3. What can we learn from earthquake waves?

This lesson can be performed as a lab. Display several seismograms. Make a transparency of the seismogram shown in the text. Using a seismogram, locate the three types of waves. Elicit that the different rates at which each travels accounts for lapse of time between each wave. Have pupils explain why large time differences mean greater distances from the focus. Show how a graph can be constructed of these time differences and how distances can be determined quickly.

Discuss triangulation. Using the example given in the text and a map, show how an epicemeter is located.

Several scales have been developed to judge the intensity of an earthquake. The Mercalli scale uses observed effects, as does the Rossi-Forel scale. The scale used today is the Richter scale, based on the magnitude of the wave recorded on the seismograph.

*Answer These*
1. a
2. a
3. a
4. a
5. c
6. c

## 4. How does magma change the earth's surface?

Prepare a transparency or large diagram of the features of intrusive volcanism as seen on page 129. Point out that there is a tremendous amount of magma located within the earth's crust. The magma may never reach the surface, and many underground formations result. Discuss these formations. Display pieces of granite and gabbro. Review the formation of igneous rocks.

*Answer These*
1. b
2. a
3. c

*Now Try This*
magma
vulcanism
igneous
dome

## 5. What is a volcano?

You can dramatically produce a simulated volcanic eruption. Make a model volcano out of clay and include a crater. Place some granular ammonium dichromate into a small crucible. Put a two inch magnesium ribbon into the chemical for use as a fuse. Place the crucible into the center of the model volcano. Light the magnesium fuse with a Bunsen flame. **Caution: Move the pupils away from the demonstration table. Warn them not to look directly at the burning magnesium ribbon.**

Using the demonstration and the diagrams on pages 130 and 131, discuss the parts of a volcano. Using the diagrams, compare types of volcanoes. Assign reports on famous volcanoes. Show films of volcanic eruptions.

1. Magma escaping to the surface.
2. A crack in the crust.
3. A hill of cinders, lava, and ashes that pile up around a volcano.
4. Paricutin.
5. Hawaiian Islands

## 6. How do we describe mountains?

The next two modules are devoted to landscape regions. Mountains together with plateaus and plains, form these major regions. Find out which of your pupils have vacationed in the mountains. Prior to the lesson, have these pupils bring in photos of the region.

Have the class make a list of various mountains and mountain ranges around the world. Point out that groups of mountains form a mountain range, and a group of mountain ranges form a mountain belt. Have pupils define and describe a mountain.

Challenge the class to explain how mountains form. Tell them to look back through unit 6 at Modules 1, 4, and 5. Review folding as discussed in Module 1. Use the photograph at the bottom of page 122 to show a syncline and anticline. Reinforce the concept with sheets of colored paper as illustrated on pages 122 and 123.

Demonstrate how fault-block mountains form. Construct blocks of wood (or use 2 shoe boxes), as illustrated at the bottom of page 122.

Review volcanism. Refer to the diagrams on pages 128 and 131 to explain domed mountains and volcanic cones. Refer back to the list of mountains and mountain ranges and assign pupils to research the kind of mountain each one represents. Have them bring in pictures, diagrams and drawings of the various types of mountains.

Use photographs, diagrams, transparency overlays and maps to teach this lesson. Raised plastic relief maps are available from A.J. Nystrom of Chicago. Scientific supply houses also have landform and landscape models.

*Answer These*
1. a
2. b
3. b

*Now Try These*
1. D
2. A
3. E
4. B
5. C

## 7. How do we describe plains and plateaus?

Elicit that the three major kinds of landscape regions are mountains, plains, and plateaus. Define a plain as a large, flat area of usually low elevation.

Have pupils recall the various agents of erosion and how each wears down the land. Point out how erosion is one way plains form. Review the process of deposition and guide pupils to see how layers can be deosited to build up a plain. Have pupils explain how a volcano can build up a plain.

On the board, list the various ways plains form. Include the upward movement of coastal land or the lowering of the water. At this point, develop the concepts that landscape development is a very slow process and that the earth is constantly changing.

Define a plateau as a plain of high elevation. Show pictures and slides of the Grand Canyon, which is located in the Colorado Plateau. Have pupils observe the horizontal layers that form the plateau. Make use of pictures, slides, topographic maps and models to teach the modules on landscape. The ESCP Stereo Atlas

published by Macalaster Scientific Company is another good visual aid.

Display a large map of the United States. While you locate the major landscape areas on this map, have pupils do the same with the map on page 134.

If time permits, use the Finding Out More to discuss the various "file" stages of mountains, plains, and plateaus. Use visual aids showing mesas, buttes, canyons, ravines, and monadnocks.

*Answer These*
1. a
2. c
3. b
4. a

## 8. What is the theory of continental drift?

Pose the following problem to the class: Is it possible for the continents to be moving? Present the evidence.

Display a large map and direct pupils' attention to the similar configurations of the east coast of South America and the west coast of Africa. Direct their attention to the map on page 137 of their texts. Again ask the pupils if it is possible that one big continent could have split and each of the parts have drifted away.

Using the map in the chapter, discuss the other similarities. Similarity of rocks and minerals, similarity of mountain formations, and similarity of the remains of living things. (Note: At this point the subject of fossils has not been introduced. Therefore, refer to "remains," such as shells and imprints of shells.) You may wish to discuss how different forms of life develop in different continents when the continents are separated. However, if the continents are connected, the same or similar forms of life can move back and forth from continent to continent. Thus, the same forms of life develop on all the continents.

Point out that the remains of tropical life have been found near the poles. Challenge pupils to explain how such forms of life could have survived the cold climates of the polar regions. Lead them to conclude that at one time, these regions were closer to the equator and that over very long periods of time, they drifted toward their present polar positions.

At this point you could introduce and discuss the magnetic properties of ocean floor rocks. Point out that the earth is like a giant bar magnet with a magnetic field. Use a compass and a bar magnet to demonstrate and explain the magnetic poles. Tell the class that certain iron-rich rocks form with their atoms in alignment with the magnetic poles. From a study made of these rocks, scientists have discovered that the earth's magnetic poles have reversed many times. If we know the pattern of change, we can trace the movement of a continent by studying the direction in which the atoms of the iron-rich rocks are aligned.

Summarize the lesson by listing the evidence which supports the theory of continental drift.

*Answer These*
1. b
2. a
3. a

## 9. What are crustal plates?

Draw a diagram on the board or use a transparency to explain that the plates are pieces of solid crust and mantle floating on a partially molten mantle. Demonstrate how the plates move with two blocks of wood floating in a fish tank. Use color to divide each block into a top and bottom half. The blocks of wood represent the lithosphere, with the upper half representing the crust and the lower half representing the upper mantle portion. Float the two blocks so that they touch each other. Place your hand in the water under the wood and force a piece of chalk up between the two blocks. Direct the pupils to observe how the blocks move apart. Point out that there is a force pushing upward through the lithosphere which forces the plates apart.

Direct the pupils' attention to the mid-ocean ridge shown in the diagram on page 139. Tell the class that magma is pushing up through this ridge. Elicit that it is the force of the magma that causes the plates connected to the ridge to spread apart.

Referring to the diagram of convection currents within the earth, point out that while molten material is pouring onto the surface at one point, at another region rock material is moving down into the earth.

*Answer These*
1. c
2. b
3. c
4. b

*Now Try This*
1. MANTLE
2. CURRENTS

## 10. How does plate motion affect the earth's crust?

Have pupils recall from the previous lesson the force that causes the plates to move. Using a large map, guide the pupils to see that as the magma forces its way through the ridge, the North and South American plates move away from the European and African plates. Elicit from the pupils that the floor of the Atlantic Ocean is spreading and getting wider.

Using a transparency or board drawing, lead pupils to see how plates may lock together and pressure builds up. Have the class theorize what may happen when the plates come apart. Point out that this is one way an earthquake develops. Have the pupils explain why earthquake zones are located along the edges of plates.

Use blocks of wood to demonstrate other plate motions. Locate the San Andreas fault on the map. Demonstrate the plate motion along the fault. Assign reports on the San Andreas fault. Display pictures that show displacement of features located along the fault.

Use two soft-covered books to demonstrate what happens when two plates meet. Show how one moves under the other and how the upper one folds upward. Elicit from the pupils that this upward fold forms a mountain range.

Summarize the lesson by having the pupils develop an understanding of the association between faults, earthquakes, and volcanoes and the edges of crustal plates.

*Answer These*
1. c      3. b
2. a      4. c

## UNIT 6: REVIEW

### Fill In the Blank
1. the Ring of Fire
2. ocean trench
3. ocean floor spreading
4. crustal plates
5. continents
6. anticline
7. syncline
8. fissure
9. surface wave
10. tremor

### Multiple Choice
1. c   2. c   3. a   4. b
5. a   6. b   7. c   8. a

## UNIT 7. THE RECORD IN THE ROCKS

### 1. How can you learn about the earth's past?

To introduce the topic of historical geology, compare the earth scientist to a detective. The earth scientist looks for clues and evidence that reveal the earth's past. Discuss the various techniques that the earth scientist uses to learn about the earth's history.

Place a sheet of colored paper on a table. Cover it with a different colored sheet. Continue this procedure to illustrrate the law of superposition. Younger rocks are usually found on top of older ones. Show pictures of the Grand Canyon and discuss the age of the layers.

Review the parts of the atom. Define isotope and radioactivity. Point out that uranium-238 is a radioactive element. It loses particles from its nucleus and eventually changes to an isotope of lead. It takes 4½ billion years for half of all the uranium in a rock to become lead (half-life). The change takes place at a constant rate, and nothing will affect the rate of change. By measuring the percent of lead and uranium in an igneous rock, the age of the rock can be determined. This method can be used with other elements. Carbon-14 is the isotope of carbon that is used to date organic remains. It has a half-life of 5,600 years. Carbon-14 dating cannot be used for remains much over 50,000 years old.

*Answer These*
1. c
2. c
3. c

*Now Try These*
URANIUM
CARBON

### 2. What are fossils?

Display a fossil impression. Define a fossil as the remains or evidence of animals and plants that lived on earth in the past. A paleontologist studies fossils to learn about events in prehistoric times (before written records). Make a fossil impression by placing a seashell in clay. Remove the shell and fire the clay in a kiln. Use a diagram or transparency to show how fossils form in sedimentary rocks.

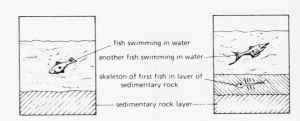

Display fossils of molds and casts. The "Do This at Home" can serve as a classroom activity.

*Answer These*
1. bones, shells, footprints, plant and animal remains, impressions (casts and molds)
2. We find fossils of them. A fossil may be a footprint, a bone, or an impression of a bone.
3. The soft parts of the animal rot away before they can form fossils.
4. Actual parts of the body of the animal; molds; casts.

### 3. How were some fossils formed?

Freeze a bean seed in an ice cube and display it in class. Discuss the Siberian mammoth and the La Brea tar pits in California. Show films or filmstrips on fossils. Assign reports on dinosaurs and other prehistoric animals. Have pupils bring in pictures, charts, and models. A trip to a museum of natural history would allow the pupils to view fossils of dinosaurs.

*Answer These*
1. b
2. a
3. c
4. c
5. b

### 4. What can we learn from fossils?

Tell the pupils that fossils of sea life were found in desert regions in Arizona and that coral fossils were found in the Antarctic. Point out that coral grows in warm, shallow waters. Have the pupils describe the ancient climates these regions must have had. Give other examples, such as glacial deposits in New York City and the Petrified Forest in the Arizona desert.

Have pupils speculate on why dinosaurs became extinct. Discuss other extinct animals and endangered species. Use the example of the horse to illustrate the subject of mutations. Use filmstrips to show how life changed through the ages. Point out that humans did not live on earth at the same time as dinosaurs.

*Answer These*
1. Fossils tell us how living things have changed through the ages.
2. The horse's size, teeth, legs, and toes have changed.
3. Man appeared about 1 or 2 million years ago. (Note: New fossil discoveries seem to be pushing the origin of man-like species farther and farther into the past. In October, 1974, fossils classified as the genus *Homo* 4 million years old were reported.)

*Now Try This*
FOSSIL

### 5. What is the geologic time scale?

This lesson can be presented as a laboratory experience. Use actual fossils or kits of plastic fossils. If models of fossils are not available, pictures could be substituted. Obtain pictures of crabs, crayfish, lobsters, starfish, lampshell, octopus, and squid. Have students make comparisons. Pupils can use clay and plaster of Paris to make their own collection of fossils.

Using a diagram or transparency, point out that some fossils are found only in a certain layer of sedimentary rock. This proves that these animals lived only at this time and then became extinct. Review how the law of superposition can tell the age of a fossil.

Develop the use of index fossils in determining the age of sedimentary rocks. Discuss the chart on page 153 and emphasize
  (a) timetable of earth's history,
  (b) division into eras,
  (c) how long ago,
  (d) time each form of life lived and died out (dinosaur, vs. man).
Use filmstrips to show different types of life forms.

Refer to the idea in Module 1, Unit 1, that earth scientists are detectives. Piecing together the history of life on earth and the actual dates of particular life forms is like making the pieces of a jigsaw puzzle fit. Some rocks can be dated by radioactivity. This helps us to date sedimentary rocks that are found with them. If certain fossils are found in these rocks, but not in earlier or later

rocks, these fossils become index fossils. They can help us date other rocks that contain these fossils, when other dating methods are not available. This in turn helps us date still other rocks nearby; and so on.

*Answer These*
1. b
2. c
3. b
4. b
5. a

### 6. What happens to the remains of living things?

Make charcoal as described in the experiment on page 154. Display examples of fossil fuels. Assign reports on each. Have the pupils examine samples of peat, lignite, bituminous coal, and anthracite coal. Show a filmstrip on the formation of coal. Discuss sedimentary and metamorphic forms of coal. Many petroleum companies provide films on natural gas and oil formation.

*Answer These*
1. Carbon.
2. Wood, coal, natural gas, petroleum.
3. They are believed to come from the remains of living things.

## UNIT 7: REVIEW

**Modified T/F**
  1. F, petroleum
  2. T
  3. F, LEAD
  4. F, EPOCH
  5. T
  6. T
  7. T, IN THE OCEAN
  8. T
  9. F, MOLD
  10. F, ADAPTING

**Multiple Choice**
1. c   2. a   3. c   4. b
5. b   6. b   7. a   8. a

## UNIT 8. WATER

### 1. What makes water change its phase?

Display some ice cubes in one beaker and some liquid water in another beaker. Direct pupils' attention to the liquid collecting in the beaker with the ice cubes. Elicit that the ice is melting and changing to liquid water. Guide the class to understand that water and ice are different phases of the same substance. Ice is simply solid water.

Ask pupils why ice melts in the room, while water freezes in the freezer section of a refrigerator. Elicit that it is warmer in the room than in the freezer. Heat is needed to melt a solid. The air in the room is warmer than the ice, and heat moves from the air to the ice, causing it to melt. Water placed in a freezer is warmer than the air around it. Heat moves from the water, causing it to cool and change from a liquid to solid ice.

It can be pointed out here that not all solids change directly into liquids when heat is added. Some solids (e.g. dry ice, or frozen carbon dioxide, and iodine crystals) change directly into gases. The process is called sublimation.

Boil some water in another beaker. Elicit that steam (water vapor) represents another phase of water (gaseous state). Use this illustration to develop the concept that liquids can change to gases with the addition of heat.

Elicit that solids can be changed to liquids and liquids to gases by adding heat. From this draw the inference that gases can be changed to liquids and liquids to solids by removing heat.

Point out that the changing of a liquid to a gas is called evaporation.

*Answer These*
1. solid
2. absorb
3. absorb
4. gas
5. give up

*Now Try This*
rain - liquid
snow - solid
water vapor - gas
ocean - liquid
river - liquid
cloud - liquid (tiny droplets of water)
steam - gas (true steam is an invisible gas)
ice - solid
lake - liquid
fog - liquid (tiny droplets of water)
mist - liquid (tiny droplets of water)
puddle - liquid

## 2. What is the water cycle?

Evaporation of liquids can be demonstrated using alcohol, perfume, or ammonia. If allowed to stand in an open container in front of the classroom, these liquids will evaporate, and diffusion will carry the molecules through the room. Review the mechanics of evaporation from the previous lesson. Elicit that sunlight supplies the heat energy for evaporation of surface water on earth.

Place a beaker of ice cubes over some boiling water. Have the pupils observe water condensing on the outside of the beaker. Identify this as condensation. Point out that the water condensing on the beaker does not come from the ice cubes.

Using the drawing on page 161, explain the water cycle. Trace evaporation of water from oceans, rivers, lakes, soil, plants and animals into the air. Elicit that as the air cools water vapor condenses. Point out that clouds are tiny droplets of water. Define precipitation.

Develop the concept that water evaporated in one part of the world may fall as precipitation in another part. Point out that water falling toward the earth may evaporate before it even hits the earth, hence a water cycle within a water cycle.

*Answer These*
1. oceans, rivers, lakes and soil
2. Air conditioning water vapor loses heat. The water vapor condenses into tiny droplets of water forming clouds.
3. The absorption of heat causes water to evaporate from the surface of the earth. Cooling causes the water vapor in the air to condense and return to the earth as some kind of precipitation.

*Now Try This*
1. snow
2. rain

## 3. How does water get into the ground?

Pour a small amount of water into a beaker of soil. Let the pupils observe how the water sinks down through the soil. Review soil porosity and permeability.

Refer to the diagram on page 162 when discussing the water table. Demonstrate the water table by placing gravel into an empty fish tank. Give the gravel an irregular surface. Pour some water into the tank and have the pupils observe how it saturates the lower portion of the gravel. Add more water and observe how the level of water rises. Note the formation of lakes in the shallow hollows at the surface.

Teach water retention as a laboratory exercise. Set up several funnels, each containing different sized particles. Set the funnels on a stand and pour water into each one. Have the pupils measure the amount of water retained by each sample. Be sure that all of the particles are dry before using or reusing them.

*Answer These*
1. b
2. a
3. c
4. a

## 4. What is hydrology?

Elicit that 3/4 of the earth's surface is water. Then have the class make a list of all the places water can be found. Have them conclude that most of the water found on earth is in the oceans. Have pupils recall the fact that ocean water is salty and cannot be used directly for drinking or agriculture.

Discuss the importance of fresh water. Have pupils relate stories of persons caught in the desert without water. Bring in articles about drought-stricken areas. Describe how civilizations developed where there was an abundance of fresh water (e.g. the fertile crescent). Have the class speculate how long one would survive without fresh water.

Point out that only 3% of all water on earth is fresh water, and most of that is frozen in polar ice caps. Develop the idea of the importance of studying methods of collecting and conserving fresh water.

Define the word hydrology. Point out that the prefix hydro means "pertaining to water." Give examples of other words containing this prefix (e.g. hydrant, hydrolysis, hydroelectric power, hydrologist). Discuss the work of hydrologists and why their work is so important. Invite an employee of the local water company to explain some of their operations.

Review the water cycle and guide pupils to see that the total amount of water on earth does not change. Lead them to see that the demand for more fresh water is increasing. Point out that, at this moment, the supply is sufficient. Ask them what effect pollution has on the supply of fresh water and what will happen if the demand becomes greater than the supply.

*Answer These*
1. a
2. c
3. b

## 5. What is hard water?

The presence of chloride, sulfate, and bicarbonate salts of calcium, magnesium and iron cause "hard" water. When soap is added to hard water, metallic salts are precipitated. Thus, much soap is wasted before a cleaning lather can form, and the salts often form a scum on the water that can cause stains in clothing.

Motivate the lesson by adding a few drops of liquid soap (not detergent) to one test tube containing distilled water and to a second test tube containing hard water. Shake both well and have pupils observe the lack of suds or lather in the tube containing hard water. (Hard water can be produced by dissolving a small amount of calcium bicarbonate in water.)

Hard water can cause boiler scale to form in pipes carrying heated water. The carbonate precipitates clog the pipes, as the photograph on page 167 illustrates.

*Answer These*
1. b   2. b   3. a   4. b

## 6. How is water purified?

Motivate the lesson by asking where our drinking water comes from. Elicit the fact that it comes from wells and/or reservoirs, and therefore has to be purified.

Demonstrate sedimentation by mixing some clay and sand in water and allowing the suspension to stand.

Demonstrate coagulation by adding some soil to a 100 ml graduated cylinder containing 80 ml of water. Agitate the cylinder to mix the soil. Add 15 ml of saturated alum solution and 5 ml of concentrated ammonium hydroxide. Have pupils observe the clearing of the suspension.

Demonstrate filtration by filtering some clay out of a water suspension.

You may wish to relate aeration of drinking water with aeration of water in a fish tank.

*Answer These*
1. c          3. b
2. c

*Now Try This*

| A | B |
|---|---|
| Sedimentation | Standing |
| Coagulation | Adding chemicals that make small particles clump together |
| Filtration | Passing through a filter |
| Chlorination | Adding chlorine |
| Aeration | Spraying into the air |

## UNIT 8: REVIEW

**Matching**
1. hydrologist
2. hydrology
3. saturated
4. pores
5. ground water
6. absorb
7. phase
8. precipitation
9. cycles
10. evaporation

**Multiple Choice**
1. c   2. b   3. a   4. b
5. c   6. a   7. c   8. c

## UNIT 9. THE OCEANS

### 1. How can we study the oceans?

Using a large wall map, show the pupils that all of the oceans are connected. Elicit the fact that about three-fourths of the earth's surface is covered by water. Ask the pupils to name the different oceans. Assign reports on famous oceanographers, such as Mathew Maury, Edward Forbes, John Brooke, C. Wyville Thomson, Fridtjof Nansen, William Beebe, Jacques Yves Cousteau, Jacques Piccard, and Donald Walsh. Include experiments done by Alexander the Great. Assign reports on Sealab I and II, the Trieste, H.M.S. Challenger, the Alvin, and other oceanographic vessels or projects. Assign the making of posters and models of oceanographic instruments.

Display various instruments used in oceanographic studies. If a body of water is nearby, plan a trip to demonstrate the use of the various instruments. If your area has a local scuba club, invite someone from the club to discuss diving, and if possible, to give a demonstration.

Use a ripple tank to show that waves are reflected when they strike a surface. A glass tray placed on the stage of an overhead projector will serve for this demonstration. A ruler can be used to set a wave in motion at one end of the tray. Pupils will see the wave travel to the far end of the tray and bounce off. Draw an analogy between the water waves and sound waves. Stress that this ripple tank is merely a model designed to help in understanding the nature of sound waves and echoes. Guide the pupils to see how echoes can be used to determine ocean depths. Work out a problem to illustrate how it is done. Display sounding charts. These can be obtained from any institution which offers courses in oceanography.

*Answer These*
1. a          4. a
2. c          5. a
3. b

*Now Try These*
1. c          4. b
2. f          5. e
3. a          6. d

2. 4500 meters

### 2. How does the temperature of ocean water vary?

This lesson could be conducted as a lab. Charts showing temperature readings of ocean water at various depths at one location could be plotted on a graph. In a class discussion of the graphed data, the following items should be noted:
(a) The temperature remains fairly constant for a certain depth.
(b) The temperature decreases rapidly after that point until it reaches a deeper point.
(c) At that depth the temperature stops dropping and remains constant. Identify the upper layer as surface water, the second layer at the thermocline, and deep water below the thermocline. Have pupils explain why the temperature of the surface water or mixed water layer remains fairly constant. Elicit that sunlight warms this layer. Wave action, currents, and winds keep this upper layer mixing, thus keeping the temperatures of this layer about the same.

A graph showing surface readings at various latitudes could also be constructed. Pupils should be able to explain that surface waters around the equator are warmer than those at the poles. Show pictures of ice floating in polar waters.

Demonstrate how the addition of salt lowers the freezing point of water. Half fill 2 beakers with distilled water. Dissolve 10 grams of salt in one beaker. Place a thermometer into each beaker. If dry ice is available place both beakers into the dry ice and have the class note the temperatures at which the water in both beakers turns to ice. If you cannot obtain dry ice, place both beakers in a freezer overnight. Have the class note that the distilled water is frozen while the salt water is a slush. Have pupils recall what happens when salt is thrown on an icy sidewalk.

*Answer These*
1. b
2. b
3. a
4. a
5. b

## 3. What changes the salinity of ocean water?

Exhibit 2 beakers, one (labeled A) half filled with tap water and another (labeled B) half filled with seawater. (To compare artificial seawater see T.E. Unit 5, Module 11.) Review why seawater tastes salty.

In another beaker, mix 35 g of salt in 965 ml of water. Have pupils note the amount of each material. Tell them that the solution being mixed is similar to seawater. Ask how they can tell which of the first two samples is most like this imitation seawater. Elicit that the seawater and imitation seawater both taste salty. Allow a pupil to taste a drop of each sample.

Define the term salinity. Elicit that the salinity of seawater is 35 parts per thousand. Explain how this solution is made. Ask how the salinity of a solution can be increased or decreased.

Point out that the salinity of seawater varies slightly from place to place. Ask what conditions could change the salinity of seawater. Guide pupils to conclude that rivers pouring fresh water into the ocean and constant rainfall will lower the salinity of ocean water in those local areas. On the other hand, in warm regions with a high evaporation rate, the salinity will be increased.

*Answer These*
1. a
2. b
3. a
4. a
5. b
6. a

*Now Try These*
1. dilute
2. salinity

## 4. What does the ocean floor look like?

Have the pupils examine the profile of the ocean floor shown in this lesson. Have them recall from the previous lesson how soundings make it possible to obtain such a picture. Using the profile, identify the shelf and slope. Display a large world map which uses color to indicate ocean depths. Point out that in certain areas, the shelf is narrow (western coast of U.S.), and in other areas, it extends over 100 miles in width (between Siberia and Alaska). Locate and discuss the continental slope. Point out that the slope drops sharply to the ocean basin.

Review the significance of ridges from the lesson on Continental Drift. Locate the ridge on the profile. Elicit from the pupils that islands form where the tops of the ridge extend above sea level. Assign a report on Surtsey.

If reports were assigned in lesson 1, have a pupil read the report on the bathyscaphe Trieste I. Discuss what Piccard and Walsh observed. Ask different pupils to locate several deep trenches on the world map. Compare the height of Mt. Everest with the depth of the Mariana Trench.

There are several good relief maps of the ocean floor that are large enough for class use. *National Geographic*, June 1968, has an insert map of the Atlantic Ocean, and the issue of October 1969 has one of the Pacific Ocean. *Time Life* books have one of each Ocean also.

Assign reports and have the pupils start a picture collection of the various features of the ocean floor.

*Answer These*
| | |
|---|---|
| 1. b | 3. a |
| 2. c | 4. a |

## 5. What materials make up ocean sediments?

Have pupils recall how ocean dredges obtain samples of sea floor sediments. Also refer back to Module 11, Unit 5, which deals with the disposition of material that erodes from the land. Elicit that much of the material settles on the continental shelf and slope. Have pupils describe what materials one might expect to find there. Challenge the pupils to explain why little of the sediment from the land reaches the ocean basins.

Describe the material that makes up the ocean floor. Use a bioscope to show slids of globigerina, radiolaria and diatoms. Guide pupils to see how these microscopic animals form the ooze of the ocean basin.

Have the pupils recall what an iceberg is. Guide them to see how an iceberg can be the source of some ocean floor sediment.

Trace volcanic ash and meteoritic dust from its point of origin to the ocean basin floor.

This would be an appropriate time to use films or filmstrips describing the physical features of the ocean floor and its sediments.

*Answer These*
1. a
2. c
3. b
4. c
5. a

*Now Try These*
1. SEDIMENT
2. OOZE

## 6. What causes ocean currents?

Define surface ocean currents as rivers of water flowing in the ocean. Have pupils recall that winds cause waves. Point out that winds also cause surface currents throughout the oceans.

Locate the Gulf Stream on a large wall map. Use red chalk to draw arrows on the map showing the direction of movement of the Gulf Stream. Elicit from the class that it is a warm current because it comes from the equatorial region. Direct attention to the fact that the current follows a curved path. Tell the class that all winds and surface ocean currents curve because the earth is turning (rotating).

Distribute notebook-sized world maps and lead pupils in locating other ocean currents. Instruct them to use a red pencil to draw arrows showing a warm current and a blue pencil for cold currents. Use colored chalk on the wall map to show cold and warm currents. Printed charts of ocean currents can be obtained from the Oceanographic Office of the U.S. Navy in Washington, D.C.

Discuss the effect of a warm current passing by a cold land mass. Point out that London, England, is farther north than all of the cities in Maine. Yet, the average wintertime temperature in London is several degrees warmer than that in Maine because of the Gulf Stream.

To demonstrate density currents prepare a solution of colored water using vegetable dye. Place the solution in the refrigerator for about one hour. Slowly pour the cold solution into a tank of water at room temperature. Point out that the cold water is denser than the water at room temperature. Have the pupils observe how the cold water sinks. Discuss how cold polar water moves along the bottom of the ocean.

Repeat the same demonstration substituting a colored super-saturated salt solution for the cold water solution. Elicit from the pupils that salt water must be denser than fresh water.

*Answer These*

| | |
|---|---|
| 1. b | 3. a |
| 2. a | 4. c |

## 7. What kinds of life are found in the ocean?

Elicit from the pupils the names of plants and animals found in the sea. Show pictures of various sea plants and animals and discuss the life activities of several of them. Compare them to the activities of some land animals.

Pose the question, "What do fish eat?" Elicit that they may eat other fish or insects or plants. Draw the following diagram on the board:

**large fish** $\xrightarrow{\text{eat}}$ **smaller fish** $\xrightarrow{\text{eat}}$ **plankton**

Introduce the class to plankton. Point out that plankton is the primary source of food for much of the life found in the sea.

Identify the diagram as a food chain. Some animals are the primary source of food for all living things, since the green plants can make their own food.

Assign reports on sea life—both plant and animal. If you are located close to the ocean, have pupils bring in seaweed. Seaweed can be preserved for display purposes. Set up salt-water and fresh-water aquaria. Have pupils collect and bring in as many forms of sea life as they can. Gallon jars can serve as the tanks. It is possible to use one air filter for 5 jars. Instruct pupils not to put too much into each jar. This activity can be conducted as a long-term project and may develop into a mini-course of marine biology.

*Answer These*

1. a
2. b
3. c
4. b
5. a

*Now Try This*

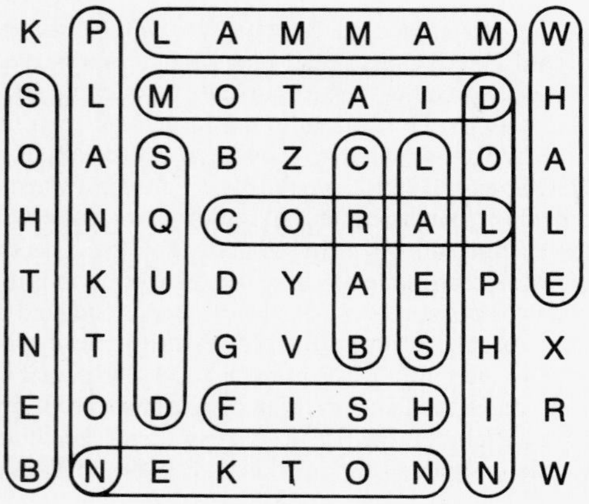

## 8. Where do we find life in the ocean?

Develop the concept that the environment is composed of all living and nonliving things that surround an organism. Have students examine their own environment. Guide them to see that light, water, air and temperature are some of the physical factors of an environment. It is important to point out that environments can change with place and time and these changes can be sudden or gradual.

Have pupils make a listing of the features of a marine environment which should include light, food source, temperature, salinity, water pressure and oxygen content.

Using a large wall chart and the diagram on page 186, describe the divisions of the marine environment.

Have pupils establish the fact that plants need light in order to grow. Elicit that light cannot penetrate too deeply into the water. Guide the pupils to see that most plant life is found at the upper level of the sea. Have the pupils explain why most animal life is found in this region too.

Elicit that temperature decreases with depth. Point out that pressure also increases with depth, and that a certain depth pressure is so great that it can crush a human. Have pupils describe the kind of organism that can live at such depths. Display photographs of organisms that live at that depth and deeper. Such photos can be found in National Geographic, Life Nature Series, and other books dealing with marine biology. Assign reports on how various forms of marine life adapt to their different environments.

Where possible, samples of seawater brought back from a beach field trip can lead to numerous laboratory lessons and class projects.

*Answer These*

1. a
2. b
3. a
4. b

*Now Try This*

1. splash zone
2. abyssal zone
3. bathyal zone
4. abyssal zone
5. abyssal zone
6. splash zone
7. bathyal zone
8. neritic zone
9. splash zone
10. bathyal zone

## UNIT 9: REVIEW

**Fill In the Blank**

1. echo
2. sun
3. −2°C
4. salinity
5. continental shelf
6. marine organisms
7. northern hemisphere
8. equator
9. diatoms
10. benthos

**Multiple Choice**

1. b   2. a   3. c   4. c
5. a   6. b   7. a   8. a

26

# UNIT 10. THE ATMOSPHERE

## 1. What is air?

As described in the text, a plastic bag can be used to demonstrate that air takes up space. When a glass is inverted over a floating cork in a tank of water, it can be noted that neither the cork nor the water can enter the glass when it is pushed down. Elicit the conclusion that there is air in the glass which prevents the water and cork from entering.

For further demonstration, the Finding Out More section illustrates that air takes up space. A discussion covering the reason why a liquid pours more easily from a can with 2 holes than with only one hole should follow. A triple-beam balance, as shown on page 191, can be used to weigh air. If a balance is not available a meter stick suspended on a string can be substituted.

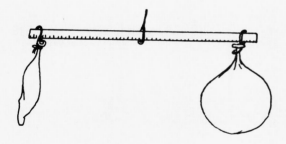

NOTE. Inflate one balloon to its limit so that the weight difference is significant.

This lesson can be used to introduce or review the concept that anything that occupies space and has mass is matter. It should be pointed out that air is matter. Hold up a glass and ask the pupils to describe the air inside. The chart on page 190 can be used to point out that the air is a mixture of gases. Reports can be assigned on each of these gases.

*Answer These*
1. Air is a colorless, odorless, and tasteless mixture of gases. It is made up of nitrogen, oxygen, argon, carbon dioxide, and other gases.
2. Air can be weighed by placing a deflated balloon on a balance and noting its weight. Then the balloon is filled with air and weighed again.
3. (a) carbon dioxide — 0.04%
   (b) argon — 0.94%
   (c) nitrogen — 78%
   (d) oxygen — 21%

## 2. What do we know about the gases in air?

Demonstrate that air is needed for burning by placing an inverted glass over a burning candle. Ask why the flame goes out.

Perform the experiment with the cork and candle on page 192 to show that only some of the air is used for burning. In performing this experiment, make a small depression in a wide cork. Use a short candle to prevent the cork from capsizing.

Refer to the chart on page 190 and list the gases found in air. Have the class recall that oxygen is needed for burning. Challenge the pupils to explain why the water rose in the cylinder. Set up the steel wool demonstration on page 192 together with a control test tube. Be sure there is no grease on the steel wool. Discuss the purpose of a control for an experiment.

After a day or two have the pupils note the rusting of the steel wool. Have them compare the level of the water in each tube and explain the reason the water rose in the test tube with the steel wool. Determine the percent of oxygen used up. Divide the height the water rose in the test tube by the total length of the tube. Then multiply this answer by 100.

Have the pupils recall the properties of carbon dioxide. Permit the pupils to read homework reports on carbon dioxide. Bromthymol blue can also be used to test for carbon dioxide. Carbon dioxide will change the color from blue to yellow or colorless. Use a chart to develop the carbon dioxide–oxygen cycle. Elicit the understanding that burning and breathing put carbon dioxide into the air while green plants remove it.

Direct the pupils' attention to the drawing of the nitrogen cycle on page 193. Elicit the concept that plants remove nitrogen from the soil. Display a package of fertilizer and have the pupils identify nitrogen compounds in it. Elicit the conclusion that fertilizer is added to the soil to replace the nitrogen removed. Display a leguminous plant or show a chart of leguminous plants. Point out the nodules on the roots of these plants and explain that bacteria live in these nodules. Tell the class that the bacteria take nitrogen from the air and make it usable in the soil.

*Answer These*
1. Fires need oxygen to burn. A covered fire will use up this oxygen and when there is no longer any oxygen left the fire will go out.
2. All of the oxygen will combine with the steel wool. This is about one-fifth or 20% of the air.
3. Plants get nitrogen from nitrogen compounds in the soil. These nitrogen compounds may have been produced by certain bacteria taking nitrogen from the air.

*Now Try These*
1. oxygen
2. carbon dioxide
3. nitrogen
4. carbon dioxide

## 3. What are the layers of the atmosphere?

Refer back to the diagram on page 12 and elicit the fact that the ocean of air that surrounds the earth is called the atmosphere.

Using the diagram on page 194 point out that the atmosphere can be described in terms of various regions or layers.

Ask pupils to suggest various methods that could be used to explore the layers of the atmosphere. Responses might include mountain-climbing expeditions, airplane observations, high-altitude balloons, or space satellites.

Using the diagram lead pupils to recognize that the troposphere is the layer closest to the earth's surface. Point out that this is a region of changing weather conditions. Establish the fact that within the troposphere the temperature decreases as the altitude increases.

Have pupils locate the tropopause. Direct them to see that the troposphere and stratosphere are separated by the tropopause. Point out that the tropopause varies in height, higher over warmer regions on earth than over colder ones.

Describe the stratosphere. Discuss why airplane pilots prefer to travel in this region. Point out that occupants of an airplane must be protected against low pressures, extreme cold, and lack of oxygen while traveling in this region. Discuss the importance of ozone in this layer.

Describe the ionosphere. You may want to review the structure of the atom in discussing ions. Using the diagram on page 195, explain how radio waves are bounced off this layer and sent around the earth. Microwaves and TV waves are not stopped by this layer. Satellites are used to reflect these waves back to earth. You may want to show pictures of the aurora which occurs in the ionosphere.

*Answer These*
1. Troposphere.
2. Stratosphere.
3. The ionosphere reflects these waves back to earth. The earth can also reflect these radio waves back to the ionosphere. In this way a radio signal can be sent around the earth.

*Now Try This*
1. troposphere
2. stratosphere
3. ionosphere
4. stratosphere
5. stratosphere
6. troposphere
7. ionosphere
8. stratosphere
9. troposphere
10. stratosphere

## 4. How does the earth get its heat?

Perform this as a laboratory lesson. Allow pupils to examine a radiometer. Show how it operates in sunlight but stops when the sunlight is blocked. Pupils may conclude that heat and light energy from the sun cause the movement of the radiometer. Call attention to the fact that there is a vacuum between the earth and sun. Pupils may conclude that heat and light may travel through "empty space." Identify heat and light movement through space as radiation. Have the pupils focus the sun's rays with the magnifying glass on a piece of white paper and a piece of carbon paper. Caution pupils to do this part of the experiment exactly as directed in order to avoid serious burns and injuries.

Permit pupils to obtain two identical containers (juice cans or collecting bottles). One should be painted black, the other white. Pupils should place a stopper and thermometer in each container. Both containers are placed in direct sunlight or about ½ meter from a source of heat (a 100-watt lamp). Have the pupils record the temperatures on the thermometers each minute for 5 minutes. Allow them to compare readings.

Using the illustration on page 197, discuss what happens to the sun's incoming solar radiation.

*Answer These*
1. Most of the earth's heat comes from radiation from the sun.
2. Light-colored clothing reflects light. Dark-colored clothes absorb light. When light is absorbed by the dark clothing it is changed to heat. Therefore, in the summer light-colored clothes are cooler.
3. On a cloudy day, the clouds absorb or reflect some of the sun's radiant energy. The energy does not reach the earth, and so the earth is cooler.

*Now Try This*
RADIANT

## 5. How is the atmosphere heated?

Demonstrate heat transfer by conduction by attaching a 15-cm strip of copper to a stand. Place a small piece of crayon on the end attached to the stand. Heat the other end of the strip. Direct the pupils' attention to the melting wax. Elicit the conclusion that heat is being transmitted along the metal.

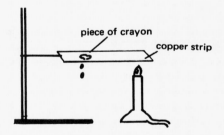

Review the concept that heat energy is related to the motion of molecules. Use marbles, a glass tray, and an overhead projector to show a model of conduction. Cover about three-fourths of the bottom of the tray with a single layer of marbles. Place the tray on the overhead projector. Agitate the marbles at one end of the tray. Pupils will note that the disturbance is "conducted" to the marbles at the other end.

Using the diagram on page 198, point out that the lower layer of the atmosphere, which touches the earth, is heated by conduction. Explain how the lower layer is also heated by the earth, which radiates heat originating from absorbed sunlight.

Demonstrate how the sun's short-wave radiation is converted into long-wave radiation and "trapped" in the lower atmosphere. Place two clear plastic shoeboxes in direct sunlight. Put a thermometer into each box and place a cover on one of the boxes. Have the class observe the temperature of both boxes over a period of time. Explain how the short waves are transmitted through the clear plastic. Point out that these waves are converted into long waves which cannot pass out through the plastic. Challenge pupils to explain why on a sunny day a closed car gets hotter inside the car than it is outside. Explain why this is called the "greenhouse effect."

*Answer These*
1. Conduction is the movement of heat between objects that are in contact.
2. The lower atmosphere touching the warmed earth is heated by conduction.
3. The earth absorbs radiant energy from the sun and becomes warm. The warmed earth then gives off radiation.

*Now Try This*
1. ABSORBED    2. RADIATES    3. CONDUCTION
The Finding Out More section can be conducted as a laboratory lesson.

## 6. How does heat move in the air?

Perform the demonstration with the balloon on page 200. Challenge pupils to account for the behavior of the balloon. Allow the flask to cool. Elicit the concept that air tends to expand when heated and contract when cooled. You may wish to point out that if heated air is prevented from expanding (as in a stoppered flask or in an auto tire), its pressure will increase. Reinforce this concept with an air thermometer. Ask pupils to explain how the thermometer works.

Demonstrate the convection box to the class. If a convection box is not available, one can be constructed with a fish tank and plywood cover. A one-inch drill can be used to make the holes. Elicit the understanding that when the air around the candle is heated, it expands, becomes lighter, and rises. Show the results of closing off the supply of cool air by closing the opening that contains the smoking cord. The convection currents will stop. Elicit examples of convection currents in air. Pupils may be familiar with hot air rising from radiators, stoves, hot pavement, etc. Use a pinwheel to show that the heat from a fire, illuminated light bulb, or hot plate moves upward by convection currents. Refer to the Do This At Home experiment and discuss how large balloons are used for travel. (Some pupils may have seen the movie "Around the World in 80 Days," which contained balloon scenes.)

*Answer These*      *Now Try This*
1. a                    1. conduction
2. c                    2. radiation
3. c                    3. convection

## 7. Which warms up faster, land or water?

Elicit the concept that on a hot summer day the land gets hot while the water stays cool. At night the reverse is true; the sand feels cooler than the water. Have the class set up the experiment as shown in the diagram. The thermometers should not touch the container. Place both thermometers just below the surface of the water and sand. Direct pupils to turn on the light and record the temperature each minute for 10 minutes. Then have them turn off the light and record the temperature each minute for 10 minutes.

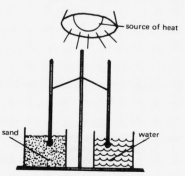

Challenge the class to explain why the land heats faster than the water. List the answers on the board. (a) The land is a better absorber of the sun's radiation; (b) the sun's rays go deep into the water, while on the land all of the heat remains at the surface; (c) water, being a liquid, can distribute the heat by convection currents, while the solid land cannot; and (d) water needs more heat to raise its temperature than land does.

Reason (d) refers to the specific heat of water in relation to other substances. It is not necessary to use the term specific heat. Use the Finding Out More section to demonstrate the specific heat of various materials.

*Answer These*          *Now Try This*
1. water      4. b       ACROSS     DOWN
2. a          5. a       3. radiant  1. water
3. c                     5. no       2. land
                         6. yes      4. no

## 8. What is air pressure?

Pose the question: What is air? Review that air is a colorless, odorless, and tasteless mixture of gases. Elicit a statement that air is matter. Define matter as anything that occupies space and has mass. Because of its mass, air has weight. Develop the relationship between weight and pressure. Elicit that air has weight and it exerts a pressure.

Use the demonstration on page 205 to demonstrate air exerts pressure. Challenge pupils to explain why the cardboard does not fall. Hold the glass in different directions and elicit the concept that the cardboard does not fall because air exerts pressure in all directions. Demonstrate and discuss how air pressure helps us do work. Place a straw in a glass of water. Place a finger over the end of the straw and lift the tube from the water. Have the class observe the water in the straw. Remove you finger from the straw. Have a pupil explain why the water remained in the straw when the finger was over the end of the straw and why the water fell out when the finger was removed.

Demonstrate and have the class explain the working of a chemistry pipette and a medicine dropper.

Set up a bottle with water. Insert a glass tube into a one-holed rubber stopper. Fit the stopper into the bottle. Ask a pupil to "suck up" the water. After several tries have the pupil remove the stopper and try again. Have the pupils explain why the water would go up the straw only when the stopper is off. Point out that air pressure allows us to drink with a straw.

*Answer These*
1. c          4. a
2. a          5. c
3. a

*Now Try This*
1. air
2. pressure

## 9. How much pressure does air have?

Perform the demonstration with the tin can on page 206. (Use a can shaped like the one shown in the drawing.) Before starting, measure the length and width of each slide and calculate the surface area of the sides of the can. Have the class note the steam coming out of the can. Remove the can from the heat before replacing the cap. The results will be dramatic. To speed up the procedure pour cold water over the can. Explain that as the can cools, the steam condenses. The pressure inside becomes less than that outside, and the can is crushed.

Using measurements made on the can calculate the total force on each side of the can. The students should be willing to grant that this amount of force is more than ample to crush the can. Then ask why the can is not crushed in normal use, since this outside pressure is always present. (Normally, the air pressure inside the can balances the pressure outside.) Have the pupils measure a book or their desk tops and calculate the total force of the air pressure being exerted on it.

Use marbles, a glass tray, and an overhead projector to show a model of the molecules in air. Use a few marbles spread far apart to illustrate air molecules high in the atmosphere. Add more marbles, and then point out that there are more air molecules closer to the earth. Guide the pupils to see that many more molecules are closer together and therefore produce a greater pressure. Tell the pupils the story of the Magdeburg hemispheres and demonstrate them before the class (NOTE: Have 2 pupils try to pull them apart while 2 other back up the first pair in case the hemispheres come apart.) If the hemispheres are not available use a plumber's plunger to hold up a lab stool. Wet the rubber plunger first. Have the class suggest other devices that use air pressure (e.g., suction-cup toys, canning jars, syringes, etc.).

*Answer These*
1. After the air was removed from the inside of the hemispheres, the air pressure outside was so great that 16 horses couldn't pull them apart. Air pressure can sometimes be stronger than a force of 16 horses.
2. 1,000 grams
3. There are more air molecules closer to the earth than there are high on a mountain. This greater amount of air produces a greater pressure.

## 10. How is air pressure measured?

Perform the demonstration on page 208. Begin with a small glass and use taller and taller cylinders. Ask the class to explain what keeps the water from falling down. Point out that at sea level air pressure can hold up a column of water 1,000 cm high.

Relate the following story to the class. It has been said that Otto von Guericke made a barometer filled with water. He constructed a long tube, over 1,000 cm (34 feet) tall. It ran from his cellar right up through and a little above the roof of his house. Water stood in the tube up to the 1,000 cm level. Von Guericke had placed a large wooden figure floating on top of the water within the tube. When the weather was nice, the figure could be seen, but when the weather was bad the figure and the water moved down below the roof. The townspeople thought von Guericke was involved with evil spirits and made him remove his weather device.

Display a jar of mercury. Allow a student to hold the jar (carefully!) and describe its weight. Tell the class that mercury is 13.6 times heavier (denser) than water. Elicit the concept that air pressure can support a column of water (1,000 cm), but only a much shorter column of mercury (76 cm). Construct a mercury barometer. Make sure the barometer tube is clean. Attach a funnel to the tube to prevent the mercury from spilling out. As you fill the tube hold it at about 45° angle to prevent bubbles of air from being trapped inside. If a bubble is trapped, tap the side of the tube so that it may rise to the top. When the tube is filled and contains no bubbles, disconnect the funnel and close the end with your finger. Invert the tube with the open end placed below some mercury in a small dish. Remove your finger and clamp the tube vertically to a stand. Use a meter stick to measure the height of the mercury above the level of the mercury in the dish. Use the diagram of the mercury barometer on page 208 to guide pupils to the understanding that it is the outside air pressure that supports the column of mercury in the tube.

Exhibit an aneroid barometer. Use the diagram on page 209 to explain how this type of barometer works.

Refer to the Finding Out More section and discuss why a barometer can be used to measure height above the ground. Point out that the altimeter used in airplanes to determine the airplane's height above the ground is actually an aneroid barometer.

*Answer These*
1. c
2. a
3. b

## 11. Why does air pressure change?

Refer back to Module 5 and review the concept of heat energy and its relation to the motion of molecules. Have the class recall the demonstration using the marbles, glass tray, and the overhead projector. Using the marbles, show how the heat makes the molecules move further apart. Remove some of the marbles and elicit the conclusion that for that area the weight of the air is now less than before.

Lead pupils to further conclude that warm air is lighter than cool air. Reverse the procedure to show that cool air is heavier than warm air. Using the same demonstration, lead pupils to conclude that since there are fewer air molecules in warm air as compared to cool air, a large volume of warm air has less weight and therefore exerts less pressure than the same volume of cool air. Reinforce the learning of this concept by asking the class to compare the air pressure on a warm sunny day with that of a cold winter day.

Students will probably have difficulty in understanding why the addition of water vapor molecules to air does not *increase* the weight of the air (for example, the way water adds to the weight of a sponge). The explanation is that the number of molecules in a given volume of air remains the same as the water vapor is added. Therefore, each water molecule takes the place of an air molecule. Since water molecules weigh less than air molecules, the total weight of a given volume of moist air is less than that of dry air.

A better analogy than the sponge is an elevator car that can hold a fixed number of people, say, 15 people. If 3 heavy people leave the car and 3 lighter ones take their places, the car will weigh less.

Use the Finding Out More Section to discuss problems encountered at high altitudes. Assign reports on high-altitude expeditions.

*Answer These*
| | |
|---|---|
| 1. warm | 4. cool |
| 2. warm | 5. moist |
| 3. cool | 6. dry |

*Now Try These*
1. PRESSURE
2. HEAVIER
3. LESS
4. DECREASES

## 12. How does air pressure change around the earth?

Elicit a statement that the equator is a warm region while the polar regions are cold. Using the diagram on page 212, direct the pupils' attention to the fact that the equatorial region receives the sun's direct rays whereas the polar regions receive slanted rays.

Demonstrate that direct rays are more intense than slanted rays by shining a beam of a slide projector or flashlight on a piece of cardboard. Lines drawn on the cardboard make observations easier. After shining the light directly on the cardboard, tilt it away from the light. Have the class compare the areas covered by the light each time and the intensity of the light each time. Refer back to the diagram on page 198 and review how the atmosphere is heated. Elicit from the pupils the fact that air above the poles is cold.

Review Module 11 and have the pupils identify the equator as a region of low pressure while the poles are regions of high pressure. Direct the pupils' attention to the Finding Out More section and establish the fact that cold air, being heavy, tends to move down, forcing warm air upward. Lead the pupils to see that this is convection.

*Answer These*
1. b
2. a
3. b

*Now Try This*
ACROSS
4. equator

DOWN
1. slanted
2. heat
3. poles

## 13. How are winds formed?

Review convection currents with the class. Refer back to the demonstrations in Module 6. Tell the pupils that the up-and-down movements of the air are called air currents.

Refer to the diagram at the top of page 214 and direct the pupils' attention to the cool, heavy air currents. Elicit the concept that this cool air moves down to the earth's surface.

Have the pupils recall how the smoke in the convection box was carried down with the cool air and moved along the bottom toward the candle. If dry ice is available, place a chunk in a 200-ml. beaker three-fourths full of water. Place the beaker on a table. (The dry ice cools the surrounding air and causes the water vapor in this air to condense.) Direct the pupils' attention to the movement of the cloud of moisture over the rim of the beaker. Have the pupils note how it moves down and outward over the surface of the table. Tell the class that similar horizontal movements of air over the earth are called winds.

Review the fact that polar regions are areas of high pressure and the warm equatorial regions are areas of low pressure. Elicit the concept that winds move from areas of high pressure toward areas of low pressure. To illustrate how fast winds move, use the analogy of sliding down a hill. Elicit the notion that the steeper the hill the faster you move. Point out that the greater difference between pressures the greater the speed of the winds.

Assign reports on the jet stream.

*Answer These*
1. a      3. a
2. b      4. unequally

*Now Try This*
1. Chicago to New York
2. New York to Boston
3. Philadelphia to New York

## 14. Which way does a wind blow?

Some sort of large visual device will prove helpful in teaching planetary winds. A large chart of a circle representing the earth can be displayed on the board. Different colored areas to denote pressure belts can be attached in the proper places as the development progresses. An overhead projector using a transparency and overlays showing pressure belts may also prove successful. As you develop the pressure belts have the pupils copy them into their notebooks.

Review that the polar regions are areas of high pressure and the warm equatorial region is one of low pressure. Mark these three pressure regions on your chart or transparency and have the pupils copy them on their charts. Point out the other high and low pressure belts. Locate them on your chart and have the students copy them.

Review that winds move from areas of high pressure toward areas of low pressure. Go back to the pressure-belt diagram and construct a diagram of the planetary wind systems. Remind pupils that a wind is named for the direction it comes from. Elicit the names of the winds, such as northeast and southeast blowing toward the equator, or northeast blowing away from the north pole. Have the class identify each wind belt drawn on the diagram.

*Answer These*
1. d
2. spins
3. west
4. east

*Now Try This*
Copy the diagram at the bottom of page 216. The names of the winds and pressure areas are, from north to south:
  High
Northeast
  Low
Southwest
  High
Northeast
  Low (Equator)
Southeast
  High
Northwest
  Low
Southeast
  High

## 15. What causes local winds?

Ask if any pupils recall sitting on a beach in the summer. Ask if they can remember which way the wind blows during the day. If they sit facing the ocean, does the wind hit their faces or does it hit the backs of their heads?

Refer back to Module 7. Review the experiment: "Which heats faster, land or water?"

Review how the atmosphere is heated. Elicit the fact that during the day the air over the land is warmer than the air over the water.

Lead the pupils to see that a low air pressure exists over the land and high air pressure over the water. Establish the idea that convection currents are set up between the land and the water and a breeze from the water to the land results. Have the class recall that winds are named for their source, and so this is called a sea breeze. Direct the pupils' attention to the diagram on page 218. Using the same development discuss nighttime breezes.

Refer to the diagram on page 219 and develop with the pupils an understanding of mountain and valley breezes.

Introduce the effect of seasonal changes on land and ocean. Establish the idea that during the winter the ocean is warmer than the land and during the summer the ocean is cooler than the land.

Display a large world map. Direct the pupils' attention to India. Discuss the wind direction over this country during the winter and summer.

*Answer These*
1. b     3. c
2. a     4. c

*Now Try These*
1. MONSOONS
2. SEA
3. LAND

## 16. How do we measure winds?

Display a wind vane. Demonstrate that it points in the direction the wind is coming from. Assign the construction of a wind vane as a project. Direct pupils to the directions given in the Do This at Home section on page 221.

Display an anemometer. Elicit the notion that it measures wind speed. Point out that the box under the cups produces a small amount of electricity. The anemometer is connected to a meter. The faster the cups turn the more electricity is produced. This is recorded by the meter and this tells the observer the wind's speed. Assign the construction of an anemometer as a home project. Allow pupils to use any materials and any design that will work.

Direct the pupils' attention to the chart on page 221. Have the pupils make daily observations and record their results.

Send out helium-filled balloons with attached cards in self-addressed stamped envelopes. Ask the receiver of the card to list the date, time, and location that the balloon was recovered. This activity will help illustrate how weather balloons are sent aloft and the pupils will enjoy getting the cards back. Discuss how wind speed and wind direction are determined by use of weather balloons.

*Answer These*
1. a    2. c    3. a    4. b

## UNIT 10: REVIEW

**Matching**
1. anemometer
2. rotate
3. water vapor
4. pressure
5. conduction
6. transmit
7. radiation
8. ion
9. nitrogen
10. air

**Multiple Choice**
1. a    2. c    3. a    4. a
5. c    6. a    7. c    8. c

# UNIT 11. WEATHER AND CLIMATE

## 1. How does water get into the atmosphere?

Make a large streak on the board with a wet sponge. Elicit the understanding that the mark begins to disapper because the water evaporates into the air. You may wish to introduce the molecular model of the evaporation process. Then have the class list sources from which water may evaporate and enter the air.

Bring a bunsen burner flame close to the board. Direct the pupils' attention to the water formed on the board. Lead the pupils to conclude that burning adds water vapor to the air.

Have a pupil breathe on the board. Draw attention to the water formed. Lead the pupils to conclude that breathing also adds water to the air. Cover a plant with a plastic bag and place it in direct sunlight. Tie the bag around the lowest part of the stem. After about 20 minutes the inside of the bag should become covered with moisture. Elicit the idea that plants give off water to the air. Tell the class that this process is called transpiration.

Establish the fact that water vapor is a gas which cannot be seen. Clouds, fog, mist, and steam are composed of tiny droplets of water and can be seen.

Discuss how heat and fans speed up the rate of evaporation. Use the Find Out More section on page 225 to discuss how these factors increase the rate.

*Answer These*
1. b     3. c
2. a     4. a

*Now Try These*
1. Evaporate
2. Ocean

## 2. What is humidity?

Review the previous lesson on how water gets into the atmosphere. Define humidity as the amount of water vapor in the air.

Display three beakers of different sizes. Demonstrate that each has a different capacity.

Display three sponges of different sizes. Place each sponge in a pan of water and let it soak up as much water as it can hold. Squeeze the water out of each sponge and measure the water each can hold. Establish the idea that each sponge has a different capacity. Recall that air can hold water, and the amount it holds is called its capacity. Have the pupils recall the demonstration in Module 6, Unit 10. Review the concept that air expands when heated and contracts when cooled. Elicit that warm air has a greater capacity than cool air. Point out that the capacity of air changes with the temperature.

Introduce the term absolute humidity and define it.

*Answer These*
1. c     3. a
2. b     4. a

## 3. What is relative humidity?

Review the terms humidity, capacity, and absolute humidity. You will again use the materials used in the previous lesson. Fill a beaker to its capacity. Allow a sponge to soak up as much water as it can. Elicit the understanding that it, too, is filled to its capacity. Introduce the term saturation. Define it and relate it to the atmosphere.

Refer to the diagram on page 229. Pour the water out of the beaker several times so that different amounts remain. Compare the amount of water in the beaker to the amount it can hold. Use fractions as well as percentages to describe how full the beaker is.

Discuss the amount of moisture in the air. Keep referring back to the beaker and its contents. Introduce and define relative humidity. Have the pupils do some problems in determining the relative humidity of the air. Assign reports on the T.H.I., refer to the Finding Out More section, and discuss the relationship between temperature and humidity.

*Answer These*
1. a        3. c
2. c        4. b

*Now Try These*
1. CAPACITY
2. HALF
3. PERCENT

## 4. How can we measure relative humidity?

The following can be performed as a laboratory lesson. Use the exercise mentioned in the first paragraph on page 230 to show that evaporation cools the surface from which it evaporates. Elicit the concept that heat is needed to cause a substance to evaporate. When the substance evaporates it removes heat from the surrounding area. Demonstrate that the faster a substance evaporates the cooler it leaves the surrounding area. Dip one thermometer into alcohol and one into water; then place them on a stand together with a dry thermometer. Have the pupils read the temperatures recorded by each thermometer. Elicit the conclusion that the alcohol evaporates the fastest.

Review capacity, absolute humidity, and relative humidity of the atmosphere. Lead pupils to see that the lower the relative humidity the faster the rate of evaporation.

Distribute simple psychrometers to the pupils. Direct their attention to the wet- and dry-bulb temperatures on the psychrometer. Demonstrate how to operate the psychrometer. Moisten the cloth on the wet bulb and spin the thermometers. Use the chart on page 231 to show the pupils how to find relative humidity. Allow each pupil to determine the relative humidity of the air. Continue to find the relative humidity for several days and note patterns for weather prediction. Assign as a project the construction of a hair hygrometer. Discuss the effect of moisture on hair length.

Distribute strips of blotting paper coated with cobalt chloride. Refer to Do This At Home section on page 227.

*Answer These*
1. c        3. a
2. c        4. c

*Now Try This*
37%
87%
50%

## 5. How does water come out of the air?

Review evaporation. Elicit the understanding that water will change from a liquid to a gas when heat is added to it.

Elicit that condensation is the opposite of evaporation. When the air is cooled some of the water vapor in it may change from a gas to a liquid. Have the pupils recall that warm air can hold more moisture than cool air. Develop the concept that when air cools, its capacity decreases. When the capacity and the absolute humidity

are equal the air is saturated. The cooler the air, the less is its capacity to hold moisture and condensation occurs.

The Do This At Home section can be performed as a classroom laboratory exercise. Have the pupils record the dew point of the air in the room. Permit the pupils to cite examples of dew formation. Ask why dew forms late at night or early in the morning. Discuss the formation of frost. Ask the pupils to give examples of frost formation.

*Answer These*
1. a        3. c
2. b        4. c

*Now Try These*
1. DEW
2. FROST

## 6. Why does it rain?

Review the concept that cooling the air to its dew point will cause the water vapor in it to condense. Have the pupils recall exhalation on a cold winter day. Elicit the memory that exhaled air is warm (37°C) and filled with moisture. When exhaled air hits the cool outer air, moisture in it condenses and we see a cloud of "smoke."

To show how clouds form, set up the demonstration shown in the diagram. Have a pupil pump air into the jar containing a small amount of water. (The rubber stopper may pop up, therefore hold it down with your hand.) After 4 or 5 strokes with the pump release the pinch clamp. A faint cloud may appear. Add some chalk dust or smoke from a burning match to the jar and perform the demonstration again. A cloud should form.

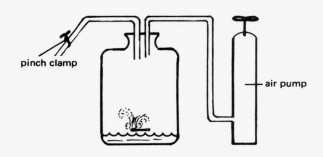

Another way to demonstrate how a cloud forms would be to place a small amount of water in a wide mouth jar (restaurants use salad dressing or pickles from such large jars). Cover the jar with a rubber membrane. Shake the jar for about 30 seconds. Remove the rubber and add some chalk dust or smoke. Replace the rubber tightly and, with your fist, push the membrane into the jar. After 10 seconds remove your fist quickly and observe the cloud that forms within the jar.

Tell the pupils that when air is compressed it warms up and when it expands it cools.

A $CO_2$ cartridge of the type used at home to make seltzer can be used to demonstrate cooling by expansion. Allow the pupils to feel the cartridge before and after puncturing. Elicit the observation that the expansion of the escaping gas cools the surrounding area.

Direct the pupils' attention to the cloud-forming demonstration. Develop with them the understanding that in both jars the air was compressed. This warmed the air and allowed the air to pick up some water. When the pressure was released the air cooled and some of the water condensed to form a cloud. Point out that dust or smoke was needed for the cloud to form.

Explain to the class that rising air is cooling and expanding. Elicit the concept that clouds form when water vapor cools into droplets of water that collect around particles of dust or smoke.

A fog is a cloud that forms near the ground. Demonstrate the formation of a fog by filling a flask with hot water. Pour out most of the water, leaving about one inch at the bottom. Place an ice cube over the opening of the flask. Have the pupils explain why a fog forms in the flask.

Discuss the formation of rain and snow with the class. Make snow in the classroom with the compressed $CO_2$ fire extinguisher. The demonstration works well on warm days with high humidity. (Give one short blast with the extinguisher. **Be sure that after each use the extinguisher is checked to see that it is still usable for extinguishing fires.**)

Discuss the various forms of precipitation and explain their differences. Assign reports on the different forms of precipitation. Have the pupils make simple rain gauges. Ask for reports on "cloud seeding" and artificial rainmaking.

*Answer These*
1. Clouds are made up of billions of tiny water droplets and ice crystals that form around dust and other particles in the air.
2. A fog is a cloud that forms near the ground.
3. Rain, snow, sleet, hail.
4. Snow is formed from crystals of ice; rain forms from droplets of water.

## 7. How do we identify clouds?

Films, filmstrips, photographs, and actual observations should be used in this lesson to describe cloud types.

Construct the following chart with the class as you describe the shapes and explain how the various types of clouds are formed.

| Name of cloud | Description | How formed |
|---|---|---|
| cirrus | light and feathery | formed from ice crystals high in the troposphere |
| cumulus | big and puffy with flat base | formed in vertical columns as currents of warm air rise rapidly |
| stratus | spread out in blanket-like layers | low clouds |

Assign the taking of pictures of clouds. (Use a filter on the camera.) Identify the clouds in the pictures and post them on a bulletin board. Have the pupils make daily observations of the types of clouds. Relate cloud types to the daily weather conditions.

*Answer These*
1. a
2. c
3. b

*Now Try This*
1. stratus
2. cumulus
3. cirrus

## 8. How does weather affect us?

The day before this lesson assign newspaper weather reports. Develop a list of factors which describe weather using these reports.

Discuss and list occupations and industries that rely on weather forecasts. Be sure to include personal needs.

At this time, have the students begin making their own weather observations. Allow 5 minutes each day for groups of pupils to make and record weather observations. Try to arrange for the observations to be made at the same time each day. Assign some pupils to observe during the weekends. Review care and operation of instruments used in making these observations. Rotate assignments so that all have an opportunity at each weather factor. Initial observations should be done together. After that, check the students' measurements periodically. Daily observations should include air pressure, air temperature, amount of precipitation during the last 24 hours, appearance of the sky and the type of clouds, wind speed, wind direction, and relative humidity. Make the observations for about 2 weeks and then look for patterns such as humidity and precipitation or air pressure and precipitation. Have the class elect a group to become the school weather forecasters. Compare the class observations with newspaper reports.

Discuss the difference between climate and weather. Ask pupils to bring in almanacs. Discuss the accuracy of almanac weather predictions.

*Answer These*
1. b
2. c
3. a

*Now Try This*
1. e      4. a
2. b      5. c
3. d

## 9. How do we get our weather?

Review with the pupils how the atmosphere is heated. Refer back to page 198 if necessary. Use the sea breeze as an example and have the pupils recall how air above the land and water gets its heat characteristics. Ask a pupil to describe the atmosphere of a room that houses an indoor swimming pool. Elicit the observation that the air is warm and damp. Point out that the water from the pool evaporates into the air. Have the pupils describe and explain the atmospheric conditions of a greenhouse, sauna, and indoor skating rink.

Define and describe an air mass. Describe the various types of air masses. Guide the pupils to see that air masses above a region take on the temperature and humidity of that region.

Use the overhead projector and a transparency of the United States to illustrate the various types of air masses and where they form. Use overlays to trace the movement of air masses across the country.

Have the pupils explain how air masses bring various types of weather to a region. Challenge the pupils to explain how observation of movement of air masses can help predict weather.

*Answer These*
1. b
2. a
3. c
4. c

*Now Try This*

| Type of air mass | Kind of weather it brings | Where formed |
|---|---|---|
| Continental polar | cold, dry | over land, at the poles |
| Maritime polar | cold, moist | over water, at the poles |
| Continental tropical | warm, dry | over land, at the equator |
| Maritime tropical | warm, moist | over water, at the equator |

## 10. What happens when air masses meet?

Review air masses and point out that the leading edge of the air mass is known as a front. An oversimplified demonstration can be used to illustrate fronts. Fill a large bottle halfway with water and fill the rest with heavy motor oil. Have the pupils identify the water as being more dense than the oil. Stopper the bottle and turn it on its side. Direct the pupils' attention to the movement of the liquids. Tell the class that the boundary between the two fluids represent a front. Elicit the fact that cold air is denser than warm air. Allow the pupils to point out that the water represents a cold air mass and the oil a warm air mass. Direct their attention to the water moving under the oil and the oil sliding over the water. Have the pupils note the turbulence that occurs along the "front" where the two fluids are in contact.

Discuss the characteristics of a cold air mass: dense, high pressure, dry, low temperatures; and those of a warm air mass: low pressure, moist, and high temperature.

Develop the sequence of events when a cold air mass meets with a warm air mass. Refer to the diagram on page 242. Using the diagram on page 243, develop the sequence of events when a warm air mass comes in contact with a cold air mass.

Discuss what is meant by a stationary front.

*Answer These*
1. east     5. a
2. c        6. a
3. changes  7. b
4. b

*Now Try This*
1. cold
2. warm
3. stationary

## 11. What is a station model?

This lesson can be performed as a laboratory lesson. Refer back to Module 8 and discuss how a weather forecast is constructed. Using the symbols on pages 244 and 245, construct a station model on the board. Construct a second one on the board, and allow the pupils to place the proper symbols in the proper places.

In discussing the millibar unit used to show air pressure, have the pupils recall that millimeters of mercury were used with the barometer. Point out that the millibar is another unit of measurement that is used to measure air pressure. Prepare a list of readings taken at different cities and have the pupils construct station models for each. Then have the pupils examine station models for other cities and have them make a list of the various weather factors for each city.

*Answer These*
1. c        3. b
2. c        4. b

## 12. How do we read a weather map?

Prepare and distribute a data sheet listing weather factors such as temperature, pressure, wind direction and velocity, dew point, cloud cover, and amount of precipitation for several cities around the United States. Using the overhead projector and a transparency of the United States construct a weather map with the class. Hand out United States maps so that each pupil can follow along. Refer to the map on page 246. Locate the cities and draw the symbol for cloud cover and precipitation on the map. Add wind direction and wind speed. Then add the temperature. On a separate transparency locate various points of air pressure (include some points of equal pressure.) Develop with the class that lines can be drawn to connect points of equal pressure. Iso (meaning same) lines that connect points of equal pressure are called isobars. Any place located on the same line would have the same pressure. Construct a series of isobars. Establish with the pupils a "high" and a "low." Place the isobar transparency on top of the U.S. transparency. Discuss the type of weather associated with "highs" and "lows." Have the pupils develop the chart found on page 247.

Identify the symbols for the various fronts and draw them on the transparency. Have the pupils look at the weather map on page 246 and identify the various symbols. Discuss the weather of several cities.

Display a series of weather maps for a two-week period. Lead the pupils to see how the highs and lows move across the country. Challenge pupils to explain how a study of weather maps can help predict weather. Organize a field trip to a local weather station.

*Answer These*
1. c
2. b
3. b
4. a

*Now Try This*
a. Richmond
b. Buffalo
c. Phoenix
d. Bismark, Denver, Buffalo
e. Chicago, Miami, Phoenix
f. Buffalo
g. Richmond, Denver
h. Miami
i. Chicago

## 13. What factors determine climate?

To begin the lesson, tell different groups of pupils that they are going on a trip to different regions of the world, such as the North Pole, the Congo jungle, the Sahara desert, etc. Have each group discuss among themselves and then report back to the class the type of clothing they will be taking along.

Guide pupils to see that the type of clothing worn in a region is determined by the region's weather. Have pupils describe the weather conditions of each region. Draw attention to the fact that some regions have the same weather almost all year long (Congo, Sahara), while others have changeable weather (Boston, Moscow). Define climate as the average weather over a long period of time. Elicit that temperature and moisture are important factors of climate.

Have pupils recall that the equator is a warm region while the polar regions are cold. Using the diagram in Module 12, Unit 10, review the fact that the equatorial region receives the sun's direct rays whereas the polar region receives slanted rays. Discuss with the pupils how latitude affects climate.

Have pupils recall that within the troposphere temperature decreases as altitude increases. Use examples such as snowcapped mountain peaks during the summer to illustrate this fact.

Review the fact that water heats up and cools off slower than does land. Develop with the class the effect that a large body of water will have on the climate of a nearby land area. Use a map to locate several cities of the same latitude, some inland and some coastal. Have pupils check almanacs or atlases to find the annual temperature ranges of the various cities. Compare the figures for the inland cities to those of the coastal cities. Lead pupils to see how the presence of nearby water moderates the temperature.

Have pupils recall the effect of ocean currents on the temperature of nearby areas. Elicit that winds as well as ocean currents bring warm air from warm areas. Develop with the pupils the way in which winds affect climate. Point out that moving air can carry moisture. Air moving from over the ocean is moist, whereas air from a land area is dry.

Review the concept that cooling air to its dew point will cause water vapor in the air to condense. Using a diagram, show how mountains force air to rise up over them. Guide pupils to see how this rising air causes the windward side of a mountain to be moist and the leeward side to be dry.

It is important to note that the topic of climate brings together many of the concepts developed in the unit on meteorolgy. It is here that the pupil has to apply these concepts.

Answer These
1. a        4. c
2. a        5. b
3. a

Now Try This
1. hot, wet        3. hot, dry
2. mild, wet       4. cold, wet

## 14. How can we classify climates?

Display pictures of two different tropical rainforest regions. Have pupils identify the climates shown on the pictures. Point out that even though the two locations are in different regions, their climates are similar. Repeat this procedure using pictures of two different desert regions. Lead pupils to see that classification of climates is based on similarities that occur in a region.

Using pictures showing vegetaion, have the pupils note that different plants grow in different climates. Lead the pupils to see that types of vegetation can be used to classify climates.

Have the pupils recall from the previous lesson that temperature and moisture are the two most important factors in describing climates. Review the relationship between latitude and temperature. Using a transparency of a world map, divide the earth into high, middle, and low latitude temperature zones. Temperature zones are established by using average monthly temperatures. The high latitutdes are regions where the average monthly temperature is never above 10°C (50°F). The low latitudes never have an average monthly temperature below 18°C (64°F). The middle latitudes lie between these two.

Describe the moisture content of a region, refer to the plant-moisture relationship used in the text. A more exact method is the ratio of rainfall to evaporation. If the ratio is less than 0.4, the climate is arid; between 0.4 to 0.8 it is semi-arid; between 0.8 to 1.2 it is subhumid; and greater than 1.2 is considered to be humid. At this time you may wish to discuss the relationship between precipitation and evaporation in describing the moisture content of the region.

Refer to the chart in the lesson for specific climates. Assign reports on each region. If possible, try to coordinate the study of climate with the social studies department. There are many films on this topic, and they could be shown as a joint venture.

Answer These
1. b        3. c
2. a        4. c

Now Try This
1. e        4. c        7. f
2. d        5. f
3. a        6. g

**Modified T/F**
1. T                              6. F, STRATUS
2. F, HUMID                       7. T
3. F, FALLS                       8. F, RELATIVE HUMIDITY
4. F, METEOROLOGIST              9. T
5. T                             10. F, EVAPORATION

**Multiple Choice**
1. b    2. b    3. c    4. b
5. a    6. a    7. c    8. c

## UNIT 12. NATURAL RESOURCES

### 1. What are the earth's resources?

This unit investigates our environment and our affect upon it. The students will identify natural resources, make judgments about how they are used or misused, and then consider ways of improving the use of these resources. They should be made aware of environmental problems and methods proposed to correct these problems. One outgrowth of this unit should be the active involvement in some community conservation project.

Review the meaning of environment. Elicit that materials we get from the earth that are needed for us to live are called natural resources. Have pupils make a list of some natural resources. The list should include water, air, land, trees, plants, fuels, and minerals (metals and non-metals).

Point out that some of our resources are renewable and some non-renewable. Have them explain what these terms mean. Allow them to identify which of our natural resources are renewable and which are not. Have them explain their choices. Mention fuels and energy resources but allow for an in-depth discussion during the next lesson.

Provoke class discussion by asking, "Are things the same today as they were 100 years ago?" Continue the questioning with, "How have they changed and what has caused these changes in our environment?" Guide pupils to see that population has increased over the years, and it is continuing to increase. Have pupils continue the discussion of how population growth has affected the use of our natural resources.

Encourage students to set up bulletin boards around the school with charts, drawings, and reports depicting current environmental problems. Have students write to local newspapers suggesting possible solutions to these problems. Civic leaders can be contacted to help organize local recycling stations or other conservation programs in the community.

Answer These
1. water, air, soil, forests, minerals, oil, gas, coal
2. water, air, soil, forests
3. minerals, oil, gas, coal
4. More people need more land to live on and grow food on. They also need more pure water and air.
5. Conservation is a way to make our natural resources last longer.

Now Try These
1. a. renewable (soil)
   b. non-renewable (natural gas)
   c. nonrenewable (oil)
   d. renewable (trees)
   e. non-renewable (trees)
   f. renewable (water)
2. Student answers will vary

## 2. What are our main energy resources?

Review the module on fossile fuels. Elicit that coal, oil, and natural gas are fossil fuels. Display samples of each. Discuss how each was formed. Elicit that these fuels are non-renewable natural resources. Have pupils explain how each supplies us with energy.

Assign reports and have pupils make models showing how fuels are mixed. Have them also construct maps showing areas of coal, oil and natural gas deposits. Make the pupils aware of the problems of fossil fuel shortages (both real and economically produced) and pollution from their use.

Use a water wheel to show how moving water can turn the blades of an electric generator. (A simple water wheel can be constructed out of styrofoam and pop sticks.) Cut the styrofoam in a wheel shape and push the pop sticks in the outer rim of the wheel. Then push a pencil into the center of the wheel and direct water at the blades.

Explain the differences between potential and kinetic energy. Using a diagram, guide pupils to see how the potential energy of water stored behind a dam is converted into kinetic energy of moving water that turns the blades of an electric generator. Elicit that water power is a renewable resource. Compare the use of water power to that of fossil fuel in the production of electricity.

Make a pinwheel and ask the class how this could be considered as a source of energy. Elicit that windmills use the energy of moving air. Discuss how windmills are being used today as a source of electric power. Have pupils construct workable models of windmills and water wheels that show how both can be used as modern-day producers of electricity. A windpowered generator can be purchased from several scientific supply houses. It consists of six blades connected to a D.C. generator and a 1.5 volt bulb to show electrical output. There are commercial organizations that will send literature and plans for actual full scale windmills.

Invite speakers from local utility companies to discuss how energy is supplied to your community.

| Answer These | Now Try These |
| --- | --- |
| 1. b | 1. FOSSIL |
| 2. a | 2. RENEWABLE |
| 3. b | 3. WINDMILLS |
| 4. c | |

## 3. What will be our future energy resources?

Exhibit newspaper articles relating to the gasoline shortages of the 1970's. Show pictures of the long lines of cars waiting at the gas pumps. Refer to the previous lesson and discuss why the shortage occurred and the possibility of it happening again. Review the conservation measures that have been undertaken and those that have been suggested.

Attach a solar cell to a solar cell motor and using sunlight or a high intensity bulb demonstrate how light energy can be converted into electrical energy. Point out that most solar energy, which is free, goes unused. Show pictures and diagrams of homes using solar collectors and discuss how they operate. The United States Department of Energy has prepared a series of activities in energy called Solar II which involves experiments related to solar energy.

Display pictures of volcanoes, geysers and hot springs. Describe these features and have pupils recall that there are very high temperatures within the earth. Discuss geothermal energy and how it can be used.

Show pictures of the Bay of Fundy at high and low tides. Using drawing and diagrams, guide pupils to an understanding of how the tides are being used to produce electricity.

Elicit that nuclear energy is another alternative form of energy. Review the parts of the atom and, with the aid of a diagram, describe nuclear fission. Using a large diagram, explain the workings of a nuclear power plant. Guide pupils to see the pros and cons of using nuclear energy to produce electricity.

*Answer These*
1. c    2. c    3. a    4. b    5. a

## 4. What causes air pollution?

Motivate the lessosn by exhibiting a used air conditioner filter (it is best kept in a closed plastic bag) and an unused filter. Elicit that the filter removes solid particles from the air. These small solids are called particulates. Air contains particulate pollutants and chemical pollutants. Chemical pollutants are gases, e.g. sulfur dioxide ($SO_2$), and carbon monoxide (CO). Point out that some pollutants enter the air by natural process, such as ashes from volcanoes, and pollen from plants. Develop the fact that the environment can handle natural pollutants. Discuss the water cycle, nitrogen cycle, carbon dioxide–oxygen cycle, and the effects of these natural cycles in maintaining the composition of the atmosphere. Point out that human activities are creating a pollution problem that can't be overcome by natural processes.

This lesson can be used to motivate pupils toward long-range studies of pollution. Discuss causes of air pollution and assign projects or reports on such topics as the effect of pollutants on various organisms, or ecosystems, and the effects of pollution on man.

Invite speakers representing conservationist groups, airline and automobile industry, and highway construction firms to address the class on the subject of air pollution.

*Answer These*
6. oxygen    7. c    8. b

## 5. What causes water pollution?

Have pupils recall how ground water and rivers carry material in them. Tell the pupils that pollutants consists of particles suspended or dissolved in the water. Some examples of suspended particles are oil, silt, and non-degradable plastics. Define non-degradable pollutants as substances that cannot be broken down into harmless products.

Discuss the means by which waste is normally removed from the environment by scavengers and decay-causing bacteria. Elicit from the pupils that water pollution, like air pollution, results when human activities upset the balance of nature. Water pollutants also include disease-causing bacteria, which enter the environment in human waste. Point out that water pollution often results from inadequate methods of sewage and garbage disposal.

Discuss the effects of water pollution on man. Encourage discussion on the relationship of population density to pollution.

Call attention to the Finding Out More section and discuss thermal pollution. Point out that warmer water holds less oxygen than cooler water. Discuss the effects that increased water temperature can have on life in a river.

Assign reports on the effects of detergents and fertilizers in our waters. At this point you may have time to discuss other forms of pollution. Introduce the problem of radiation and noise pollution. Assign reports on these subjects.

*Answer These*
1. Pollutants can be dissolved materials or suspended particles.
2. c
3. c

## 6. How can we prevent pollution?

Review the various types of pollution from the previous lessons. Elicit from the pupils that increased pollution could pose a very serious threat to all life on earth. Establish with the class that a pollution problem exists.

Point out the three steps in approaching the problem of pollution: (1) to be aware that a problem exists; (2) to get a commitment to do something about the problem; (3) to work towards finding a solution. It is important to have the pupils note that in some cases, all of these steps cannot be attained at the present time.

Encourage discussion about cleaning up our polluted environment. Assign committees to work on projects and reports on how different pollution problems can be helped.

Plan for trips to sewage treatment plants, water purification plants, air monitoring centers and local industrial plants. Invite speakers to discuss what is being done to control and clean up pollution.

Many films and printed material are available from government and private industries on the subject of pollution control.

*Answer These*
1. a   2. a   3. b   4. c   5. c

## UNIT 12: REVIEW

**Matching**
1. pesticide
2. algae
3. fertilizer
4. smog
5. nuclear energy
6. solar energy
7. geothermal energy
8. kinetic energy
9. potential energy
10. conservation

**Multiple Choice**
1. b   2. b   3. c   4. a
5. b   6. a   7. c   8. a

## UNIT 13. ASTRONOMY

### 1 Why study about the stars and outer space?

Many young people show a keen interest in the study of planets and stars. Elicit a definition of astronomy from the pupils. Have the class suggest areas of astronomy they would like to investigate. List all the topics suggested on the board.

Display satellite photographs of the earth and the moon. Point out that our government is interested in astronomy and space science. Tell the pupils that the government has spent and is spending billions of dollars on a space program. Have the pupils suggest reasons for this interest. Use the board to list the factors suggested. Some possibilities include:
   a. learn more about the universe
   b. explore the moon and the planets
   c. conduct experiments to find out how to maintain life in space
   d. search for life on other planets
   e. improve methods of forecasting weather
   f. improve national defense
   g. test various scientific laws
   h. produce better methods of communication
   i. develop a better understanding of how other bodies in space affect our planet

Present a historical development of space exploration and assign reports on such topics as: I.G.Y., Sputnik, Robert Goddard, Explorer, Project Mercury, Alan Shepard, John Glenn, Project Gemini, Spacelab, Viking, and other related space programs.

*Answer These*
1. False   4. True
2. True   5. False
3. True

*Now Try These*
1. Astronomy
2. Satellite

## 2. What are the tools of astronomy?

Demonstrate the difficulty of viewing distant objects. Hold up a book while standing at the front of the room. Ask a pupil in the rear of the room to try to read what is written on a page. Establish the fact that stars and planets are difficult to study because they are so far away. Elicit that the telescope is an instrument used to view distant celestial bodies.

Conduct this lesson as an introduction to the instruments used by astronomers. Develop the fact that there are different types of telescopes. On the board list the three main types of telescopes: refracting, reflecting, and radio. Display or show pictures of each instrument and identify their parts. Point out that the refracting telescope uses lenses while the reflector uses mirrors. Emphasize that these are optical telescopes. Guide the pupils to see that these instruments collect light from distant objects. Later lessons will explain in detail how each works.

Explain the operation of the radio telescope. Assign reports on the operation and use of the radio telescope. Elicit from the pupils that astronomers do not look through radio telescopes. Lead pupils to understand that radio signals are picked up by the antenna. Some confusion may develop over the term radio signal. Students usually think of radio signals as messages sent out by some form of intelligent life. Point out that astronomers do not listen for messages. Rather, they analyze radio waves produced by celestial bodies. These radio waves are sometimes converted to sound waves, but more frequently they are recorded on a graph. Lead the pupils to recognize that a radio telescope can be used anytime, no matter what the weather or time of day. Compare the radio telescope to radar, and discuss the work of Karl Jansky.

Display a spectroscope and identify its parts. Tell the pupils that the spectroscope is used to analyze light. The spectroscope will be discussed in greater detail in a later lesson.

*Answer These*
1. b   2. b   3. a   4. c

*Now Try This*
DOWN
1. stars
3. light
4. spectroscope

ACROSS
2. telescope
5. cloudy
6. radio
7. sun
8. larger

## 3. How does a refracting telescope work?

This lesson can be conducted as a laboratory exercise. Allow pupils to construct simple refracting telescopes.

Draw a diagram of a simple refracting telescope, and have the pupils identify the objective lens and the eyepiece lens. Guide the pupils to see how the objective lens collects light. You might wish to use an optics kit to demonstrate how a convex lens gathers light. Such kits are available from scientific supply houses.

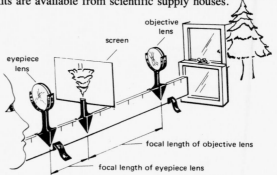

Mount the lens on a meter stick, as shown in the drawing. Aim the lens at some distant object. Demonstrate how to focus the image formed by the object on a screen. Allow pupils to observe how the lens makes the object appear smaller, brighter, and sharper. Point out that the distance from the lens to the screen is the focal length of the lens. Find the focal length of several different lenses. Use the lens with the longest focal length as the object lens and one with a shorter focal length as the eyepiece lens. Place the lens on the meter stick, on opposite sides of the screen, at the proper focal distances from it. Remove the screen and view the object through both lenses. Ask the pupils to describe the image formed.

*Answer These*
1. a   2. c   3. c   4. c

*Now Try These*
1. refracted   2. light

## 4. How are mirrors used in telescopes?

This lesson can be performed as a laboratory exercise. Allow the pupils to construct a simple reflecting telescope, using a meter stick, screen, concave mirror, and convex lens.

Display a concave mirror and have pupils observe how it curves inward in the center. Have the pupils observe themselves in the mirror, and elicit that this mirror is the type often used as a shaving or make-up mirror. Using an optics kit, demonstrate how a concave mirror gathers light. Draw a diagram of a simple reflecting telescope on the board, and point out the locations of the mirror and lens in the telescope.

Have the pupils construct a simple reflecting telescope. Direct them to mount a screen at the center of the stick and to aim the stick at some distant object. Using a concave mirror, demonstrate how to focus the image of the distant object on the screen. Allow the pupils to observe and describe the image formed on the screen. As shown in the drawing, have the screen extended to one side of the stick, and the mirror placed at a slight angle in order to produce a better image. Ask the pupils to observe and describe the image formed by the mirror.

Demonstrate how to view the image formed by the mirror through the convex lens. Have the pupils observe and describe the image formed.

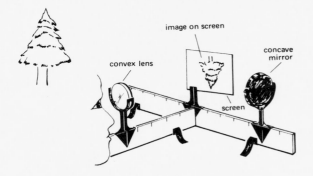

Compare the features of the reflecting telescope with those of the refracting telescope. Consider such things as:
a. the length of the tube
b. the total weight, and the distribution of the weight
c. the amount of work needed to construct the lens and the mirror

Assign reports on the Yerks telescope, Hale telescope, and other large optical telescopes throughout the world.

*Answer These*
1. c   2. b   3. c   4. a   5. b   6. a   7. c

*Now Try These*
1. d   2. a   3. c   4. c   5. b

## 5. How do we study light from the stars?

This lesson can be conducted as a laboratory exercise.

Direct a light through a prism and project a spectrum onto a screen. Have the pupils identify the colors of the spectrum.

If possible, display a spectroscope and have the students identify the parts. You may be able to borrow a spectroscope from a local high school or college.

Demonstrate that different elements give off colors when heated to sufficient temperatures. Explain how the spectroscope is used to identify elements. Use a chart to show the spectra of several elements. Point out that each element has its own spectrum. Compare the methods of identifying elements through their spectra with the method of identifying individuals through their fingerprints.

Distribute diffraction gratings and allow the pupils to examine them. Explain that a diffracting grating can be substituted for a prism. Diffraction gratings and diffraction grating spectroscopes are available through most scientific supply houses. A diffraction grating spectroscope can be constructed using a diffraction grating and a cardboard tube, as shown in the Find Out More section of this module. Have the pupils tape the diffraction grating to one end of a tube, and tape some black construction paper to the other end. Make a small slit in the construction paper and demonstrate how to use the spectroscope. **CAUTION: Warn the pupils not to look at the sun.** Direct them to look at an incandescent lamp, the bright sky, and a fluorescent lamp. Distribute crayons and instruct the pupils to draw the spectra they see. Some pupils may note the appearance of a spectrum on both sides of the slit. Tell them to pay attention to only one spectrum.

Have the pupils observe the spectra of variuos gases. Use an induction coil to light up the gas tubes. If the gas tubes are not available, perform flame tests for different elements as the pupils look on through their spectroscopes. Sodium, copper, barium, and strontium compounds will produce varied spectra. Keep the room as dark as possible. Outside light can affect the spectra produced. Direct the pupils' attention to the intensity and amount of color produced. Some spectra may have a greater intensity or cover a larger area in one band than in another.

With some classes, you may wish to discuss how the spectroscope helps to determine a star's motion (Doppler effect), temperature, and age.

*Answer These*
1. b   2. c   3. a   4. a

*Now Try These*
1. prism   2. light   3. spectrum   4. temperature, size, age

## 6. What unit of distance do astronomers use?

Elicit that distances on earth can be measured in centimeters, meters, and kilometers. Use a large chart or transparency to show a table of the planets and their distances from the sun. Guide the pupils to appreciate the fact that, because distances in space are so great, much larger units than those used for ordinary purposes are needed to measure these distances. Express the distance between the earth and the sun as 150 million kilometers. From this, develop the concept of the astronomical unit. To give the pupils some idea of the relative distances of the planets from the sun, use the chart of astronomical units in the Now Try These section, and draw them to scale on the board.

Point out that distances to the stars are so great that even a unit as large as the astronomical unit becomes too difficult to work with. Using the given speed of light as 300,000 kilometers per second, lead the pupils through all the mathematical calculations necessary to determine the distance light travels in one year. Help them to appreciate just how long it would take them, traveling at the speed of light, to reach various stars. As an example, you might point out that when scientists in the Viking program sent a radio signal to the spacecraft on Mars (which is much closer than even the nearest star), the signal took about 20 minutes to reach that planet.

Use the demonstration in the Finding Out More section to illustrate parallax. Point out that this is one method of determining distance to closer stars.

*Answer These*
1. a    2. b    3. b

*Now Try These*
1. Mercury, Venus, Earth, Mars, Jupiter, Saturn, Uranus, Neptune, Pluto
2. The sun

## 7. What are constellations?

Write the following on the board: Aquarius, Leo, Pisces, Ursa Major, Ursa Minor, Orion, Capricorn, Libra. Elicit that these are the names of star constellations. Pupils may recognize some of these constellations as zodiac signs. Point out that zodiac signs are named for constellations that occupy a specific region of sky (the ecliptic).

Elicit that constellations are groups of stars that seem to suggest certain patterns in the sky. Display a transparency or chart of the northern sky and point out some well-known constellations. Guide the pupils to see that the constellations provide a means of locating and identifying various stars. Identify Polaris as the first star in the handle of Ursa Minor and Mizar as the second star in the handle of Ursa Major.

Identify such well-known constellations as Ursa Major, Ursa Minor, Orion, and Cassiopeia. Assign reports on the constellations and the objects their shapes represent. Have the pupils make charts and construct devices to project the constellations on a screen.

Discuss why different constellations are visible at different times of the year. Mount pictures of the constellations on the walls around the room. Move around the room with a globe, pointing out how different constellations come into view at different times during the year.

Star charts can be obtained from magazines, such as *Sky and Telescope*, or from the local planetarium or college. Use a star chart appropriate for the time of the year you are teaching the topic.

*Answer These*
1. b    2. c    3. a    4. c    5. a

*Now Try These*
1. BIG DIPPER        3. RIGEL
2. ORION             4. CASSIOPEIA

## UNIT 13: REVIEW

### Fill In the Blank
1. The Hunter            6. Newton
2. Orion                 7. Galileo
3. second                8. year
4. Proxima Centauri      9. navigator
5. The spectrum         10. location

### Multiple Choice
1. c    2. c    3. a    4. a
5. a    6. c    7. b    8. a

## UNIT 14. STARS

### 1. What can we learn from a star's light?

This lesson can be performed as a laboratory exercise. Elicit from the students that the sun and the stars are composed of hot gases. Point out that most people have never really looked carefully at stars. Many pupils find it hard to believe that stars are different colors. Use the constellation Orion as an example. Demonstrate how to locate and recognize Orion. Display a color slide or photograph of this constellation. (If you are taking your own photographs, a 15- or 30-second exposure should produce good results.) Direct the pupils' attention to Betelgeuse and Rigel. Elicit from the class that Betelgeuse is a red star and Rigel is white.

Use a nichrome wire to demonstrate that temperature can affect brightness. Guide the pupils to see the longer the wire is held in the flame, the hotter and brighter it becomes. **Caution: If pupils are going to take an active part in this demonstration, advise them as to the proper safety procedures to be followed.**

Display a photoelectric cell connected to a meter and explain how it works. Photoelectric meters, light meters, and exposure meters can be purchased from a scientific supply house or photography shop. A selenium photoelectric cell attached to a galvanometer can be substituted for the photoelectric meter. An inexpensive cell and meter can be purchased at any electronics store. Check the sensitivity of the meters before allowing the pupils to work with them. Caution them not to place the light source too close to the cell, or they may damage the meter.

Using the meter, demonstrate the relationship of distance to brightness. Have students observe that as the distance between the bulb and the meter increases, the intensity of the light decreases. Using different size bulbs, demonstrate the relationship between star size and brightness.

Summarize the lesson with a discussion of the magnitude of a star.

*Answer These*
1. b    2. a    3. b    4. a

*Now Try These*
1. The brighter star is closer to the observer.
2. The brighter star is hotter.
3. The brighter star is larger.

### 2. How are stars classified?

Exhibit a hand-operated magneto. Pupils may recogize this as the instrument used to demonstrate how electricity is generated. Turn the handle slowly at first and then increase the speed. Ask pupils to describe what they observe. Elicit that as the speed increased, the bulb got brighter and its color changed from red to orange to yellow to white. Repeat the demonstration so that all can note the color changes. Have pupils recall that the brightness of a star is dependent upon its size, distance and temperature. Compare the light bulb to a star, and guide them to see that the color of a star is also determined by its temperature. White stars are hotter than yellow stars, which are hotter than red stars.

Display a classroom chart of the Hertzsprung-Russell diagram. Direct the pupils' attention to the temperature scale at the bottom of the diagram. Guide them to see the relationship between the scale and the colors. Direct the pupils to the magnitude scale and explain that absolute magnitude is a star's true brightness.

Show pupils how a star is placed on the diagram. Lead them to understand how color, size, and absolute magnitude allow us to place a star on the diagram and to identify it as a giant, supergiant, dwarf, or main sequence star.

| Answer These | | Now Try These |
|---|---|---|
| 1. c | 3. c | 1. c |
| 2. a | 4. b | 2. white dwarfs |

## 3. What is the life history of stars?

Have pupils read the introductory paragraph on page 288. Elicit that stars are masses of hot gases. Point out that they are using up these gases at a tremendous rate by converting them into energy. (Save any further discussion of the topic of nuclear fusion for a future lesson.) Have pupils conclude that in time, a star converts most of its mass into energy and then dies away. Ask what they think is in store for the sun, which is a star. Tell them that it is midway in its life cycle and has about 5 billion more years to go, before it "burns out."

Develop the concept that stellar material under gravitational force is pulled together to form the beginnings of a star. Display the H-R diagram and show where this young star would appear on the diagram. Lead pupils to see that as the star gets older, it gets brighter and hotter. Locate this star along the main sequence curve in the H-R diagram. Have the pupils conclude that stars in the upper left part of the main sequence curve are older stars.

Explain what causes the formation of red giants. Tell the pupils that this stage lasts a relatively short time compared to main sequence stars. This accounts for the fact that red giants are fewer in number than main sequence stars. Describe novas and supernovas. Tell students that in 1054, the Chinese recorded the occurrence of a supernova. It burned brightly for two years and could even be seen by day. Show pictures of the Crab nebula, which contains the debris of a supernova.

| Answer These | | Now Try These |
|---|---|---|
| 1. a | 4. b | 1. gravity |
| 2. b | 5. b | 2. nova |
| 3. c | | |

## 4. What other kinds of stars have been observed?

A week before presenting this lesson, assign reports on pulsars, quasars, black holes, cepheids, pulsating stars, neutron stars, binary stars, and star clusters. Gather as much visual material as possible. Contact the school librarian and request a list of available books containing information on this topic.

Elicit that stars shine with a steady light produced by converting mass into energy. Discuss the fact that astronomers have discovered some stars that do not behave like those discussed to this point. Such stars are called variable stars. Briefly discuss some of the reasons why certain stars do not produce a "steady" light.

Discuss pulsars and quasars. Review the radio telescope and point out how valuable it has been in studying these stars. Discuss how a black hole forms and how it affects everything surrounding it.

| Answer These | |
|---|---|
| 1. b | 4. c |
| 2. a | 5. Hotter, brighter |
| 3. b | |

## 5. What are galaxies?

Obtain as many photographs and drawings of galaxies as possible. Many filmstrips have excellent illustrations of the various types of galaxies.

Display a photograph of the constellation Andromeda. Identify the spots of light on the photo as stars. Point out the one fuzzy patch that is not a star at all, but a galaxy. (It is located across from the star Mirach). Define galaxy.

Display a photograph of a nebula and point out the difference between a nebula and galaxy. At times, the location of a nebula interferes with the determination of the brightness of a galaxy. Review how the study of light from celestial bodies helps determine their distances, sizes and shapes.

At this point it is important that the pupils develop some appreciation of the vast number of galaxies that exist and of the immense distances between them. Point out that we see millions of stars in our own Milky Way galaxy, and in the universe there are millions of galaxies, each with billions of stars. Discuss distances and review the concept of the light-year. Point out that astronomers have found the closest galaxies to be a few million light years away from ours. Most of them are smaller and dimmer than ours. The three galaxies that can be seen without a telescope are Andromeda in the Northern Hemisphere and the two Magellanic clouds in the Southern Hemisphere.

Use photographs and drawings to describe the three types of galaxies. Examples of spiral galaxies are our own Milky Way, Andromeda (M31) and the Whirlpool galaxy (M51). Galaxies identified by "M" numbers indicate credit given to the French astronomer Charles Messier (1730–1817). "NGC" stands for the New General Catalogue, which also lists galaxies with a number. Tell the pupils that the center of the spiral galaxy consists of old stars, red in color, whereas the spiral arms contain millions of younger stars together with clouds of dust and gases. The entire galaxy rotates in space like a pinwheel.

Examples of Elliptical galaxies are NGC 205, NGC 221 found in the constellation Andromeda and NGC 3193 in the constellation Leo.

Examples of Irregular galaxies include the Large Magellanic Cloud found in the constellation Dorado, the Small Magellanic Cloud in the constellation Tucana and NGC 5195 in the constellation Canes Venatici.

*Answer These*
1. b   2. b   3. a   4. c

*Now Try These*
2. A nebula is a large cloud of gas and dust that reflects light from other stars. A galaxy is a group of stars that give off their own light.

## 6. What is the Milky Way?

Motivate the lesson by asking the class how they would address an envelop from a distant planet in another galaxy to a friend on earth. On the chalkboard draw the envelope to include:
a) Friend's name
b) Address
c) City, State, Zip
d) Earth, Sun-Solar System
e) Milky Way Galaxy, Universe

Review the different types of galaxies. Elicit that our galaxy is a spiral type called the Milky Way. Using a photograph of a spiral galaxy (M51 is a good example), review the characteristics of this type of galaxy.

Develop the understanding that since we can't leave our galaxy to make direct observations, we must rely on comparisons with other galaxies and indirect observations. Use the analogy of the basketball court on page 295 to explain why it is so difficult to determine the size and shape of our galaxy. Tell the class that even though we can't see all the stars in our galaxy the ones we do see are all members of the Milky Way.

Using a photograph of the Milky Way point out that the bright band of light is a concentration of thousands and thousands of stars.

The presence of dust and gas prevents the Milky Way from being far brighter, but on a clear dark night it is visible to the naked eye. This band of light is thicker when viewed from the Southern Hemisphere.

Use the drawing on page 294 to describe the Milky Way and locate the Sun. Review light-years when describing the diameter and thickness.

Tell the class that the entire galaxy rotates in space. Inform the pupils that all of the stars travel at different speeds. Our sun moves at a speed of about 250 km/sec, and it takes some 200 million years to make one complete revolution around the center. You might want to mention that the stars in each constellation change their positions because of this motion and that the Big Dipper and other constellations may not have the same shapes thousands of years from now.

The Milky Way is getting harder and harder to see due to light pollution from the earth. You might like to discuss how light pollution has affected the location of observatories and general observations.

*Answer These*
1. a   2. a   3. a   4. c

## UNIT 14: REVIEW

### Matching
1. Milky Way
2. nucleus
3. neutrons
4. gravity
5. black dwarf
6. nova
7. white dwarf
8. supergiant
9. cepheid
10. galaxy

### Multiple Choice
1. b   2. c   3. b   4. a
5. c   6. b   7. c   8. c

## UNIT 15. THE SUN AND ITS FAMILY

### 1. How does the sun affect the earth?

Introduce the lesson by posing the question found in the first paragraph on page 298: "What would happen on earth if the sun stopped shining?" Guide the pupils to see that the sun is the prime source of all the earth's energy. Trace various forms of energy on the earth to the sun.

Distribute a small piece of blueprint paper to each pupil, and instruct them to place a small object, such as a key or coin, on top of the paper. After 15–20 minutes, have the pupils examine the paper and explain what caused the color to fade. Relate this to the fact that many storekeepers have amber-colored sheets in their window to protect the merchandise from fading.

Make a past of silver nitrate or silver bromide and demonstrate how sunlight causes it to turn darker. Relate this reaction to the subject of photography. A discussion of this topic often leads to extracurricular activities in photography. Assign reports and projects on cameras and developing and printing of photographs. Pupils may show an interest in forming a school photography club.

Display a small green plant and discuss the process of photosynthesis. Use a word equation to show how carbon dioxide and water combine during photosynthesis to form glucose (a type of sugar) and release oxygen. Be sure to include energy as one of the "ingredients" of the process. Emphasize the role of the sun in furnishing the energy, and point out that the energy is stored in the glucose (or other plant products). Relate this stored energy to the energy still present in fossil fuels.

Elicit from the pupils that vitamin D is sometimes called the sunshine vitamin. Discuss how the sun's ultraviolet rays help the body produce vitamin D. Also discuss how these rays destroy harmful bacteria and can be used to preserve food.

Stress the harmful effects of the sun. Point out that too much sun can cause eye damage, harmful burns to the skin, and skin cancer. Assign projects and reports on the value of suntan lotions in protecting the skin against the sun's rays.

*Answer These*
1. c   2. a   3. a   4. c

*Now Try These*
1. carefully; burn   2. heat

### 2. What is the moon?

Display a photograph of the moon and ask the pupils to identify it. Elicit that the moon is a satellite of the earth. On the board, define a satellite as a body that moves around a larger one in space. Point out that the name of our natural satellite is Moon. Show a chart or transparency listing the other planets and their satellites. Emphasize the proper use of the term "moon." Point out that Mars has no moons; it has two satellites, each with their own names. Only the earth has a satellite named Moon.

Display additional photographs of the moon, and ask the pupils to describe the various features they see, such as mountains, plains, and craters. Assign reports on how these craters may have been formed.

On the board, list the moon's distance from Earth (380,000 km), its diameter (3,200 km), and its gravity (1/6 that of earth). Using these facts, lead into a discussion of other facts about the moon, such as: the presence (or lack) of surface moisture; ability to support life; range of surface temperatures; and geology of the surface.

Assign reports on Project Apollo, and have pupils discuss reasons for lunar exploration. Use maps of the moon to locate lunar landing sites. Excellent topographic maps of the moon can be purchased from Aeronautical Chart and Information Center, United States Air Force, St. Louis, Missouri, 63118. Discuss Galileo's seas (or mare), and locate them on the moon maps.

*Answer These*
1. b   2. a   3. a   4. c

*Now Try These*
1. 10 kg
2. There is no atmosphere and, thus, no wind on the moon; therefore, the pinwheel would not turn.
3. 360 centimeters

### 3. What are the motions of the moon?

Introduce the concept of luminous and nonluminous bodies. Make the distinction between light from the sun (a luminous body) and light from the moon (which is reflected sunlight).

Use a large slate glove to demonstrate rotation and revolution. Lead the pupils to understand that every time the moon makes one rotation, the earth makes $27\frac{1}{3}$ rotations. With the globe, illustrate that one revolution of the moon also takes $27\frac{1}{3}$ days. Duplicate the diagram on page 302 to show the period of revolution and rotation.

Draw the diagram on page 303 on the board and guide the pupils to see why we see only one side of the moon. Divide the slate globe into four equal sections by drawing lines from pole to pole. Shine a light on the globe, and demonstrate that each part is illuminated at one time or another. Walk around the room and slowly rotate the globe, so that the same side faces the class throughout your "revolution." From this, have pupils understand that we see the same side of the moon throughout its period of revolution.

*Answer These*          *Now Try These*
1. b   2. a   3. c   4. c      1. rotation   2. revolution

## 4. How does the moon change its appearance?

Display a calendar and have the pupils note the dates of new, full, first, and last quarter moons. Elicit that these are the phases of the moon. Have the pupils determine the period of time between each phase, and the time from one new moon phase to the next. Have the pupils recall that the moon shines by reflected light. Review the periods or rotation and revolution.

Construct a loop from a wire coat hanger, and use it to illustrate the moon's orbit around the earth. Use a softball to represent the earth and describe its orbit as being parallel to the floor. Place the wire hanger at a slight angle to the "earth's" horizontal orbit. Demonstrate that the moon is sometimes "above" and sometimes "below" the earth's orbit.

Draw a diagram on the board similar to the one on page 305 to represent various positions of the moon in its orbit around the earth. Guide the pupils to see why the moon changes its appearance during the month.

Divide the class into several groups or teams. Darken the room and distribute a lamp and softball to each group. Make sure that the light from one group does not interfere with that of any other group. Have the pupils shine the lamp on the ball, and then move the lamp to different positions around the ball. Direct them to use the diagram on the board as a reference. Have the pupils note how much of the ball is illuminated at each position. Caution them not to look directly at the light. Check to see that, during full moon phase, no shadows are allowed to eclipse the moon. (Save this for the next lesson.)

Assign a moon observation for the next four weeks. Have the pupils keep a record of the phases, and the time and date each occurs. Encourage them to make drawings of how the moon appears each night.

*Answer These*
1. b  2. a  3. c  4. b

*Now Try These*
1. h    5. b
2. f    6. d
3. a    7. c
4. e    8. g

## 5. How does a lunar eclipse occur?

Divide the class into several groups of pupils and distribute a softball, a small styrofoam (or ping-pong) ball, and a lamp to each group. Direct them to shine the light on the softball (earth) and then place the ping-pong ball (moon) in the umbra of the softball. Caution the pupils not to look directly into the light. Darken the room as much as possible and check to see that the light from one group does not interfere with that of other groups.

Have the pupils draw a diagram showing the positions of the lamp and the two balls. Elicit that the moon can enter the umbra of earth's shadow only during full moon phase. Refer to the diagram on page 306 and have the pupils label the moon, sun, earth, umbra, and penumbra on their diagrams. Using the diagrams, guide the pupils to see the difference between a total and partial eclipse.

Using a wire hanger and a softball, as in the previous module, demonstrate why a lunar eclipse does not occur every month at full moon phase.

Draw the diagram from page 306 on the chalkboard, and add the earth's atmosphere to the diagram. Explain that the moon is never totally blacked out from view during an eclipse because the earth's atmosphere acts as a lens, which refracts come of the sun's light into the earth's shadow. This refracted light illuminates the moon's surface slightly.

*Answer These*
1. b  2. b  3. a  4. c

*Now Try These*
1. full moon
2. The earth's shadow is cast on the dark (or night) side of the earth.
3. A total lunar eclipse occurs when the entire moon moves into the earth's umbra; a partial eclipse occurs when part of the moon moves into the earth's umbra.
4. If the earth's shadow does not fall on the moon, there will be no eclipse.

## 6. How does a solar eclipse occur?

Elicit that the sun in the center of our solar system, and discuss the fact that many ancient people regarded the sun as a god. Display pictures of the Greek god Apollo, the Egyptian god Ra, the Japanese flag, the Mexican caledar, and Mayan Temples.

Discuss how the various cultures represented by these items prayed to the sun. Elicit from pupils that many people worshipped the sun because it gave them heat and light. Relate the incident involving a solar eclipse in Mark Twain's *A Connecticut Yankee in King Arthur's Court*. (The film version of this novel makes for an excellent assembly program.) Point out that the previous lesson dealt with a lunar eclipse, while this one is concerned with a solar eclipse.

Display photographs of a total solar eclipse. Direct the pupils' attention to the sun's corona. Draw a diagram showing the different zones of the sun. Discuss the characteristics of the photosphere, chromosphere, and corona.

Conduct this lesson as you did the last one, changing the position of the moon from full moon to new moon. Have the pupils compare the earth's umbra with the moon's umbra. Point out the reason why fewer peope view a solar eclipse than a lunar eclipse. Using the diagram on page 308, show the pupils the difference between a total and partial solar eclipse.

*Answer These*
1. c  2. b  3. c  4. c

*Now Try This*

| DOWN | ACROSS |
|------|--------|
| 1. penumbra | 4. lunar |
| 2. solar | 5. umbra |
| 3. sun | |

## 7. Where does the sun get its energy?

On the board, list the sun's diameter and temperature. Point out that by using a spectroscope, scientists have determined the sun's composition. Have the pupils recall that the sun is composed of hot gases that give off light and heat. Use a match to illustrate that the sun would have used up its gases long ago, if ordinary burning were responsible for the heat and light. Challenge the class to explain how the sun produces heat and energy.

To explain the difference between an ordinary chemical reaction, such as oxidation, and a nuclear reaction, such as the fission of uranium atoms or the fusion of hydrogen atoms, you may wish to go into the structure of the atom. In chemical reactions, only the electrons of atoms are involved. They change their positions and may give up some energy. This is the energy given off by reactions such as burning.

Nuclear reactions involve changes in the nuclei of atoms. The energies involved are many times greater. In fact, a measurable change in mass can be observed as the result of a nuclear reaction. Ask the class if they are familiar with the law of conservation of matter. Tell them that in a fusion reaction, some mass actually disappears. Write Einstein's formula $E = mc^2$ on the board. Explain in terms of the equation how mass can be changed to energy. Point out that $c$ is the speed of light, and that this large number is *squared* in the formula. That explains why very smallchanges in mass in a nuclear reaction can result in the emission of enormous amounts of energy.

*Answer These*

| 1. b | 3. a |
| 2. b | 4. c |

*Now Try These*

| 1. yellow | 3. energy |
| 2. hydrogen | 4. thermonuclear |

## 8. What are some features of the sun?

Review the physical features of the sun. Exhibit a globe of about 20 inches in diameter and hold up a B.B. Ask the pupils to guess how many B.B.s would fit into the globe. Draw an analogy between the size of the earth and sun. Point out that approximately one million B.B.s would fill the 20-inch globe and that is the same number of earths that would fit into the sun.

Display a photograph of the sun and point out that it is the photosphere that they see. Describe the photosphere as the lowest layer of the sun's atmosphere. It is so bright that it blocks out the other two layers of the sun's atmosphere.

Have pupils describe sunspots. A telescope or binoculars can be directed at the sun to project the sun's image through the eyepiece onto a piece of paper.

Tables containing Wolf's sunspot numbers can be used to illustrate the sunspot cycle of 1749 to 1965. Have pupils plot and graph the number of sunspots for each year. Have them observe how the number of sunspots increases over a period of 10–11 years.

Develop the understanding that the photosphere rotates. Elicit that the photosphere is gaseous. Point out that various regions rotate at different speeds. The equatorial region takes 25 days for one rotation, while the polar region requires 34 days.

Show photographs of solar flares and discuss how these affect us on earth. Mention solar winds.

*Answer These*

1. b    2. c    3. a    4. c    5. b

## 9. What is the sun's upper atmosphere?

Show a picture of a cross section of the sun. Draw it on the chalkboard and have the pupils label the photosphere, chromosphere and corona.

Display photographs of different eclipses of the sun. Review the solar eclipse. Have pupils identify the moon's shadow, the chromosphere, and the corona on the photos. Point out that the chromosphere and corona are visible only during a total eclipse. Have pupils also note that the corona take on different shapes during different solar eclipses. Some pupils might like to research what astronomers think may cause these different shapes.

Show photographs of prominences and discuss the dangers of viewing the sun improperly, especially during a solar eclipse. Cite examples of eye damage that has resulted from unheeded warnings.

The teaching of this unit requires the use of many photographs, films and filmstrips. Excellent filmstrips have been written on the features of the sun. One such filmstrip can be used at this point to sum up the material presented. Photographs can be obtained from scientific supply houses and planetariums such as the Yerkes, Mount Wilson, and Palomar observatories. Periodicals such as *Sky and Telescope* have articles, maps, and photographs that may prove useful. A science film classic, "Our Mr. Sun," produced by Bell Telephone, has valuable footage of various features of the sun.

*Answer These*

Across

| 1. b | 4. c |
| 2. b | 5. a |
| 3. a | |

*Now Try This*

| Across | Down |
| 1. CHROMOSPHERE | 4. CORONA |
| 2. ECLIPSE | 5. PHOTOSPHERE |
| 3. WEAK | 6. RED |

## 10. What do we know about the inner planets?

Review the meaning of the term satellite from Module 2 of this unit. Ask if the sun has any satellites. Pupils should respond that the planets are actually satellites of the sun.

From Module 3 of this unit, review the concept of luminous and illuminated bodies. Elicit that bodies that give off their own light, like the sun, are luminous, while bodies that shine by reflecting light, like the moon, are illuminated. Ask pupils how planets differ from stars. Responses should include the fact that stars are much larger than any of the planets and that stars are luminous while planets are illuminated. The fact that planets appear brighter than stars is explained by the fact that the planets are so much closer to earth than even the nearest star (except for the sun).

Discuss unmanned space probes. You may wish to have pupils do some library research on this topic and prepare written reports. The photograph of Mercury crossing the sun on page 316 was reconstructed by computers. Data from Skylab was transmitted in digital form to computers on the ground.

After the class has read the section titled Exploring Mars (page 317), lead a discussion concerning the possibility of life on that planet.

*Answer These*

| 1. a | 3. c |
| 2. c | 4. a |

*Now Try These*

1. Mercury, Venus, Earth, Mars, Jupiter, Saturn, Uranus, Neptune, Pluto
2. Mercury, Pluto, Mars, Venus, Earth, Uranus, Neptune, Saturn, Jupiter
3. All three surfaces have numerous craters.
4. The canyons appear to have been created by erosion by running water. However, at the present time there is no liquid water on Mars.

## 11. What do we know about the outer planets?

This lesson should be conducted mainly as a class discussion after pupils have read the material on pages 318 and 319. You may wish to have pupils do some research and report writing on the Pioneer and Voyager space probes.

Information from the Pioneer program (see Finding Out More, page 319) indicates that the bands or belts of dark clouds on Jupiter's surface are produced by convection currents in the atmosphere. Jupiter is also one of three planets known to have a magnetic field (Mercury and Earth are the others). Instruments on Pioneer X measured Jupiter's magnetic field, or magnetosphere, and found that it extends nearly 50 times the diameter of the planet.

Pupils are often interested in the fact that the existence of Neptune (and later Pluto) was predicted before the planet was ever seen. Irregularities in the predicted orbit of Uranus led to the prediction and later discovery of Neptune. Similar irregularities in Neptune's orbit led to the discovery of Pluto. You may wish to assign research and report projects on these and other facts about the planets that are not covered in Modules 10 and 11.

*Answer These*

Jupiter . . . Saturn . . . Uranus . . . Neptune . . . Pluto . . . clouds . . . bands . . . red spot . . . rings . . . densities . . . star

## 12. What else do we know about the solar system?

When discussing this lesson, emphasize the first sentence on page 320. Pupils should understand that the solar system includes *all* of the objects that orbit the sun.

Many films and filmstrips dealing with the solar system are available. Use of these and other audiovisual materials will provide an appropriate summation of this unit.

*Answer These*
1. False. The solar system includes all objects that orbit the sun, such as asteroids, comets, and meteors.
2. False. Asteroids do not come from outer space. This group of rocks is a permanent member of the solar system and circles the sun in an orbit between Mars and Jupiter.
3. True.
4. False. The tail of a comet is made up mostly of thin gas.
5. True.

*Now Try These*
1. Sun, planets and their satellites, asteroids, comets, and meteors.
2. The asteroids circle the sun in a regular orbit. Meteors are traveling toward earth, caught up by the earth's gravity.
3. A meteorite is a meteor that strikes the earth's surface.

## UNIT 15: REVIEW

### Modified T/F
1. F, BAD
2. T
3. T
4. F, FULL
5. T
6. F, SURFACE
7. T
8. T
9. F, SATURN
10. F, COMETS

### Multiple Choice
1. a  2. c  3. b  4. c
5. a  6. b  7. a  8. c

## UNIT 16. MOTION IN THE SOLAR SYSTEM

### 1. What is inertia?

Demonstrate the principle of inertia with a cloth and some dishes. Place the dishes on the cloth, and elicit that a force is needed to make the dishes move. Pull the cloth slowly, and the dishes move along with the cloth. Then pull the cloth quickly from under the dishes. Challenge the pupils to explain why the dishes remain behind. Practice this demonstration several times before you do it in class. Don't hesitate; one short jerk is enough. Use a smooth cloth, such as silk, about the size of a face towel. Try not to pull the cloth up or down, just straight out.

Write Newton's Law of Inertia on the board, and ask the pupils to try to explain its meaning. Discuss examples of inertia in a car making a quick start or stop. Lead the pupils to see tht objects in space keep moving because there are no outside forces acting on them.

Have the pupils demonstrate inertia with a marble and a piece of paper folded into a V-shaped groove. Direct pupils to first place the marble on a flat surface. Then have them tilt the paper and allow the marble to move down the groove. Have them explain why the marble does not move on the flat surface, why it moves down the groove, and why it stops. Use a pie plate or saucer to produce changes in the direction of movement of the marble.

Note that the Do This At Home section contains a modification of the dishes and tablecloth demonstration.

*Answer These*
1. b  2. b  3. b

*Now Try These*
1. inertia  2. force

### 2. Why do the planets circle the sun?

Throw a small object in the air. Elicit that gravity is a force that pulls all objects toward the earth, and this force causes the object to fall. From the previous lesson, review the effects of an outside force (in this case gravity) on an object in motion.

Throw a ball across the front of the room, and direct the pupils' attention to the fact that the object follows a curved path. Refer to the diagram on page 326, and guide the pupils to understand that more than one force is affecting the ball. Because of inertia, the object tends to continue traveling in a straight line. At the same time, an outside force (gravity) acting on the ball pulls it down. The effects of these two forces results in a curved path.

Review the concept of gravitational attraction and elicit that this attraction exists between all bodies in the universe. Perform the demonstration shown on page 327 to illustrate that it is this attraction that keeps the planets from flying off into space.

Divide the class into several teams and distribute a tack and a piece of string to each team. Direct the pupils to tie the tack to one end of the string and a pencil to the other end. Have them push the tack through a clean sheet of paper into a soft piece of wood or a magazine. Instruct them to move the pencil in a straight line. Have them observe that even though they try to move the pencil in a straight line, the string causes the pencil to circle the tack. Compare the motion of the pencil to the motions of the planets, and the force exerted by the string to the gravitational attraction of the sun.

*Answer These*
1. b  2. c  3. b

*Now Try These*
1. Rivers always flow "downhill" (from areas of higher elevation to areas of lower elevation). The gravitational attraction of the earth for the water causes a river to flow. Gravity "pulls" the water downhill.
2. The earth's gravity holds the atmosphere in place. If there were no gravity, the atmosphere would disperse into space.

### 3. What is the shape of the earth's orbit?

Elicit from the pupils that a cirlce is a figure with all points on the outer edge equidistant from the center. Tell them that the earth's average distance from the sun is 150 million kilometers. Display a chart or transparency showing the approximate distances between the earth and the sun at various times during the year, as shown here:

| Time of year | Approximate distance between the earth and sun |
|---|---|
| April 1 | 150 million kilometers |
| July 1 | 152 million kilometers |
| October 1 | 150 million kilometers |
| January 1 | 147 million kilometers |

Direct the pupils' attention to the fact that the earth–sun distance is sometimes greather than 150 million kilometers and sometimes less. Guide them to see that if the earth's orbit were a circle, the distance between the earth and sun would always be the same. Have them draw the shape that the earth's orbit seems to have.

Draw an ellipse on the board and have the pupils describe its shape. Label the major axis and foci of the ellipse. Elicit that the earth travels in an elliptical orbit around the sun. Point out that the sun is located at one focus of the ellipse. Label the sun on your diagram.

Tell the pupils to apply the dates found in the table to the figure. Many pupils will question the earth being closest to the sun during our winter and farthest from the sun during our summer. Lead them to understand that distance from the sun has no affect on the seasons. Point out that the change in distance between the earth and sun is very slight compared to the total distance involved.

Show the pupils how to use a compass. Demonstrate how a string looped around two tacks can be used to draw an ellipse. Distribute two tacks, a piece of string, and a compass to each pupil, and direct them to draw a circle and to label its center. Instruct them to construct several radii and to measure each one. Elicit that all of the radii of a circle are equal.

Have them construct an ellipse and label one of the foci as the sun. Direct the pupils' attention to the chart of distance between the earth and sun, and have them indicate where the earth will be in its orbit at various dates. Point out that the earth revolves counter-clockwise around the sun.

Have the pupils recall that the closer a planet is to the sun, the greater the gravitational attraction. Develop the idea that the greater the gravitational force between the sun and planet, the faster the planet travels. From this concept, elicit that the earth moves faster in its orbit in January than in July. Direct the pupils' attention to the chart on page 329. Guide them to see that the closer a planet is to the sun, the greater is its orbital velocity.

*Answer These*
1. elliptical   2. perihelion   3. increases   4. January   5. July

## 4. How do we know that the earth turns?

Elicit from the pupils that the earth rotates on its axis as it revolves around the sun. Point out that ancient people believed that the earth remained still while all other celestial bodies moved around it. List the names of Ptolemy, Nicolaus Copernicus, Tycho Brahe, and Johannes Kepler on the board. Introduce the historical aspects of astronomy, and assign reports on these men. Introduce the terms geocentric and heliocentric in relation to Ptolemy and Copernicus, and define each of these terms on the board.

Challenge the students to present evidence that the earth rotates. Elicit that the changing of day and night are caused by the earth's rotation. Using a globe and a lamp in a darkened room, demonstrate how rotation produces day and night.

Display a photograph of star trails above the north pole. Using a camera, explain the procedure involved in taking time exposure pictures. Guide the pupils to see how stars produce circular lines of light on the film as the earth rotates below them. Assign the taking of such pictures as a project.

Demonstrate the Coriolis effect with a slate globe. Point out that the earth rotates from west to east. On a stationary globe, draw a line from the pole to the equator. Then slowly rotate the globe as you again draw a similar line. Guide the pupils to see how the line curves. For further details of the deflection of winds on the earth's surface, see Module 14, Unit 10.

Display a photograph of a Foucault pendulum. The pendulum shown on page 331 is the Smithsonian Institution in Washington, D.C. However, similar pendulums demonstrating the earth's rotation are located in various buildings throughout the country. Lead the pupils to understand that the pendulum does not really change its direction of swing. It is the rotation of the earth beneath the pendulum that causes the direction to appear to change.

Elicit that the earth's shape is slightly oblate. The circumference around the equator is slightly greater (68 km) than it is around the poles. Explain that centrifugal force due to the earth's rotation is responsible for this slight bulging at the equator.

Point out that the tracking of satellites in polar orbits has also provided evidence of the earth's rotation.

*Answer These*
1. b   2. c   3. b   4. c

*Now Try These*
1. AXIS          3. CURVE
2. PENDULUM      4. OCEAN CURRENTS

## 5. Why do we have day and night?

Using a Trippensee Planetary Model, demonstrate that the earth's axis is tilted 23½° from a perpendicular to the path of orbit (ecliptic). Trippensee Planetary Models are available at most scientific supply houses. Have the pupils observe that the earth's axis always tilts in the same direction as the earth revolves around the sun. This concept is called parallelism. Elicit that the North Pole always points toward Polaris, the North Star.

Elicit that the side of the earth facing the sun has day, while the side away from the sun has night. Review from the previous lesson that the earth's rotation causes day and night to alternate.

Prepare a transparency of a large circle. Add lines to represent the earth's equator and 23½° and 66½° north and south parallels. Use a colored overlay to illustrate night and day. Have the pupils locate the sun. Show the earth with the axis in a vertical position, and point out that all the lines have equal amounts of daylight and darkness, with day and night being equal in time.

Using a protractor, tilt the earth circle transparency 23½°. Refer to the transparency and the Trippensee Planetary Model to develop an understanding of how the lengths of day and night change as the earth moves to different locations in its orbit.

Direct the pupils' attention to the Arctic Circle and ask why Alaska is called the land of the midnight sun when the Northern Hemisphere is tilted toward the sun. Point out that when days are long in the Northern Hemisphere, the reverse is true in the Southern Hemisphere.

Using a globe, demonstrate the direction of the earth's rotation, and the apparent motion of the sun across the sky.

*Answr These*                    *Now Try This*
1. a   2. b   3. b   4. c   5. a      axis

## 6. Why do the seasons change?

Have the pupils recall that the shape of the earth's orbit is elliptical. Elicit that the earth is closer to the sun during our winter than during our summer. Lead the pupils to conclude that distance from the sun does not affect the seasons.

Using the Trippensee Planetary Model, have the pupils recall that the earth is tilted 23½° from the vertical. Using the diagram on page 335, illustrate that some parts of the earth receive direct rays of the sun and that other parts receive slanted rays.

Using a flashlight and graph paper, demonstrate that direct rays cover a smaller area than do slanted rays. Develop with the class the idea that direct rays are more intense because they cover a smaller area. Elicit from the pupils that direct rays produce more heat.

Use the Trippensee Planetary Model and transparency of the earth to show the positions of the earth at different seasons. Have the pupils construct a diagram showing the position of the earth and the angle of the rays as the earth moves along its orbit. Elicit from the pupils that the days are longer when the Northern Hemisphere is tilted toward the sun. Summarize with the class that the angle of the sun's rays and the length of day determine the seasons.

*Answer These*
1. c   2. a   3. b   4. b   5. c

## 7. How do we measure time?

Demonstrate the need for developing accurate methods of measuring time by having several students stand quietly by their seats. Instruct them to close their eyes and to sit down after they think two minutes have passed. Have the rest of the class check on how well they estimate time. Question the pupils as to what method they used in their estimation.

Elicit from the pupils different ways to express time, e.g. days, months, years, seasons, hours, minutes, seconds, etc. List these examples on the board, and discuss how the earth's motions determine the day and year. Point out that the length of a month was originally related to the phases of the moon.

Guide the pupils to understand that hours, minutes, and seconds were created by and for the convenience of man. Track back some devices man has invented to measure time. Show examples of a sundial, sand glass, water clock (clepsydra), hour candle, and a burning rope and knots. Assign the construction of similar devices as projects. Have the pupils construct a sundial and allow them to try it out of doors. Discuss why corrections must be made when comparing sundial time to mean solar time.

Assign reports on the calendar, daylight savings time, time zones, international dateline, and the names of the months and days of the week.

Direct the pupils' attention to the chart on page 337 and discuss the length of day on other planets. Refer to the chart on page 329 and compare the length of a year on each planet.

*Answer These*
1. a   2. b   3. a   4. b

*Now Try This*
1. Year   2. Month   3. Day

## 8. What are time zones?

Have pupils display the sundials they constructed for the last session. Ask them to identify the gnomon and the plane. Review why corrections must be made when comparing sundial time to mean solar time.

Using a transparency or map, review what is meant by meridian or longitude. Guide the class to see that the earth moves through 360° during one complete rotation. Elicit that a day is divided into 24 hours. Develop the idea that there is one hour difference for each 15° of longitude (360° ÷ 24 = 15). Demonstrate this with a globe.

Elicit that solar noon is determined by the location of the sun. Develop the concept that the sun arrives earlier to the east of the meridian and later to the west. Show the class how confusion in time results without the establishment of time zones. Locate and identify the time zones in continental United States.

Have the pupils conduct an activity to identify the relationship of time zones to locations on the earth. Prepare a map of the world and instruct the pupils to locate the longitude of various cities around the world. Have pupils make a tube out of the map and place it on top of a prepared circle listing the hours of the day.

Have pupils identify daytime and nighttime. Instruct them to line up one city at solar noon. Then have them identify hours of the day at various cities around the world. Elicit that as you travel west, you gain time; on an eastward journey, you lose time.

*Answer These*
1. a
2. b
3. a

*Now Try These*
1. a) Eastern     d) Central
   b) Pacific      e) Eastern
   c) Eastern      f) Mountain

2. a) 7:00 p.m.
   b) 6:00 p.m.
   c) 8:00 p.m.
   d) 8:00 p.m.

## 9. What causes tides?

On the bulletin board, display a tide chart from a newspaper, almanac, or fishing magazine. Elicit that the tides are daily changes in the level of the earth's oceans and seas, and relate the changes of tides to pupils' experiences at the beach. Have them note that the time between high tide and low tide is approximately six hours, and that high tide and low tide occur twice each day.

Review the concept of gravitational attraction from the previous lesson. Emphasize that the moon's gravity exerts a force of attraction on everything on the earth: the oceans, the atmosphere, and the solid earth itself. Point out that the movement of water we see as tides is the most obvious evidence of the moon's attraction.

Inform the class that the force of attraction between two objects is directly related to the distance between them. That is, the closer together the objects are, the greater will be the force of attraction between them. Refer to the diagram on page 245. Guide the pupils to see that the gravitational attraction is strongest between the moon and the side of the earth that is facing the moon. Since water is able to flow freely, it responds to the moon's gravitational "pull" by piling up on the side of the earth that is nearest the moon, thus producing a high tide.

At the same time, an indirect high tide is produced on the opposite side of the earth as a result of the moon's pull on the solid earth. The earth responds to the moon's gravity by moving slightly toward the moon. As the solid earth moves, the water on the side of the earth farthest from the moon is "left behind," resulting in a high tide on that side of the earth.

Using the diagram, lead pupils to see that low tides are produced by the movement of water to high tide locations. The low tide occurs at points 90° from high-tide locations.

You may also wish to point out the fact that high and low tides do not occur at the same time every day. Elicit from the class the fact that high tides occur on the sides of the earth that face toward and away from the moon. Review the moon's rotation around the earth and develop the idea that the moon is in a slightly different position in space relative to the earth each day. Since high tides "line up" with the moon's position, these tides occur at a slightly different time each day.

*Answer These*
1. b   2. c   3. a

*Now Try This*

| ACROSS | DOWN |
|--------|------|
| 2. flood | 1. moon |
| 4. change | 3. gravity |
| 6. beach | 5. ebb |

## 10. What causes the tides to change?

Review the fact that the gravitational attraction between the moon and the earth causes tides. Have the pupils recall that as distance between two objects increases, gravitational force between the objects decreases. Discuss the fact that Isaac Newton first explained the Law of Gravitation. (Point out that there is little truth to the story than an apple falling on his head gave him the idea.) Explain to the class that the force of attraction between two objects depend upon the masses of the objects as well as the distance between them. Explain that as mass increases, gravitational force increases. Discuss the fact that due to differences in mass, gravity on the moon is less than that on earth, while gravity on the sun is greater than that on earth.

Establish the fact that the sun also has an effect on the earth's tides. Challenge the pupils to explain why the sun's influence on the tides is less than that of the moon, given the fact that the sun has a greater mass and greater gravitational force than the moon. Elicit that the reason for this difference is the fact that the moon is much closer to the earth than is the sun. Recall that as distance between two objects increases, the gravitational attraction between them decreases.

Use the diagram on page 342 to guide the pupils to see that when the sun and moon are lined up, there is an increase in the total gravitational attraction affecting the earth. Elicit that this increase will cause the high tides to be higher than usual, and the low tides lower than usual. Have the pupils observe that such an alignment occurs twice a month—at new moon phase and at full moon phase.

Using the diagram on page 343, explain neap tides and elicit that they occur at first and last quarter phases of the moon.

If the pupils live near the beach, assign as a project a tide-moon observation. Have pupils record the heights of the tides and the corresponding phases of the moon.

Assign reports about areas with great tidal range, such as the Bay of Fundy in Nova Scotia. Show pictures of this area at low and at high tides. Have the pupils also prepare reports on the Passamoquody Power Plant in Maine, and the ways in which fishermen and ship captains use the tides.

*Answer These*
1. Newton
2. larger
3. distance
4. increase
5. higher
6. decrease
7. lower
8. twice

*Now Try These*
1. spring tide
2. neap tide
3. spring tide
4. spring tide
5. neap tide
6. neap tide
7. spring tide
8. both tides
9. neap tide
10. neap tide

## 11. What makes a rocket move?

Have a pupil on roller skates or a skateboard toss you a basketball. Be sure to select a pupil who is capable of balancing himself on skates or skateboard to perform this demonstration. Direct the class to observe that the pupil moves in the opposite direction of the thrown ball. Repeat the demonstration several times. Each time instruct the pupil to throw the ball a little harder. Have the class observe that the harder he throws the ball, the farther he moves backward.

On the board, write Newton's Law of Action and Reaction: "For every action, there is an equal reaction in the opposite direction." Ask the pupils to explain the demonstration in terms of this law. Elicit other examples which illustrate this law such as a recoiling rifle, jumping off a small boat, and a rotating lawn sprinkler. Inflate a balloon and let it go. Have the pupils identify the action and reaction and explain what make the balloon move.

Display pictures of rockets. Draw a diagram of a rocket and have the pupils identify and label its parts. Write the letters LOX on the diagram of the rocket and identify this as an abbreviation for liquid oxygen. Elicit that rockets must carry their own oxygen, because there is no air in space to supply the rocket with oxygen needed for the burning of the fuel.

Assign reports on various types of rockets. Have the pupils report on such men as Robert Goddard and Werner von Braun, who were associated with the development of rockets.

*Answer These*
1. c   2. a   3. b   4. c

## 12. How can rockets travel into space?

Extend a ruler halfway over the edge of a table. Place a styrofoam ball on the end of the ruler that is resting on the table. Using a downward motion of your hand, strike the extended end of the ruler, thereby flipping the ball in the air. Have the pupils recall rocket motion from the previous lesson and identify the action and reaction in this demonstration. Elicit that gravity causes the ball to fall back down. Flip the ball again this time using a greater force. Guide the pupils to see that the greater the downward force of your hand, the higher the ball rises. Elicit from the pupils that a great force is needed to move a rocket up from the earth's surface. Point out that this great force can be created by getting the rocket to move very fast. Discuss the terms thrust and escape velocity.

Challenge the pupils to devise a method of attaining a velocity of 40,250 kilometers per hour (escape velocity on earth). Elicit that a great deal of fuel is needed to attain this speed, and this additional fuel makes the rocket heavier. Using the diagram on page 346, introduce the concept of the multistage rocket. Display photographs of multistage rockets, and lead the pupils to see how the rocket becomes lighter as it moves along. Have the pupils recall the gravitational force between two objects becomes less as the distance between them increases. Guide them to see that less fuel is needed as the rocket moves farther from the earth.

Have the pupils recall the law of inertia (refer back to Module 1). Elicit that no fuel is needed to keep the spaceship moving in space, because there is nothing to slow down the rocket's motion.

*Answer These*
1. a   2. c   3. a   4. c

*Now Try This*

| ACROSS | DOWN |
|---|---|
| 2. multistage | 1. velocity |
| 4. rocket | 3. inertia |
| 6. gravity | 5. thrust |

## 13. How is space being explored?

This lesson should be conducted mainly as a class discussion.

Pupils should be made aware of the fact that there are several "types" of unmanned space probes. Some, like the probes to Venus, send back information until they reach the planet's surface, where they are destroyed. Some unmanned probes are designed to orbit a planet for long periods of time, sending back data all the while. Such probes may send landers to the planet's surface to furnish even more information. Pioneer X is designed to leave the Solar System. However, during its flight, it passed close enough to several planets to send back valuable information about those planets.

The idea of living and working on a space station can be used to stimulate a lively discussion.

*Answer These*
1. c   2. a   3. b   4. a

## UNIT 16: REVIEW

**Matching**
1. friction
2. ellipse
3. rotation
4. leap year
5. solar noon
6. ebb tides
7. flood tides
8. spring tides
9. thrust
10. neap tides

**Multiple Choice**
1. b   2. b   3. c   4. a
5. c   6. a   7. b   8. c

# CONCEPTS AND CHALLENGES IN EARTH SCIENCE

# CONCEPTS AND CHALLENGES IN

# Earth Science

## SECOND EDITION

LEONARD BERNSTEIN

MARTIN SCHACHTER

ALAN WINKLER

STANLEY WOLFE

**STANLEY WOLFE**
*Project Coordinator*

**Globe Book Company, Inc.**
A CEBCO BOOK
New York/Cleveland/Toronto

## ALAN WINKLER

Alan Winkler has taught science in the New York City Public Schools for more than twenty-five years. He has served on several science curriculum committees for the New York City Board of Education, was a writer of the science course of study for Grades 6, 7, and 9, and prepared a special-purpose laboratory program for earth science in Grade 9. Mr. Winkler has also been a consultant in the preparation of filmstrip series in earth science.

## LEONARD BERNSTEIN

Leonard Bernstein is the Director of the Isaac Newton School for Mathematics and Science in New York City. His success in science teaching was nationally featured in an article published in the *Wall Street Journal*. Mr. Bernstein is an author of science textbooks and serves as a consultant and lecturer on science teaching methods for college classes, National Science Foundation Institutes, and in-service workshops. He has been a member of the New York City Science Curriculum Revision Committee and has served as consulting editor to the New York City Division of Curriculum Development.

## MARTIN SCHACHTER

Martin Schachter is Assistant Principal, Supervision of Science, at Frederick Douglass Intermediate School in New York City. He is a member of the Science Standing Committee of the Bureau of Science for the New York City Board of Education, an instructor in Teacher-Training Workshops in Science sponsored by the New York City Board of Education, and an author of many of the science courses of study in use in the New York City Junior High and Intermediate Schools. Mr. Schachter is a Past President of the Junior High School-Intermediate School Chairmen's Association; a member of American Mensa Ltd.; a consultant for Mississippi Educational Television; an instructor in Science Update, sponsored by the New York City Board of Education; and a lecturer in science education.

## STANLEY WOLFE

*Project Coordinator*

Stanley Wolfe is Assistant Principal supervising science and mathematics at Peter Rouget Intermediate School in New York City. He has had wide experience in the development and implementation of middle-school science curricula and has participated in the writing of the current New York City Science Curriculum for Grades 6, 7, 8, and 9. He has also written an eighth-grade career guidance course of study. Mr. Wolfe is a past Coordinator of the New York City Science Fair.

ISBN: 0-87065-462-4

Printed in the United States of America

9  8  7  6  5  4

# CONTENTS

**Measuring 1**

SEEDLESS *raisins*

NET WT. 15 OZ.    425 GRAMS

PITTED PRUNES

NET WT. 12 OUNCES
340 GRAMS

**How much?** When you shop, you want to get the most for your money. When you buy chopped meat, you want to know how much meat is in the package. The label on the package tells you how much it weighs. Weight is one way of describing the amount of something. Weight is one of the properties of matter that can be measured. Length, area, and volume are also properties we can measure. To find out things about matter, we must describe its properties. Many properties can be measured.

▶ **What are some properties of matter that we can measure?**

**Units of mass.** We buy chopped meat by the pound. The pound is a <u>unit</u> (YOU-nit) of weight. Scientists do not use weight to mean the amount of something. They use the word mass. They measure mass in grams. The gram is a unit of mass in the <u>metric system</u> (MEH-tric SIS-tem). A nickel has a mass of about 5 grams. Weight and mass are related, but they are not the same. You will learn more about weight and mass in another lesson.

▶ **What unit is used to measure mass in the metric system?**

**Too much is too many.** The gram is sometimes too small for certain measurements. The mass in grams comes out in large numbers. A person may have a mass of 75,000 grams. The mass of a car may be as much as 1,500,000 grams. It would help to have a larger unit of mass. Then the numbers would be smaller.

▶ **Why is the gram sometimes too small for measuring masses?**

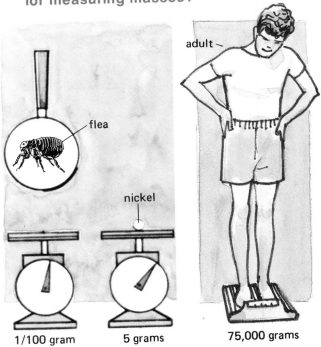

flea

nickel

adult

1/100 gram        5 grams        75,000 grams

**Cutting it to size.** For large objects, the gram may be too small. For small objects, the gram may be too big. The mass of an insect may be only 1/100 of a gram. The metric system can solve this problem.

| PREFIX | | MEANING |
|---|---|---|
| mega- | (MEG-uh) | one million (1 000 000) |
| kilo- | (KILL-uh) | one thousand (1 000) |
| hecto- | (HEC-tuh) | one hundred (100) |
| deca- | (DEC-uh) | ten (10) |
| deci- | (DESS-ih) | one tenth (1/10) |
| centi- | (SEN-tih) | one hundredth (1/100) |
| milli- | (MILL-ih) | one thousandth (1/1 000) |
| micro- | (MIKE-roh) | one millionth (1/1 000 000) |

Look at the table. A prefix (PREE-fix) can be used to change the size of a unit. It can make the unit larger or smaller. "Kilo-" (KILL-uh) is a prefix that means 1000. A <u>kilogram</u> (KILL-uh-gram) is 1000 grams. The mass of large objects is measured in kilograms. A person with a mass of 75 000 grams has a mass of 75 kilograms. "Centi-" (SEN-tih) is a prefix meaning 1/100. An insect with a mass of 1/100 of a gram has a mass of 1 centigram.

▶ **What is a kilogram?**

**Just a minute!** You have a date at 8:00. How long must you wait? Scientists say that the earth is 5 billion years old. How old are you? Time is not matter. But time matters! It is important to measure time. In daily life, we use many different units to measure time. The second, the minute, the hour, the day, the year, and the century (100 years) are units of time. The second is the main unit of time in the metric system.

▶ **What is the unit for measuring time in the metric system?**

## WHAT YOU LEARNED

1. The amount of matter is called its mass.
2. In the metric system, mass is measured in grams.
3. Prefixes are used to make units larger or smaller.
4. Time is measured in seconds.

## SCIENCE WORDS

**unit** (YOU-nit)
   an amount that is used to measure things
**gram**
   a unit of mass in the metric system
**metric system** (MEH-trick SIS-tem)
   the units of measurement used by scientists
**kilogram** (KILL-uh-gram)
   1 000 grams

## ANSWER THESE

1. Write the following masses in order from the smallest to the largest.
   milligram
   kilogram
   microgram
   hectogram
   centigram
   gram
2. Use the table of prefixes to find the meaning of each of these:
   microsecond
   millisecond
   megaton

## NOW TRY THESE

1. How many seconds are there in a century? Give your answer in megaseconds.
2. Scientists sometimes measure the cost of scientific equipment in "megabucks." A large atom-smasher may cost 500 megabucks to build. What do you think that means?

## FINDING OUT MORE

The International Bureau of Weights and Measures is located near Paris, France. The standard unit of mass is kept there. This mass is exactly 1000 grams or 1 kilogram. Each nation keeps a copy of this mass in its own national laboratory. This is done so that scientists all over the world can be sure they are measuring mass in the same units. The standard kilogram is made of a platinum-iridium alloy that will not rust. It is carefully protected against damage. What might happen if this standard mass became scratched?

# How do we measure size?

**The long and the short of it.** In the metric system, we measure length and distance in a unit called the <u>meter</u> (MEE-ter). We use prefixes to make larger and smaller units of length. A <u>kilometer</u> (KILL-uh-mee-ter) is 1000 meters. A <u>centimeter</u> (SEN-tih-mee-ter) is 1/100 of a meter. A <u>millimeter</u> (MILL-ih-mee-ter) is 1/1000 of a meter. The table compares the units of length.

▶ **What is the unit of length in the metric system?**

| | |
|---|---|
| 10 millimeters | = 1 centimeter |
| 1000 millimeters | = 1 meter |
| 100 centimeters | = 1 meter |
| 1000 meters | = 1 kilometer |

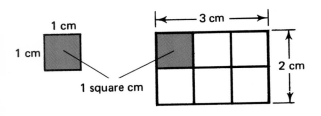

Length x Width = Area
3 cm x 2 cm = 6 square centimeters

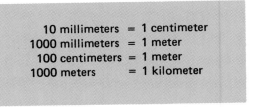
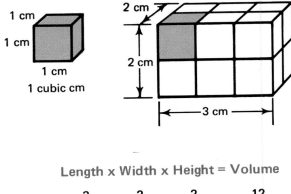

Length x Width x Height = Volume
3 cm x 2 cm x 2 cm = 12 cubic centimeters

**Measuring area.** Look at the drawing of the square. Each side of the square is 1 centimeter long. The area of the square is 1 square centimeter. Now look at the drawing of the rectangle. Its length is 3 centimeters. Its width is 2 centimeters. You can see that the rectangle contains 6 square centimeters. Its area is 6 square centimeters. You can find the area of a rectangle by multiplying its length by its width.

▶ **How can we find the area of a rectangle?**

**Measuring volume.** Look at the drawing of the cube. Each edge of the cube is 1 centimeter long. The volume of the cube is 1 cubic centimeter. Now look at the drawing of the box. Its length is 3 centimeters. Its width is 2 centimeters. Its height is 2 centimeters. Its volume is 12 cubic centimeters. The volume of a box can be found by multiplying its length by its width by its height.

▶ **How can we find the volume of a box?**

**Volume of liquids.** Volume is measured in cubic centimeters. Volume can also be measured in units called <u>liters</u> (LEE-ters). The volume of liquids is often measured in liters. A liter is the same as 1000 cubic centimeters. A box that is 10 centimeters on each side has a volume of 1000 cubic centimeters (10 × 10 × 10 = 1000). One liter of a liquid will exactly fill the box. A milliliter (MILL-ih-lee-ter) is 1/1000 of a liter. A milliliter is the same as 1 cubic centimeter.

▶ How many cubic centimeters are there in 1 liter?

**Abbreviating units.** Milligram, kilometer, and cubic centimeter are long words. It takes a lot of space and a lot of time to write them out. We abbreviate (uh-BREE-vee-ate), or shorten, the names of units. For example, km is the abbreviation for kilometer. To abbreviate units of area and volume, we use a small 2 to show square units and a small 3 to show cubic units. To abbreviate square centimeters, we write cm². To abbreviate cubic centimeters, we write cm³. The table shows the abbreviations for units in the metric system.

▶ How would we abbreviate 100 cubic centimeters?

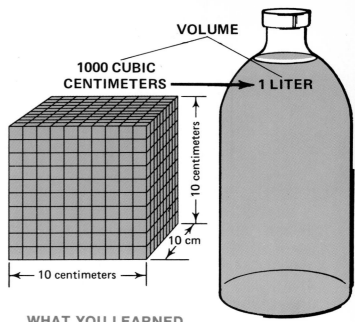

| NAME OF UNIT | ABBREVIATION |
|---|---|
| gram | g |
| kilogram | kg |
| milligram | mg |
| meter | m |
| kilometer | km |
| centimeter | cm |
| millimeter | mm |
| square centimeters | cm² |
| cubic centimeters | cm³ |
| liter | L |
| milliliter | mL |

**WHAT YOU LEARNED**

1. The unit of length is the meter.
2. Area is measured in square units.
3. Volume is measured in cubic units.
4. A liter is the same as 1000 cubic centimeters.
5. Units can be abbreviated.

**SCIENCE WORDS**

**meter** (MEE-ter)
   the unit of length in the metric system
**kilometer** (KILL-uh-mee-ter)
   1000 meters
**centimeter** (SEN-tih-mee-ter)
   1/100 of a meter
**millimeter** (MILL-ih-mee-ter)
   1/1000 of a meter
**liter** (LEE-ter)
   1000 cubic centimeters

**ANSWER THESE**

1. The unit of length is the
   a. meter
   b. liter
   c. kilogram
2. The volume of liquids is measured in
   a. square centimeters
   b. cubic liters
   c. liters
3. Width × height × length of a box equals its
   a. area
   b. weight
   c. volume

5

# How do we determine density?

The small density of the material in this bag makes the bag easy to lift.

**Size can fool you.** Did you ever pick up a large object and find that it was lighter than you thought? Or find that a small object was surprisingly heavy? This happens because objects are made of different materials. An object that is heavy for its size is made of dense material. We say that the material has a high density (DEN-suh-tee).

▶ Why are some small objects very heavy?

**Numbers for density.** The density of a material can be expressed by a number. For example, the density of iron is 8 grams per cubic centimeter (8 g/cm³). This means that a piece of iron with a volume of 1 cubic centimeter will have a mass of 8 grams. The density of gold is 19 g/cm³. This means that a piece of gold with a volume of 1 cm³ has a mass of 19 grams. A mass of 19 grams is more than twice 8 grams. Gold is more than twice as dense as iron. If a piece of gold and a piece of iron are the same size, the gold will have a weight and mass more than twice as much.

▶ What is the mass of 1 cm³ of a metal if the density of the metal is 11 g/cm³?

**Density and size.** The density of a material does not depend on the amount of material you have. A large piece of iron has the same density as a small piece. If you cut a copper rod into two pieces, each piece will have the same density as the whole rod.

▶ How will the density of a large piece of gold compare with the density of a small piece of gold?

**Density and temperature.** The density of a material changes slightly with changes in temperature. This happens because a material usually becomes slightly larger as it is heated. There is less mass in a cubic centimeter than before, so the density is less. If the temperature does not change, then the density will not change.

▶ What happens to the density of a material as the temperature changes?

**Measuring density.** If we want to find the density of a material, we must first have a piece of the material. The size of the piece doesn't matter. Then we must measure the volume of the piece and its mass. The mass divided by the volume gives the density. Here is an example. Suppose a certain piece of lead

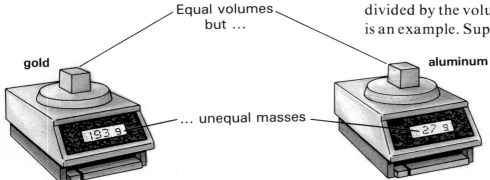

Equal volumes but ...

gold

... unequal masses

aluminum

If two objects have the same volume, then the object with the greater mass will have the greater density.

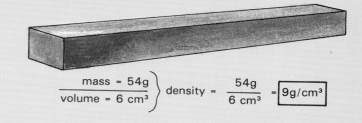

Both bars are made of the same metal. The density of the metal is the same no matter how large or small the piece of metal. The density of the metal is 9 grams per cubic centimeter, or 9 g/cm³.

has a mass of 72.0 grams. Its volume is 6.00 cubic centimeters.

$$\text{density} = \frac{\text{mass}}{\text{volume}}$$

$$= \frac{72.0 \text{ grams}}{6.00 \text{ cubic centimeters}}$$

$$= 12.0 \text{ grams per cm}^3$$

▶ If you know the mass and the volume of an object, how do you find its density?

**Identifying different materials.** Density is one of the ways of describing materials. Different materials have different densities. The density of a material can help us identify it. The chart shows the densities of several different materials.

▶ According to the chart, what is the density of aluminum?

| Material | Density at Room Temperature (grams per cubic centimeter) |
|---|---|
| cork | 0.2 |
| alcohol | 0.8 |
| water | 1.0 |
| aluminum | 2.7 |
| iron | 7.9 |
| lead | 11.3 |
| mercury | 13.6 |
| gold | 19.3 |

## WHAT YOU LEARNED

1. Objects that are heavy for their size are made of dense materials.
2. A large piece of a material has the same density as a small piece.
3. Density changes slightly with temperature.
4. Density is the mass of a piece of material divided by its volume.
5. Density helps identify a material.

## SCIENCE WORDS

**dense**
heavy for its size

**density** (DEN-suh-tee)
a number describing how dense a material is

## ANSWER THESE

1. Small objects that are very heavy are said to be
   a. hard
   b. massive
   c. dense
2. We can find the density of an object by
   a. dividing its mass by its volume
   b. dividing its volume by its mass
   c. adding its mass and volume
3. As the mass of an object increases, its density
   a. increases
   b. decreases
   c. remains the same
4. A large piece of aluminum has a density
   a. greater than a smaller piece
   b. less than a smaller piece
   c. the same as a smaller piece
5. Different materials have densities
   a. that are the same
   b. that are different
   c. that depend on their size

## NOW TRY THESE

1. An object has a volume of 10 cm³ and mass of 27 g. Name the material that the object is made of. (See the chart.)
2. The chart below shows the volume and mass of three objects: R, S, and T. Find out which two objects were made of the same material.

| Object | Volume | Mass |
|---|---|---|
| R | 20 cm³ | 22.6 g |
| S | 5 cm³ | 39.5 g |
| T | 15 cm³ | 118.5 g |

# UNIT REVIEW

*Do the following questions on a separate sheet of paper.*

**Matching**   *Write down each of the measurements in Column I. Next to each measurement from Column I write the measurement from Column II that is the same.*

|   |   |
|---|---|
| **Column I** | **Column II** |

**Group A**

1. 1000 milligrams
2. 10,000 grams
3. 0.1 gram
4. 0.1 kilogram
5. 0.01 gram

10 mg
100 mg
1 g
100 g
10 kg

**Group B**

6. 10 centimeters
7. 1000 centimeters
8. 1000 millimeters
9. 0.1 kilometer
10. 1000 meters

1 km
10 m
100 mm
100 m
100 cm

**Multiple Choice**   *Write the letter of the choice that best completes the statement or answers the question.*

1. The gram is a unit of
   a. mass
   b. weight
   c. volume
2. The prefix for 1000 is
   a. milli-
   b. kilo-
   c. micro-
3. A rectangle 4 cm × 6 cm has an area of
   a. 10 square centimeters
   b. 24 square centimeters
   c. 24 cubic centimeters

4. A bottle marked 1.5 liters has a volume of
   a. 500 cubic centimeters
   b. 1.5 cubic liters
   c. 150 milliliters
5. To find the density of a material, divide its
   a. volume by its mass
   b. weight by its mass
   c. mass by its volume

# UNIT 1

# Studying the Earth

## Unit Lessons

1. How does a scientist study the earth.
2. What are the parts of the earth?
3. What is the inside of the earth like?
4. What is a globe?
5. What is a map projection?
6. How do we find places on a map?
7. How do you read a map?
8. What are contour lines?
9. What is a topographic map?

## Goals and Objectives

After completint this unit, you should be able to:

- understand how a hypothesis is formed.
- name and describe the layers of the earth.
- explain why maps of the earth are usually distorted.
- read the symbols on a map and work with latitude and longitude.
- give a description of an area by examining a topographic map of it.

# How does a scientist study the earth?

As the Viking 2 spacecraft sat on Mars, a camera inside took this photo on September 6, 1976.

**What's going on here?** Scientists have many questions about the earth. For example, they would like to know how the earth's mountains, valleys, and oceans formed. They would like to know what causes earthquakes and when the next big one will happen. To help answer such questions, scientists make observations (ob-zer-VAY-shuns). Observations are made with the senses. Scientists look, listen, taste, smell, and feel in order to get facts about the world around them. You, too, can use your senses to learn about the things around you.

▶ **How can we get information about the world around us?**

**Is there life on Mars?** On July 20, 1976, scientists put the Viking lander on the planet Mars. They wanted to study Mars the way scientists study the earth. But it was too difficult for human beings to go to Mars. Instead, they sent instruments (IN-struh-ments) to Mars to make observations. These instruments took the place of human senses. Cameras took pictures of the Martian landscape. Instruments examined the atmosphere on Mars and observed the weather. Other instruments did chemical experiments to look for signs of life. One of the instruments looked for magnetic materials. The results of all these observations were sent back to earth. Radio and television signals carried these messages.

▶ **How did scientists make observations on the planet Mars?**

**"Seeing is believing."** Most people trust their senses. But the senses can be fooled. The senses also have limits. Many things are too small to be seen with the eyes alone. Some things are too far away to be seen. We use microscopes and telescopes to help us see them. Some sounds are so soft we can't hear them. We use amplifiers (AM-pluh-fy-ers) to make them louder. Our senses need help. Instruments are used to help our senses make observations.

▶ **How do instruments help our senses?**

**Observations in science must be accurate.** Instruments help us make accurate measurements. We use a ruler to find out how long something is. We use a scale or balance to find its weight. We use a thermometer to find its temperature. Instruments can make a record of observations even when nobody is there. We can study the record later. Instruments help the senses make accurate observations.

▶ **What do we need to make accurate observations?**

**Elementary, my dear Watson.** Detectives and earth scientists work in the same way. Detectives make observations and look for clues. From the clues they guess how a crime was done and who did it. Earth scientists also look for clues about the earth. From the clues they guess how mountains are formed, or how continents move. They don't make wild guesses. Their guesses are based on accurate observations and careful thinking. Scientists call this type of guess a <u>hypothesis</u> (hy-POTH-uh-sis). A hypothesis needs to be proved correct. More experiments and observations are needed to test whether a hypothesis is correct.

▶ What is a hypothesis?

## WHAT YOU LEARNED

1. Scientists make accurate observations to help answer questions about the world.
2. People use their senses to make observations.
3. Instruments are used to help the senses make observations.
4. Scientists use observations to make a hypothesis.
5. Experiments are done to test whether a hypothesis is correct.

## SCIENCE WORDS

**observation** (ob-zer-VAY-shun)
a fact about our surroundings obtained by using our senses
**instrument** (IN-struh-ment)
something that helps our senses make accurate observations
**hypothesis** (hy-POTH-uh-sis)
a guess based on accurate observations

## ANSWER THESE

1. To answer questions, scientists make
   a. observations
   b. rules
   c. clues
2. To observe something, scientists use
   a. guesses
   b. their senses
   c. a notebook
3. The senses are helped by
   a. books
   b. drawings
   c. instruments
4. In an experiment the scientist must
   a. make neat notes
   b. make accurate measurements
   c. take care not to spill anything
5. A hypothesis must be
   a. proved correct
   b. accepted
   c. discarded

## NOW TRY THESE

1. List the five human senses.
2. Explain how your senses could help you make observations of each of the following: a rock, a river, a gas.
3. List two instruments that can be used to aid your sense of sight, and tell how each one helps.

# What are the parts of the earth?

**What shape is the earth?** Look at the photograph of our planet, earth. This picture was taken out in space. What does the earth look like? The earth is shaped like a ball, or sphere (SFEER). The earth is a large sphere.

▶ **What is the shape of the earth?**

**The water.** What do you think the blue part of the photograph is? It is the water on the earth. Most of our planet is covered with water. About ¾ of the earth's surface is water. Water is found in the oceans, rivers, and lakes. The part of the earth's surface that is water is the hydrosphere (HY-dro-sfeer).

▶ **What is the hydrosphere?**

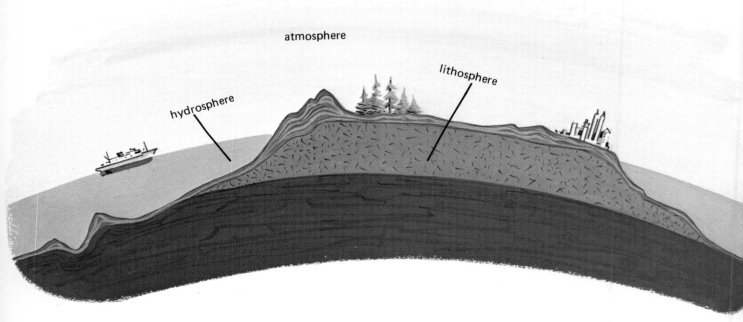

atmosphere

lithosphere

hydrosphere

**The land.** Land is the solid part of the earth. Mountains are raised lands. Valleys are the lower lands between the mountains. The countries of the world are parts of the land. The hard solid part of the earth that makes the land is called the lithosphere (LITH-o-sfeer). There is lithosphere under the oceans, too.

▶ **What parts of the earth make up the lithosphere?**

**The air.** There is another part of the earth around the lithosphere and the hydrosphere. This part is called the atmosphere (AT-muh-sfeer). The atmosphere is made of air. The atmosphere is the air that covers all the other parts of the earth.

▶ **What is the atmosphere?**

**WHAT YOU LEARNED**

1. Our planet earth is a large sphere or ball.
2. Water covers ¾ of the earth. This is called the hydrosphere.
3. The solid part of the earth is called the lithosphere.
4. The air around the earth makes up the atmosphere.

**SCIENCE WORDS**

**sphere** (SFEER)
   a ball or globe
**hydrosphere** (HY-dro-sfeer)
   the part of the earth's surface covered by water
**lithosphere** (LITH-o-sfeer)
   the solid part of the earth
**atmosphere** (AT-muh-sfeer)
   the air around the earth

**ANSWER THESE**

1. Name the three parts of the earth.
2. How much of the earth's surface is the hydrosphere?
3. On which part of the earth do we find your school?

**FINDING OUT MORE**

Earth science is a broad subject. It is not only the study of the rocks and minerals found on the land. Some earth scientists study the oceans. Others study the weather. Still others study earthquakes and volcanoes. Even the study of outer space is important to earth scientists.

Earth scientists work in many different areas.

# What is the inside of the earth like?

**Cutting the earth in half.** Did you ever plan to dig a hole through the earth to the other side? What do you think the earth would look like on the inside? The inside of the earth can be compared to a hard-boiled egg. If you cut a hard-boiled egg with the shell on, you see that the egg has different layers. The earth is made of layers, too.

▶ **How can the earth be compared to a hard-boiled egg?**

**The crust of the earth.** The shell of the egg is the outside layer. The earth has an outside layer, too. It is called the crust. The shell of the egg is very thin. The earth's crust is about 30 kilometers thick. Could you say the crust is very thin? Yes! To get to the center of the earth, you would have to dig about 6,500 km. Compared to 6,500 km, 30 km is not much. Compared to the whole earth, the crust is very thin.

▶ **What is the outer layer of the earth called?**

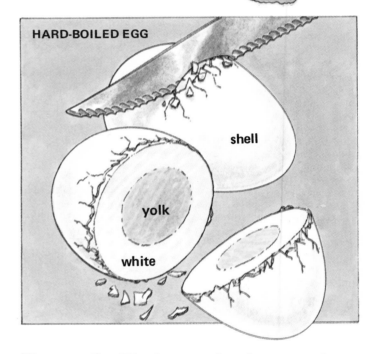

HARD-BOILED EGG

shell

yolk

white

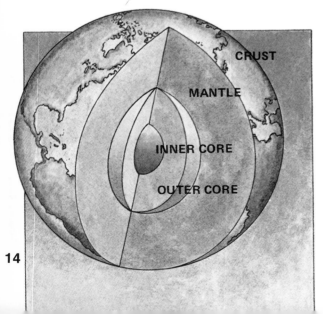

CRUST

MANTLE

INNER CORE

OUTER CORE

**The mantle.** The layer under the crust of the earth is called the mantle (MAN-tull). The mantle could be compared to the white of the egg. As you can see in the drawing, it is much thicker than the crust. The mantle is about 3,000 km thick.

▶ **What is the layer of the earth found under the crust called?**

14

**The core.** The center part of the earth is called the <u>core</u>. It can be compared to the yolk of the egg. But the core of the earth is made up of two layers, not just one. They are the outer core and the inner core.

► **What is the center of the earth called?**

## WHAT YOU LEARNED

1. The earth has four layers: the crust, the mantle, the outer core, and the inner core.
2. The crust is the thin outside layer of the earth.
3. The mantle is the second layer. It is much thicker than the crust.
4. The core is the center part of the earth. It is made up of the outer core and the inner core.

## SCIENCE WORDS

**crust**
   the thin outside layer of the earth
**mantle** (MAN-tull)
   the thick layer of the earth just under the crust
**core**
   the center part of the earth

## ANSWER THESE

1. Name the two layers that make up the center of the earth.
2. Which layer of the earth can you touch?
3. What is the name of the layer just below the crust of the earth?

## NOW TRY THIS

Copy these sentences and complete the rhymes.
1. Run like the wind and kick up the dust;
   It settles right back on the earth's _____.

2. You will need a shovel with a very long handle
   To dig to the earth's second layer, the _____.

3. You could dig and dig and dig still more,
   But you won't even reach the earth's outer _____.

## DO THIS AT HOME

Get a cupcake that has icing on top and marshmallow or other filling inside. Push a straw through the top into the center of the cupcake. Now pull the straw out and cut it open. What do you find inside the straw? How could an experiment like this one be used to find out about the inside of the earth?

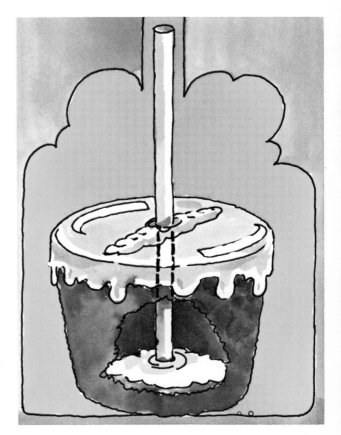

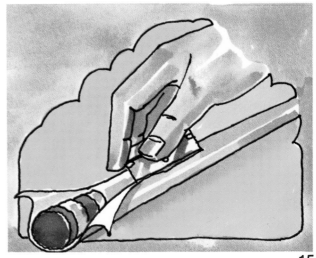

# What is a globe?

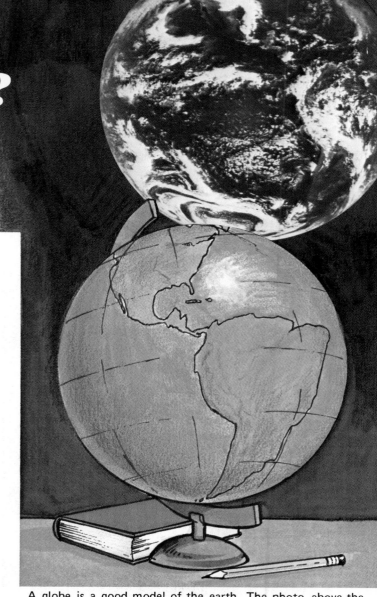

**The shape of things.** An astronaut out in space can see the whole earth. Down here on the ground it is hard to imagine what the whole earth looks like. To study the whole earth, we make a <u>model</u> (MOD-ul) of it. A model is something that represents the real thing. The best model of the earth is a globe. We can study many things about the earth by using a globe.

▶ **What is the best model of the earth?**

**Got the world on a globe.** Look at a globe. It shows a correct picture of the whole earth. The surface is rounded like the earth's surface. Directions are shown correctly on a globe. Land and ocean areas have their true shape. The land and ocean areas are also drawn to scale. The scale shows how sizes on the earth and on the globe are related. For example, a river that is 1000 km long on the earth may be 10 cm long on the globe. Another river that is 2000 km long will be 20 cm long on the same globe. If one area is twice the size of another on the earth, it will be twice the size on the globe, too. All land and ocean areas on the globe are in their true size to scale.

▶ **Why is a globe a good model of the earth?**

A globe is a good model of the earth. The photo above the globe was taken 35,000 kilometers from earth.

**Globes can't always be used.** On a globe you can look at only half the world at one time. Most globes are too small to show details. Larger globes are too big to handle. They can't fit into your books or be carried to school. What is needed is a flat model that represents the earth. This flat model is called a map. A map can show the whole earth at once. Or it can show a small part of the earth with more detail. One way to study the earth is to study a map of it.

▶ **What is a map?**

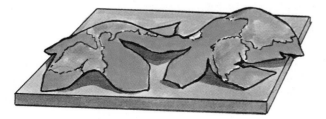

A hollow sphere will rip if you try to push it flat.

**Got the world on a map.** Can a map be made just by flattening a globe? Not really. When a globe is flattened, it rips or crumples. A globe can show all shapes, distances, and directions correctly. A flat map can not do this. If the shapes on a map are correct, the distances may be wrong. If the distances are right, the shapes or directions may be wrong. We say that the maps are distorted (dis-TORT-ed) or that they have distortions (dis-TOR-shuns). All maps of large areas are distorted in some way.

▶ **What may be distorted on a map of the earth?**

### WHAT YOU LEARNED

1. A globe is the best model of the earth.
2. Globes are not always easy to use.
3. Flat maps are distorted in some way.

### SCIENCE WORDS

**model** (MOD-ul)
  something that represents the real thing
**distorted** (dis-TORT-ed)
  not showing correct distance, shape, or direction

### ANSWER THESE

1. A map is a
   a. plan
   b. model
   c. photograph
2. The best model of the earth should be drawn on a
   a. large piece of paper
   b. plastic cone
   c. globe
3. Globes can't always be used because they
   a. cost too much
   b. are too small to show detail
   c. are distorted
4. All flattened maps are
   a. free of distortion
   b. distorted in some ways
   c. completely distorted

### NOW TRY THESE

Find the words.
1. A map is a

2. Best model of the earth

### FINDING OUT MORE

Maps are not used only to study land and water areas. Some maps show locations of mineral resources. Others show where certain crops are grown or materials are manufactured. Weather maps give a picture of conditions in the sky. Climate maps show the amount of rainfall and the average temperature in different places. A star map shows us where to find different stars in the sky.

# What is a map projection?

**Mapmaker, mapmaker, make me a map.**
Try to flatten a globe, and it will only rip.
You must use other methods for making
flat maps. Here are a few ways.

Use a clear plastic globe. With a crayon
draw some dark lines on the globe. Show
countries, rivers, lakes, and oceans. Then
cut the globe into two equal halves. Each
half is called a hemisphere (HEM-uh-
sfeer). Place a light at the center of one
hemisphere, as shown. Hold a piece of paper so that its center touches the hemisphere. Shine the light through the hemisphere. Shadows of the lines drawn on the
hemisphere fall on the paper. We say that
these lines are projected (pruh-JEK-ted)
onto the paper screen. Trace over these
lines to make a flat map. Maps made in this
way are called map projections (pruh-JEK-
shuns).

▶ What is a hemisphere?

line shadow

line on hemisphere

**Different map projections.** Placing the
screen in different ways makes different
kinds of map projections. A flat screen
may touch the globe at one point, as in the
way just described. Or the screen may be
wrapped around the globe like a tube. It
may also be wrapped to form a cone. The
lines that fall on the screen are then traced.
The screen can then be unrolled to form a
flat map.

▶ What makes one map projection
different from another?

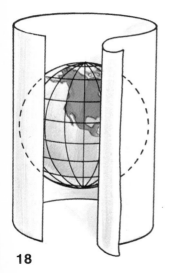

The screen may be
wrapped around the
globe like a tube.

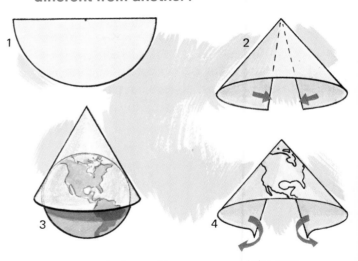

The screen may be formed into a cone, and the cone
placed over the globe.

**Map distortions.** Different map projections show different types of distortion. Where the screen is close to the globe, the projected lines will show little distortion. Where the screen is farther from the globe, there will be greater distortion. Look at the screen wrapped to form a tube around the globe. The globe and screen touch along the equator. Areas near the equator will be projected with little distortion. Areas far from the equator will be projected with great distortion. On such a map, Greenland will appear larger than South America. (See the map on page 21). Actually, South America is eight times as large as Greenland. You can see this on a globe.

The size of the area being mapped also affects the amount of distortion. A map of a large area will contain some large distortions. Maps of small areas show almost no distortions.

▶ **Does a map of a large or a small area show more distortions?**

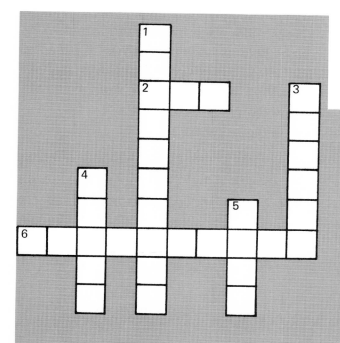

## WHAT YOU LEARNED

1. The lines and shapes on a globe can be projected onto a flat surface.
2. There are different types of map projections.
3. Different map projections show different distortions.

## SCIENCE WORDS

**hemisphere** (HEM-uh-sfeer)
  one half of a globe or sphere
**map projection** (pruh-JEK-shun)
  flat map made with the help of a globe

## ANSWER THESE

1. A map formed on a screen from a globe is called a
   a. screen map
   b. global map
   c. map projection
2. All maps are
   a. distorted more in some places than in others
   b. distorted in the same way
   c. distorted near the equator
3. To make a map projection, the screen
   a. may be wrapped around the globe like a tube
   b. should not touch the globe
   c. should be a sphere

## NOW TRY THIS

Copy the blocks for the crossword puzzle onto a sheet of paper. Use the clues below to complete the puzzle.

## DOWN

1. Half of a globe
3. Surface on which lines are projected
4. Round model of the earth
5. What happens to a globe when you try to flatten it

## ACROSS

2. Flat model of the earth
6. Map made by tracing lines from a globe onto a screen

**19**

# How do we find places on maps?

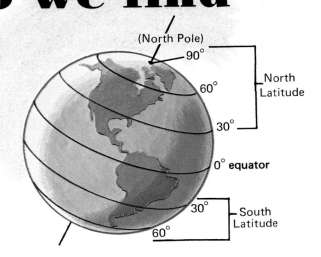

SOME PARALLELS AT 30° INTERVALS

**Splashdown!** A space capsule splashes down in the Pacific Ocean. Navy boats rush to pick up the astronauts. How can a tiny space capsule be found in a huge ocean? We can imagine streets and avenues in the ocean. They are the lines you see on maps of the earth. These lines are called parallels (PAR-uh-lels) and meridians (muh-RID-ee-uns). Parallels and meridians are imaginary lines on the earth that help us determine positions.

▶ **What are parallels and meridians?**

**A street named Equator.** Parallels run horizontally around the earth. The equator (uh-KWAY-ter) is the longest parallel. It divides the earth in half. Other parallels locate places north or south of the equator. The amount by which a place is north or south of the equator is called its latitude (LAT-uh-tood). Latitude is measured in degrees. The equator is at 0° latitude. The North Pole is at 90° north latitude. The South Pole is at 90° south latitude. A point on earth can be anywhere from 0° to 90° north or south latitude.

▶ **What is latitude?**

**Where it's at.** Meridians are lines going from pole to pole. They locate places east or west of a special meridian called the

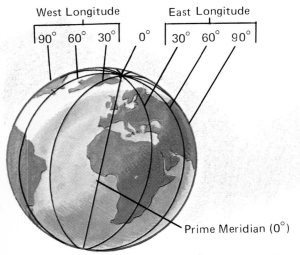

SOME MERIDIANS AT 30° INTERVALS

GLOBE SHOWING MERIDIANS AND PARALLELS

prime meridian. The prime meridian is the starting meridian. It passes through Greenwich, England. The amount by which a place is east or west of the prime meridian is called its <u>longitude</u> (LON-jih-tood). Longitude is also measured in degrees. There are 180° of east longitude and 180° of west longitude. Lines of latitude and longitude cross. If you know the latitude and longitude of a place on the earth, you can find the place on a map. Every place on earth has its own latitude and longitude.

▶ **What is longitude?**

## SCIENCE WORDS

**parallels** (PAR-uh-lels)
   imaginary lines running horizontally around the earth
**meridians** (muh-RID-ee-uns)
   imaginary lines running from the North Pole to the South Pole
**latitude** (LAT-uh-tood)
   the number of degrees by which a place on earth is north or south of the equator
**longitude** (LON-jih-tood)
   the number of degrees by which a place on earth is east or west of the prime meridian

## WHAT YOU LEARNED

1. Parallels and meridians are imaginary lines on the earth.
2. Latitude and longitude tell us the location of places on the earth.

## ANSWER THESE

1. Imaginary lines running horizontally around the earth are
   **a.** meridians
   **b.** parallels
   **c.** longitudes
2. Imaginary lines running from pole to pole are
   **a.** meridians
   **b.** parallels
   **c.** latitudes
3. Latitude and longitude are measured in
   **a.** days
   **b.** kilometers
   **c.** degrees
4. The latitude of the North Pole is
   **a.** 0°
   **b.** 90° S
   **c.** 90° N
5. The largest possible degree of longitude is
   **a.** 41°
   **b.** 90°
   **c.** 180°

## NOW TRY THIS

Find the latitude and longitude of the points marked A to F on the map. Tell if the latitude is north or south and if the longitude is east or west.

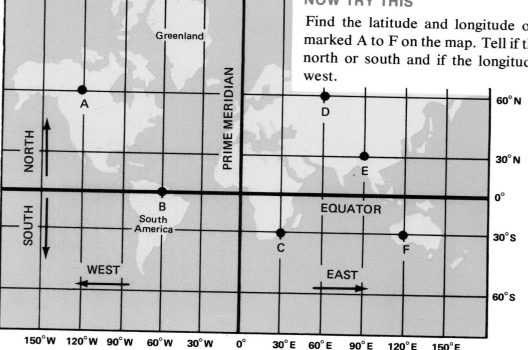

21

# How do you read a map?

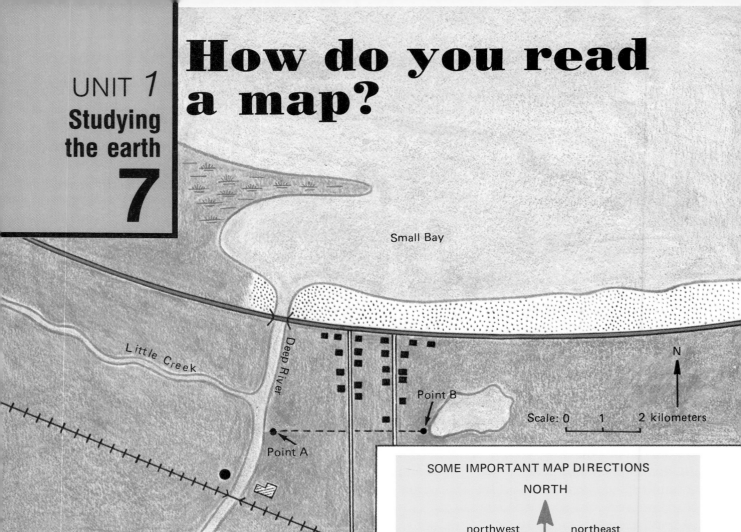

Small Bay

Little Creek

Deep River

Point B

Point A

N

Scale: 0    1    2 kilometers

**Directions on a map.** Look at Deep River on the map. The river flows toward the top of the map into Small Bay. On most maps the top is the direction north. Deep River is flowing north. If the top of the map is north, the bottom of the map is south. East is to your right, and west is to your left. Some maps show directions on them. If you look at the map again, you will see an arrow marked *N* near the map scale. This arrow shows the direction north.

Most directions are not exactly north, south, east, or west. We have special words for these in-between directions. For example, the direction between south and east is called southeast. Can you see that Little Creek is flowing southeast?

▶ **What direction is toward the bottom of many maps?**

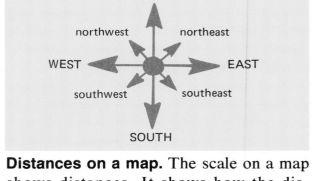

SOME IMPORTANT MAP DIRECTIONS

NORTH

northwest     northeast

WEST                          EAST

southwest     southeast

SOUTH

**Distances on a map.** The scale on a map shows distances. It shows how the distance on the map compares to the real distance on the earth. Look at the scale on the map. A ruler will tell you that the distance between the *0* and the *1* is 1 cm. This means that each centimeter of distance on the map represents a distance of 1 kilometer on the earth. Measure the distance on the map from point *A* to point *B*. It is 4 cm. This tells you that the distance on the earth from point A on the river to point B on the lake is 4 kilometers.

▶ **What does the scale on a map show?**

**Showing objects on a map.** Simple drawings are used to show real objects on a map. For example, the small black squares on the map show the locations of houses. Simple drawings like these are called symbols (SIM-buls). Many different symbols are used on maps. The most common symbols are listed in the table.

▶ How are real objects shown on a map?

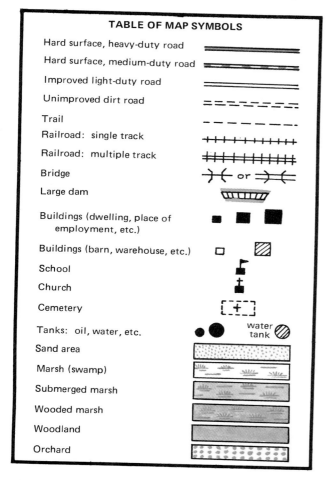

TABLE OF MAP SYMBOLS

| | |
|---|---|
| Hard surface, heavy-duty road | |
| Hard surface, medium-duty road | |
| Improved light-duty road | |
| Unimproved dirt road | |
| Trail | |
| Railroad: single track | |
| Railroad: multiple track | |
| Bridge | or |
| Large dam | |
| Buildings (dwelling, place of employment, etc.) | |
| Buildings (barn, warehouse, etc.) | |
| School | |
| Church | |
| Cemetery | |
| Tanks: oil, water, etc. | water tank |
| Sand area | |
| Marsh (swamp) | |
| Submerged marsh | |
| Wooded marsh | |
| Woodland | |
| Orchard | |

**Color on a map.** Color has a meaning on maps. Anything made by people is usually colored black. Symbols for houses, railroads, and bridges are black on a map. Blue is used to show bodies of water. Lakes, rivers, and swamps are colored blue. Forests and woods are colored green. Color helps to tell one feature from another.

▶ What would be the color of the ocean on a map?

## WHAT YOU LEARNED

1. On most maps, the top is the direction north.
2. The map scale is used to measure distances on a map.
3. Map symbols are used to represent real objects.
4. Color may be used on a map to show different features, such as woods, water, and buildings.

## SCIENCE WORDS

**map scale**
a map feature that tells how map distances compare to real distances on earth

**map symbols** (SIM-buls)
simple drawings used on a map to represent real objects

## ANSWER THESE

1. The direction to your right on a map is usually
   a. north
   b. south
   c. east
2. Distances on a map are shown by a
   a. symbol
   b. map scale
   c. river
3. The following symbol ⟩⟨ represents a
   a. bridge
   b. swamp
   c. school
4. On a map the symbol for a school would be colored
   a. red
   b. green
   c. black

## NOW TRY THESE

Use the map on page 22 to answer these questions
1. In what direction would you travel to go from point B to point A?
2. How many kilometers is it from point B to the bridge on the road?
3. In what part of the map is the swamp?
4. How many buildings are shown on the map?

# What are contour lines?

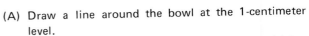

(A) Draw a line around the bowl at the 1-centimeter level.
(B) Continue drawing lines around the bowl for higher levels.
(C) Look down on the bowl from above.

**Ups and downs.** The level of the water in the oceans is about the same from place to place. The average level of water in the oceans is called <u>sea level</u>. Heights of places on land are measured from sea level. The top of a mountain may be 1000 meters above sea level. A point on the ocean's bottom may be a certain number of meters below sea level. The distance of a point above or below sea level is called <u>elevation</u> (el-uh-VAY-shun). Mt. Everest is the highest mountain on earth. The elevation of Mt. Everest is 8.8 kilometers.

▶ **What is elevation?**

**Shaping up.** One way of showing elevations on a map is by drawing <u>contour</u> (CON-toor) <u>lines</u>. The idea of contour lines can be shown as follows. Use a clear plastic box and a bowl. Starting at the bottom of the box, make marks on the outside of the box one centimeter apart. Put the bowl upside down in the box. Slowly add water to the box until it is up to the one-centimeter mark. Where the water level touches the bowl, draw a line around the bowl with a wax pencil. This is the 1-centimeter contour line of the bowl.

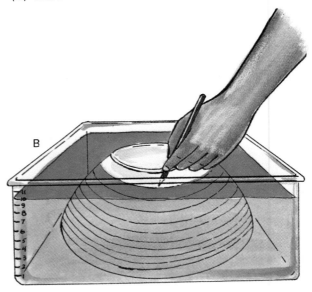

Now add more water until it is up to the second centimeter mark. Again draw a line around the bowl. This is the 2-centimeter contour line. Keep doing this until the bowl is covered by the water. Each line on the bowl is 1 centimeter higher than the one below it.

▶ **How high up from the bottom of the box is the 4th contour line?**

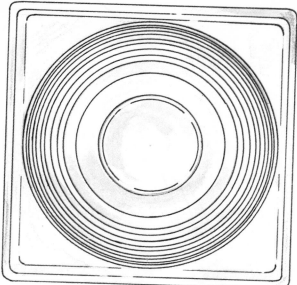

c

**Drawing a contour map.** Take the bowl out of the box. Pour the water out of the box. Then put the bowl back into the box. Put a plastic cover on the box, and tape a thin plastic sheet to the cover. Look straight down on the bowl. You will see all the contour lines looking like rings, one inside another. Draw these rings on the plastic sheet. You will have a contour map of the bowl. The outside ring is the 1-centimeter contour line. It shows all the places on the bowl that have an elevation of 1 centimeter. The second ring is the 2-centimeter contour line. The smallest ring shows the highest elevation that you drew on the bowl.

▶ If a place on the bowl has an elevation of 2.5 cm, between which two contour lines would it be?

## FINDING OUT MORE

Farmers with hilly ground are careful to plow in a certain way. They plow along a line whose points are at the same elevation. This makes the furrows run across the slope of the hill. Water collects in the furrows and sinks into the soil. The furrows stop the water from running down the hill and carrying away valuable topsoil. This kind of plowing is called contour plowing.

## WHAT YOU LEARNED

1. The level of water in the oceans is about the same from place to place.
2. Heights of places on land are measured from sea level.
3. A contour line on a map shows all points having the same elevation.

## SCIENCE WORDS

**sea level**
the average level of water in the oceans

**elevation** (el-uh-VAY-shun)
the distance of a point above or below sea level

**contour** (CON-toor) **line**
a line on a map showing points having the same elevation

## ANSWER THESE

1. The elevation of a mountain refers to its
    a. length
    b. width
    c. height
2. The elevation of a mountain is measured from
    a. sea level
    b. the floor of a valley
    c. the base of the mountain
3. A contour line on a map
    a. shows points having different elevations
    b. shows points having the same elevation
    c. shows points that are 1 centimeter apart

# What is a topographic map?

AN ISLAND

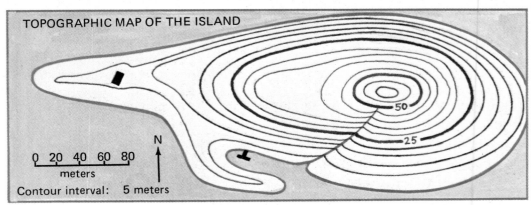

TOPOGRAPHIC MAP OF THE ISLAND

50

25

0  20  40  60  80
meters

N

Contour interval:  5 meters

**Topographic maps.** A land map with contour lines is called a topographic (top-uh-GRAF-ik) map. Look at the topographic map. The brown lines are contour lines. Every place on the same line is at the same height above sea level. Every fifth line is heavier than the others. These heavy contour lines have a number on them. The number shows the elevation of that line in meters. Where the contour lines are close together, the land has a steep slope. Where the lines are far apart, the land has a gentle slope.

▶ **What kind of slope is shown by contour lines that are close together?**

**Between the lines.** The difference in elevation between one contour line and the next is called the contour interval (IN-ter-vul). In the case of the bowl shown on page 24, the contour interval was 1 centimeter. On the topographic map of the island, the contour interval is 5 meters. A large contour interval is used for maps of regions with mountains. A small contour interval is used for flat regions.

▶ **What regions use a large contour interval?**

Hilly area near a large body of water and a topographic map of the same area.

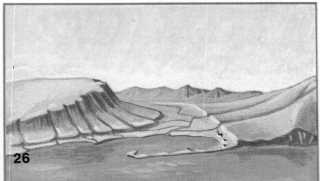

200

100

100

**Color me high.** Contour lines are not the only way to show elevations. Some maps use color for this purpose. Regions high up on mountains are shown in one color. Regions near sea level are shown in another. Still other colors are used for elevations that are in between. A special color may be used for land that is below sea level.

▶ **How is color used on a map to show elevation?**

A MAP USING COLORS TO SHOW ELEVATIONS

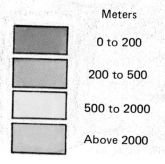

Meters

0 to 200

200 to 500

500 to 2000

Above 2000

## WHAT YOU LEARNED

1. A land map with contour lines is called a topographic map.
2. Each contour line shows the same change in elevation from one line to the next.
3. Contour lines that are close together show land with a steep slope.
4. Some maps use different colors to show elevations.

## SCIENCE WORDS

**topographic** (top-uh-GRAF-ik) **map**
a land map that uses contour lines to show elevations

**contour interval** (IN-ter-vul)
the difference in elevation between two neighboring contour lines

## ANSWER THESE

1. To show elevations a topographic map uses
   a. different colors
   b. shading of one color
   c. contour lines

2. On a topographic map, the difference in elevation between two neighboring contour lines is called the
   a. slope
   b. contour interval
   c. altitude
3. On a topographic map, a flat area will have contour lines that are
   a. straight
   b. close together
   c. far apart
4. Instead of using contour lines, some maps show elevations by using
   a. colors
   b. circles
   c. squares

## NOW TRY THESE

1. According to the map on this page, what is the difference between the elevations in the eastern half and the western half of North America?
2. Why do you think the contour interval is large on topographic maps of regions with mountains?

# 1 Review

*Do the following questions on a separate sheet of paper.*

**Matching** *Write down each of the statements in Column I, leaving one line of space after each statement. On the blank line following each statement, write the word or phrase from Column II that is described by that statement.*

### Column I

1. Something that represents the real thing.
2. A ball or globe.
3. Distance above or below sea level.
4. The thick, middle layer of the earth.
5. The air around the earth.
6. Flat map made with the help of a globe.
7. Imaginary line running horizontally around the earth.
8. One half of a globe or sphere.
9. Showing incorrect distance, shape, or direction.
10. The center part of the earth.

### Column II

elevation
parallel
hemisphere
map projection
model
distorted
core
mantle
sphere
atmosphere

*Do the following questions on a separate sheet of paper.*

**Multiple Choice** *Write the letter of the choice that best completes the statement or answers the question.*

1. The countries of the world are located on the
   a. hydrosphere
   b. lithosphere
   c. atmosphere
2. The thin outer part of the earth is called the
   a. shell
   b. mantle
   c. crust
3. A map differs from a globe in that a map must be
   a. distorted
   b. many different colors
   c. pocket-sized
4. 42° north is a measure of
   a. temperature
   b. longitude
   c. latitude

5. You can compare distances on the earth to distances on a map using a
   a. yardstick
   b. piece of string
   c. map scale
6. Sea level is about the same
   a. all over the world
   b. as land level
   c. except in Africa
7. A topographic map provides information about
   a. people in other countries
   b. the elevation of land
   c. buried objects
8. The difference in elevation between two neighboring contour lines is
   a. impossible to measure
   b. very small
   c. the contour interval

# UNIT 2

# Minerals of the Earth

## Unit Lessons

1. What are elements?
2. What are chemical symbols?
3. What is a compound?
4. What are chemical formulas?
5. What materials make up the crust of the earth?
6. How can you identify a mineral?
7. What else can help you identify minerals?
8. How does a mineral split or break?
9. What are some special properties of minerals?
10. Why do we study minerals?
11. What are gems and precious stones?

## Goals and Objectives

After completing this unit, you should be able to:

- understand why elements are the simplest kind of substance.
- differentiate between elements and compounds.
- recognize chemical formulas as a kind of scientific shorthand.
- name the most common elements and minerals that make up the earth.
- explain how minerals can be identified.
- list the many ways in which we use, or enjoy minerals.

# What are elements?

**Pass the sugar.** You know that many materials can change. For example, milk can turn sour. Iron nails can rust. Sugar will change if we heat it in a test tube. At first the sugar turns brown and becomes sticky. Then the sticky, brown material becomes a hard, black solid. This black solid is carbon.

Something else happens while we are heating the sugar. Drops of a colorless liquid form near the top of the test tube. This liquid is water. By heating sugar, we can get carbon and water.

▶ What two substances can we get from sugar by heating it?

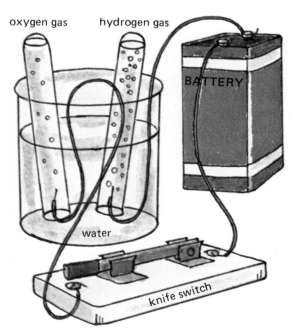

oxygen gas    hydrogen gas

BATTERY

water

knife switch

**Can water be changed?** The picture shows a beaker of water. Two test tubes filled with water are upside down in the beaker. A wire runs into each test tube. When the switch is pushed down, an electric current flows through the wires and through the water. When this happens, bubbles of gas rise from the ends of the wires. The gases collect in the test tubes. Chemical tests can show that the gases in the test tubes are different. One is hydrogen (HY-druh-jen). The other is oxygen (OK-sih-jen).

▶ What two gases can we get from water by sending an electric current through it?

**Elementary, dear Watson.** From sugar we were able to get carbon and water. Carbon and water are simpler substances than sugar. From water we were able to get hydrogen and oxygen. Hydrogen and oxygen are simpler substances than water. You might think we could do something to carbon to get simpler substances from it. But we can't. We can't get simpler substances from hydrogen or oxygen, either. Carbon, hydrogen, and oxygen are elements (EL-uh-ments). Elements are the simplest kind of substance.

▶ **What are elements?**

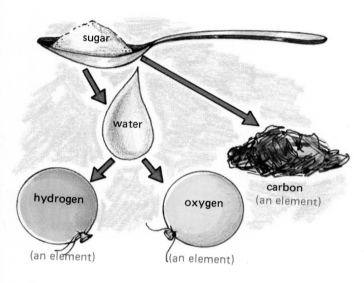

Sugar is made up of three elements. Water is made up of two.

## Elements can be solids, liquids, or gases.

More than 100 elements are now known. Most of these elements are solids at room temperature. Carbon, gold, silver, iron, and copper are examples of solid elements. Some elements are gases at room temperature. Hydrogen, oxygen, and nitrogen are gases. A very few elements are liquids at room temperature. Mercury and bromine are liquid elements.

▶ Are most elements liquids, solids, or gases?

## WHAT YOU LEARNED

1. Heating sugar produces carbon and water.
2. Passing an electric current through water produces the gases hydrogen and oxygen.
3. Elements are the simplest kind of substance.
4. Most elements are solids at room temperature.
5. All substances are made up of one or more elements.

## SCIENCE WORDS

**hydrogen** (HY-druh-jen)
  the element that combines with oxygen to make water
**oxygen** (OK-sih-jen)
  the element that combines with hydrogen to make water
**element** (EL-uh-ment)
  a substance of the simplest type

## ANSWER THESE

1. A substance that is an element is
   **a.** sugar
   **b.** water
   **c.** oxygen
2. A substance that will "pop" when placed near a burning splint is
   **a.** oxygen
   **b.** hydrogen
   **c.** water
3. A substance that will cause a burning splint to burst into flames is
   **a.** oxygen
   **b.** hydrogen
   **c.** water
4. The simplest kind of substance is called
   **a.** an element
   **b.** a mixture
   **c.** a compound
5. Two elements that are liquids at room temperature are
   **a.** hydrogen and oxygen
   **b.** mercury and bromine
   **c.** carbon and gold

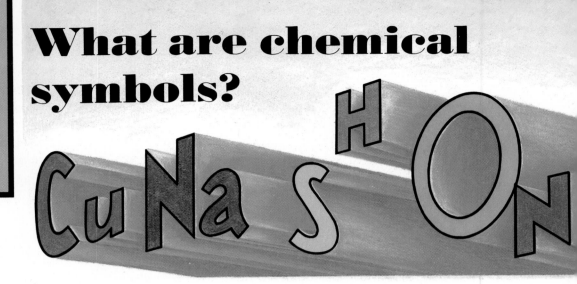

# UNIT 2
## Minerals of the earth
### 2

# What are chemical symbols?

**Chemical symbols.** Secretaries use shorthand to write words quickly. Shorthand takes less time and space to write. Scientists also use shorthand to write the names of the elements. The shorthand for the name of a chemical element is called a chemical symbol (SIM-bul). For example, *S* is the chemical symbol for the element *sulfur*. Scientists use chemical symbols to save time and space.

▶ **What do chemical symbols stand for?**

**Writing chemical symbols.** Each element has its own symbol. For some elements, only one capital letter is used. For example, H stands for hydrogen, O stands for oxygen, and C stands for carbon. For all the other elements, two letters are used. The first letter is always a capital, and the second is a small letter. Mg is the symbol for the element magnesium. Al stands for aluminum. Ca stands for calcium. Many times the letter or letters in a symbol come from the name of the element

| Element | Symbol | Some Important Uses | Element | Symbol | Some Important Uses |
|---|---|---|---|---|---|
| aluminum | Al | light metal used in making airplanes, buildings, pots and pans | neon | Ne | gas that lights up red in neon signs |
| bromine | Br | used in photography, medicines, insecticides | nickel | Ni | metal used in coins |
| calcium | Ca | metal found in teeth, bones, sea shells, chalk | nitrogen | N | main gas in the air; important element for all living things |
| carbon | C | found in coal, oil, gas, living things, inks, and pencil leads | oxygen | O | gas necessary for respiration; aids burning |
| chlorine | Cl | found with the element sodium in table salt, and in chemicals to kill germs in swimming pools | platinum | Pt | expensive metal used in jewelry |
| | | | potassium | K | found in fertilizers |
| chromium | Cr | shiny metal used on bumpers of some cars | silicon | Si | used in electronics and in compounds for making glass |
| copper | Cu | metal used for electric wires, pots and pans | silver | Ag | used in tableware, jewelry, photography, and medicines |
| gold | Au | metal used for jewelry | sodium | Na | soft metal that combines with chlorine to make table salt |
| helium | He | gas much lighter than air; used in blimps and balloons | sulfur | S | used to make sulfuric acid and some medicines |
| hydrogen | H | flammable and explosive gas, lightest of all gases | tin | Sn | used to make the inside of tin cans |
| | | | tungsten | W | metal wire inside light bulbs that gets white hot |
| iodine | I | used on cuts and wounds to kill germs | uranium | U | metal used in some nuclear reactions |
| iron | Fe | strong metal used in construction of buildings | zinc | Zn | metal used in dry cells and batteries |
| lead | Pb | metal used in automobile batteries and in fishing and diving weights | | | |
| mercury | Hg | heavy, poisonous liquid used in some thermometers | | | |

SOME OF THE BETTER KNOWN ELEMENTS

in English. Sometimes they come from the name of the element in Latin. The Latin name for sodium is *natrium*. The symbol for sodium, Na, comes from the first two letters in *natrium*.

▶ **How many letters are there in a chemical symbol?**

**Different names.** The names of elements may differ around the world. Sulfur is called *sera* in Russian, *gafrim* in Hebrew, and *azufre* in Spanish. But the symbol for sulfur is *S* in all countries. The names may change, but the symbols are always the same. Chemical symbols are a <u>universal</u> (you-nuh-VER-sul) language that all scientists understand.

▶ **What is the symbol for sulfur in Russian, Hebrew and Spanish?**

**Practice makes perfect.** The best way to learn the symbols is to use them over and over. Many will be used throughout this book. Look at the chart. It shows some common elements. Read some of their important uses and copy their symbols into your notebook.

▶ **What is the best way to learn the symbols of the elements?**

## WHAT YOU LEARNED

1. Chemical symbols are a shorthand for the names of the elements
2. Using chemical symbols helps scientists save time and space.
3. Chemical symbols always have one or two letters. One-letter symbols are always a capital letter, while only the first letter is a capital in two-letter symbols.
4. The symbols for the elements are the same throughout the world.

## SCIENCE WORDS

**chemical symbol** (KEM-uh-kul SIM-bul)
a kind of shorthand used to write the names of chemical elements

**universal** (you-nuh-VER-sul)
worldwide, throughout the world

## ANSWER THESE

1. Which of the following could not be a chemical symbol? **a.** Ptu **b.** No **c.** I
2. Symbols of elements come from the
   **a.** Latin name of the element
   **b.** English name of the element
   **c.** Latin and English names of the elements
3. Match the elements in column A with their symbols in column B and their uses in column C.
   Example:
   **a.** tungsten, W, metal wire in light bulbs

| Col. A | Col. B | Col. C |
|---|---|---|
| **a.** tungsten | Br | light metal used in airplanes |
| **b.** hydrogen | Ag | metal used in automobile |
| **c.** bromine | Pb | batteries |
| **d.** aluminum | Ca | metal found in bones and |
| **e.** neon | W | teeth |
| **f.** uranium | Cu | metal used in nuclear |
| **g.** calcium | Ne | reactions |
| **h.** copper | H | used in tableware |
| **i.** lead | U | metal wire in light bulbs |
| **j.** silver | Al | flammable, explosive gas |
| | | used in photography, |
| | | medicine, and insecticides |
| | | metal used in electric wire |
| | | gas that lights up red |

## NOW TRY THESE

1. Use the symbols below to find the names of the elements needed to complete the crossword puzzle.

| **Across** | **Down** |
|---|---|
| **1.** Al | **2.** Pb |
| **5.** Sn | **3.** Hg |
| **8.** O | **4.** N |
| **9.** Na | **6.** Ne |
| | **7.** Au |

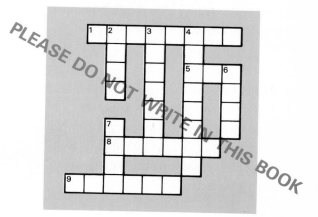

# What is a compound?

Objects made of iron are attracted to a magnet.

**Describing iron.** Iron is an element. It has many uses. Paper clips, most nails, pins and needles, and many machine parts are made of iron. Hold a magnet near some paper clips. Anything made of iron is attracted to a magnet. Objects that are attracted to a magnet are usually made of iron.

▶ What happens when anything made of iron is brought near a magnet?

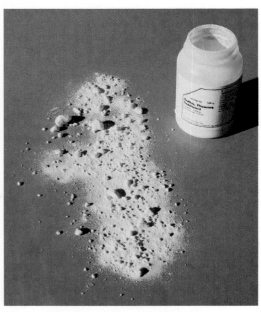

The yellow powder is the element sulfur.

**Look at sulfur.** Sulfur is also an element. It has a yellow color. Grind some pieces of sulfur into a fine, soft powder. Burning the powder produces a gas with an irritating smell. This gas is poisonous. Sulfur should be burned only in a fume hood.

Facts about substances that help to describe them are called properties (PROP-er-teez). The yellow color of sulfur is a property of sulfur. The fact that sulfur burns is another of its properties. That burning sulfur produces an irritating gas is still another of its properties. Some of the properties of two different substances may be alike. But two different substances are always different in at least some of their properties.

▶ What are two properties of sulfur?

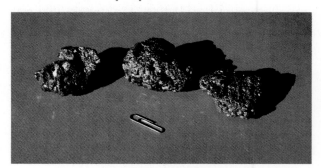

Pyrite is a mineral commonly known as "fool's gold."

**Fool's gold.** Pyrite (PIE-RIGHT) is a mineral that can be found in the ground. It has beautiful gold-clored crystals. Some people mistake it for gold. In fact, it is sometimes called fool's gold. Pyrite is composed of the elements iron and sulfur. But if you look at pyrite, you will see that it is unlike either element. Pyrite does not burn, although sulfur does. Unlike iron, pyrite is not attracted to a magnet. Pyrite is an example of a compound (KOM-POUND). A compound is any substance formed from two or more elements.

The properties of a compound are different from the properties of the elements that make up the compound.

▶ **What is a compound?**

**Another compound.** Water is a compound. It is made up of the elements hydrogen and oxygen. Hydrogen is a flammable gas. Oxygen is a gas that "supports combustion" (come-BUS-chun). "Supports combustion" means that oxygen itself does not burn, but it is needed to make other things burn. You would certainly not use either hydrogen or oxygen to put out a fire. But water, the compound made from these elements, is often used for this purpose. The properties of water are different from the properties of either hydrogen or oxygen.

▶ **What elements are water made from?**

Sodium, an element which is a metal, is so soft it can be easily cut with a knife.

**A tasty compound.** Table salt is another common compound. It is made up of two elements. One of these is the metal sodium. Sodium is so soft it can be cut with a knife. The other element is chlorine. Chlorine is a green gas. Both elements are poisonous. When they combine, they make table salt, a substance we eat every day.

▶ **What elements make up table salt?**

## WHAT YOU LEARNED

1. Elements can be identified by their properties.
2. Elements lose their own properties when they form compounds.
3. A compound is a substance that is a combination of two or more elements.
4. Compounds have properties that are different from the properties of the elements they are composed of.

## SCIENCE WORD

**compound** (KOM-POUND)
  a substance made up of two or more elements

**properties** (PROP-er-teez)
  facts about a substance that help to describe it

## ANSWER THESE

1. A metal that is attracted by a magnet is
   **a.** iron   **b.** sodium   **c.** gold
2. A yellow powder that burns with a bad smell is
   **a.** sodium   **b.** hydrogen   **c.** sulfur
3. A substance that is an element is
   **a.** water   **b.** pyrite   **c.** iron
4. Fool's gold is
   **a.** water   **b.** pyrite   **c.** iron
5. A substance made by the combination of two or more elements is called
   **a.** a mixture
   **b.** a compound
   **c.** a simple substance
6. A compound
   **a.** has the same properties as those of its elements
   **b.** has new properties
   **c.** has no properties
7. A substance that is a compound is
   **a.** oxygen   **b.** hydrogen   **c.** water

## NOW TRY THIS

Make two columns on your paper. At the head of one column write "Element." At the head of the other write "Compound." Then place the following substances under the proper heading.

1. aluminum   5. oxygen   9. mercury
2. water   6. sugar   10. pyrite
3. salt   7. hydrogen   11. bromine
4. carbon   8. chlorine   12. gold

# What are chemical formulas?

**Pass the salt.** Chemical symbols are a shorthand way to write the names of elements. Chemical symbols are used to write chemical formulas (FOR-myoo-luhs). Chemical formulas are a shorthand way to write the names of compounds. The symbols for sodium and chlorine are Na and Cl. NaCl is the chemical formula for the compound made from sodium and chlorine. This compound is called sodium chloride. Sodium chloride is the chemical name for table salt.

▶ What is a chemical formula?

**What's a compound made of?** Chemical formulas tell several things about compounds. They tell what elements are in the compound. The formula NaCl tells us that NaCl is made up of the elements sodium (Na) and chlorine (Cl). The formula for a compound made from iron (Fe) and sulfur (S) is FeS. Pyrite is another compound made from iron and sulfur. Its formula is $FeS_2$. The meaning of the 2 in the formula $FeS_2$ is explained in the next paragraph. The chart shows other compounds and their formulas.

▶ What does a formula tell us?

**The meaning of subscripts.** Formulas tell more than just what elements are in a compound. They also tell the relative (REL-uh-tiv) number of atoms of each element in the compound. Atoms are the tiny particles of matter making up elements. The formula of aluminum oxide is $Al_2O_3$. The small numbers after the Al and O are called subscripts (SUB-SKRIPTS). Subscripts are written slightly below the line. In this case, the subscripts tell us that there are 2 atoms of aluminum (Al) for every 3 atoms of oxygen (O) in aluminum oxide.

When a subscript is the number 1, the 1 is left out. For example, the formula for water is $H_2O$. There are really two subscripts in this formula, but only one is written. There is a 2 following the H and a 1 (left out) following the O. The formula tells us that in water there are 2 atoms of hydrogen for every 1 atom of oxygen.

▶ What does the formula $Al_2O_3$ tell you?

| SOME COMPOUNDS AND THEIR FORMULAS | | |
|---|---|---|
| Compound | Elements in the Compound | Formula of the Compound |
| cinnabar | mercury (Hg and sulfur (S) | HgS |
| galena | lead (Pb) and sulfur (S) | PbS |
| zincite | zinc (Zn) and oxygen (O) | ZnO |
| hydrogen chloride | hydrogen (H) and chlorine (Cl) | HCl |

## THE MEANING OF CHEMICAL FORMULAS

| Formula | Name | Meaning of the Formula | |
|---|---|---|---|
| | | Elements | Relative Number of Atoms |
| $Al_2O_3$ | aluminum oxide | aluminum oxygen | two aluminum atoms for every three oxygen atoms |
| $H_2O$ | water | hydrogen oxygen | two hydrogen atoms for every one oxygen atom |
| $NaCl$ | table salt | sodium chlorine | one sodium atom for every one chlorine atom |
| $H_2SO_4$ | sulfuric acid | hydrogen sulfur oxygen | two hydrogen atoms and four oxygen atoms for every one sulfur atom |
| $CHCl_3$ | chloroform | carbon hydrogen chlorine | three chlorine atoms for every one hydrogen and one carbon atom |

## WHAT YOU LEARNED

1. Chemical formulas are a kind of shorthand used to write the names of compounds.
2. Chemical symbols are used in writing chemical formulas.
3. Chemical formulas tell what elements are in a compound and the relative number of atoms of each element.

## SCIENCE WORDS

**chemical formula** (FOR-myoo-luh)
a kind of shorthand scientists use to give information about chemicals

**subscripts** (SUB-SKRIPTS)
numbers appearing slightly below the line in chemical formulas

## ANSWER THESE

1. Which of the following is NOT a compound?
   a. $H_2O$
   b. $Al_2O_3$
   c. $O_2$
2. How many elements are in the chemical whose formula is $CO_2$?
   a. one
   b. two
   c. three
3. In a glass of water (formula: $H_2O$), the number of hydrogen atoms is
   a. twice the number of oxygen atoms
   b. half the number of oxygen atoms
   c. neither answer **a** nor answer **b**

## NOW TRY THIS

Copy on a separate piece of paper the information given below. On the blanks on your paper fill in the names of the elements found in each compound.

| Compound | Formula | Names of Elements | Relative Number of Atoms |
|---|---|---|---|
| 1. carbon dioxide | $CO_2$ | | |
| 2. calcite | $CaCO_3$ | | |
| 3. cinnabar | $HgS$ | | |
| 4. magnesium chloride | $MgCl_2$ | | |
| 5. aluminum sulfide | $Al_2S_3$ | | |

# What materials make up the crust of the earth?

**Rocks.** The crust of the earth is made of rocks. Stones in a field are broken pieces of the rocky crust. Dirt and soil are made of rock that has been broken into very small bits. There are many different kinds of rocks. Rocks are made of materials called <u>minerals</u> (MIN-uh-ruls).

▶ **What are the materials in rocks called?**

**Minerals.** The crust of the earth is made of rocks, and rocks are made of minerals. What is a mineral? A mineral may be made of a single element. Gold is an example of a mineral with only one element in it. A mineral may also be made of a single compound. <u>Quartz</u> (KWORTZ) is a mineral that is made of silicon dioxide ($SiO_2$). Silicon dioxide is a compound of silicon (Si) and oxygen (O). The chart lists some minerals and their formulas. Some minerals are elements. The rest are compounds.

▶ **What are minerals made of?**

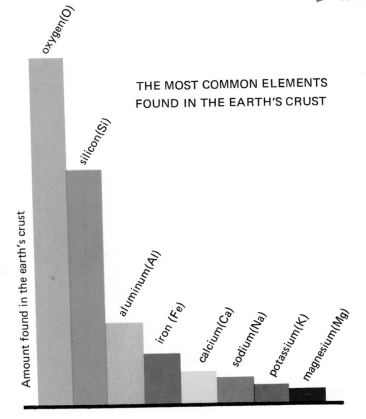

THE MOST COMMON ELEMENTS
FOUND IN THE EARTH'S CRUST

Amount found in the earth's crust

oxygen(O)
silicon(Si)
aluminum(Al)
iron (Fe)
calcium(Ca)
sodium(Na)
potassium(K)
magnesium(Mg)

| SOME MINERALS AND THEIR FORMULAS | |
| --- | --- |
| **MINERAL** | **FORMULA** |
| gold | Au |
| silver | Ag |
| copper | Cu |
| quartz | $SiO_2$ |
| calcite | $CaCO_3$ |
| halite | NaCl |
| galena | PbS |
| pyrite | FeS |

**The elements in the earth's crust.** Almost all of the elements can be found in the earth's crust. But most of the crust is made of just eight elements. The bar chart lists these eight elements and shows their symbols. The chart also shows the amount of each element in the crust. They are listed in order. Oxygen makes up the largest amount. Silicon is next. Aluminum is third. Magnesium is eighth (the last element in the list). These eight elements can make many different compounds. There are many different minerals in the earth's crust.

▶ **Name the eight elements that make up most of the earth's crust.**

## WHAT YOU LEARNED

1. The crust of the earth is made of rocks.
2. Rocks are made of minerals.
3. A mineral is made of one element or one compound.
4. Eight elements make up almost all the minerals on earth.

## SCIENCE WORDS

**mineral** (MIN-uh-rul)
a material found in the crust of the earth
**quartz** (KWORTZ)
a mineral made of silicon dioxide

## ANSWER THESE

1. What materials make up the crust of the earth?
2. Name some minerals that are made of one element.
3. Name some minerals that are made of compounds.

## FINDING OUT MORE

A geologist (jee-OL-uh-jist) is a scientist who studies the earth. Geologists collect rocks and min-

erals and find out what they are made of. Some geologists study mountains and valleys. They try to find out how and when the mountains and valleys were formed. Sometimes, the geologists make maps of the land. They also try to find useful materials in the earth's crust, such as coal, oil, iron, and copper. What the geologist learns helps us build dams, canals, highways, and bridges.

## NOW TRY THIS

Copy the diagram on a piece of paper. Fill in the words that answer the clues.

**Down**
1. The number of elements that make up most of the crust of the earth.
3. The most common element in the earth's crust.

**Across**
2. A scientist who studies the earth.
4. What minerals are made up of.

PLEASE DO NOT WRITE IN THIS BOOK.

# How can you identify a mineral?

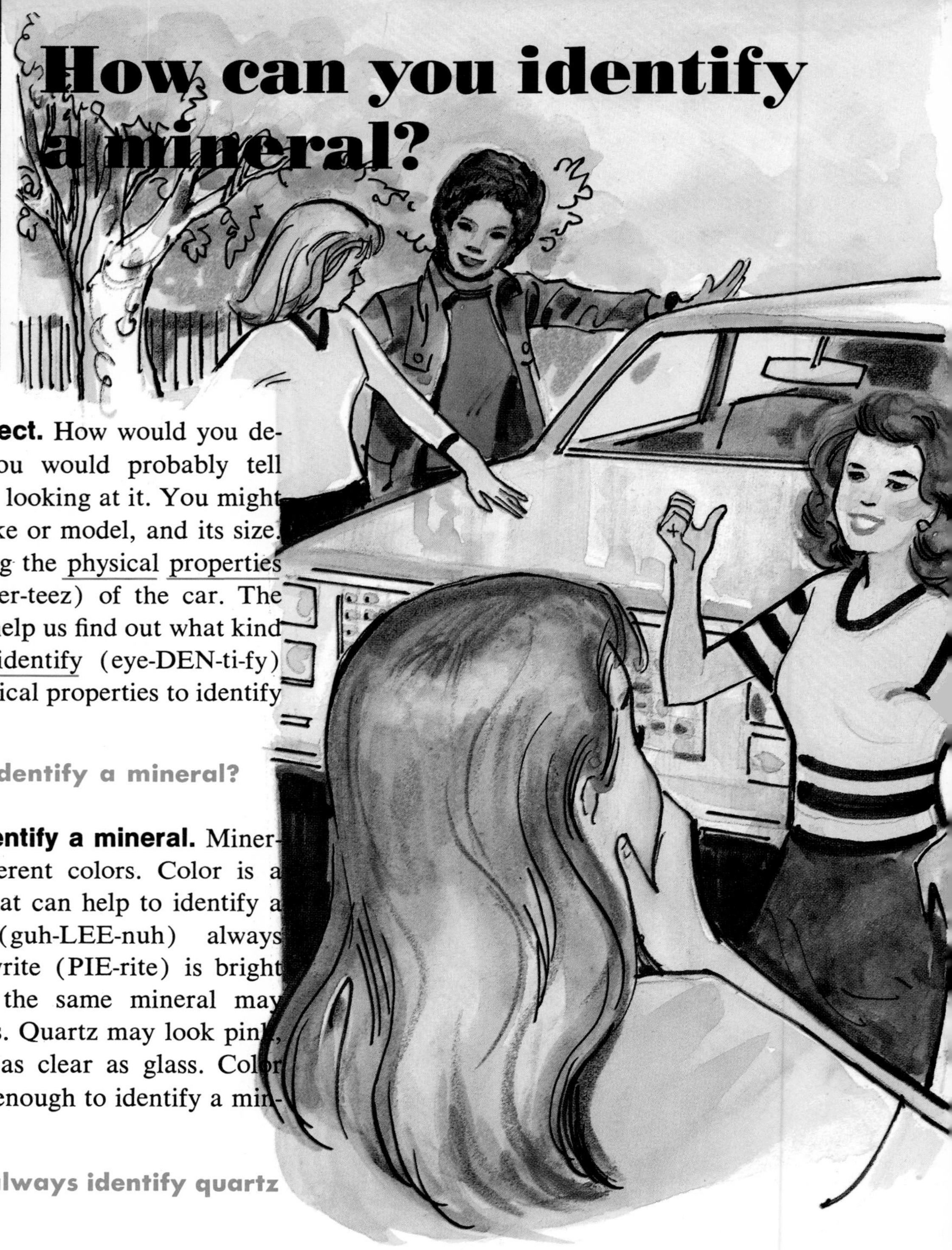

**Describing an object.** How would you describe this car? You would probably tell what you can see by looking at it. You might tell its color, its make or model, and its size. You would be telling the physical properties (FIZ-uh-kul PROP-er-teez) of the car. The physical properties help us find out what kind of car it is. They identify (eye-DEN-ti-fy) the car. We use physical properties to identify minerals, too.

▶ **How can you identify a mineral?**

**Color helps us identify a mineral.** Minerals have many different colors. Color is a physical property that can help to identify a mineral. Galena (guh-LEE-nuh) always looks dark gray. Pyrite (PIE-rite) is bright yellow. Sometimes the same mineral may have different colors. Quartz may look pink, or milky white, or as clear as glass. Color alone is not always enough to identify a mineral.

▶ **Why can't we always identify quartz by its color?**

PYRITE

CALCITE

**Luster helps us identify a mineral.** Luster (LUSS-ter) means the amount of shininess of an object. Some minerals look metallic (shiny like a metal). Others look dull. Pyrite looks like gold. It has a metallic luster. Calcite (CAL-site) usually has a dull luster.

▶ **What is luster?**

**Hardness helps us identify a mineral.** If a mineral scratches a piece of glass, it is harder than glass. If the glass scratches the mineral, the mineral is softer than glass. Try to scratch glass with your fingernail. Do you see a mark? No, glass is harder than your nail. Diamond is the hardest of all minerals. It will scratch glass. Glass will scratch calcite. Calcite is softer than glass and softer than diamond. If a diamond is real, it will scratch glass. Scratching can be used to test for all minerals.

▶ **How can we show that diamond is harder than glass?**

**Diamond scratching glass**

**Glass scratching calcite**

## WHAT YOU LEARNED

1. Minerals can be identified by their physical properties.
2. Color, luster, and hardness are physical properties of minerals.

## SCIENCE WORDS

**physical properties** (FIZ-uh-kul PROP-er-teez)
   facts about an object that help identify it
**identify** (eye-DEN-ti-fy)
   tell what something is
**luster** (LUSS-ter)
   the amount of shininess of a mineral or object

## ANSWER THESE

1. Color alone cannot be used to identify a mineral because
   a. most minerals have no color
   b. all minerals have the same color
   c. the same mineral may have different colors

2. Luster can be
   a. wet, dry, or damp
   b. metallic, glassy, or dull
   c. red, yellow, or green

3. If a mineral leaves a scratch on a piece of glass, that mineral is
   a. harder than the glass
   b. softer than the glass
   c. stronger than the glass

## NOW TRY THIS

Scientists have made a list of minerals in order of their hardness. This list can be used to identify minerals by testing their hardness. Use the chart to tell which is harder:
   1. diamond or topaz
   2. quartz or talc
   3. calcite or gypsum
   4. feldspar or quartz

| MINERAL | HARDNESS TEST |
|---|---|
| 1. talc | softest, can be scratched by your fingernail |
| 2. gypsum (JIP-sum) | soft, can also be scratched by fingernail (but not by talc) |
| 3. calcite | scratched by a copper penny |
| 4. fluorite (FLOO-uh-rite) | scratched by steel knife or a nail file, but not easily |
| 5. apatite (AP-a-tite) | scratched by steel knife or a nail file, but not easily |
| 6. feldspar (FELD-spar) | knife cannot scratch it, and it can scratch glass |
| 7. quartz | scratches glass and steel |
| 8. topaz (TOH-paz) | can scratch quartz |
| 9. corundum (ko-RUN-dum) | can scratch topaz |
| 10. diamond | can scratch all others |

# What else can help you identify minerals?

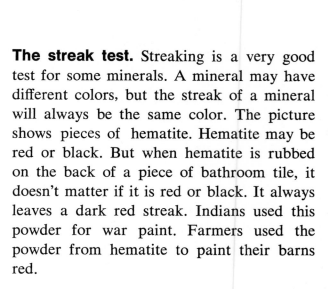

**The streak of a mineral.** Did you know that the white chalk in your classroom is a mineral? White chalk is made of the mineral calcite. Write on the board with a piece of chalk. Look closely at the chalk mark. What is it made of? It is a powder left by the chalk. Calcite leaves a white powder when it is rubbed on something. Many other minerals leave a powder in the same way. Scientists call this powder the streak (STREEK) of the mineral.

▶ **What is the streak of a mineral?**

Black Hematite

Red Hematite

Streak of black hematite

Streak of red hematite

**The streak test.** Streaking is a very good test for some minerals. A mineral may have different colors, but the streak of a mineral will always be the same color. The picture shows pieces of hematite. Hematite may be red or black. But when hematite is rubbed on the back of a piece of bathroom tile, it doesn't matter if it is red or black. It always leaves a dark red streak. Indians used this powder for war paint. Farmers used the powder from hematite to paint their barns red.

▶ **What color is the streak of hematite?**

**Mass.** The mass of an object is a measure of how much matter there is in it. We usually find the mass of an object by weighing it. If one object has twice as much mass as another, it will also weigh twice as much. Weight is the force of gravity acting on an object. The weight of an object can change. An object on the moon weighs only 1/6 as much as on the earth. But its mass stays the same. Mass is measured in grams and kilograms.

▶ **How do we usually find the mass of an object?**

**Density.** Another way to identify a mineral is to use its density. Recall that density is the amount of mass that takes up a certain volume. Suppose a piece of mineral looks like pyrite and has a mass of 40 grams. Suppose its volume is 5 cubic centimeters. Then the density of the mineral is

$$\frac{40 \text{ grams}}{5 \text{ cubic centimeters}} = 8 \text{ g/cm}^3$$

But pyrite has a density of about 5 g/cm³. The unknown mineral may look like pyrite but its density tells us it can't be pyrite. It must be something else. Density helps us to identify minerals.

▶ **If a mineral looks like pyrite, what can we do to see if it really is pyrite?**

## WHAT YOU LEARNED

1. A streak is the powder mark left by a mineral when it is rubbed on something.
2. The streak of a mineral can help identify the mineral.
3. The mass of an object is a measure of how much matter there is in it.
4. Density tells how much matter there is in a certain volume of material.
5. Density can help identify a mineral.

## SCIENCE WORDS

**streak** (STREEK)
the powder a mineral leaves when it is rubbed

**mass**
a measure of how much matter there is in an object

**density** (DEN-si-tee)
the mass of an object divided by its volume

## ANSWER THESE

1. How would you do a streak test for a mineral?
2. Why is the streak test useful?
3. How can density help identify a mineral?

## NOW TRY THESE

In the picture there are several letters. Can you find them? The letters can be arranged to make a science word. What is the word?

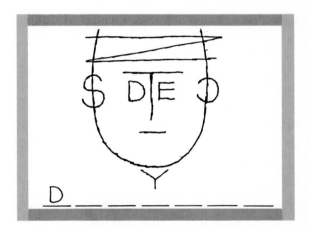

## LOOKING BACK IN SCIENCE

In ancient times, a king asked a goldsmith to make a crown of gold. The king gave the goldsmith one kilogram of gold. The goldsmith was not honest. He kept some of the gold and put in copper instead. The goldsmith made sure the crown's mass was 1 kilogram when he brought it to the king. The king thought he had been cheated, but he didn't know how to prove it. He asked a famous scientist named Archimedes (ar-kim-EE-deez) to help him. Archimedes compared the mass of the crown with the space it took up. He knew the density of pure gold. He found that the density of the crown was different. So he knew it couldn't be pure gold. The goldsmith was punished for stealing the king's gold.

# How does a mineral split or break?

**Some minerals break along flat surfaces.**
Did you ever see the inside of an old iron?
There is a material in it that looks like thin
layers of plastic, one on top of another. This
material is a mineral called mica (MY-ca).
Mica "peels off" or splits in flat sheets. Many
minerals break or split into pieces with
smooth, flat surfaces. This splitting is called
cleavage (CLEE-vidge).

▶ **What is cleavage?**

**Minerals can have different kinds of
cleavage.** Mica will always split into thin
sheets. But when galena breaks, it forms little
cubes like dice. And when feldspar breaks,
it looks like steps. The cleavage of a mineral
is always the same for that mineral. Cleavage
can help us identify a mineral.

▶ **What mineral has a cleavage that
looks like sheets? Like dice? Like
steps?**

**Some minerals do not have cleavage.**
You saw that galena breaks into little cubes
with flat surfaces. Galena has cleavage. But
if you break asbestos (az-BESS-tose), you
get splinters. Copper breaks with sharp edges.
When flint breaks, some of it may look like
the outside of a shell. These minerals break
with uneven surfaces. The way they break
is called fracture (FRAC-choor). Asbestos
has a splintery fracture. Flint has a shell-
like fracture.

▶ **What is breaking with uneven surfaces called?**

asbestos
splintery fracture

obsidian
shell-like fracture

## WHAT YOU LEARNED

1. A mineral that breaks along a flat, smooth surface has cleavage.
2. Minerals may have different kinds of cleavage.
3. Minerals that don't have cleavage have fracture.
4. The cleavage or fracture of a mineral can help identify the mineral.

## SCIENCE WORDS

**cleavage** (CLEE-vidge)
the splitting of a mineral along a flat surface

**fracture** (FRAC-choor)
the way a mineral breaks along uneven surfaces

## ANSWER THESE

1. How are fracture and cleavage different?
2. Which mineral will split into thin sheets?
3. Which mineral forms cubes when it breaks?

## NOW TRY THIS

Match the words in Column A with those in Column B.

| Column A | Column B |
|---|---|
| 1. galena | a. uneven surfaces |
| 2. mica | b. splintery fracture |
| 3. flint | c. cubic cleavage |
| 4. asbestos | d. flat surfaces |
| 5. cleavage | e. shell-like fracture |
| 6. fracture | f. sheet-like fracture |

## FINDING OUT MORE

### Diamond Cutting

One of the most skilled workers in the world is the diamond cutter. A diamond is a rough lump when it is first found in the earth's crust. The diamond cutter's job is to make a beautiful jewel from the rough diamond. To do this, he studies the diamond for many hours to find its cleavage surfaces. If it is a large diamond, he may break it into smaller pieces with a hammer and chisel. Then he cuts and polishes the pieces along their cleavage surfaces. If he makes one mistake, the diamond may be ruined, and thousands of dollars may be lost.

# What are some special properties of minerals?

**The shape of a mineral.** Would you ever think of putting minerals on your food? You do this every time you put salt on your food. Earth scientists call this mineral halite. The grains of salt are called crystals (CRISS-tals). A crystal is a piece of a mineral that has a definite shape.

▶ **What is a crystal?**

**Crystals of the same mineral always have the same shape.** Diamond crystals have one shape. Quartz crystals have another shape. Salt crystals have still another shape. These different crystal shapes help tell one mineral from another. But crystal shape alone is not a sure test. The crystals of two different minerals sometimes have the same shape.

▶ **How can crystal shapes help us identify a mineral?**

diamond

quartz   halite

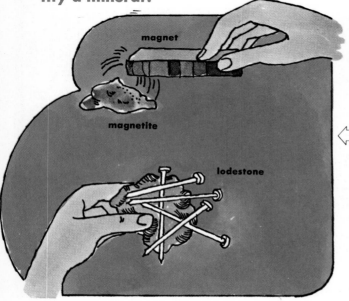

magnet

magnetite

lodestone

**A natural magnet.** You know that iron is a metal that is attracted to a magnet. Did you know that there is a mineral that is attracted to a magnet? This mineral is called magnetite (MAG-nuh-tite). It has iron in it. You can use a magnet to test for magnetite. Magnetite that is found as a natural magnet is called lodestone.

▶ **How can you use a magnet to identify magnetite?**

**A mineral that fizzes in acid.** Calcite is a mineral that is easy to identify. It is soft. It has cleavage. It is usually white or clear. And there is an easy test to make sure it is calcite. Just put a drop of weak hydrochloric acid on the mineral. If it bubbles or fizzes, it is calcite. Calcite is the only mineral that fizzes in acid. So this is a sure test for calcite.

▶ **What chemical can you use to identify calcite?**

## WHAT YOU LEARNED

1. Minerals are made of crystals that have a definite shape.
2. Magnetite can be identified by its magnetic properties.
3. Calcite can be identified by testing it with weak hydrochloric acid.

## SCIENCE WORDS

**crystal** (CRISS-tal)
   a piece of a mineral with a definite shape
**magnetite** (MAG-nuh-tite)
   a mineral that is attracted to a magnet

## ANSWER THESE

1. How are diamonds, quartz, and salt alike?
2. What mineral can you identify with a magnet?

## NOW TRY THIS

Unscramble the underlined words.
1. Diamonds are very rahd and have a lystrac shape.
2. Iron is attracted by the mineral tamnegite.
3. Acid is used to test for ticleac.

## WHAT'S HAPPENING

Ever since diamonds were discovered, people have dreamed of making them out of cheaper materials. In 1955, scientists finally succeeded in making small diamonds from graphite. These diamonds are like real diamonds. They are not as large or as beautiful as the ones found in the earth's crust. But they are just as hard as natural diamonds. They are used to make drills and cutting tools for industry.

## DO THIS AT HOME

Look at some salt and some sugar under a magnifying glass. Also look at sand under a magnifying glass. Look at the shape of the salt crystals. Look for the crystals of the sugar and sand. How are the crystals different from each other?

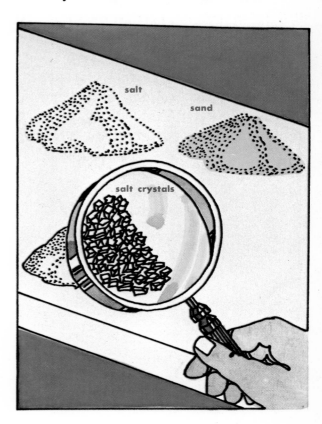

# UNIT 2
## Minerals of the earth
# 10

# Why do we study minerals?

**Many minerals are useful.** Diamond crystals are beautiful. They are used to make jewelry. Diamonds are also the hardest of all minerals. They are used for cutting and drilling through hard materials. Gypsum is another useful mineral. It is used to make plaster of Paris. Many walls and ceilings are made of this material. Here is a chart of some other minerals and their uses. ⟺

To find out how minerals can be used, we must study them.

▶ **What is one reason for studying minerals?**

**We get many metals from minerals.** Some minerals are important because of the metals they contain. We can take the metal out of the mineral and use it. A mineral that has a lot of metal that can be taken from it, is called an <u>ore</u> (OR). Miners dig ores out of the ground. Some ores are listed in the chart. ⟺

▶ **What is an ore?**

| Mineral | Uses |
|---|---|
| quartz | glass, sandpaper, telephone, radio |
| feldspar | porcelain, china, dishes |
| mica | insulators, toasters, irons, motors |
| talc | talcum powder |
| calcite | cement, building materials |

| Ore | Chemical Formula | Metal Removed |
|---|---|---|
| bauxite | $Al_2O_3$ | aluminum |
| hematite | $Fe_2O_3$ | iron |
| pyrite | $FeS$ | iron |
| galena | $PbS$ | lead |

48

## WHAT YOU LEARNED

1. Minerals are studied because they are useful.
2. An ore is a mineral that contains a metal that can be removed easily.

## SCIENCE WORD

ore (OR)

a mineral that has a large amount of metal in it

## ANSWER THESE

1. List five common minerals and one use for each.
2. List the metal that is found in
   a. bauxite
   b. galena
   c. pyrite
   d. hematite

## NOW TRY THIS

Copy the diagram and fill in the spaces.

**Across**
1. mineral containing iron
4. mineral containing aluminum

**Down**
2. mineral containing lead
3. mineral containing iron

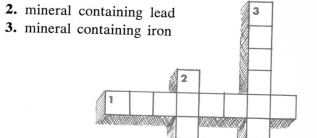

PLEASE DO NOT WRITE IN THIS BOOK.

**FINDING OUT MORE**

Most metals are found as ores. How do we get the metals out of the ores? Put some black copper oxide and powdered charcoal into a test tube. Heat the test tube. Then pour the mixture into a glass of water. Pieces of shiny copper will fall to the bottom of the glass. The charcoal will float on top. *What metal did you remove from the ore?*

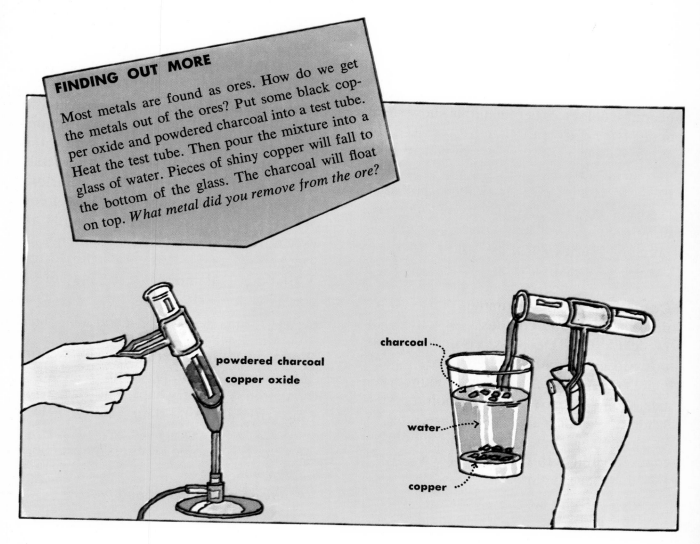

powdered charcoal
copper oxide

charcoal
water
copper

49

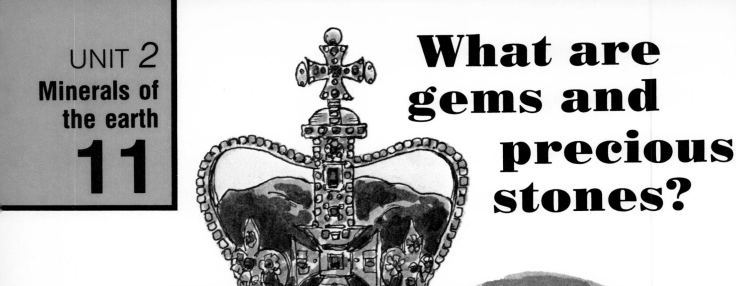

# What are gems and precious stones?

**Minerals of beauty.** Have you ever seen how beautiful some minerals look? Some have perfect crystal shapes. Some sparkle or shine when light hits them. Some have beautiful colors. When minerals show such beauty, they are called gemstones (JEM-stones). Gemstones may be cut and shaped into gems (JEMS). Some gemstones are hard to find and are called precious (PRESH-us) stones. Other gemstones are more easily found, and are called semiprecious (SEM-ee-PRESH-us) stones.

► **What are gemstones?**

**Corundum gems.** Corundum (kuh-RUN-dum) is a mineral composed of aluminum oxide ($Al_2O_3$). Deep red corundum crystals are called rubies (ROO-bees). Sapphires (SAF-ires) are blue corundum crystals. Some gems show a six-pointed star when they reflect light. The star seems to be inside the gem. Rubies and sapphires that reflect light this way are called star rubies and star sapphires.

► **What is a star sapphire?**

**Valuable carbon.** Coal is composed of the element carbon. Diamonds are also composed of carbon. Heat and pressure within the earth change coal to diamond crystals. Diamond crystals are usually colorless. They may also be yellow, red, blue, green, or black. Darkly colored diamonds are very rare and most valuable. Diamonds are weighed in units called carats (KAR-uts). A one-carat diamond has a mass of 0.2 gram.

► **What is the mass of a 1-carat diamond?**

**Rings on your fingers.** Are you wearing any jewelry? Most precious or semiprecious stones are very hard. They last a long time without losing their beauty. That is one reason why gems are used in jewelry. The chart lists some precious and semiprecious gems.

► **Why do gems make good jewelry?**

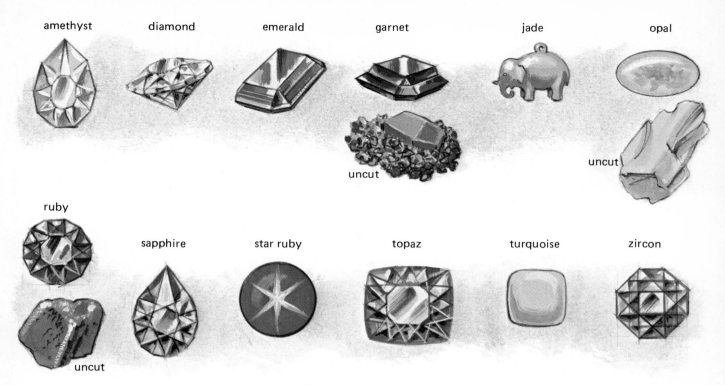

amethyst    diamond    emerald    garnet    jade    opal

uncut

uncut

ruby

sapphire    star ruby    topaz    turquoise    zircon

uncut

PRECIOUS AND SEMIPRECIOUS GEMS

## WHAT YOU LEARNED

1. Minerals that show beauty are called gemstones.
2. Precious gemstones are very scarce.
3. Rubies and sapphires are forms of corundum.
4. Heat and pressure within the earth change carbon into diamonds.
5. Gemstones are very hard and last a long time without losing their beauty.

## SCIENCE WORDS

**gemstones** (JEM-stones)
   minerals that show some form of beauty
**gem** (JEM)
   a cut or shaped gemstone
**corundum** (kuh-RUN-dum)
   a mineral composed of aluminum oxide
**ruby** (ROO-bee)
   a deep red corundum gemstone
**sapphire** (SAF-ire)
   a blue corundum gemstone
**carat** (KAR-ut)
   a unit of mass for gems, equal to 0.2 gram

## ANSWER THESE

1. Compared to precious stones, semiprecious stones are
   a. just as rare
   b. not as rare
   c. more rare
2. Deep red corundum is called
   a. emerald    b. sapphire    c. ruby
3. A five-carat diamond has a mass of
   a. 0.2 g    b. 1 g    c. 5 g
4. An emerald is
   a. red    b. yellow    c. green

## FINDING OUT MORE

**Manufactured gems.** Most gems can now be made in the laboratory. Rubies, sapphires, emeralds, and even diamonds are being made. These gems can be made more perfect than those discovered in nature. The jewels of a 17-jewel watch are often manufactured rubies or sapphires. Since manufactured gems are not rare, they are not as valuable as natural gemstones.

# UNIT 2 Review

*Do the following questions on a separate sheet of paper.*

**Fill in the Blank**     *Write down the statements in Column I. Where there is a blank line in each statement, write the word or phrase from Column II that best completes the meaning of the statement.*

| **Column I** | **Column II** |
|---|---|
| 1. Rubies and sapphires are made of the mineral_____. | subscript |
| 2. Bauxite is an example of a(n) _____. | streak |
| 3. A crystal is a piece of a mineral with a definite_____. | universal |
| 4. One way to identify a mineral is by its_____. | corundum |
| 5. The luster of a mineral is a(n)_____. | minerals |
| 6. Rocks are made up of_____. | physical property |
| 7. The number appearing slightly below the line in a chemical formula is called a(n)_____. | hydrogen |
| | shape |
| 8. A substance made up of two or more elements is called a(n)_____. | ore |
| 9. Something that is the same worldwide is _____. | compound |
| 10. The element that combines with oxygen to make water is_____. | |

**Multiple Choice**     *Write the letter of the choice that best completes the statement or answers the question.*

1. Sugar is not an element because
   a. it is sweet
   b. it can be burned
   c. it can be broken down into different substances
2. Scientists use chemical symbols
   a. to save time and space
   b. so no one can copy their work
   c. because many scientists cannot read Latin
3. The crust of the earth is made up mostly of the element
   a. quartz
   b. oxygen
   c. aluminum
4. A diamond can scratch glass because
   a. it has sharp edges
   b. people are not careful
   c. glass is softer than diamond

5. If a woman goes to the moon, her mass will
   a. remain the same as on the earth
   b. be 6 times greater
   c. be 6 times smaller
6. Hydrochloric acid can help identify the mineral
   a. galena
   b. calcite
   c. quartz
7. A valuable gemstone made of carbon is
   a. diamond
   b. opal
   c. star sapphire
8. A mineral that breaks into flat sheets is
   a. feldspar
   b. mica
   c. asbestos

# UNIT 3

# Rocks and How They Form

## Unit Lessons

1. What kinds of rocks are in the earth's crust?
2. How are igneous rocks formed?
3. How can you identify igneous rocks?
4. How are sedimentary rocks formed?
5. How are sedimentary rocks formed from living things?
6. How can you identify sedimentary rocks?
7. How are metamorphic rocks formed?
8. What do some metamorphic rocks look like?

## Goals and Objectives

After completing this unit, you should be able to:
- differentiate between igneous, sedimentary, and metamorphic rocks.
- explain how igneous rock is formed from molten material.
- describe how particles become cemented together to form sedimentary rock.
- explain how heat and pressure can change igneous and sedimentary rock into metamorphic rock.

# What kinds of rocks are in the earth's crust?

**Classifying things.** Did you know that you are classified information? What school do you go to? What class are you in? Classification (CLASS-i-fi-CAY-shun) is grouping things that are alike in some way. What are some ways that you are like the other students in your class?

▶ **How do we classify things?**

**How does classifying things help us to study them?** There are many things we want to study. If we were to study each by itself, we would never have enough time to finish. We group things together so that we may save time and make study easier. Cars are grouped by price, size, and style. Dogs are classified by breeds, such as poodles, shepherds, and collies. Biologists classify things as living or non-living. Chemists classify elements as metals or non-metals.

▶ **Why do we classify things?**

**Classifying rocks.** There are many different rocks in the earth's crust. All of them can be classified according to the way they were formed. Some rocks form when melted materials cool and become solid. These are called igneous (IG-nee-us) rocks. Other rocks form when pieces of minerals and rocks become cemented together. They are called sedimentary (sed-uh-MEN-tuh-ree) rocks. A third type of rock forms when other rocks are heated and pressed together for a long time. They are known as metamorphic (met-uh-MOR-fic) rocks.

▶ **What kind of rock is made by pressure and heat?**

lava (melted rock)

igneous rock (solid rock)

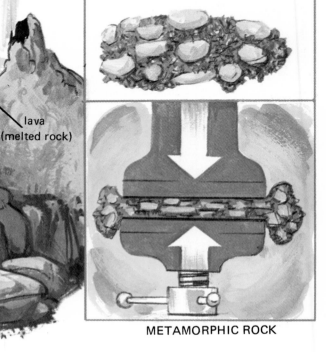

SEDIMENTARY ROCK

METAMORPHIC ROCK

**Why study rocks?** Some scientists study rocks to find new uses for them. There is another reason for studying rocks. Rocks tell a story about the earth's past. Some rocks tell us a story of a mountain being built up. Other rocks tell us about mountains that were worn down. Rocks also tell us about great seas that once covered the land, and about thick sheets and rivers of ice. Rocks tell us that there have been many changes on the earth.

▶ **What can we learn about the earth by studying rocks?**

## WHAT YOU LEARNED

1. Classification makes scientific study easier.
2. Rocks can be classified as igneous, sedimentary, or metamorphic.
3. Rocks tell us about the earth's past.

## SCIENCE WORDS

**classification** (CLASS-i-fi-CAY-shun)
  grouping things together that are alike in some way
**igneous** (IG-nee-us) **rocks**
  rocks formed from the cooling of hot, melted materials
**sedimentary** (sed-i-MEN-tuh-ree) **rocks**
  rocks formed by the cementing of materials together
**metamorphic** (met-a-MOR-fic) **rocks**
  rocks formed when other rocks are put under great heat and pressure

## ANSWER THESE

1. What is classification?
2. The three groups of rocks found in the lithosphere are _____, _____, and _____.

## NOW TRY THESE

1. Find the word in the puzzle.

2. A kind of rock.

3. Rocks tell us about the earth's _____.

## DO THIS AT HOME

Look for rocks near your home. Collect as many as you can. Tell how they look. How many rocks look the same? How many look different? You are classifying rocks. What can you do to try to identify the rocks?

# How are igneous rocks formed?

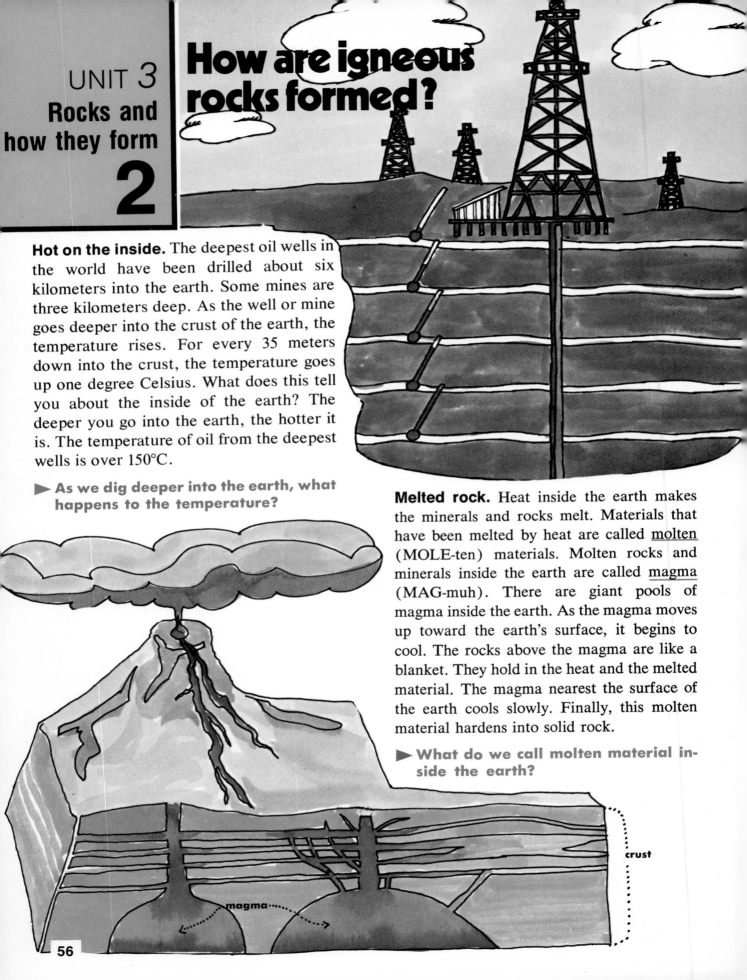

**Hot on the inside.** The deepest oil wells in the world have been drilled about six kilometers into the earth. Some mines are three kilometers deep. As the well or mine goes deeper into the crust of the earth, the temperature rises. For every 35 meters down into the crust, the temperature goes up one degree Celsius. What does this tell you about the inside of the earth? The deeper you go into the earth, the hotter it is. The temperature of oil from the deepest wells is over 150°C.

▶ As we dig deeper into the earth, what happens to the temperature?

**Melted rock.** Heat inside the earth makes the minerals and rocks melt. Materials that have been melted by heat are called molten (MOLE-ten) materials. Molten rocks and minerals inside the earth are called magma (MAG-muh). There are giant pools of magma inside the earth. As the magma moves up toward the earth's surface, it begins to cool. The rocks above the magma are like a blanket. They hold in the heat and the melted material. The magma nearest the surface of the earth cools slowly. Finally, this molten material hardens into solid rock.

▶ What do we call molten material inside the earth?

crust

magma

**Igneous rocks.** Sometimes the magma inside the earth pushes through the crust onto the surface. The hot liquid that comes out of the earth is called lava (LAH-vuh). The rocks that form when lava cools and becomes solid are called igneous rocks. Igneous rocks are also formed when magma cools and hardens inside the earth. The word *igneous* comes from a Latin word meaning fire.

▶ **What kind of rock is formed when magma cools and hardens?**

## WHAT YOU LEARNED

1. Heat inside the earth causes rocks and minerals to melt.
2. Igneous rocks form when magma cools and becomes solid.
3. Igneous rocks also form when lava cools and becomes solid.

## SCIENCE WORDS

**molten** (MOLE-ten)
  melted
**magma** (MAG-muh)
  melted rocks and minerals inside the earth
**lava** (LAH-vuh)
  magma that comes through the earth's surface

## ANSWER THESE

1. How do we know that the inside of the earth is very hot?
2. What is magma?
3. What is lava?

## LOOKING BACK IN SCIENCE

Have you ever thought about how the earth began? Scientists believe that in the beginning, all the earth was hot, molten material. After millions of years, the outside cooled and hardened. What kind of rocks formed? Scientists think the first rocks to cover the earth were igneous rocks. Even today we have proof that the earth is hot on the inside. Volcanoes throw out tons of lava from inside the earth. What type of rocks do we find near volcanoes?

## NOW TRY THIS

Find the hidden word in each picture.

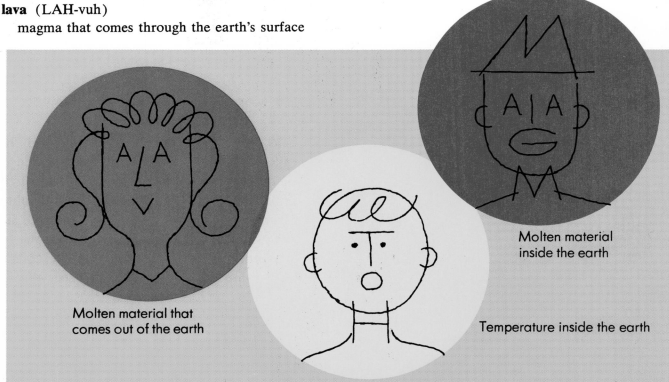

Molten material that comes out of the earth

Molten material inside the earth

Temperature inside the earth

# How can you identify igneous rocks?

GRANITE

quartz

feldspar

mica

**A mixture of minerals.** Igneous rocks are made up of several different minerals. Granite (GRAN-it) is a common example of an igneous rock. It is made up almost entirely of three minerals. These minerals are quartz, feldspar (FELD-spar), and mica (MY-kuh). The quartz crystals in granite look like pieces of broken glass. Feldspar crystals are usually pink or cream-colored. Mica crystals have a dark color. The types of minerals in an igneous rock help to identify it.

▶ **What is one way to identify an igneous rock?**

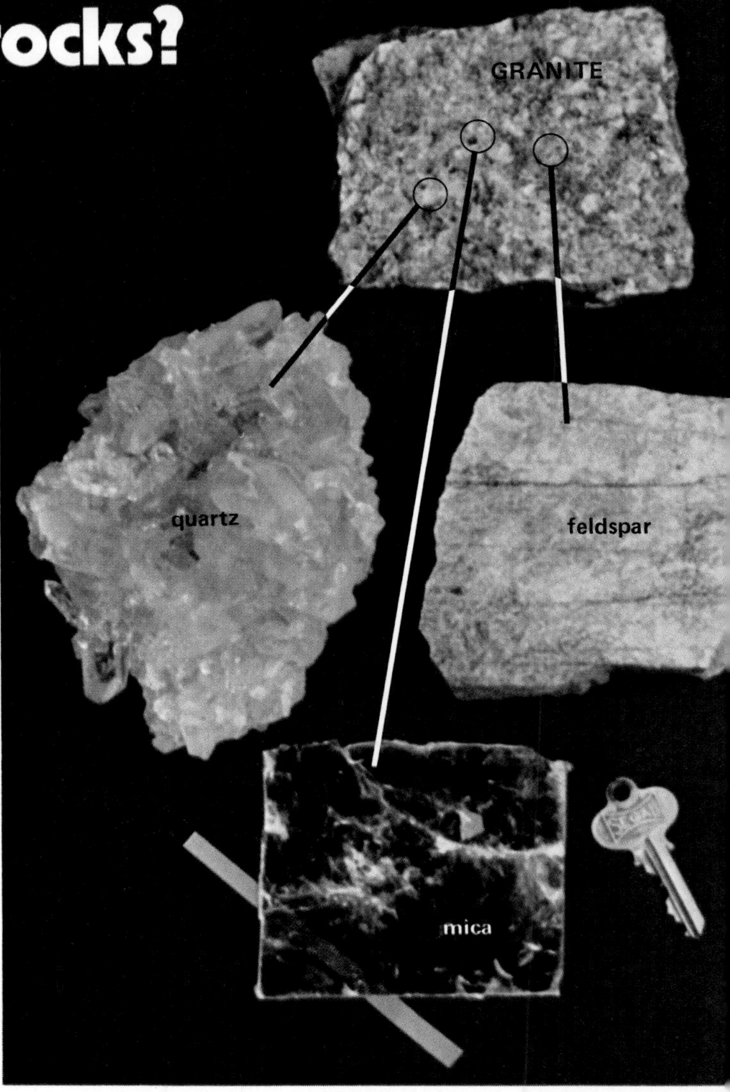

granite

rhyolite

The granite in this picture is made up mostly of small bits of quartz, feldspar, and mica. The picture shows larger samples of these minerals. The key shows their size. Note that you can see the strip of paper through the mica.

⟺ **The size of the crystals.** Granite and rhyolite (RY-o-lite) are igneous rocks made up of the same minerals. How can you tell the difference between granite and rhyolite? Granite has large crystals, and rhyolite has very small crystals. You can see and feel the different crystals in granite. But the crystals in rhyolite are too small to be seen. We say that granite has a coarse <u>texture</u> (TEKS-cher) and rhyolite has a fine texture. The texture of an igneous rock helps to identify it.

▶ **What kind of texture does an igneous rock with large crystals have?**

**Forming crystals.** You can find out why some rocks have large crystals and others have smaller crystals, or none at all. Heat some sulfur in a dish until the sulfur melts. Let it cool slowly. Then melt some more sulfur in another dish. Pour this melted sulfur into a beaker of cold water. The sulfur will cool quickly. You cannot see crystals in the sulfur that cooled quickly in the cold water. But if you look at the sulfur that cooled slowly in the first dish, you can see its crystals. The slower an igneous rock cools, the larger its crystals are.

▶ **Why do some igneous rocks have large crystals?**

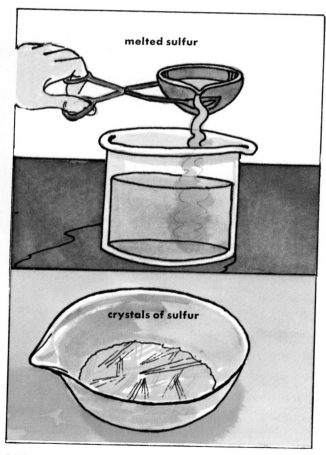

melted sulfur

crystals of sulfur

## WHAT YOU LEARNED

1. Igneous rocks can be identified by the minerals in them.
2. Igneous rocks can be identified by the size of their crystals.
3. The slower an igneous rock cools, the larger its crystals are.

## SCIENCE WORD

**texture** (TEKS-cher)
  the size of the crystals in a rock

## ANSWER THESE

1. Describe the igneous rock called granite.
2. Describe the igneous rock called rhyolite.
3. Compare the texture of an igneous rock that cooled slowly with one that cooled quickly.

## NOW TRY THIS

Riddle: What is it?
  1. It is made of granite.
  2. It may be put above someone's head and the person will never know it.
(The answer is upside down at the bottom of this page.)

## DO THIS AT HOME

Here are some pictures of different kinds of igneous rocks. Look at the pictures carefully. Then tell if each rock cooled slowly from magma inside the earth's crust, or quickly from lava outside the crust.

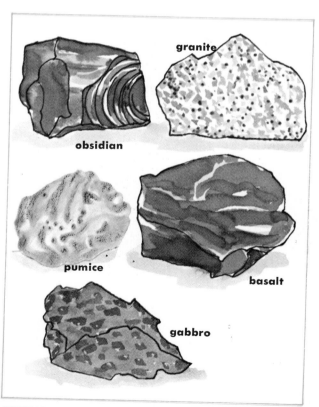

obsidian

granite

pumice

basalt

gabbro

Answer to riddle: tombstone

59

# How are sedimentary rocks formed?

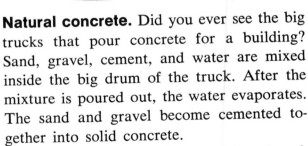

**Making sedimentary rocks.** Mix several teaspoons of mud and several teaspoons of sand in a jar of water. Stir the mixture, and then let it stand for a while. What happens to the mixture? The solid materials settle to the bottom of the jar. The sand settles first because it is heavier. The materials that settle to the bottom are called <u>sediments</u> (SED-uh-ments).

Sediments are found on the bottoms of oceans and lakes. Layers upon layers of sediment collect there. The layers are pressed together for thousands of years. The small, solid <u>particles</u> (PAR-tick-uls) become cemented together to form solid rock. This kind of rock is called sedimentary rock.

▶ **How is sedimentary rock formed?**

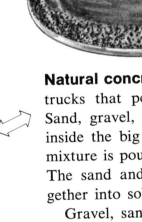

**Natural concrete.** Did you ever see the big trucks that pour concrete for a building? Sand, gravel, cement, and water are mixed inside the big drum of the truck. After the mixture is poured out, the water evaporates. The sand and gravel become cemented together into solid concrete.

Gravel, sand, and other particles of rock settle to the bottom of lakes and oceans. There are minerals dissolved in the water. As the water evaporates, the minerals act like cement. This cement covers the particles of sediment. The pebbles and grains of sand become cemented together. This causes the mixture to harden into sedimentary rock. Sedimentary rock is natural concrete.

▶ **What makes the particles of sediments stick together in sedimentary rocks?**

**Rocks from the water.** Dissolve several tablespoons of salt in a beaker of water. Pour the water into an evaporating dish. Heat the dish until all the water is gone. What is in the dish now? You can see lumps of salt.

Water evaporates from salt lakes and shallow seas. The salt is left behind. It forms the mineral called halite. Rock salt is a sedimentary rock made of halite. Limestone (LIME-stone) is another kind of sedimentary rock formed when water evaporates. In this case, the water had calcite dissolved in it.

▶ **How are sedimentary rocks like rock salt and limestone formed?**

## WHAT YOU LEARNED

1. Sedimentary rocks are formed when particles of rock are pressed and cemented together.
2. Some sedimentary rocks form when water containing dissolved minerals evaporates.

## SCIENCE WORDS

**sediment** (SED-uh-ment)
  solid material that settles to the bottom of a lake or ocean
**particle** (PAR-tick-ul)
  a small piece of a solid material
**limestone** (LIME-stone)
  a sedimentary rock made of calcite

## ANSWER THESE

1. Material that settles at the bottom of lakes and oceans is called
   a. cement
   b. sediment
   c. beach
2. Sedimentary rocks are formed when particles of sand and gravel are
   a. cemented together
   b. dissolved
   c. heated together

3. The cement for sedimentary rocks is made of dissolved
   a. concrete
   b. minerals
   c. salt
4. Sediments usually form layers with the heaviest particles at the
   a. top
   b. middle
   c. bottom
5. Limestone is sedimentary rock made from the mineral
   a. calcite
   b. halite
   c. quartz

## NOW TRY THESE

Unscramble the following words:
   a. mesident
   b. norceect
   c. mendsietary
   d. peavortea

## DO THIS AT HOME

Mix some plaster of Paris and gravel in a paper cup. Add water and stir until the mixture gets creamy. Let the mixture stand until it gets hard. Then, rip off the paper cup. Why can you call this a sedimentary rock?

plaster of Paris and gravel

# How are sedimentary rocks formed from living things?

**Rocks from shells.** Look at the picture. It shows a sedimentary rock called coquina (coh-KEE-nuh). Can you tell what coquina is made of? Look at the tiny shells that make up this rock. Can you identify some of the shells? There are clam shells, snail shells, and many other types of sea shells.

▶ **What is coquina made of?**

**How coquina is formed.** There are always many shells near the edge of an ocean beach. These shells were the outside covers of animals that lived in the ocean. When the animals died, their shells sank. In time, these shells pile up in layers. Minerals dissolved in the water help to cement the shells together. The cemented shells form coquina.

▶ **How is coquina formed?**

shell limestone

**Shell limestone.** Shell limestone is another sedimentary rock made from shells. Look at the picture of shell limestone. You cannot see the shells, because they were broken up into very small pieces. This happens when sea shells are washed up· onto the land. The waves then break the shells into smaller and smaller pieces. The pieces of broken shells pile up and become part of the beach. Sometimes, a whole beach is made up only of broken sea shells. Shells of sea animals are made of calcium carbonate (CAL-see-um CAR-buh-nate). This is the same as the white mineral calcite. A beach made of broken shells is usually very white. After a long time, the fine pieces of shell become cemented together. They form shell limestone.

▶ **How is shell limestone formed?**

## WHAT YOU LEARNED

1. Some sedimentary rocks are formed when the shells of sea animals are cemented together.
2. Shell limestone is made of the mineral calcite from broken shells.

## SCIENCE WORD

**coquina** (coh-KEE-nuh)
   sedimentary rock formed from sea shells that are cemented together

## ANSWER THESE

1. Why is coquina a sedimentary rock?
2. How is shell limestone the same as coquina?
3. How is shell limestone different from coquina?
4. How do sea animals build up beaches?

## NOW TRY THESE

Copy these into your notebook, and complete the rhyme.
1. Coquina is a rock that is easy to tell, because it's made up of broken _____.
2. Shell limestone forms on many beaches, when shells are broken into _____.
3. If a beach is very white, it may be made of the mineral _____.

## DO THIS AT HOME

Place a few drops of vinegar on a sea shell. Does it bubble? Try it with a piece of coquina or limestone. What mineral bubbles when acid is placed on it? What mineral do we find in sea shells and limestone?

## FINDING OUT MORE

Along the coast of England, there is a city called Dover. Dover is known for its famous white cliffs. These white cliffs are made of natural chalk. Natural chalk comes from the shells of microscopic animals. These cliffs were once under water. For millions of years, bits of shells settled to the bottom. Gradually, these thick layers of chalk were built up.

The chalk cliffs of Dover

# How can you identify sedimentary rocks?

**Rocks with big pieces.** You learned that many sedimentary rocks are made of pieces, or particles, of other rocks. These particles are cemented together. Sedimentary rocks are classified according to the size of their particles. Look at the picture of the rock called conglomerate (con-GLOM-er-it). It is a sedimentary rock made of pebbles and gravel.

▶ **What kind of particles make up conglomerate?**

CONGLOMERATE

**Rocks with smaller pieces.** The particles in sand are smaller than gravel. But you can still see and feel them. Sandstone (SAND-stone) is a sedimentary rock. Its name tells you that it is made up of particles of sand. It feels gritty, like sandpaper. If you look closely at sandstone, you can see the small particles of sand. The most common mineral in sandstone is quartz.

▶ **What do we call the small particles that make sandstone?**

SANDSTONE

**Rocks with very small pieces.** Did you know that mud and clay are made up of particles of rock? The particles of mud and clay are very small. Most of them are too small to see. Shale is a sedimentary rock made from particles of mud and clay. The small particles have been pressed and cemented together into layers. You can see the layers in a piece of shale. When shale is wet, you can smell the mud and clay from which it was made.

▶ **How big are the particles that make shale?**

SHALE

**Limestone caves.** Look at this picture of an underground cave. There are rocks that look like icicles. But they are not made of ice. They are limestone made of calcite.

These limestone rocks are forming by evaporation. Water dripping into the cave has calcite dissolved in it. A little water evaporates before it drips down. It leaves a little calcite behind. Where the water falls, it also leaves a little calcite. Slowly, the calcite forms "icicles" that hang from the ceiling. Other calcite "icicles" grow up from the floor. Sometimes they meet and form a solid column of limestone rock.

► **What is the name of the rock found in underground caves?**

## WHAT YOU LEARNED

1. The size of the rock particles can be used to identify sedimentary rocks.
2. The sedimentary rock called conglomerate is made of pebbles and gravel cemented together.
3. Sandstone is made of particles of sand cemented together.
4. Shale is made of particles of mud and clay cemented together.
5. Limestone is formed in underground caves by evaporation.

## SCIENCE WORDS

**conglomerate** (con-GLOM-er-it)
    sedimentary rock made of pebbles and gravel
**sandstone** (SAND-stone)
    sedimentary rock made of sand
**shale**
    sedimentary rock made of mud and clay

## ANSWER THESE

1. Name three sedimentary rocks.
2. What sedimentary rock is made from mud and clay?
3. What is the difference between shale and sandstone?
4. The sedimentary rock with the largest particles cemented together is
    a. sandstone
    b. conglomerate
    c. shale
5. When shale is wet it smells like
    a. mud
    b. fish
    c. salt
6. "Icicles" hanging in underground caves are mostly made of
    a. granite
    b. limestone
    c. sandstone

## DO THIS AT HOME

Put some Epsom salts in two small glasses of water. Keep adding the salts until no more will dissolve in the water. Then place one end of a string in one glass, and the other end of the string in the other glass. Let the string hang between the glasses, without touching the table. Water will drip from the center of the string. (Put a dish under the string to catch the dripping water.) Let the glasses and the string stand for a day. You will find that you made your own Epsom salt "icicle." How is this like what happens in a cave?

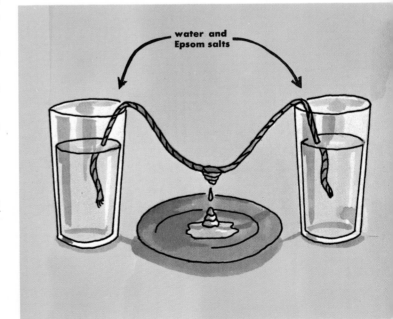

water and Epsom salts

# How are metamorphic rocks formed?

SHALE

**+**

HEAT OF THE EARTH

PRODUCES

SCHIST

**Heat can change rocks.** To make a cake, you mix eggs, flour, sugar, and milk. Then you bake the mixture in an oven. The cake looks nothing like the eggs, flour, sugar, or milk. They have been changed by the heat of the oven.

The inside of the earth is like an oven. Heat inside the earth "bakes" the rocks and changes them. The changed rocks are called metamorphic (met-uh-MOR-fick) rocks. Sedimentary rocks and igneous rocks can be changed to metamorphic rocks by heat in the earth.

▶ **What causes rocks to change into metamorphic rocks?**

**Heat causes chemical changes.** Magma is a hot, liquid rock inside the earth's crust. Magma moves into cracks in sedimentary rocks. It can also flow between the layers of sedimentary rocks. The heat of the magma causes a chemical reaction. Chemical elements in the magma react with chemical elements in the rocks. New minerals are formed from the minerals in the magma and the rocks. These new minerals form new rocks. The new rocks are metamorphic rocks.

▶ **Why can magma cause metamorphic rocks to form?**

**Pressure can change rocks.** Tons and tons of rocks push down on the rocks below them. The weight of the rocks causes great pressure (PRESH-ur). This great pressure causes chemical changes in the minerals of the rocks. New minerals and new rocks are produced. The new rocks are metamorphic rocks. Metamorphic rocks form deep within the earth's crust.

▶ **What makes metamorphic rocks form deep within the earth's crust?**

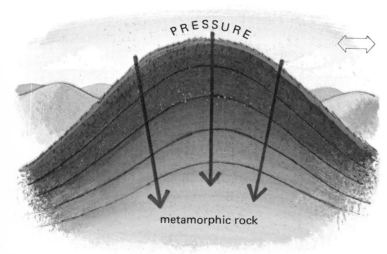

PRESSURE

metamorphic rock

## WHAT YOU LEARNED

1. Metamorphic rocks are formed from igneous and sedimentary rocks.
2. Metamorphic rocks are formed by heat, chemical reactions, and pressure.
3. Metamorphic rocks form deep within the earth's crust.

## SCIENCE WORDS

**metamorphic** (met-uh-MOR-fic) **rocks**
rocks formed by changes in other rocks
**pressure** (PRESH-ur)
a pressing force

## ANSWER THESE

1. List three ways that metamorphic rocks are formed.
2. Explain how heat produces metamorphic rocks.
3. Why are most metamorphic rocks formed deep within the earth's crust?

## NOW TRY THIS

Find the word that shows a way that metamorphic rocks are formed.

Across:
1. The change caused by magma touching other rocks.
2. Type of rocks formed from molten magma.
3. Molten liquid inside the earth.
4. Rock formed from heat, pressure, and chemical reactions.

When you have filled in all the words in the puzzle, you will find a mystery word. What is it?

## FINDING OUT MORE

Here is a chart that lists some sedimentary and igneous rocks, and the metamorphic rocks they can be changed to.

| ROCK CHANGED | METAMORPHIC ROCK FORMED |
|---|---|
| 1. granite | gneiss |
| 2. shale | schist |
| 3. shale | slate |
| 4. limestone | marble |
| 5. sandstone | quartzite |

## WHAT'S HAPPENING

**Islands Made by Animals**

There are certain very small animals that live in warm, shallow sea water. These animals are called coral (COR-ul). They have shells and skeletons made of calcium carbonate. These animals attach themselves to the parts of islands under water. Their shells become cemented to the island. Over thousands of years, these shells build up and form a coral reef around the island. Sometimes, the whole top of an island is made of coral. Bermuda is an island made of coral.

CORAL REEFS

67

# What do some metamorphic rocks look like?

**How can you identify metamorphic rocks?** Get a box of flat toothpicks. Snap each toothpick in half, but leave the halves attached. Place the toothpicks in a paper bag and shake the bag. Then pour the toothpicks from the bag onto a table. Look at the flat sides of the toothpicks. They face in different directions. Now place a book on top of the toothpicks and press down. Remove the book and look at the toothpicks again. What has happened? Many have flattened out.

When rocks are placed under pressure, the mineral crystals in them flatten out. The minerals form bands and layers. The bands are used to identify metamorphic rocks.

► **What is one way to identify metamorphic rocks?**

**Common metamorphic rocks.** Gneiss (NICE) is a metamorphic rock. Look for the bands of minerals in the picture of gneiss. Schist (SHIST) is another metamorphic rock. Some schist has a lot of mica in it. You can see the flattened pieces of mica in schist.

Compare gneiss and schist to granite. All three rocks have some of the same minerals. But granite is an igneous rock. Its minerals are not found in bands. Gneiss and schist are metamorphic rocks. They have been changed by heat and pressure. Their minerals are found in bands.

► **Name two common metamorphic rocks.**

**Other metamorphic rocks.** Slate looks like shale, but slate is much harder. When shale is put under pressure, it changes into slate. The minerals in slate are lined up in layers. That is why slate breaks into flat sheets. Slate is used for blackboards because it breaks into sheets. Another metamorphic rock is marble. Marble is formed from limestone. When limestone is under heat and pressure, it changes into marble. Marble is used as a building stone.

► **What metamorphic rocks do shale and limestone form?**

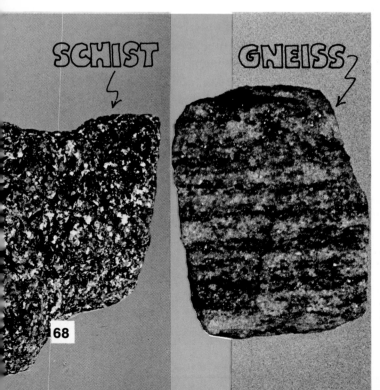

SCHIST

GNEISS

## WHAT YOU LEARNED

1. Pressure causes the minerals in metamorphic rocks to line up in bands.
2. Metamorphic rocks can be identified by their bands.

## SCIENCE WORDS

**gneiss** (NICE)
   a metamorphic rock with bands of minerals
**schist** (SHIST)
   a metamorphic rock showing minerals flattened into bands or layers
**slate**
   a metamorphic rock made from shale and that breaks in flat sheets

## ANSWER THESE

1. What causes the bands in some metamorphic rocks?
2. Name a metamorphic rock that forms from shale.
3. Slate looks very much like shale except that slate is
   **a.** harder   **b.** lighter   **c.** darker
4. The mineral calcite is found in limestone. Calcite is also found in
   **a.** gneiss
   **b.** schist
   **c.** marble

5. Quartz is found in sandstone. What metamorphic rock also contains quartz?
   **a.** marble
   **b.** quartzite
   **c.** slate

## NOW TRY THIS

Fill in the blanks to find out what makes up the crust of the earth.

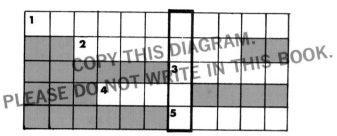

**Across**
1. Rock formed from heat, pressure, and chemical changes.
2. Rock formed from magma.
3. The outer layer of the earth.
4. It is made of minerals.
5. A sedimentary rock that forms slate.

## FINDING OUT MORE

Look at this chart of a rock cycle. It shows how one class of rock may be changed to another class.

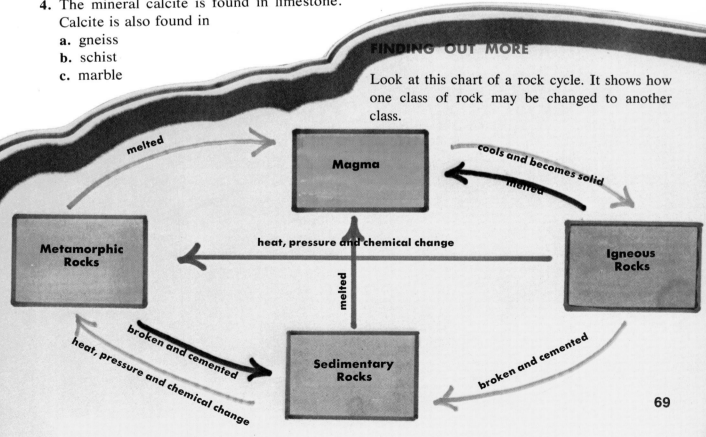

69

# 3 Review

Do the following questions on a separate sheet of paper.

**Fill in the Blank**     *Write down the statements in Column I. Where there is a blank line in each statement, write the word or phrase from Column II that best completes the meaning of the statement.*

| Column I | Column II |
|---|---|
| 1. When limestone is under heat and pressure, it changes into _____. | conglomerate |
| 2. A metamorphic rock used to make blackboards is _____. | classification |
| 3. Rocks that are formed by the cooling of magma are called _____. | slate |
| 4. A sedimentary rock made up of pebbles and gravel is a _____. | lava |
| 5. A rock formed from the shells of clams and snails is _____. | marble |
| 6. Solid material that settles to the bottom of a lake or ocean is called _____. | quartzite |
| | igneous rocks |
| 7. An example of an igneous rock with large crystals is _____. | coquina |
| 8. The hot liquid that comes out of the earth is _____. | sediment |
| 9. Grouping things together by their similarities is called _____. | granite |
| 10. Metamorphic sandstone is _____. | |

Do the following questions on a separate sheet of paper.

**Multiple Choice**     *Write the letter of the choice that best completes the statement or answers the question.*

1. Sedimentary rocks are
   a. formed from cemented fragments of rock
   b. very rare
   c. formed from melted materials

2. Metamorphic rocks are formed by
   a. low heat and high pressure
   b. low heat and low pressure
   c. high heat and high pressure

3. Melted rocks and minerals inside the earth are called
   a. oil
   b. magma
   c. metamorphic

4. Granite is usually made up of
   a. quartz, feldspar, and mica
   b. quartz, feldspar, and sulfur
   c. rhyolite, quartz, and mica

5. The slower an igneous rock cools,
   a. the finer its texture will be
   b. the coarser its texture will be
   c. the softer it will be

6. Limestone is a sedimentary rock made up of
   a. halite
   b. gravel
   c. calcite

7. Shells are cemented together to form rock by
   a. minerals dissolved in the water
   b. the animals that live in the shells
   c. melted rock from inside the earth

8. Metamorphic rocks form
   a. at the surface of the earth
   b. deep within the earth
   c. in the middle of the oceans

# 4 Wearing Down the Earth

## Unit Lessons

1. What are physical and chemical changes?
2. What is mechanical weathering?
3. What is chemical weathering?
4. What factors affect the rate of weathering?
5. What is soil?
6. How may one soil differ from another?
7. What is a soil profile?
8. How do soils differ in different climates?
9. What are some chemicals in the soil?
10. What are basic and acidic soils?
11. What life is found in soil?

## Goals and Objectives

After completing this unit, you should be able to:

- differentiate between physical and chemical changes.
- understand how the earth is worn down by physical and chemical weathering.
- explain how soil is a product of weathering and organic processes.
- describe different kinds of soil in terms of texture, layering, pH, and climate.
- name the chemicals commonly found in soil, as well as some of the life forms.

# What are physical and chemical changes?

**There'll be some changes made.** Break a piece of chalk. Peel a small piece of mica from a large sample. What happens? The size and shape of each substance were changed. But each substance still has the properties it had to start with. The chalk can still be used to write on the board. It is still chalk. The smaller piece of mica has the same properties as the larger piece. The smaller piece has the same hardness. It has the same density. It gives the same streak test. The smaller piece is still mica. A change that does not change the properties of a substance is called a physical (FIZ-uh-kul) change.

Breaking something is a physical change.

▶ What kind of change takes place when chalk is broken in two?

**Making new substances.** Burning wood is a very different kind of change from breaking chalk. As wood burns, carbon dioxide gas and water vapor rise from the burning wood. Scientists can detect these two gases even though neither gas can be seen.

Both of these gases are new substances produced by the burning wood. When the burning is finished, there is no more wood left. Ash remains in its place. Burning wood produces carbon dioxide, water vapor, and ash. The properties of each of these substances are different from the properties of the wood. The burning of wood has produced new substances. Changes that produce new substances are called chemical changes.

▶ What new substances are formed as wood burns?

**Rocks and physical changes.** Rain, wind, and other things in nature wear down rocks. Tiny pieces may break off a rock and get washed or blown away. The grains of sand on a beach come from sandstone. (See page 64). The tiny pieces of clay in streams come from shale. Grains of sand have the same properties as the material in sandstone. Clay particles have the same properties as the material in shale. When small pieces of rock break from larger ones, a physical change takes place.

▶ What kind of change takes place when sandstone breaks apart into sand?

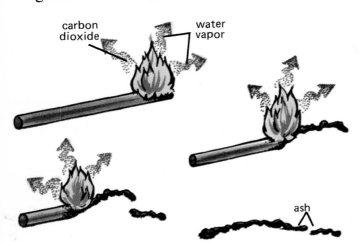

carbon dioxide

water vapor

ash

Burning is a chemical change.

**Hematite (left) and limonite (right).** These two minerals have the same chemical formula as iron rust.

**Chemical changes in rocks.** Dip an iron nail in water. Then leave it exposed to the air. After some time, rust forms on the nail. Rust is iron oxide. Its formula is $Fe_2O_3$. It is a new substance formed when iron combines with oxygen from the air. Some minerals, such as magnetite and pyrite, have iron in them. When rocks containing these minerals are exposed to the air, iron rust forms. This is a chemical change. New minerals form called hematite and limonite. Hematite and limonite have the same chemical formula as iron rust, $Fe_2O_3$.

▶ **What happens to minerals containing iron when they are exposed to the air?**

## WHAT YOU LEARNED

1. A physical change does not change the properties of a substance.
2. A chemical change is a change that produces new substances.
3. The breaking of a rock is a physical change.
4. A chemical change takes place when the minerals in a rock change from one kind to another.

## DO THIS AT HOME

Wet some steel wool. Press it down to the bottom of a test tube. Half fill a glass with water. Stand the test tube upside down in the water. Examine the test tube and the steel wool every day for a few days. What happened to the steel wool? What kind of a change took place? What happened to the water inside the test tube? The water took the place of a gas removed from the air in the test tube. What gas do you think it was? What happened to the gas?

## SCIENCE WORDS

**physical** (FIZ-uh-kul) **change**
a change that does not change the properties of a substance

**chemical change**
a change in which one or more new substances are produced

## ANSWER THESE

1. Breaking off a small piece of mica from a large sample is a
   a. chemical change
   b. physical change
   c. chemical and physical change
2. Changes that produce new substances are
   a. chemical changes
   b. physical changes
   c. neither chemical nor physical changes
3. When wood burns
   a. carbon dioxide alone is produced
   b. water vapor alone is produced
   c. both carbon dioxide and water vapor are produced
4. After a rock undergoes chemical change, the rock will
   a. contain new minerals
   b. contain no new minerals
   c. remain unchanged

## NOW TRY THIS

Tell whether each of the following is a chemical change or a physical change.

1. A rock breaks into many pieces.
2. A match burns.
3. A tin can rusts.
4. A sidewalk becomes cracked by a tree root.
5. Bubbles come off calcite that is placed in acid.

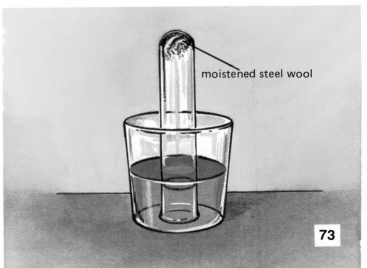

moistened steel wool

# What is mechanical weathering?

The roots of trees can break a rock wall.

**The weathering of rocks.** If you wanted to build something that would last a long time, you might use rocks and stones. Many old buildings are made of stone. Some have lasted for thousands of years. But they will not last forever. As time passes, small pieces of a rock will break away. Sometimes cracks appear in rocks and they split into pieces. The breaking down of rocks mainly from the action of the weather is called weathering. Weathering often takes place very slowly. People usually do not notice it happening.

▶ What is weathering?

**Mechanical and chemical weathering.** Changes in the weather cause large rocks to break into pieces. Except for their size, the small pieces are the same as the rock itself. They have the same composition as the rock.

This kind of weathering is called mechanical (muh-KAN-ih-kul) weathering. Sometimes, as a rock weathers, chemical changes take place in the rock. Then the surface of the rock and the small pieces that come from the rock change their composition. This kind of weathering is called chemical (KEM-ih-kul) weathering. Chemical weathering is discussed in the next lesson.

▶ What is mechanical weathering?

**Freezing water can cause mechanical weathering.** Some rocks have tiny holes called pores. Other rocks have cracks or splits. Water enters these openings. During cold weather, the water turns into ice and

Breaking a rock into pieces does not change the composition of the pieces. The pieces are made up of the same material as the rock.

Weathering can break a wall apart.

expands. The rocks crack, and the cracks become larger. Weathering produced by the action of freezing water is called <u>frost</u> <u>action</u>. Frost action takes place in regions where water keeps freezing and melting. Potholes that form in the street during cold water are caused by frost action.

▶ What is frost action?

**Mechanical weathering by plants.** Look at the sidewalk near a tree. Are there cracks in the sidewalk? The roots of the tree may have caused the cracks. The roots of plants can crack rock. When the roots are tiny, they grow into small cracks in the rock. As the roots grow larger, they cause the rock to break. The roots of a tree can crack and lift up the sidewalk. They can also break the rock of a mountain.

▶ How do plants cause weathering?

## WHAT YOU LEARNED

1. The breaking down and wearing away of rocks is called weathering.
2. Mechanical weathering is weathering without a chemical change taking place.
3. Chemical weathering is weathering that takes place as a result of chemical changes.

4. The freezing and melting of water can cause mechanical weathering.
5. The roots of growing plants can cause mechanical weathering.

## SCIENCE WORDS

**weathering**
the breaking down and wearing away of rocks

**mechanical** (muh-KAN-ih-kul) **weathering**
weathering in which chemical change does not take place

**chemical** (KEM-ih-kul) **weathering**
weathering in which chemical change takes place

**frost action**
mechanical weathering caused by the freezing and melting of water

## ANSWER THESE

1. The type of changes in the earth's surface caused by mechanical weathering is
   a. a chemical change
   b. a physical change
   c. both a chemical and physical change
2. When water freezes, it
   a. expands
   b. contracts
   c. melts

## NOW TRY THESE

1. Explain why sidewalks may crack in the winter.
2. Why shouldn't trees be planted near underground water pipes?
3. How are potholes formed?

## FINDING OUT MORE

Animals and plants help frost action. Some animals dig holes and tunnel through the ground. Even ants and earthworms dig tunnels. The roots of plants also make passages for water to get into the ground. Water fills these holes and tunnels. Frost action then goes to work when the water freezes.

# What is chemical weathering?

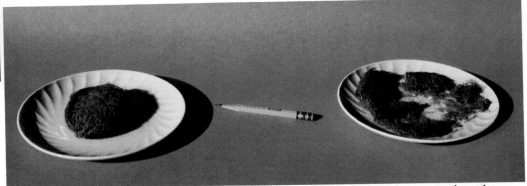

After a wire pad has rusted, it breaks apart easily. This change in properties shows that rusting is a chemical change.

**Chemical change.** Rust is produced when iron combines chemically with oxygen in the air. The properties of rust are different from the properties of iron and oxygen. For example, rust has an orange-brown color. It does not look like iron or oxygen. Also, an iron wire can be bent back and forth. When the wire rusts, it will break apart when bent. The formation of rust from iron and oxygen is a chemical change. During a chemical change, new substances are formed. These substances have new properties. They are different from the substances that were there before the chemical change took place.

▶ **What happens when oxygen combines with iron?**

**Oxidation.** Oxidation (ok-suh-DAY-shun) is one kind of chemical weathering. Oxidation is the chemical change that takes place when oxygen combines with another substance. The formation of rust when iron combines with oxygen is oxidation. Iron compounds in a rock may undergo oxidation. The rock weakens and turns into a kind of rust.

▶ **What happens to a rock when it undergoes oxidation?**

**Hydration.** Hydration (high-DRAY-shun) is the chemical reaction of water with other substances. When the minerals in a rock undergo hydration, the rock swells up and crumbles.

▶ **What happens to the minerals in rocks when they undergo hydration?**

**Acid reactions.** Carbon dioxide is a gas found in the air. When it rains, carbon dioxide dissolves in the water to form carbonic (car-BON-ik) acid. When this acid touches limestone or marble, a chemical reaction takes place. The carbonic acid dissolves the limestone or marble. The rock containing these minerals then falls apart. The reaction of carbonic acid with minerals is called carbonation (car-buh-NAY-shun).

Acids also form from the decay or wastes of plants and animals. These acids can also cause chemical changes in the minerals in rocks. The new substances formed by the chemical changes can often be worn down more easily. Chemical weathering takes place when rocks undergo chemical change.

▶ **What can acids do to minerals?**

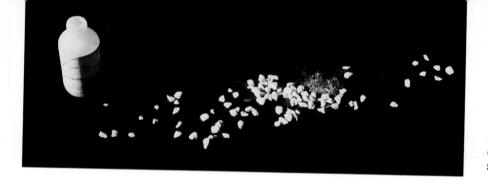

The marble chips shown here and limestone rock will both be dissolved by rain water that is slightly acid.

Old buildings, such as this one in Paris, show the effects of weathering.

## WHAT YOU LEARNED

1. During a chemical change, new substances are formed.
2. Oxidation is the chemical reaction of oxygen with other substances.
3. Hydration is the chemical reaction of water with other substances.
4. Carbonation is the chemical reaction of carbonic acid with other substances.
5. Chemical weathering takes place when rocks break apart as a result of chemical change.

## SCIENCE WORDS

**chemical change**
a process in which substances are changed to new substances

**oxidation** (ok-suh-DAY-shun)
the chemical reaction between oxygen and other substances

**hydration** (high-DRAY-shun)
the chemical reaction between water and other substances

**carbonation** (car-buh-NAY-shun)
the chemical reaction between carbonic acid and other substances

## ANSWER THESE

1. Why must steel bridges be painted?
2. An example of oxidation is
   a. the reaction of carbonic acid and limestone
   b. water dissolving rock salt
   c. the rusting of iron
3. An example of hydration is
   a. the reaction of carbonic acid and limestone
   b. water dissolving rock salt
   c. the rusting of iron
4. An example of carbonation is
   a. the reaction of carbonic acid and limestone
   b. water dissolving rock salt
   c. the rusting of iron
5. When water combines with carbon dioxide, the result is
   a. rust
   b. carbonic acid
   c. marble

## NOW TRY THIS

What is the difference between mechanical weathering and chemical weathering?

## FINDING OUT MORE

Weathering is normally a slow process. Today we are speeding up the process of weathering. Automobiles are putting gases from exhaust pipes into the air. Factory smokestacks are also sending waste gases into the air. Some of these gases make an acidic solution when they mix with rain water. Rain water polluted in this way is called acid rain. Acid rain is causing rocks and minerals to weather faster. It is destroying the rocks used in buildings as well as those found in the field. In some cities buildings are beginning to crumble and fall apart from acid rain.

# What factors affect the rate of weathering?

**Moisture.** All rocks do not weather at the same rate. Some rocks weather faster than others. Moisture in the air affects the rate of rock weathering. The more water, the faster the weathering. Oxidation, carbonation, and hydration work faster in a moist region. Moisture speeds up chemical weathering. Weathering takes longer in a dry region.

▶ **How does moisture affect weathering?**

**Temperature.** Frost action takes place when water freezes. Two things are needed for frost action to take place. Water must be present. Then there must be the right changes in temperature. If the temperature stays too warm, the water won't freeze. If the temperature stays too cold, the ice won't melt. When the temperature often rises and falls above and below the freezing point of water, frost action speeds up.

▶ **What two factors affect the rate of frost action?**

**Surface area.** All kinds of weathering weaken rocks. Finally, the rock breaks up into pieces. The surface area of all the pieces is greater than the surface area of the whole rock. The greater surface area leaves more of the rock exposed to the weather. As a rock is broken into smaller pieces, it weathers faster.

▶ **How does the surface area of a rock affect the rate of weathering?**

**The nature of the rock.** Different kinds of rock weather at different rates. Quartz weathers slowly while feldspar weathers much faster. The tiny holes that are in porous rocks allow water to enter. In colder climates, frost action causes these rocks to weather faster than rocks that have no pores. Sandstone is a porous rock. Shale is nonporous.

Rocks containing iron weather by oxidation at a faster rate than many rocks lacking iron.

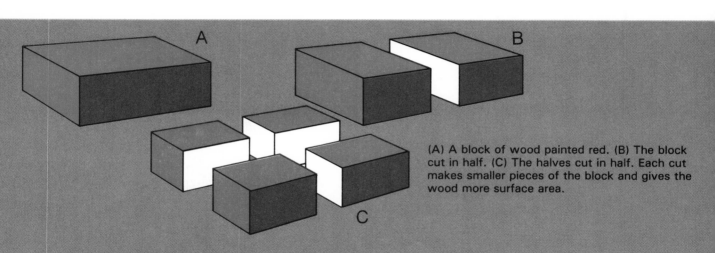

(A) A block of wood painted red. (B) The block cut in half. (C) The halves cut in half. Each cut makes smaller pieces of the block and gives the wood more surface area.

Before this rock was broken into pieces, all of its surface was painted red. In this photo, all of the rock not colored red is new surface produced by breaking the rock.

Carbonation causes rocks that dissolve in acid to weather faster than rocks that resist the attack of acids.

Rocks differ in the way they are made up. These differences make one kind of rock weather faster than another.

▶ Why does sandstone weather faster than shale?

## WHAT YOU LEARNED

1. In a moist climate, rocks weather faster.
2. Repeated freezing and melting temperatures cause rocks to weather faster.
3. The greater the surface area of a rock, the faster it will weather.
4. A rock broken into pieces weathers faster than the whole rock.
5. The rate of weathering depends upon the kind of rock.

## ANSWER THESE

1. As the amount of moisture in a region increases, the rate of weathering
   a. increases
   b. decreases
   c. remains the same
2. As the season gets closer to summer, the rate of weathering due to frost action
   a. increases
   b. decreases
   c. remains the same
3. As a rock is broken into smaller and smaller pieces, the rate of weathering
   a. increases
   b. decreases
   c. remains the same
4. If a rock contains more quartz than feldspar,
   a. it weathers faster
   b. it weathers slower
   c. the rate of the weathering is not affected

## FINDING OUT MORE

**Cleopatra's Needle.** In 1880 a large stone monument was moved from Egypt to New York City. This stone, called Cleopatra's Needle, had writings carved on it. The climate in Egypt is hot and dry. This monument had not changed for over 3,000 years in Egypt. Within a short time the hot and cold, moist climate of New York changed it. Most the carvings on the stone weathered away.

A section of Cleopatra's Needle

# What is soil?

**The importance of soil.** Most plants need soil in order to grow. Without soil, there would be very few plants. Many animals eat plants. Without soil to grow plants, these plant-eating animals could not live. Other animals hunt and kill plant-eating animals for food. Without soil, few things could live on earth.

▶ Why is soil important for life on earth?

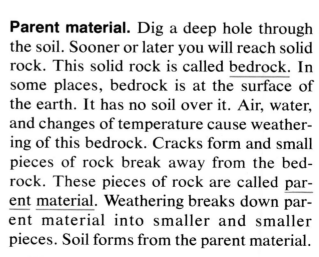

exposed bedrock

parent material

Rocks break away from weathering bedrock. These rocks are the parent material that will break into small pieces and become an important part of the soil.

**Parent material.** Dig a deep hole through the soil. Sooner or later you will reach solid rock. This solid rock is called bedrock. In some places, bedrock is at the surface of the earth. It has no soil over it. Air, water, and changes of temperature cause weathering of this bedrock. Cracks form and small pieces of rock break away from the bedrock. These pieces of rock are called parent material. Weathering breaks down parent material into smaller and smaller pieces. Soil forms from the parent material.

▶ What changes bedrock to parent material?

**80**

**Plant growth.** There are spaces between the tiny particles of weathered bedrock. These spaces are filled with air and moisture. Some plants are able to take root in this material. These plants and their remains form acids. The acids cause chemical weathering of the rocks. Weathering of the bedrock speeds up. The weathering goes deeper into the bedrock. More parent material is broken down into tiny particles of minerals. The layer of mineral particles becomes thicker. Material from the decaying remains of animals and plants is formed. The remains of living things are called <u>organic</u> (or-GAN-ik) <u>materials.</u> Organic materials become mixed with the mineral particles. This mixture is called <u>humus</u> (HYOO-mus). Humus becomes a part of the soil.

▶ What is organic material?

**Soil.** Soil is a mixture of a number of things. Soil is made mostly of rock and mineral particles. It also contains air, moisture, and living and dead things. Soils are not exactly the same everywhere. Different bedrocks produce different soils. Climate also has an effect on the formation of soil. In one climate one type of thing can live in the soil. Other climates are suitable for other types of living things.

▶ Why may one soil be different from another?

## WHAT YOU LEARNED

1. Parent material is the pieces of rock that break away from bedrock.

2. As weathering breaks down parent material, soil starts to form from the tiny pieces.
3. Soil continues to form as organic materials mix with tiny rock particles.
4. Soil contains rock and mineral particles, air, moisture, and living and dead organic material.

## SCIENCE WORDS

**bedrock**
   the solid rock that lies under the soil
**parent material**
   the pieces of rock that break away from bedrock
**organic** (or-GAN-ik) **material**
   the material making up things that are now alive or were once alive
**humus** (HYOO-mus)
   material formed from the decaying remains of animals and plants

## ANSWER THESE

1. The solid rock found under the soil is called
    a. parent rock
    b. organic rock
    c. bedrock
2. The rocks that break away from the bedrock are called
    a. parent material
    b. organic material
    c. solid material
3. The organic material in the soil is
    a. humus
    b. parent material
    c. bedrock
4. Soil is made up mostly of
    a. organic material
    b. rock and mineral particles
    c. air and moisture

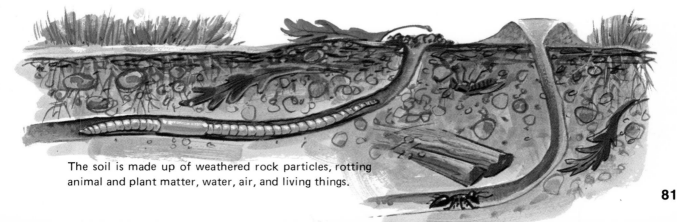

The soil is made up of weathered rock particles, rotting animal and plant matter, water, air, and living things.

# How may one soil differ from another?

**Bedrock to soil.** Weathering changes bedrock to parent material. Weathered parent material forms a large part of the soil. Limestone and granite are two kinds of bedrock. The minerals in granite are different from those in limestone. One kind of soil comes from granite bedrock. Another kind comes from limestone bedrock.

Sometimes a soil is carried from one place to another after it is formed. This can happen, for example, when water washes a

LIMESTONE ROCK

soil away. The soil will come to rest in a new place. Then the bedrock beneath the soil may differ from the parent material that formed the soil. Such a soil is called a transported (trans-POR-tid) soil. (To transport something means to carry it to another place.)

Many soils are not transported. They stay where they were formed. The parent material forming the soil is the same as the bedrock below the soil. Such a soil is called a residual (rih-ZIJ-oo-ul) soil.

▶ What are residual soils?

**That's the size of it.** The size of soil particles varies from soil to soil. Texture (TEKS-cher) is a word used to describe the size of soil particles. Sandy soils have a coarse (CORS) texture. This means that sandy soils are made up of particles of large size. Silty (SILL-tee) soils have smaller particles. Silty soils have a texture that is not as coarse as sand. Clayey (CLAY-ee) soils have the smallest-size particles. Clayey soils have a fine texture. When clayey soils are wet, they feel sticky and muddy.

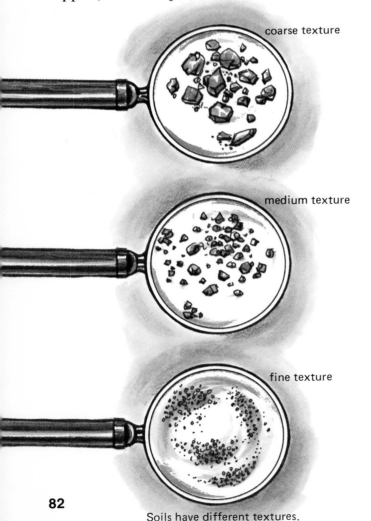

coarse texture

medium texture

fine texture

Soils have different textures.

82

Some soils are all sand. Others are all clay. Still others are all silt. Soils can also be mixtures of two or three textures. A mixture of mostly sand and silt with some clay is called loam (LOHM). Loam does not get too wet or too dry. Loam is the best soil for growing most plants.

▶ **What is meant by the texture of a soil?**

Plants do not grow well where the soil has been compacted.

**Water moves through the soil.** The texture of the soil affects the speed of water moving through it. Water sinks through some soils faster than through others. Water goes down fastest through gravel. Water passes more slowly through sand. Water hardly goes down through clay at all.

The large spaces between the particles of gravel let water pass through quickly. It takes a little longer for water to go through the smaller spaces in sand. The smallest spaces between particles are found in clay soils. Sometimes these spaces are too small for water to pass through.

Walking tends to compact (kom-PAKT), or push together, the particles in the soil. As a result, plants do not grow well in a compacted soil.

▶ **Why does water move faster through gravel than through clay?**

## WHAT YOU LEARNED

1. A transported soil has been carried away from the place where it was formed.

2. A residual soil has remained where it was formed.
3. Soils have different textures.
4. Water passes fastest through a soil with a coarse texture.

## SCIENCE WORDS

**transported** (trans-POR-tid) **soil**
a soil made of material that did not come from the bedrock below it
**residual** (rih-ZIJ-oo-ul) **soil**
a soil made of material from the bedrock below it
**texture** (TEKS-cher)
the size of particles making up a soil
**coarse** (CORS) **soils**
soils made up of large particles
**fine soils**
soils made up of small particles

## ANSWER THESE

1. Soils that have been carried away from the place where they were formed are
   a. residual soils
   b. transported soils
   c. light soils
2. Compared to sand, the texture of a silty soil is
   a. finer
   b. coarser
   c. the same
3. Loam is mostly a mixture of sand with
   a. cement
   b. gravel
   c. silt
4. Water passes most quickly through a soil that is
   a. fine
   b. coarse
   c. clayey

## FINDING OUT MORE

Soil tends to become more compact through the year. Tractors ride over the soil, pushing the particles closer together. The weight of workers picking crops compacts the soil. Rain, too, will cause the particles to move closer together. Farmers plow their fields to break up the soil before planting. This allows water to move easily into the ground.

# What is a soil profile?

A "road cut" is the name given to the rocks that are exposed when a road is built through the side of a hill.

**Soil layers.** Soil forms in layers. The top layer is the easiest to observe and study. But looking at all the layers gives a better understanding of soil. A road cut is a place where land has been cut through to make a road. Road cuts are good places to get a side view of the layers making up soil. The side view of a soil is called a soil profile (PRO-file). Each layer in the profile is called a soil horizon (hor-EYE-zun).

▶ **What is a soil profile?**

**Soil horizons.** Most soils have three layers, or horizons. Each horizon is named with a capital letter. Horizon A, the first layer, is called the topsoil. Horizon B, just below the topsoil, is called the subsoil. Horizon C is the layer below the subsoil.

▶ **What is used in naming soil horizons?**

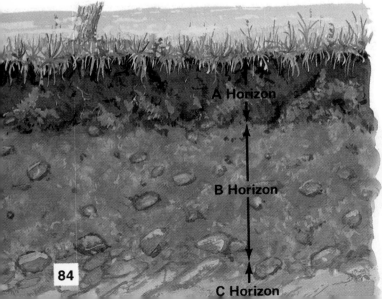

A Horizon

B Horizon

C Horizon

**Horizon A, topsoil.** Topsoil is a mixture of tiny rock particles and humus. The decayed animal and plant life making up humus give topsoil its dark color. Plants grow best in topsoil. As plants die, their remains are added to the topsoil. This makes the topsoil thicker. Larger plants can then grow in the thicker topsoil.

▶ **What gives topsoil its dark color?**

**Horizon B, subsoil.** Water moves down freely through spaces in the topsoil. This water carries with it very tiny clay particles. The clay particles fill the spaces in horizon B. They give the subsoil a red-orange color and make the subsoil hard. Water cannot pass easily through the hard subsoil. Only the roots of large plants push down into the subsoil. Subsoil is a hard soil made up of rock particles and tiny clay particles.

▶ **What gives subsoil its red-orange color?**

**Horizon C.** Horizon C contains some larger pieces of broken rock. Lower in horizon C is the solid, unbroken bedrock itself. The pieces of broken rock come from the weathering of the bedrock.

In some soils, there is no horizon B. Then, horizon C lies directly below horizon A. These soils are called immature (im-uh-TYOOR) soils. A soil containing all three

**MATURE SOIL**

**IMMATURE SOIL**

horizons is called a <u>mature</u> (muh-TYOOR) <u>soil</u>. As time passes, weathering changes immature soils into mature soils.

▶ **What lies above the solid bedrock in horizon C?**

## WHAT YOU LEARNED

1. Soil forms in layers called horizons.
2. The first layer, the topsoil (horizon A), contains humus and tiny pieces of weathered rock.
3. The second layer, the subsoil (horizon B), contains small pieces of weathered rock mixed with tiny particles of clay.
4. The third layer, horizon C, has larger pieces of rock lying above solid bedrock.
5. Immature soils have horizon C directly below horizon A, but with time these soils develop into mature soils with all three horizons.

## SCIENCE WORDS

**soil horizons** (hor-EYE-zunz)
  the different layers of soil

**soil profile** (PRO-file)
  a side view of the layers making up a soil

**topsoil**
  name given to horizon A, the top layer

**subsoil**
  name given to horizon B, the layer below the topsoil

**mature** (muh-TYOOR) **soil**
  older soils having all three horizons

**immature** (im-uh-TYOOR) **soil**
  younger soils lacking a subsoil

## ANSWER THESE

1. Soil forms in layers called
   a. horizons
   b. pieces
   c. sections
2. An important part of topsoil is
   a. fine particles of clay
   b. humus
   c. partially weathered bedrock
3. The horizon whose color comes from very fine clay particles is
   a. A     b. B     c. C
4. Subsoil is horizon
   a. A     b. B     c. C
5. How many horizons are found in a mature soil?
   a. 1     b. 2     c. 3

## NOW TRY THIS

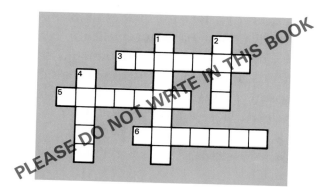

**Down**
   1. Different layers in a soil profile
   2. Particles found in subsoil
   4. Material found in topsoil

**Across**
   3. Layers of soil
   5. Horizon B
   6. Horizon A

# How do soils differ in different climates?

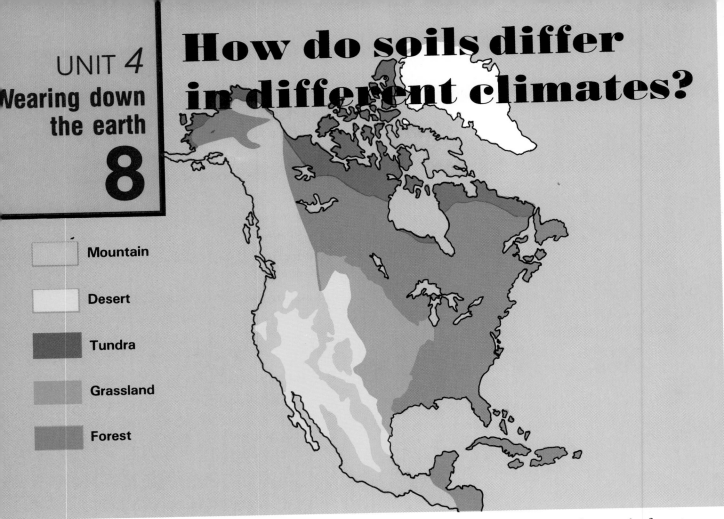

Mountain

Desert

Tundra

Grassland

Forest

**Soils differ.** There are different kinds of soils. They differe in the amount of humus. They also differ in the types and amounts of minerals in the upper horizons. Rainfall plays an important role in where minerals are found in a soil. Greater amounts of rainfall dissolve more minerals. These minerals move down from horizon A. They collect in horizon B. Knowing how soils differ is helpful to farmers and people who build roads, bridges, and buildings.

Some important kinds of soils are forest soils, desert soils, grassland soils, prairie soils, and tundra soils.

▶ **What will large amounts of rainfall do to a soil?**

**Forest soil.** Most of the eastern United States has a <u>forest soil</u>. Trees there get plenty of rain and grow tall. Shading from trees keeps many plants from growing on the forest floor. So very little humus or topsoil forms. As the rain filters down through the topsoil, it carries minerals to the subsoil. The movement of minerals from the topsoil downward is called <u>leaching</u> (LEECH-ing). Forest soils have thin topsoils with little humus or minerals in them.

▶ **Where in the United States are there forest soils?**

**Desert soil.** The western part of the United States is very dry. Few plants can grow in areas this dry. Because it doesn't rain much, minerals do not leach out of the top layer of soil. Therefore, the top layer remains rich in minerals. However, deserts don't really have a topsoil. This is because the top layer of soil in a <u>desert</u> lacks humus.

▶ **Why do only a few kinds of plants grow in a desert soil?**

Vegetation is sparce on this pine forest floor because the trees block out the sun's light.

Tundra vegetation at the base of Mt. McKinley in Alaska.

**Grassland soil.** The flat states in the midwest part of the United States get enough rainfall to support the growth of many kinds of plants, but not enough to support trees. This region is covered by grassland soils. The topsoil there is thick, black, and rich in humus. Our main farm products grow in these fertile soils.

▶ **What is the topsoil like in grassland soils?**

**Tundra soil.** Northern parts of Alaska and Canada have very cold climates. This region is called the tundra (TUN-druh). Most of the time the ground is frozen. Weathering takes place very slowly. The A and B horizons are very thin. Any plants that survive this climate have very shallow roots. Mosses and lichens (LY-kuns) are plants with shallow roots that grow in tundra soil.

▶ **How thick is the tundra soil?**

## WHAT YOU LEARNED

1. Soils are described according to the amount of humus and amount and types of minerals in the upper horizons.
2. The amount of rainfall plays an important role in making one soil different from another.
3. Types of soils found in the United States include forest soil, desert soil, grassland soil, and tundra soil.

## SCIENCE WORDS

**forest soil**
soil with a thin topsoil but in a climate wet enough to support the growth of trees

**desert soil**
soil in a dry region rich in minerals but lacking humus

**grassland soil**
soil with rich topsoil and enough rainfall to support the growth of many kinds of plants

**tundra** (TUN-druh)
soil in a cold climate with thin A and B horizons

**leaching** (LEECH-ing)
the movement of minerals downward away from the topsoil

## ANSWER THESE

1. When few plants are growing on the floor of a forest, it is because there is a lack of
   **a.** water  **b.** sunlight  **c.** a subsoil
2. There is practically no leaching in
   **a.** forest soils  **b.** grassland soils  **c.** desert soils
3. The thickest, richest topsoil is found in
   **a.** forest soil  **b.** grassland soil  **c.** desert soil
4. The type of soil found in northern Alaska is
   **a.** forest soil  **b.** tundra soil  **c.** desert soil

## NOW TRY THIS

Name the types of soil that best fit the descriptions below.

1. Found in the eastern United States
2. Having a top layer rich in minerals but lacking humus
3. Best for growing many kinds of plants
4. Frozen most of the time
5. Found in the states in the Midwest
6. Supporting the growth of mosses and lichens
7. Supporting the growth of trees but few plants
8. Found in a very dry region

# What are some chemicals in the soil?

**A fertilizer used for roses.** The 8 10 4 on the bag means that the fertilizer contains 8% nitrogen, 10% phosphorus, and 4% potassium.

**Chemicals in the soil.** Most plants need certain chemical elements for proper growth. Some of these elements are needed in larger amounts than the rest. Plants need large amounts of the elements carbon and oxygen. Carbon dioxide from the air supplies these elements. Hydrogen and nitrogen are other elements needed in large amounts. Plants take hydrogen from the water in the soil. Nitrogen comes from the organic matter in the soil. The remaining elements that plants need are found in the minerals in the soil. The soil and the air contain all the chemical elements that plants need for growth.

▶ **Where do plants get the elements they need?**

| ELEMENTS MOST PLANTS NEED FOR PROPER GROWTH |
|---|
| Elements Needed in Large Amounts |

| | | | |
|---|---|---|---|
| carbon | oxygen | hydrogen | nitrogen |
| phosphorus | potassium | magnesium | sulfur |
| | calcium | | |

| Elements Needed in Small Amounts |
|---|

| | | | |
|---|---|---|---|
| copper | chlorine | sodium | zinc |
| molybdenum | vanadium | manganese | cobalt |
| | iron | boron | |

**Taking chemicals from the soil.** Small amounts of materials in the soil dissolve in soil water. Soil water and its dissolved substances are taken in by plant roots. Both plants and leaching remove chemicals from the soil. These substances must be put back into the soil for good plant growth. Nature has a way of replacing leached chemicals. But nature works slowly. Fertilizers contain the chemicals plants need. Fertilizers are added to soil to replace these chemicals faster.

▶ **What is used to replace chemicals taken from the soil?**

**Organic fertilizers.** Natural, or organic, fertilizers come from the decay of dead animal and plant matter. They also come from animal wastes, or manure (muh-NYOOR). In fact, manure itself is an organic fertilizer. Organisms in manure can carry nitrogen compounds in manure to the soil. Dried blood, bone meal, and dead plants are other sources of the chemicals that make up organic fertilizers. The roots of certain plants, such as clover and legumes (LEG-yooms), add nitrogen to the soil. Legumes are plants like peas and beans. Farmers put this nitrogen into the soil by growing clover and legumes, and plowing the plants into the soil. Organic fertilizers contain chemicals needed for plant growth. They also help soils absorb moisture.

▶ **What are some sources of the chemicals in organic fertilizers?**

**Chemical fertilizers.** <u>Chemical</u> <u>fertilizers</u> do not come from the decay of things that were once living. Instead, the chemicals are taken from the ground and are usually treated in some way before being used as fertilizers. Fertilizers, both organic and chemical, are especially important for adding to the soil the elements that are removed fastest. These elements are nitrogen, phosphorus, and potassium. Chemical fertilizers often contain the compound ammonium nitrate as a source of nitrogen. They contain ammonium phosphate as a source of phosphorus. Potash is a source of potassium. Look at the picture of the rose fertilizer. The numbers 8-10-4 on the bag tell the percent of each element in the fertilizer. This fertilizer has 8% nitrogen, 10% phosphorus, and 4% potassium.

▶ **What compound do fertilizers contain as a source of nitrogen?**

## WHAT YOU LEARNED

1. Plants need carbon dioxide water, and minerals from the soil.
2. Organic fertilizers come from the decay of dead animal and plant matter.
3. The chemicals in chemical fertilizers come from the ground and are usually treated before being used as fertilizers.
4. The elements nitrogen, phosphorus, and potassium are removed from the soil quickly by growing things.

## SCIENCE WORDS

**manure** (muh-NYOOR)
   waste from animals

**organic** (or-GAN-ik) **fertilizers**
   fertilizers from the decay of dead animal and plant life

**chemical fertilizers**
   chemicals that come from the ground and are usually treated before being used as fertilizers

## ANSWER THESE

1. Most of the elements needed for plant growth come from
   **a.** the air    **b.** water    **c.** the soil
2. During leaching, the minerals in the topsoil
   **a.** move downward
   **b.** are put back with fertilizer
   **c.** grow upward
3. Minerals may be put back into the soil by adding
   **a.** bromthymol blue
   **b.** fertilizers
   **c.** water
4. Organic fertilizers come from
   **a.** chemicals
   **b.** decay of dead things
   **c.** the air
5. Which element comes from the addition of potash in the soil?
   **a.** nitrogen    **b.** phosphorus    **c.** potassium

## NOW TRY THIS

Solve the puzzles to find the names of three elements that are found in chemical fertilizers to help plants grow.

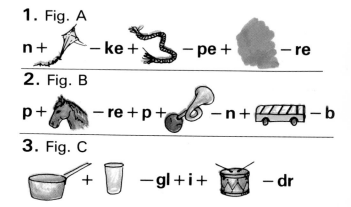

**1.** Fig. A

n + [kite] − ke + [snake] − pe + [cloud] − re

**2.** Fig. B

p + [horse] − re + p + [ball] − n + [bus] − b

**3.** Fig. C

[pan] + [glass] − gl + i + [drum] − dr

## FINDING OUT MORE

**Adding fertilizer to your garden.** Grass and trees remove many elements from your garden soil. Many gardeners save the grass cuttings and dead leaves. They are kept in a pile called compost (KOM-post). The compost pile is left standing for almost a year. It becomes organic fertilizer, which is then added back to the soil. Compost recycles elements in your garden soil.

# What are basic and acidic soils?

Pine trees and other evergreens grow best in an acidic soil. Grasses grow best in a basic soil.

**Acidic, basic, and neutral.** Some soils have a great deal of the elements calcium, magnesium, sodium, and potassium. These elements form compounds called bases. Soils with these compounds are called basic (BAYS-ik) soils. Leaching can remove chemicals that make a soil basic. An acidic (uh-SID-ik) soil is formed when most of the basic elements are removed. An acidic soil is the opposite of a basic soil. A soil that is neither acidic nor basic is called neutral (NOO-trul).

▶ What is a basic soil?

**Different soils, different plants.** Certain plants grow well in basic soils. Grasses are an example. Other plants grow well in acidic soils. Pine trees and other evergreens are examples. Farmers often call a basic soil a sweet soil. An acidic soil is called a sour soil. Some types of fertilizers make soils basic. Farmers add lime to soils to keep them basic. Lime is calcium carbonate. It is the calcium in the calcium carbonate that makes the soil basic. Other elements, such as iron, make soils acidic.

▶ Which plants grow best in acidic soils?

**Testing the acidity of soils.** Chemical indicators (IN-dih-kay-ters) can be used to tell if a soil is acidic or basic. Chemical indicators have different colors in acidic and basic soils.

Take small samples of soil from different places. A half teaspoon of soil is enough for each sample. Make a funnel out of a filter paper. Place one of the samples into the funnel. Make a tiny pinhole at the bottom of the funnel. Set the funnel on top of a test tube. Add the liquid called bromthymol (BROHM-THY-mole) blue to the soil drop by drop. Stop when the liquid drips through the funnel into the test tube. Record the color of the liquid dripping into the test tube. Repeat the test with the other samples of soil.

Bromthymol blue is a chemical indicator. It turns yellow when it passes through an acidic soil. It turns blue when it passes through a basic soil. It turns greenish-blue when it passes through a neutral soil. Record which of your samples were acidic, which were basic, and which were neutral.

▶ What effect does an acidic soil have on bromthymol blue?

TESTING THE ACIDITY OF A SAMPLE OF SOIL

BROMTHYMOL BLUE

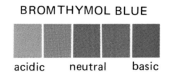

acidic    neutral    basic

**How basic or acidic is the soil?** A number can be used to tell how strongly acidic or basic a solution is. The number is called the pH of the solution. The pH of a solution usually falls between 0 and 14. A pH of 7 means a solution is neutral. A pH greater than 7 means the solution is basic. The higher the number, the more basic. For example, a pH of 10 is more strongly basic than a pH of 8. When a solution's pH is less than 7, the solution is acidic. The smaller the pH, the more strongly acidic. The acidity of a soil can be checked quickly with an instrument called a pH meter.

▶ What kind of soil has a pH of 8?

## WHAT YOU LEARNED

1. Soils may be acidic, basic, or neutral.
2. Some plants need an acidic soil to grow best, while others need a basic soil.
3. A soil can be tested to see how acidic or basic it is.
4. The pH of a soil is a number that tells how basic or acidic the soil is.

## SCIENCE WORDS

**basic** (BAYS-ik) **soil**
 a sweet soil; one having a great deal of the elements calcium, magnesium, sodium, or potassium

**acidic** (uh-SID-ik) **soil**
 a sour soil; one lacking the elements that make a soil basic

**neutral** (NOO-trul) **soil**
 a soil that is neither acidic or basic

## ANSWER THESE

1. Basic soils are sometimes called
   a. sweet
   b. sour
   c. neutral

2. Large amounts of elements such as calcium, magnesium, sodium, and potassium make a soil
   a. acidic
   b. basic
   c. neutral
3. Grasses grow best in soils that are slightly
   a. acidic
   b. basic
   c. neutral
4. Soils rich in iron tend to be
   a. acidic
   b. basic
   c. neutral
5. We can tell if a soil is basic or acidic by
   a. tasting it
   b. touching it
   c. testing it with an indicator

## NOW TRY THIS

Are the following soils basic, acidic, or neutral?

1. has a pH of 7
2. turns bromthymol blue yellow
3. called a sour soil
4. neither a sour or sweet soil
5. soil after leaching has taken place
6. pine trees grow well in this soil
7. bromthymol blue turns a greenish-blue when passed through this soil
8. opposite of sour soil
9. reads 5 on the pH meter
10. soil after lime has been added to it

## FINDING OUT MORE

**Additional information on classified soils.** A great deal of leaching takes place in forest soils. Forest soils are highly acidic. Lack of rainfall limits leaching in desert soils. Desert soils are basic. Farmers are constantly adding chemicals to their soils. These chemicals allow their crops to grow better.

THE pH ACIDITY SCALE

0 1 2 3 4 5 6 7 8 9 10 11 12 13 14

strongly acidic    weakly acidic    weakly basic    strongly basic

◄ acidic    basic ►

neutral

# What life is found in the soil?

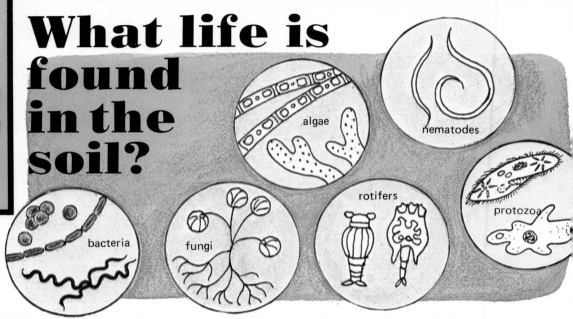

algae

nematodes

rotifers

protozoa

bacteria

fungi

**Who lives there?** There are many living things in soil. Many are too small to be seen by the naked eye. Bacteria, protozoa (PRO-tuh-zo-uh), and fungi (FUN-ji) are examples of microscopic life in the soil. The soil also contains larger forms of life, such as worms, mites, spiders, slugs, and insects. Larger animals, such as muskrats and some types of rats and mice, also make their homes in the soil.

▶ What are some animals found in soil?

**Bacteria and fungi fertilize the soil.** The remains of dead plants and animals rest in the top layer of soil. Bacteria and fungi feed on these remains. Their feeding causes dead things to rot and decay. Humus formed from decayed plant and animal material makes the soil richer. Humus is found mostly in topsoil.

▶ How do bacteria and fungi make the soil richer?

**Free nitrogen.** Nitrogen may be in a compound with one or more other elements. When in a compound, nitrogen is called combined nitrogen. Nitrogen can also exist without being combined with other elements. Then it is called free nitrogen. The nitrogen in the air is free nitrogen.

▶ What is free nitrogen?

**Out of the air, into the soil.** Plants need nitrogen to live. Most plants can not use free nitrogen. They need nitrogen in its combined form. Free nitrogen must be changed into combined nitrogen. Some soil bacteria can change free nitrogen into combined nitrogen. These bacteria are called nitrogen-fixing bacteria.

Nitrogen-fixing bacteria live in bumps on the roots of certain plants. These bumps are called nodules (NOJ-ools). Legumes (LEG-yooms) are one kind of plant that have nodules on their roots. Clover, peas, soybeans, and alfalfa are examples of legumes. Legumes help change free nitrogen in air to combined nitrogen in the soil.

▶ Why is nitrogen in the air of no use to plants?

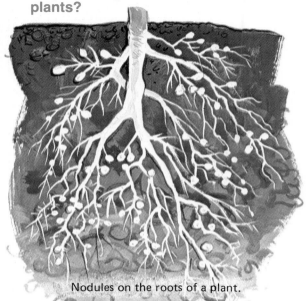

Nodules on the roots of a plant.

**Soil animals.** Spiders, mites, slugs, and insects help cause decay. They feed on smaller animals and dead plants. They begin the production of humus. Some worms and insects make tunnels in the soil. These tunnels add spaces between the particles of soil. They allow air and water to move freely through the soil. Waste materials from soil animals also help make soil more fertile.

▶ How does the earthworm help the soil?

## WHAT YOU LEARNED

1. Many things live within the soil.
2. Humus is formed when bacteria and fungi cause dead things to rot.
3. Nitrogen-fixing bacteria change free nitrogen into combined nitrogen.
4. Soil animals make spaces in the soil for air and water.

## SCIENCE WORDS

**combined nitrogen**
 nitrogen combined chemically with other elements

**free nitrogen**
 nitrogen that is not combined with other elements

**nitrogen-fixing bacteria**
 bacteria that are able to change free nitrogen to combined nitrogen

## ANSWER THESE

1. Humus is found mostly
    a. buried deep in the soil
    b. in the topsoil
    c. in the bedrock
2. Bacteria and fungi cause dead things in the soil to
    a. explode
    b. fix nitrogen
    c. decay
3. Nitrogen in a compound is called
    a. compound nitrogen
    b. free nitrogen
    c. combined nitrogen
4. An example of a legume is the
    a. soybean
    b. tomato
    c. pepper

## FINDING OUT MORE

Soils have different colors. Some are black, others brown, and still others are gray or white. Humus gives color to a soil. Humus is black. It makes soils darker. Soils with little humus are usually light in color. Desert soils are often white or gray.

# UNIT 4 Review

*Do the following review questions on a separate sheet of paper.*

**Modified True/False**    *Write down each of the following statements, leaving a blank line between each line you write. Before the number for each statement, write T if the statement is true and F if the statement is false. For the false statements, cross out the word written in capital letters and write above it a word that will make the statement true.*

1. Combined nitrogen is nitrogen combined CHEMICALLY with other elements.
2. A soil containing a great deal of calcium is a(n) ACIDIC soil.
3. Fertilizers from the decay of dead animals and plants are ORGANIC fertilizers.
4. A TUNDRA soil is a soil in a dry region, rich in minerals, but lacking humus.
5. An immature soil is an OLDER soil, lacking a subsoil.
6. COARSE soils are made up of large particles.
7. Bedrock is solid rock that lies OVER the soil.
8. The more water, the SLOWER the weathering.
9. Hydration is the CHEMICAL reaction between water and other substances.
10. A PHYSICAL changes does not change the properties of a substance.

**Multiple Choice**    *Write the letter of the choice that best completes the statement or answers the question.*

1. The breaking of a rock
   a. is a chemical change
   b. makes a new substance
   c. is a physical change
2. Frost action is an example of
   a. winter snowstorms
   b. chemical weathering
   c. mechanical weathering
3. Hydration causes the minerals in a rock to
   a. swell up and crumble
   b. stay where they are
   c. solidify
4. Humus is formed from
   a. large pebbles and boulders
   b. decaying remains of animals and plants
   c. tiny particles of dust and sand

5. Plants do not grow well in compacted soil because
   a. water cannot seep into the soil
   b. compacted soil is often poisonous
   c. it is too rocky
6. An older soil, having all three horizons, is called
   a. a mature soil
   b. a parent soil
   c. an ancient soil
7. Leaching in soils is the movement of minerals
   a. upward from the bedrock
   b. from the soil into the roots of trees
   c. downward from the topsoil
8. Nitrogen-fixing bacteria live
   a. in bumps on the roots of some plants
   b. in cracks in the bedrock
   c. in the leaves of some trees

94

# UNIT 5

# Agents of Erosion

## Unit Lessons

1. How does running water wear away the earth's surface?
2. How does a river move rocks?
3. What land shapes are produced by running water?
4. How can you tell the age of a river?
5. How does moving ice change the surface of the earth?
6. What is an ice age?
7. How do winds change the earth's surface?
8. How do waves erode the land?
9. What shoreline features are produced by wave erosion?
10. What shoreline features are built up by waves?
11. What happens to the eroded material from the land?
12. What helps to prevent erosion?

## Goals and Objectives

After completing this unit, you should be able to:
- describe how running water causes the erosion of some landforms and the deposition of others.
- explain how glaciers change the face of the earth.
- understand how winds may move particles of earth, changing the land.
- describe how the action of waves on the shoreline changes the shoreline.
- explain how a lot of eroded material ends up in the ocean and how we can slow down this erosion.

# How does running water wear away the earth's surface?

**Where does rain water go?** What happens to the rain that falls on the earth? Some rain that falls to the earth evaporates. It goes back into the air as water vapor. Some rain water sinks into the ground. The rest of the rain becomes <u>runoff</u> (RUN-off). Runoff is water that runs over the ground. It passes into streams, rivers, lakes, or oceans. It may also flow over another path. It may first fall onto city streets. It will then flow into sewer pipes. Finally, it will pass from sewer pipes into streams, rivers, lakes, or oceans.

▶ **Where can you see runoff?**

What happens to rain water? It . . .

. . . evaporates. . .

sinks into the ground . . .

. . runs over the land . . .

falls into sewer systems.

**Moving water can break rocks.** Water that is moving can make pieces of sand and gravel hit against each other. What happens when these pieces hit each other? Place some pieces of plaster and some pebbles in a jar of water. Cover the jar and shake it. What happens? The pieces of plaster break into smaller pieces. Some of the pebbles may also break. Moving water can help break rocks into smaller and smaller pieces. The breaking up of rocks by other moving rocks is called <u>abrasion</u> (uh-BRAY-zhun).

▶ **What is abrasion?**

**Water can move rocks.** Throw some chalk dust into running water. What happens? Some of the chalk dust is carried along by the water. If the water is moving fast, it can carry sand along, or even pebbles and stones. Running water doesn't only break up rocks. It also carries the pieces away. Breaking up rock and carrying it from one place to another is called <u>erosion</u> (eh-ROH-zhun). Running water can cause erosion.

▶ **What is erosion?**

**WHAT YOU LEARNED**

1. Rain that runs over the ground is called runoff.
2. Runoff finally finds its way into streams, rivers, lakes, or oceans.
3. Moving water can help break rocks into smaller and smaller pieces.
4. Running water can cause erosion.

**SCIENCE WORDS**

**runoff** (RUN-off)
  water that runs over the ground
**abrasion** (uh-BRAY-zhun)
  the wearing away of rocks by rubbing and hitting
**erosion** (eh-ROH-zhun)
  the breaking up and carrying away of materials in the earth's crust

**ANSWER THESE**

1. Where do rivers and streams get their water?
2. How does running water cause abrasion?
3. How does running water cause erosion?

**NOW TRY THESE**
In the following puzzles, there is part of a letter in each box. You can make the whole letter by adding one line. For example,

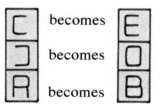

Copy each puzzle onto a piece of paper. Add a line in each box to make letters that spell science words you learned.

1. Breaking up rocks.

2. Breaking up and carrying away materials in the earth's crust.

**FINDING OUT MORE**
Small streams of water come rushing down mountains and hillsides. In the spring, snow melts and more water flows into these streams. The small streams empty into small rivers. Some rivers overflow and cause flooding. Trees on the hillsides and along the river banks can slow down the flow of water across the land. Roots of trees and other plants help prevent soil from being washed away. Many farmers used to clear all the trees from their land. This was a mistake. The rains sometimes caused a flood that removed the topsoil. Today trees are planted on the land to prevent erosion of the soil. This is called soil conservation (CON-ser-VAY-shun).

# How does a river move rocks?

source or head

banks

bed (path along the bottom)

mouth

ocean, lake, or bay

DESCRIBING A RIVER

**Describing a river.** There are many ways to describe a river. The place where a river starts is called its <u>source</u> (SORSS) or head. The bottom of a river is called its <u>bed</u>. The sides of a river are called its <u>banks</u>. The place where a river ends is called its <u>mouth</u>. The waters of some rivers flow slowly. The waters of other rivers are fast-moving. The water's speed changes along a river's path. The water often flows quickly at its head, and slowly at its mouth.

Rivers have different sizes. Some rivers are wide and shallow. Others are deep and narrow. Some rivers carry a great deal of water. Others carry only a little.

▶ **What are some ways of describing a river?**

The fast-moving water in this river is carrying with it a large amount of mud.

**Rolling down a river.** Place a book on a desk or table. Raise one end of the book about 2 centimeters. Place a marble on the raised end. Let the marble roll down the book. Now raise the end of the book higher. Again allow the marble to roll down the book. Watch how fast the marble rolls down. With a steeper slope, the marble rolls down faster.

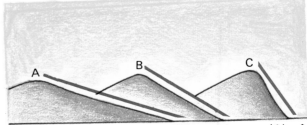

The sides of mountains have different slopes. (A) A mountain with a gentle slope. (B) A steeper slope. (C) A very steep slope. Where the slope of a river bed is steep, the current will be swift.

Water in a river acts the same way. The water in a river flows downhill. Where the slope is steep, the water moves faster. Faster-flowing water erodes the land more quickly than slow water.

▶ How does the slope of the land affect the speed of a river?

**Swelling rivers.** Heavy rains add more water to a river. So do melting ice and snow. Go to the sink and turn on the water slightly. Note the speed of the water. Now open the faucet a little more. More water flows out. It also flows out more quickly. As more water is added to a river, it flows faster. During floods, rivers move along at greater speeds.

▶ What happens to a river's speed as more water enters it?

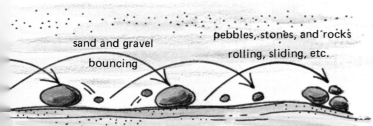

Sand and gravel often bounce along a river's bed. Larger stones and rocks may roll and slide in the direction of the moving water.

**Rolling stones.** Weathering breaks rocks into bits and pieces of different sizes. Rain water runs off over the land. It washes bits of weathered rock and soil into a river. This makes the water muddy. Small bits of mud are carried downstream by the river. Rocks roll down the sides of a river bed. They fall into the water. They are too heavy to be carried in the river like mud. But rushing water makes them roll along the bottom. Sand and pebbles also move downstream with the river. The faster a river flows, the more material it can move.

▶ How can a river move stones and pebbles?

## WHAT YOU LEARNED

1. Water travels fastest in rivers with steep-sloping beds.
2. As more water is added to a river, the river flows more quickly.
3. The faster a river moves, the more rock material it can carry downstream.

## SCIENCE WORDS

**source** (SORSS)
a river's head or place where the river starts
**bed**
the bottom of a river
**banks**
the sides of a river
**mouth**
the place where a river ends

## ANSWER THESE

1. A river empties into the ocean at its
    a. head
    b. source
    c. mouth
2. As the slope of the land gets steeper, the speed of a river will
    a. decrease
    b. increase
    c. remain the same
3. As less water enters a river, the river flows
    a. faster
    b. slower
    c. at the same speed
4. Larger rocks are moved by a river as its speed
    a. increases
    b. decreases
    c. remains the same

## NOW TRY THESE

1. Why might the same river flow quickly at its head and slowly at its mouth?
2. Why do rivers flow faster during floods?
3. Explain why rivers erode the land faster where the slope is steeper.

# What land shapes are produced by running water?

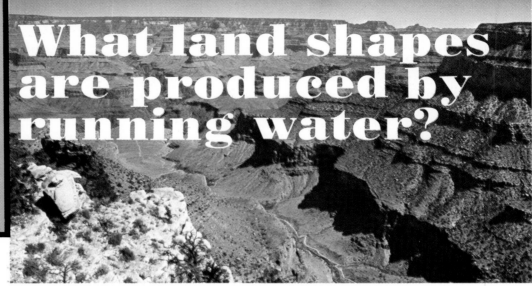

The Grand Canyon, Arizona.

**Down in the valley.** The bed of a river is usually solid rock. Pieces of rock bounce and roll along the bed of a fast-moving river. These pieces scrape the bed as they move along. Gradually, the bed is cut deeper into the land. A valley is formed. A fast-moving river may cut a very deep valley. Deep, steep-sided valleys are called canyons (KAN-yuns), gorges (GOR-jez), glens (GLENS), ravines (ruh-VEENS), or chasms (KAZMS). Over thousands of years the swift-moving Colorado River has eroded its bed. It has produced the Grand Canyon. In some places, the canyon is more than 1 kilometer deep.

▶ **What are some names for a deep-sided valley?**

**Rapids and waterfalls.** River beds are made of different rocks and minerals. Softer rocks are eroded faster than harder ones. Some parts of the river bed erode faster than others. The slope of the bed becomes steeper as the soft rock wears away. Water rushing along these steep slopes forms rapids. Waterfalls form where the steep slopes drop straight down. In time the steep slopes wear down. The rapids and waterfalls will be gone.

▶ **What happens to a river bed where the rock is softer?**

**Leveling off.** As a river bed wears down, its slope becomes flatter. The river slows down. It cannot move large rocks. It does not cut into its bed as fast as before. Instead, the river wears away its banks. The river becomes wider. It does not flow straight. It begins to flow in a wavy path. We say that the river meanders (mee-AN-ders). The river valley gradually becomes wider and flatter as the river meanders from side to side.

▶ **When does a river begin to form a wide valley?**

Niagara Falls

A meandering river is sometimes said to snake along. Do you see why?

**Slowing down.** A river slows down when its bed becomes flatter. The slow-moving water cannot move large stones and pebbles. They collect along the bed and banks of the river. This is called <u>deposition</u> (dep-uh-ZISH-un). Pieces of rock are being deposited (dih-POZ-ih-ted) by the river. As the river gets closer to its mouth, it may slow down even more. It begins to deposit smaller bits of rock, such as gravel and sand. Finally, the river reaches its mouth. Here the water is moving very slowly. Even the bits of mud in the water settle out. The mud collects at the river's mouth. This mud often forms a triangle of muddy land. This is called a <u>delta</u> (DELL-tuh). Delta is the name of a letter in the Greek alphabet. It looks like a small triangle.

▶ Where does a delta form?

ocean or other large body of water

**A delta at the mouth of a river.** The delta, shown within the dashed area, is mud that was carried down the river.

## WHAT YOU LEARNED

1. A fast-moving river may cut a deep valley.
2. Rapids and waterfalls are found where soft rock wears away.
3. A slow-moving river erodes its banks.
4. Erosion of the banks produces meandering.

5. As river water begins to slow down, it deposits large pieces of rock.
6. Where river water is flowing slowly, small pieces of rock settle out.

## SCIENCE WORDS

**meander** (mee-AN-der)
flow in a wavy path
**deposition** (dep-uh-ZISH-un)
the settling of rock material where the water in a river is slowing down
**delta** (DELL-tuh)
a mud deposit found at the mouths of some rivers

## ANSWER THESE

1. Valleys are formed when a swiftly flowing river erodes its
   a. bed
   b. banks
   c. rapids
2. A valley becomes wider when a river erodes its
   a. bed
   b. banks
   c. rapids
3. In time all waterfalls
   a. become higher
   b. become bigger
   c. disappear
4. As a river slows down, its path
   a. becomes straighter
   b. meanders
   c. becomes deeper
5. As a river slows down, the rock material carried by the water
   a. is deposited
   b. is eroded
   c. meanders

## DO THIS AT HOME

Place some pebbles, sand, and clay into a tall bottle of water. Cover the bottle and shake it up. Put the bottle down and watch the mixture settle. Do all the particles settle out at the same time? The heavier pebbles settle first, and then the sand. The clay takes the longest to settle. When a river slows down, its particles settle out of the water in the same order.

# How can you tell the age of a river?

The Niagara River is a young river, as indicated by its steep sides and fast-moving water.

**Life cycle.** Would you describe the person who delivers your mail as young, middle-aged, or old? The words *young, mature,* and *old* are used to describe their ages. Rivers have different ages, too. If you know what to look for, you can tell whether a river is young or old.

▶ What words are used to describe the age of a river?

**Youth.** The slope of a young river is steep. The water moves fast. The path of the river is fairly straight. Rapids and waterfalls appear along the way. Most of the erosion takes place at the bed of a young river. The fast-moving water forms very steep, narrow valley. Rivers flowing into other rivers are called tributaries (TRIB-yoo-ter-eez). Young rivers have few tributaries. The Colorado and Niagara (ny-AG-ruh) Rivers are examples of young rivers.

▶ What are the speed and path of a young river?

**Maturity.** As a young river becomes a mature river, its slope becomes less steep. Its waters slow down. It winds back and forth in loops called meanders (mee-ANN-ders). The rapids and waterfalls found in young rivers disappear. The mature river erodes its banks faster than its bed. It becomes wider, not deeper. Many tributaries flow into a mature river. These tributaries carry a great deal of eroded topsoil. Particles of soil and weathered rock carried by a river are called sediment (SED-uh-ment). The mature river is loaded with sediment.

At flood time, the moving water of the mature river carries much topsoil with it. The muddy water overflows its banks. When the water returns to the river, topsoil is left behind. Rich topsoil deposited alongside the river is called a flood plain. Flood plains have fertile soils.

The Missouri, Mohawk, and Ohio Rivers are mature rivers.

▶ Where does a flood plain form?

**Old age.** The slope of the bed of an old river is nearly flat. The river barely keeps flowing. Instead of tributaries flowing into the river, distributaries (dih-STRIB-voo-ter-eez) flow out. Parts of meanders become cut off from the main river. These parts form lakes shaped like a "C" and called oxbow lakes. The water

The Mississippi is a mature river.

Meanders and oxbow lakes are characteristics of an old river.

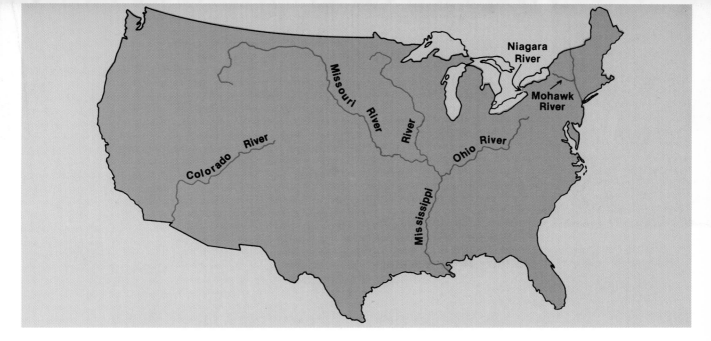

moves too slowly for erosion to take place. New sediment is deposited. Deltas form at the mouths of old rivers.

▶ **How much erosion takes place in old rivers?**

## WHAT YOU LEARNED

1. Rivers can be described as young, mature, or old.
2. Young rivers flow quickly and erode their beds.
3. Mature rivers flow slowly and erode their banks.
4. In old rivers, soil is mostly deposited in the river rather than eroded from it.

## SCIENCE WORDS

**tributaries** (TRIB-yoo-ter-eez)
   smaller rivers that flow into a larger river

**sediment** (SED-uh-ment)
   soil and other matter that has settled to the bottom of a river

**flood plain**
   an area alongside a river where soil is deposited during flooding

**meanders** (mee-ANN-ders)
   curved loops in a river

**distributaries** (dih-STRIB-yoo-ter-eez)
   smaller rivers that flow out of another river

**oxbow lake**
   a lake formed from what was once a section of a meandering river

## ANSWER THESE

Use the letters
   A — for a young river
   B — for a mature river
   C — for an old river
to tell which kind of a river each of the following statements refers to.

1. flows quickly
2. has meanders
3. hardly moves
4. has a slope that is not very steep
5. has a very steep slope
6. has hardly any slope at all
7. erodes its banks
8. has many tributaries
9. Colorado River
10. erodes its bed
11. has rapids and waterfalls
12. Missouri River
13. has steep, deep valleys
14. has few tributaries
15. has flood plains
16. forms a delta
17. has a fairly straight path
18. has oxbow lakes alongside
19. has wide river valleys
20. barely keeps flowing

# How does moving ice change the surface of the earth?

**Rivers of ice.** In the winter, snow piles up on the ground. In the spring, the snow melts. Near the tops of many mountains the air is cold all the time. The snow does not melt there in the spring or summer. More snow falls on top of the snow already on the mountains. The snow gets deeper and deeper. In some places it may be more than a kilometer deep. The snow at the bottom of the pile turns to ice. The weight of all this snow causes the ice to move. Very slowly, the snow and ice move downhill. This moving river of ice and snow is called a glacier (GLAY-sher).

▶ **What is a glacier?**

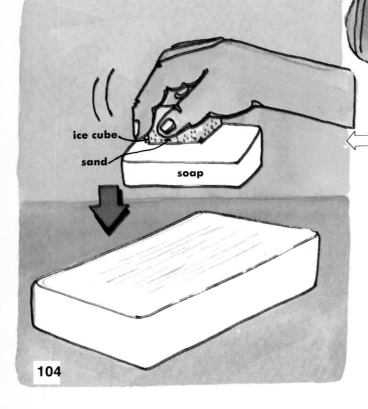

ice cube

sand

soap

**Glaciers cause erosion.** Press an ice cube into some sand. Then move the ice cube over a piece of soap: The sand frozen into the ice scratches the soap. A glacier scratches and scrapes the ground in the same way. Sand, gravel, and pieces of rock become frozen into the bottom of the glacier. As the glacier moves, it scratches the rock over which it moves. It breaks up the rock and carries these pieces along, too.

▶ **How does a glacier erode the land?**

**Glaciers make hills.** It is warmer near the bottom of a mountain than near the top. As the moving ice comes down the mountain, it begins to melt around the edges. The water runs off. But the sand, gravel, and rocks that were in the ice are left behind. This loose material from the melting glacier gradually piles up. It forms a long, low hill called a moraine (mor-AIN). A hill of sand, gravel, and loose rock at the front edge of a melting glacier is called a terminal (TUR-muh-nul) moraine.

▶ What is a terminal moraine made of?

A TERMINAL MORAINE

GLACIER

TERMINAL MORAINE

**U.S. Navy icebreakers clearing passage for ships.**

## WHAT YOU LEARNED

1. A glacier is a moving river of ice and snow.
2. A glacier erodes the earth's surface over which it moves.
3. A glacier moves loose rocks and pebbles along with it.
4. When a glacier melts, it leaves a hill of loose material called a moraine.

## SCIENCE WORDS

**glacier** (GLAY-sher)
   a moving river of ice and snow
**moraine** (mor-AIN)
   a long hill made of loose material carried and then left by a glacier
**terminal** (TUR-muh-nul) **moraine**
   a long hill of loose material formed at the front end of a glacier

## ANSWER THESE

1. What is a glacier made of?
2. What material found in a glacier wears away the land?
3. What do we call a hill of loose material along the front edge of a glacier?

## NOW TRY THESE

Unscramble the words.
1. A glacier is made of C E I and W O N S.
2. A glacier will E R E D O the surface over which it moves.
3. A moraine is made up of R S O K C and S N D A and L E G A R V broken from the ground and left by a glacier.
4. A M I N T E R A L moraine is found at the end of a glacier.

## FINDING OUT MORE

⟷

In some lands of the north, glaciers reach the ocean. When a glacier reaches the ocean, a large piece of it may break off and float away in the water. This large piece of floating ice is called an iceberg. Most of the iceberg is below the surface of the water. Many ships have crashed into icebergs. To protect ships at sea, the Navy watches for icebergs and keeps track of where they are heading. If there is a danger to ships, the Navy uses explosives to destroy the icebergs.

# What is an ice age?

An erratic in Central Park, New York City.

**Delivery by ice.** Central Park is a large park in New York City. In the park there are many large rocks. These rocks are not like the bedrock below the park. They cannot be pieces of rock that broke away from the bedrock. They must have come from some other place. In fact, they are like the bedrock found hundreds of kilometers away. These rocks must have been carried to the park. They are too heavy to be moved by running water. There is only one way these rocks could have been moved. They must have been buried in a glacier. The ice moved and brought the rocks with it. When the ice melted, the rocks were left behind. These rocks are called <u>erratics</u> (uh-RAT-iks).

▶ **What is the name of a large rock that has been moved by a glacier?**

**The cold summer.** In Central Park, summer temperatures now often go above 30°C. How could a glacier be found in so warm an area? Long ago the earth slowly got colder. As it got colder, the sheet of ice around the North Pole got larger. It finally got so large that it covered Canada and the northern United States. In places it was more than 1 kilometer thick. Such a large ice sheet is called a <u>continental</u> (kon-tuh-NEN-til) <u>glacier</u>. This period of great cold is called an ice age. There have been a number of ice ages. The last one ended about 11 000 years ago. The ice melted because the earth got warmer again. Today an ice sheet still covers Greenland. Another large mass of ice is at the South Pole. This region is called <u>Antarctica</u> (ant-ARK-tih-kuh).

▶ **When did the last ice age end?**

The edge of the ice sheet in Antarctica.

**Glacial lakes.** During the ice age, glaciers formed in river valleys. The glaciers scraped out the river valleys. They made them hundreds of meters deeper. As the climate became warmer, the ice melted. The river valleys filled with water from the melting ice. In this way the Great Lakes formed. The Finger Lakes of New York were also formed in this way. Lakes formed from glaciers are usually long and deep.

▶ **What can a glacier do to a river bed?**

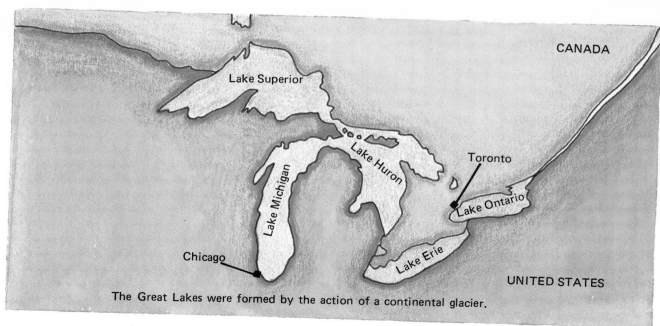

The Great Lakes were formed by the action of a continental glacier.

## WHAT YOU LEARNED

1. A large mass of ice brought large rocks to New York City from hundreds of kilometers away.
2. A continental glacier once covered Canada and the northern United States.
3. The last ice age ended about 11 000 years ago.
4. The Great Lakes were formed by the last ice-age glacier.

## SCIENCE WORDS

**erratics** (uh-RAT-iks)
   a rock carried a large distance by a glacier
**continental** (kon-tuh-NEN-til) **glacier**
   a sheet of ice large enough to cover a large part of a continent
**Antarctica** (ant-ARK-tih-kuh)
   region surrounding the South Pole, now covered by a continental glacier

## ANSWER THESE

1. Erratics can be found in
   a. New York City
   b. Miami, Florida
   c. Los Angeles, California
2. A continental glacier still covers
   a. Canada
   b. Alaska
   c. Greenland

3. An example of a lake formed by a glacier is
   a. the Great Salt Lake
   b. Lake Michigan
   c. Lake Tahoe
4. Glacial lakes are usually
   a. long and wide
   b. long and deep
   c. round and wide

## PEOPLE IN SCIENCE

**Louis Agassiz** (1807-1873)
Louis Agassiz was a Swiss scientist who studied glaciers. He was the first person to discover that a glacier moves faster in the center than at its sides. He recorded where erratics could be found. These records helped him prove that an ice sheet once covered large areas of the land. He proved that there have been ice ages.

# How do winds change the earth's surface?

dry sand

wet sand

**Moving air.** Wind is moving air. The wind can move ships across oceans. The wind can move sand and soil across land. Make two small piles of sand. Add water to one pile. Then blow across the top of each pile. The pile of dry sand blew away, or eroded. Moisture kept the wet sand from moving. Wind erodes the land mostly in a dry region (REE-jun). Wind erosion can be seen easily in a dry, sandy region, or desert (DEZ-ert).

▶ **Where can you see wind erosion?**

**Land erosion.** Take a piece of sandpaper and rub it on a piece of wood. The pieces of sand on the sandpaper wear down the wood. You supply the energy that moves the sandpaper on the wood. The wind supplies the energy that moves sand over the land. The moving sand wears particles away from rocks. The wind carries the sand and broken rock particles over the land. The wind cannot lift the particles very high. It carries most of them close to the ground. Look at the picture of an eroded rock. The lower part of the rock has been eroded the most.

▶ **What parts of rocks are eroded most by the wind?**

**Hills of sand.** Wind may be blocked by a large pile of rocks or a hill. When something blocks the wind, it slows down. Then it cannot carry the particles of sand any longer. It drops the particles it is carrying. These particles build up. They form a hill of sand called a sand dune (DEWN).

wind

leeward side

windward side

A sand dune is formed by the wind

The sand dune has two sides. The side facing the wind has a gentle slope. This is called the windward (WIND-werd) side. The side away from the wind is called the leeward (LEE-werd) side of the sand dune. The leeward side has a steep slope. The shape of a sand dune can tell you the direction of the wind.

▶ **What can the shape of a sand dune tell you?**

## WHAT YOU LEARNED

1. In dry regions, sand moved by wind wears away the land.
2. A sand dune forms when something blocks the wind that carries the sand.

## SCIENCE WORDS

**region** (REE-jun)
a place or area
**desert** (DEZ-ert)
a very dry region
**sand dune** (DEWN)
a hill formed from sand
**windward** (WIND-werd) **side**
the side of a mountain or hill facing the wind
**leeward** (LEE-werd) **side**
the side of a mountain or hill away from the wind

## ANSWER THESE

1. What causes sand to move in dry regions?
2. Where does the wind erode rocks the most?
3. What are the two sides of a sand dune?

## NOW TRY THESE

1. Why are rocks placed around the bottom of telephone poles in the desert?
2. Why are small wooden fences placed at the back of beaches in the winter?

## WHAT'S HAPPENING

In the early 1930s, the midwest was hit by a "black blizzard." There was very little rainfall, and the land was dry. The topsoil was lifted and carried away by the wind. Dust darkened the sky each day. Roads were covered by soil and dust. People feared that their homes and cars would be buried. Plants help stop the wind from eroding the ground. Today trees are planted to cover the land and slow down the wind.

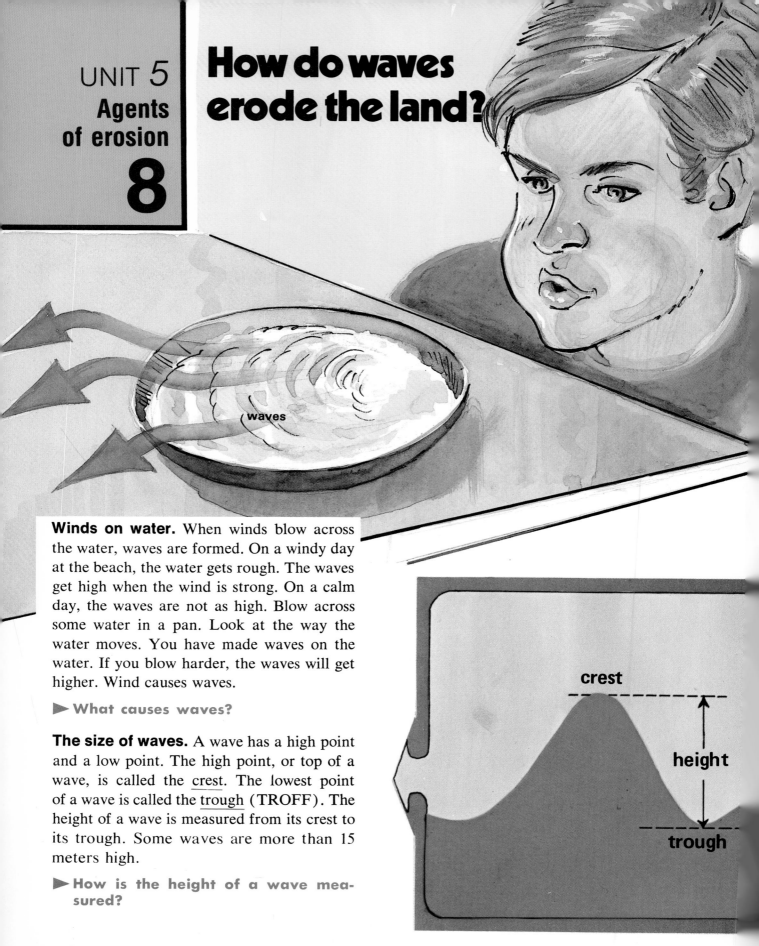

# How do waves erode the land?

waves

**Winds on water.** When winds blow across the water, waves are formed. On a windy day at the beach, the water gets rough. The waves get high when the wind is strong. On a calm day, the waves are not as high. Blow across some water in a pan. Look at the way the water moves. You have made waves on the water. If you blow harder, the waves will get higher. Wind causes waves.

► **What causes waves?**

**The size of waves.** A wave has a high point and a low point. The high point, or top of a wave, is called the <u>crest</u>. The lowest point of a wave is called the <u>trough</u> (TROFF). The height of a wave is measured from its crest to its trough. Some waves are more than 15 meters high.

► **How is the height of a wave measured?**

crest

height

trough

**Breaking waves.** The water at the shoreline is <u>shallow</u> (SHAL-oh) compared to the deeper water farther out. As a wave moves toward the shoreline, the trough touches the bottom of the shore. The wave breaks, and forms a <u>breaker</u> (BRAY-ker). The force of a breaker makes the water form white bubbles, or <u>foam</u> (FOHM). The foamy water of the breakers is called the <u>surf</u>.

▶ **What is the surf?**

**Erosion by waves.** The force of waves striking the shore can break up rocks. The pieces of rocks rub against other rocks. This abrasion (uh-BRAY-zhun) wears down the rocks and forms grains of sand. As the sand builds up, it forms a beach. The waves can erode the land by carrying the sand away.

▶ **How do waves change rocks into sand?**

## WHAT YOU LEARNED

1. Winds cause waves.
2. A wave is made up of a crest and a trough.
3. Waves hitting against the shore can cause land erosion.

## SCIENCE WORDS

**crest**
the top of a wave
**trough** (TROFF)
the bottom of a wave
**shallow** (SHAL-oh)
not deep
**breaker** (BRAY-ker)
tumbling water formed when a wave breaks

**foam** (FOHM)
bubbles formed on a liquid
**surf**
the foamy water made from breakers

## ANSWER THESE

1. Most waves are caused by
   a. people at the beach
   b. the wind
   c. big boats
2. The distance between a wave's crest and its trough is the wave's
   a. height
   b. length
   c. width
3. At the shoreline, waves break and form
   a. a wavelength
   b. sand dunes
   c. breakers

## NOW TRY THESE

Match the words in column A with the statements in column B.

| A | B |
|---|---|
| 1. wind | a. cause of breakers |
| 2. crest | b. wearing down by rubbing |
| 3. trough | c. cause of waves |
| 4. shallow water | d. bottom of a wave |
| 5. surf | e. top of a wave |
| 6. abrasion | f. foamy water |

## WHAT'S HAPPENING

A hurricane (HUR-uh-kane) is a very big storm. The winds sometimes blow at more than 150 kilometers per hour during a hurricane. Hurricanes form very high waves. These waves hit the land and wash it away. Open beaches are washed away the most. Almost every year, parts of the open beaches of Fire Island, New York, are washed away by storms. In 1900, more than 6 000 people drowned in Galveston, Texas, because of large hurricane waves. Today, lines of large rocks are built from the beaches into the ocean. These lines of rocks are called jetties (JET-tees). Jetties help keep the beaches from being eroded by wind and moving water.

# What shoreline features are produced by wave erosion?

**Shorelines are different.** Some shorelines are steep and rocky. Others are gentle and sandy. All shorelines are attacked by the force of waves. Water rushing forward throws sand against the land. Waves may wear back steep cliffs or carry sandy beaches into the sea. Waves change the shape of the shoreline. The different kinds of shapes of a shoreline are called shoreline features.

▶ **What changes the shape of a shoreline?**

**Steep and rocky.** On a rocky shore, waves pound against the bottom of the rocks. The bottoms begin to wear away. The tops of the rocks stick out beyond the bottoms. The overhanging tops finally split off and fall into the ocean. Steep-faced rocks called sea cliffs remain. In time, these cliffs are worn farther and farther inland.

Under the water, there are no pounding waves to wear away the rocks. A flat section of rock remains. This region is called a wave-cut terrace (TER-is).

▶ **What do the waves do to the rocks on a shoreline?**

**Some rocks resist erosion.** Very hard rocks may not wear away quickly. They stick out into the ocean. This bit of land is called a promontory (PRAHM-un-tor-ee).

At times only parts of a rock may be very hard. Waves cut deeply into the softer parts of the rock. The worn-away sections of the rock form sea caves. The caves are hollowed-out parts of sea cliffs.

Waves may cut all the way through a section of a promontory. A sea arch or natural bridge results. In time, the top of the arch falls into the sea. One side of the arch is left standing by itself. This tiny rock island is called a stack.

▶ **What is a promontory?**

A. Waves pound against rocky coast.

B. Part of rocky coast eaten away by waves.

C. As waves continue to eat rock away, part of the rock mass hangs out over the water.

D. Overhang breaks off and pieces are washed to sea, leaving a sea cliff and wave cut terrace.

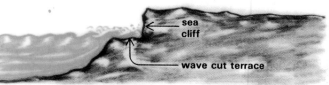

All of these unusual shoreline features were produced by wave erosion.

## WHAT YOU LEARNED

1. The action of waves changes the shape of a shoreline.
2. Steep sea cliffs are made when waves wear away the rocks on a shoreline.
3. Wave action moves a shoreline farther and farther back.
4. When a shoreline has both hard and soft rocks, wave action can produce promontories, sea caves, and sea arches.

## SCIENCE WORDS

**shoreline features**
the different shapes of a shoreline produced by wave action

**sea cliffs**
steep-faced rocks on a shoreline

**wave-cut terrace** (TER-is)
a flat section of rock remaining when the rock above was worn away by wave action

**promontory** (PRAHM-un-tor-ee)
a section of hard rock that sticks out into the ocean

**sea arch**
arch formed when waves cut through a promontory

**stack**
tiny rock island formed when the top of a sea arch falls into the sea

## ANSWER THESE

1. Along the shoreline most features are created by the force of
   a. the wind
   b. the rain
   c. the waves
2. A wave-cut terrace forms because
   a. wave action has little effect below the water
   b. the terrace is made of soft rock
   c. the temperature is lower around the terrace
3. Steep-faced cliffs found along the coast are called
   a. sea steeps
   b. sea cliffs
   c. wave-cut terraces
4. Promontories result from
   a. sea arches
   b. unequal wave erosion
   c. sea caves

## WHAT'S HAPPENING

**Great losses.** People build homes on top of sea cliffs. The view from these heights is beautiful. You can see far out over the ocean. However, storm waves erode the bases of the cliffs quickly. Then, there is nothing to hold up the houses. They fall into the sea. A person who understood earth science would know better than to buy or build a home in such a place.

# What shoreline features are built by waves?

The black sand on this beach in Hawaii was formed from weathered volcanic rock.

**Back to the sea.** Have you ever stood on a shoreline at the ocean? Water from waves is thrown forward onto the land. Then the water flows back to the sea. This backward flow is called an undertow. The undertow carries sand off the land into the sea. While the undertow carries sand out to sea, incoming waves bring sand onto the beach. On some beaches, more sand is carried away with the undertow than is brought back by incoming waves. If this goes on for long, the beach will be washed away.

▶ **What is an undertow?**

**Beaches.** Beaches form when weathered material is deposited on a shoreline by water waves. Materials that form beaches vary in size and color. Pebble beaches are found along some shorelines. Weathered quartz along the Atlantic coast produces white sands. The lava from a volcano can be weathered to form a black sand. This black sand can be found on some beaches in Hawaii and other Pacific islands. Coastlines of Florida and Bermuda have beaches made of pieces of shell.

▶ **What kind of rock can form a black sand?**

**Longshore currents.** Some ocean currents move parallel to the shoreline. These currents are called longshore currents. Longshore currents form when waves moving toward the beach at an angle meet the water in an undertow current. Longshore currents drop much of the sand they carry. The sand builds up at a distance from the shore but in the same direction as the shoreline. These underwater deposits of sand are called sandbars. Wave action may finally deposit sand above the water. An offshore bar, or barrier beach, forms. The water between the bar and the mainland is called a lagoon (luh-GOON). Miami Beach in Florida and Rockaway in New York have been built upon offshore bars.

▶ **What is the water called that lies between an offshore bar and the mainland?**

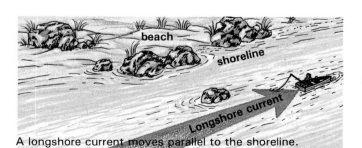
A longshore current moves parallel to the shoreline.

The city of Miami Beach was built on an offshore bar.

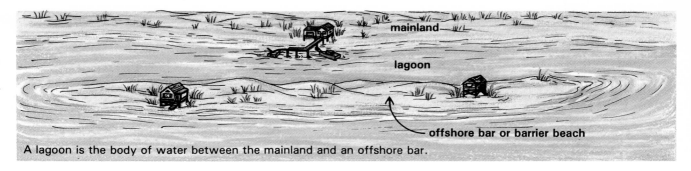

A lagoon is the body of water between the mainland and an offshore bar.

## WHAT YOU LEARNED

1. An undertow carries sand off the land into the sea.
2. Beaches are formed when weathered rock material is deposited on land by waves.
3. Longshore currents flow parallel to the shore.
4. Longshore currents deposit the sand that forms sandbars and barrier beaches.

## SCIENCE WORDS

**undertow**
backward flow of water fater a wave splashes on the shore

**beach**
shoreline covered by weathered rock material

**longshore current**
flow of water parallel to the shoreline

**sandbar**
a long underwater deposit of sand parallel to the shoreline

**offshore bar** (barrier beach)
deposit of sand sticking out of the water and running parallel to the shoreline

**lagoon** (luh-GOON)
water between an offshore bar and the mainland

PLEASE DO NOT WRITE IN THIS BOOK

## ANSWER THESE

1. How does the undertow erode a beach?
2. How do beaches form?
3. Why do the beaches along the Atlantic coast have white sand?
4. What materials form the sands on Bermuda?
5. What is the source of some sands in Hawaii?
6. List 2 features that are due to longshore currents.

## FINDING OUT MORE

**Coral reefs.** Corals (KOR-uls) are tiny animals that grow in warm, shallow waters. They attach themselves to rocks under the water. They need not move because waves and currents bring them their food. Corals absorb calcium minerals from the sea water. From the minerals they make shells to protect their soft bodies. Their shells remain attached to the rocks after they die. New corals then attach themselves to these remains. The shells gradually become cemented to form coral rock. A large build-up of coral rock is called a coral reef. Corals do not grow above the water. Coral reefs are usually just under the surface. They are a great hazard to ships.

## NOW TRY THIS

### Across

1. Line where water meets land
2. Shoreline that is covered by eroded material
4. Backward flow of water from the land to the sea

### Down

1. Long underwater deposits of sand parallel to the shore.
3. Body of water that forms between the mainland and an offshore bar
5. Longshore _____

**115**

# What happens to the eroded material from the land?

**To the sea.** Rivers flow downhill. They carry with them tons and tons of material eroded from the land. Glaciers also move large amounts of rocks and pebbles. Where does this eroded material go? Most rivers flow into other rivers, which then flow into the ocean. Glaciers move toward these rivers also. Most of the eroded material carried by rivers and glaciers is carried into the ocean.

▶ **Where does the eroded material from the land end up?**

**Minerals in the ocean.** If you ever swallowed some sea water, you know that it is salty. Salt is a mineral. Salt and other minerals dissolve in water that moves over the land. Minerals also dissolve in ground water. Much of the water carrying dissolved minerals flows into the ocean. These minerals are added to the salt and other minerals already in the ocean.

▶ **How do minerals get into the ocean?**

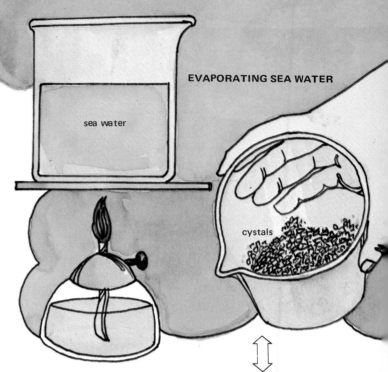

EVAPORATING SEA WATER

sea water

cystals

**How can you get the minerals out of sea water?** Place some sea water in a beaker. Heat the beaker over a very low flame to make the water evaporate. Crystals form on the glass of the beaker. These crystals are the minerals that were dissolved in the sea water.

▶ **What are the crystals that are left when sea water evaporates?**

**Test for sodium.** Salt is the most common mineral in the ocean. Salt is a compound of sodium and chlorine. The chemical formula for salt is $NaCl$. Dip a wire loop into some sea water. Place the loop over a flame. The bright yellow color of the flame is made by sodium. This is called a flame test. The bright yellow color of the flame can be used to identify sodium. Scientists also use this test to identify other minerals in sea water. Other elements make different color flames.

▶ **How can a flame test help you identify sodium?**

116

## WHAT YOU LEARNED

1. Much of the eroded material of the earth is carried into the ocean.
2. Sea water contains many dissolved minerals.

## ANSWER THESE

1. Rivers, glaciers, and ground water carry much of their material into
   a. air
   b. oceans
   c. hills
2. Evaporating sea water leaves
   a. nothing
   b. foam
   c. minerals
3. When salt water is placed in a flame, the color of the flame becomes
   a. bright yellow
   b. red
   c. blue

## FINDING OUT MORE

Salt is not the only mineral found in the ocean. Many other minerals are carried from the land into the sea. Many minerals are also found on the ocean floor. Sixty-three elements are known to be in sea water. Gold and silver are among the elements found in the ocean. If you evaporate 100 grams of sea water, 3.5 grams of minerals will be left.

| SOME MINERALS IN SEA WATER | |
| --- | --- |
| Mineral | Chemical formula |
| sodium chloride | $NaCl$ |
| magnesium chloride | $MgCl_2$ |
| magnesium sulfate | $MgSO_4$ |
| potassium sulfate | $K_2SO_4$ |
| calcium carbonate | $CaCO_3$ |

## NOW TRY THESE

1. Make a chart like the one shown below. On your chart, fill in the words where the question marks are. Then add some of your own ideas about the ocean. The first line of the chart has been filled in to help you get started.

| Material from the sea | Use |
| --- | --- |
| fish | food |
| ? | swimming |
| salt | ? |
| clams | ? |
| ? | food for fish |
| iodine | ? |
| copper | ? |
| ? | ? |

Solve the puzzles to find the science words.

2. Element that can be identified when salt is placed in a flame.

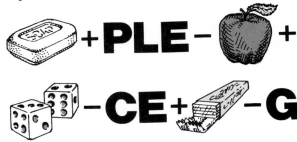

3. Write the names of the pictures in the boxes. The circled letters will be the science word.

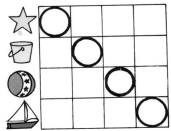

Common name for sodium chloride.

# What helps to prevent erosion?

**Breaking the fall.** On a flat surface, form a layer of sand about one centimeter deep. Fill a medicine dropper with water. Hold the dropper about 50 centimeters above the sand. Let the water fall onto the sand drop by drop. Notice how the drops form grooves in the sand. Deep grooves in the ground are called <u>gullies</u> (GUL-eez).

Hold a leaf from a plant just above the sand. Let the water drop onto the leaf. The water then drips from the leaf onto the sand. What happens to the sand this time? Leaves of trees and plants slow down falling raindrops. Leaves weaken the power of water to wash away soil.

▶ **What do leaves from trees and plants do to falling rain?**

**Holding the soil together.** Water carries away soil when it runs over the land. Roots of trees and plants cling to the soil. They help hold the soil in place. Soil with roots in it is less likely to be washed away. The roots prevent the soil from being washed away. Plants slow down the flow of running water. Slow-moving water does not erode the land quickly. Land covered with plants can prevent or slow down erosion.

▶ **How do plants prevent or slow down erosion?**

**Protection from wind erosion.** Grasses can protect the soil from the wind. They keep the wind from blowing directly on the soil. Beach grasses keep sea breezes from blowing sand away. They help prevent erosion by both wind and water. People protect their land from erosion by growing things on it.

▶ **How do grasses protect soil from erosion?**

**Dam it.** Building a dam is another way to prevent erosion. Dams slow down the flow of river water. The rate of erosion then slows down. Dams store the water from large rains and snows. They help prevent floods and erosion caused by fast-moving water.

▶ How does a dam prevent erosion?

## WHAT YOU LEARNED

1. The leaves of plants weaken the power of water to wash away soil.
2. The roots of plants hold the soil in place.
3. Grasses protect the soil from wind erosion.
4. Dams prevent floods and the erosion caused by fast-moving water.

## SCIENCE WORD

**gully** (GUL-ee)
a deep groove in the ground

## ANSWER THESE

1. As plants are removed from the ground, the speed of erosion
   a. increases
   b. decreases
   c. remains the same

2. Deep grooves formed in the ground are called
   a. dugouts
   b. gullies
   c. scoops
3. Beach erosion can be prevented by
   a. permitting swimming
   b. building docks
   c. planting beach grasses
4. The flow of a river can be slowed down by
   a. increasing the slope of the bed
   b. increasing the amount of water
   c. building a dam across the river

## NOW TRY THESE

Solve the puzzles to find the science words

1. Are made when raindrops fall on bare ground.

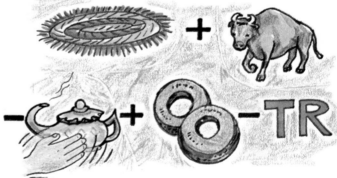

2. Slows down the flow of a river.

3. May be eroded by sea breezes.

# Review

*Do the following questions on a separate sheet of paper.*

**Matching** *Write down each of the statements in Column I, leaving one line of space after each statement. On the blank line following each statement, write the word or phrase from Column II that is described by that statement.*

| Column I | Column II |
|---|---|
| 1. Steep-faced rock on the shoreline. | runoff |
| 2. A deep groove in the ground. | bed |
| 3. A moving river of ice and snow. | meanders |
| 4. The top of a wave. | tributaries |
| 5. Water that runs over the ground. | glacier |
| 6. The bottom of a river. | erratic |
| 7. The side of a river. | crest |
| 8. A rock carried by a glacier. | sea cliff |
| 9. Smaller rivers that flow into a larger river. | gully |
| 10. Curved loops in a river. | bank |

*Do the following questions on a separate sheet of paper.*

**Multiple Choice** *Write the letter of the choice that best completes the statement or answers the question.*

1. The breaking up and carrying away of materials in the earth's crust is called
   a. runoff
   b. erosion
   c. soil conservation
2. The rate at which water flows in a river depends
   a. on the slope of the river
   b. on the amount of water in the river
   c. on the source of the river
3. A delta can form only
   a. at the head of a steep river
   b. at the mouth of a small river
   c. at the bends of a meandering river
4. A river with waterfalls and rapids is probably
   a. an old river
   b. very wide and slow
   c. a young river

5. Wind erosion occurs most easily
   a. in a dry region
   b. in a wet region
   c. in a grassy region
6. A section of very hard rock jutting out into the ocean is called
   a. a wave-cut terrace
   b. a sea cliff
   c. promontory
7. The flow of water parallel to the shoreline is called
   a. the longshore current
   b. the undertow
   c. a lagoon
8. Plants prevent soil erosion by
   a. using the soil for food
   b. holding the soil with their roots
   c. preventing water from reaching the soil

# UNIT 6 Building Up the Earth

## Unit Lessons

1. How does the earth's crust move?
2. What are earthquake waves?
3. What can we learn from earthquake waves?
4. How does magma change the earth's surface?
5. What is a volcano?
6. How do we describe mountains?
7. How do we describe plains and plateaus?
8. What is the theory of continental drift?
9. What are crustal plates?
10. How does plate motion affect the earth's crust?

## Goals and Objectives

After completing this unit, you should be able to:

- explain why faults, earthquakes, and mountains are signs that the earth's crust is under pressure.
- describe how earthquakes are located.
- name features on the earth produced by volcanism.
- classify mountain ranges on the basis of how they were formed.
- differentiate between plains and plateaus.
- give evidence for the theory of continental drift.
- describe the features found on the earth's crust where plates meet.

# How does the earth's crust move?

Damage caused by the 1964 earthquake in Alaska.

**Earthquakes.** The earth's crust is always moving, but usually very slowly. Slight movements of the ground are called tremors (TREM-ers). There are over six million tremors a year in the earth's crust. Many of these tremors are too slight to be felt. But an instrument called a seismograph (SIZE-muh-graf) can measure these movements. Earthquakes are sudden, strong movements in the earth's crust. They can cause a lot of damage.

On March 27, 1964, the ground in Anchorage, Alaska, shook with great force. When it stopped, 115 people had died. Buildings had fallen apart. Great cracks were left in the streets. All of this damage was caused by an earthquake.

▶ **What is an earthquake?**

**What causes earthquakes?** Scientists believe that pressures in the earth's crust cause earthquakes. These pressures cause the crust to break at a weak point. When the crust breaks, it moves. One part of the crust slips and slides along the other. The break in the earth's crust is called a fault (FAWLT). This movement of the ground along a fault is known as faulting (FAWL-ting). Earthquakes take place as a result of faulting.

▶ **What is a fault?**

**Layers of rock.** Sedimentary rocks usually form in flat, or horizontal (hahr-uh-ZON-tul), layers. The picture shows sedimentary rock layers that were folded, or bent and pushed up.

Get a package of colored paper. Each layer of color represents a layer of sedimentary rock. Push both ends of the paper toward the center. The pressure causes the paper to bend upward and fold. There are great pressures inside the earth's crust. The pressures cause the crust to move upward and fold.

▶ **What causes the earth's crust to move and fold?**

**FOLDED ROCK LAYERS**

fault

**Changes in the crust.** Sometimes scientists take special trips, or expeditions (eck-spuh-DISH-uns), to learn more about the earth. In 1835, a young scientist explored the Andes mountains in South America. At a height of over 4000 meters, he found the remains of sea animals and plants that lived long ago. He discovered the remains of trees that usually grow near the sea.

How did these remains get more than 4 kilometers above the sea? The scientist believed that this land was once covered by the sea. Long ago, these mountains may have been part of the ocean floor. Pressure inside the earth caused this land to rise above the ocean.

▶ **What did a scientist find high in the Andes mountains?**

## WHAT YOU LEARNED

1. An earthquake is a sudden, strong movement of the earth's crust.
2. A fault is a break in the earth's crust.
3. Pressure within the earth's crust causes it to fold and move upward.
4. Remains of sea life on mountain tops show that the mountains were once covered by the ocean.

## SCIENCE WORDS

**tremor** (TREM-er)
a slight shaking of the earth's crust

**seismograph** (SIZE-mo-graf)
an instrument that measures movements in the earth's crust

**earthquake**
sudden, strong movements in the earth's crust

**fault** (FAWLT)
a break in the crust of the earth

**faulting** (FAWL-ting)
movement in the earth's crust so that one part of the ground slides past another part

**folded**
bent and pushed upward

## ANSWER THESE

1. Earth movements caused by pressure result in
   a. folding of rocks
   b. erosion
   c. minerals in the ocean
2. Scientists believe that finding the remains of sea life on mountain tops shows that
   a. sea animals can climb mountains
   b. the mountain tops were once covered by seas
   c. giant waves can be 4 kilometers high
3. The land has not been completely worn away by erosion because
   a. it is too slow
   b. it has stopped
   c. some land is always being built up

## NOW TRY THESE

1. Why are earthquakes dangerous?
2. What is a tremor?
3. Where does the earth's crust break?

## FINDING OUT MORE

A seashore village can be wiped out by a giant wave. Often it is called a tidal wave. But this kind of wave is not caused by the tides. It may be caused by an earthquake on the ocean floor. The Japanese name for these waves is tsunami (tsew-NAHM-ee). In the middle of the ocean, tsunami are hardly noticeable. But when they hit the shore, they may rise as high as 25 meters and cause death and destruction.

**Damage caused by a tsunami**

# What are earthquake waves?

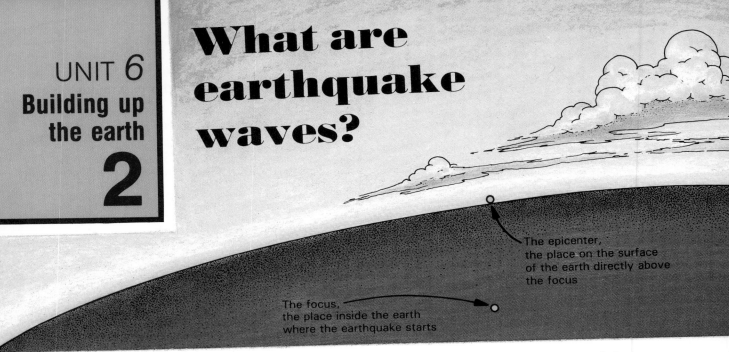

The epicenter, the place on the surface of the earth directly above the focus

The focus, the place inside the earth where the earthquake starts

**Where it all begins.** Earthquakes start inside the crust of the earth. They begin at a place along a fault in the earth's crust. The place inside the earth where a quake starts is called the focus (FOH-kus). The place on the surface of the earth directly above the focus is called the epicenter (EP-ih-sen-ter). A quake shakes the surface of the earth hardest at the epicenter.

There are three main kinds of shock waves that travel out from the focus. They are primary (PRY-mer-ee) waves, secondary (SEC-un-der-ee) waves, and surface waves.

▶ **What is the focus of an earthquake?**

**Primary waves.** Primary waves or P waves, travel the fastest of the earthquake waves.

They cause particles in materials to move back and forth in place. The wave itself moves out from the focus. A Slinky spring can show this. The wave moves along the spring as the coils move back and forth. Waves that move in this manner are called longitudinal (lon-juh-TOO-dih-nul) aves. A primary earthquake wave moves away from the focus in all directions. It can move through solids, liquids, and gases.

▶ **How does a P wave affect the particles in a material it travels through?**

**Secondary waves.** Tie a rope to a door knob. Shake the other end up and down. A wave called a transverse (trans-VURS) wave forms. When a transverse wave travels through

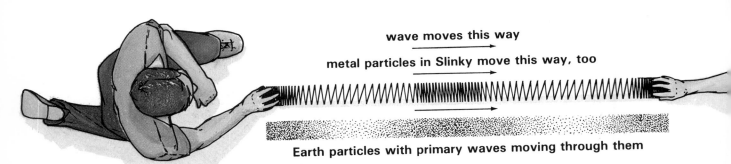

wave moves this way

metal particles in Slinky move this way, too

Earth particles with primary waves moving through them

**A longitudinal wave.** To make a longitudinal wave in a Slinky, stretch the Slinky out on the floor with a classmate holding one end still. Give the hand holding the Slinky a quick push toward your classmate. Both the particles of metal in the Slinky and the wave move in the same direction.

124

**A transverse wave.** To make a transverse wave in a Slinky, stretch the Slinky out on the floor with a classmate holding one end still. Move your hand back and forth quickly from side to side. While the wave moves from one end of the Slinky to the other, the particles of metal in the Slinky move from side to side.

a material, the particles of the material move up and down while the wave moves sideways. Secondary earthquake waves are transverse waves. They travel slower than primary waves but faster than surface waves. They cannot travel through liquids and gases.

Secondary waves are also called shear waves or S waves.

▶ **What kind of a wave is a secondary earthquake wave?**

**Surface waves.** Surface waves travel the slowest of the three kinds of earthquake waves. They move straight up from the focus to the epicenter. Then they travel along the earth's surface. They cause the most damage to buildings.

▶ **How do surface waves travel?**

## WHAT YOU LEARNED

1. Earthquakes start within the earth's crust at a place called the focus.
2. Earthquakes send out three main types of waves: primary, secondary, and surface waves.
3. Earthquake waves travel at different speeds.

## SCIENCE WORDS

**focus** (FOH-kus)
the place within the crust of the earth where an earthquake starts

**epicenter** (EP-ih-sen-ter)
place on the surface of the earth directly above the focus

## ANSWER THESE

1. Earthquakes start within the earth's crust at the
   **a.** core      **b.** focus      **c.** epicenter

2. The waves that move the fastest are the
   **a.** primary waves
   **b.** secondary waves
   **c.** surface waves

3. The waves that travel through solids, liquids, and gases are the
   **a.** primary waves
   **b.** secondary waves
   **c.** surface waves

4. The waves that cause the most damage are the
   **a.** primary waves
   **b.** shear waves
   **c.** surface waves

## FINDING OUT MORE

A seismograph (SIZE-muh-graf) is an instrument that measures earthquakes. There are several types. One kind is shown in the picture. A pen (A) is attached to a heavy weight (B). The weight hangs by a spring (C) from the rod (D). The pen touches a moving paper (E) attached to the base (F) of the seismograph.

If the earth moves, so does the base. The pen remains in place. The pen marks a wavy line on the paper if the base moves. This paper makes a record of the movements in the earth's crust.

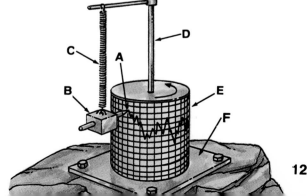

**125**

# What can we learn from earthquake waves?

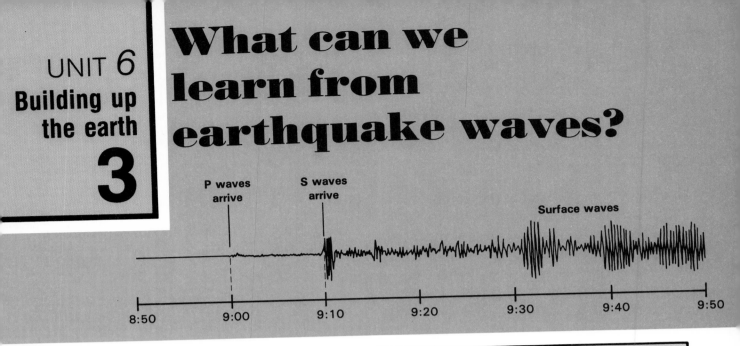

P waves arrive | S waves arrive | Surface waves

8:50    9:00    9:10    9:20    9:30    9:40    9:50

**Studying earthquake waves.** Seismologists (size-MAHL-uh-jists) are scientists who study earthquakes. They have seismographs set up all around the world. They study the wavy lines drawn by seismographs. Sheets of paper with the wavy lines drawn on them are called seismograms (SIZE-muh-grams). Studying seismograms can tell us much about an earthquake. It can tell where the focus is and the force of the earthquake.

▶ **What can a seismogram tell us?**

**Reading a seismogram.** Look at the drawing of a seismogram. The small wavy lines are from the P waves. What time did they first appear? The time scale shows 9:00. Now look at the larger wavy lines. They are from the S waves. What time did they appear? The S waves appeared 10 minutes later at 9:10. There was a 10-minute difference between the times the P and S waves arrived. Scientists can use differences in time to tell the distance of the epicenter from the seismograph. A large time difference means a large distance. A small time difference means a small distance. Charts have been prepared to change time differences into distances.

▶ **What tells how far the epicenter of an earthquake is from a seismograph?**

| Table A | |
|---|---|
| Time difference between arrival of S and P waves at seismograph station | Distance from the seismograph station to the quake's focus |
| 1 minute | 700 km |
| 2 minutes | 1200 km |
| 3 minutes | 1800 km |
| 4 minutes | 2500 km |
| 5 minutes | 3400 km |
| 6 minutes | 4500 km |
| 7 minutes | 5500 km |
| 8 minutes | 6500 km |

**Finding the epicenter.** A seismogram tells only how far away the focus is. It does not tell whether the epicenter is north, east, south, or west of the seismograph station. To find the direction, seismograms from three stations are needed. A circle is drawn on a map around each station showing how far the epicenter is from each station. There is only one point where all three circles will cross. This point shows the epicenter of the quake.

▶ **Why doesn't the distance from the epicenter to one station tell where the epicenter is located?**

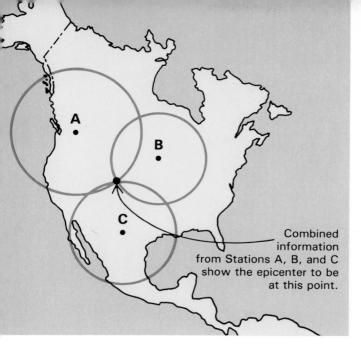

Combined information from Stations A, B, and C show the epicenter to be at this point.

**The strength of an earthquake.** In 1935 Charles Richter (RIK-ter) developed a scale for determining the strength of an earthquake. His scale is based on the size of the wavy lines on a seismogram. Large wavy lines mean a strong earthquake. Small ones mean a weak earthquake. The <u>Richter</u> <u>Scale</u> gives each earthquake a score of from 1 to 9 or more. The higher the number, the stronger the earthquake. An earthquake scoring 6 or higher can cause a great deal of damage.

▶ **What does the Richter Scale measure?**

## WHAT YOU LEARNED

1. Seismograms can tell how far away an earthquake began.
2. Differences in time between P and S waves are used to find the distance from the seismograph station to the focus.
3. Seismograms from three stations are needed to find the epicenter.
4. The Richter Scale measures how large an earthquake is.

## SCIENCE WORDS

**seismologists** (size-MAHL-uh-jists)
scientists who study earthquakes

**seismogram** (SIZE-muh-gram)
sheet of paper showing the wavy lines drawn by a seismograph

**Richter** (RIK-ter) **Scale**
scale that measures how large an earthquake is

## ANSWER THESE

1. Seismograms show
   a. wavy lines caused by earthquake waves
   b. pictures of destruction done by earthquakes
   c. maps of areas where earthquakes took place

*Look at the seismogram to answer questions 2, 3, 4, and 5.*

2. P waves first appear at
   a. 7:55
   b. 8:00
   c. 8:55
3. S waves first appeared at
   a. 8:00
   b. 8:05
   c. 8:10
4. The time between P and S waves was
   a. 5 minutes
   b. 10 minutes
   c. 15 minutes
5. According to the seismogram and the information given in Table A, the distance from the station to the focus is
   a. less than 700 kilometers
   b. 1800 kilometers
   c. more than 3000 kilometers
6. Seismograms from the following number of stations are needed to find the epicenter:
   a. 1 station
   b. 2 stations
   c. 3 stations

**SEISMOGRAM** (for questions 2, 3, 4, 5)

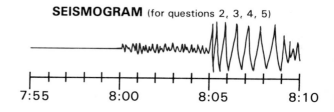

7:55          8:00          8:05          8:10

# How does magma change the earth's surface?

**DOMED MOUNTAIN**

**magma**

**Movement of the crust.** Very high temperatures within the crust of the earth melt rocks to form magma. When magma comes onto the surface, it is called lava. The movement of magma and lava is called volcanism (VOL-canism). Pressure from inside the earth causes the crust to move. The movement of layers of rock in the crust causes folds and faults. Folding, faulting, and volcanism build up the crust of the earth.

▶ **What is volcanism?**

**Building from inside.** Blow up a balloon. The pressure on the inside pushes the balloon outward. Magma deep within the crust sometimes forms giant pools. As more magma flows into these pools, pressure builds up within them. This pressure causes the crust to bend upward. A rounded mountain forms where

the crust is pushed up by the magma. The mountain looks like a dome. It is called a domed (DOHMD) mountain. The picture shows part of the Adirondack Mountains in New York State. The Adirondack Mountains are domed mountains.

▶ **What causes domed mountains to form?**

**Moving magma.** Magma moves into cracks in the earth's crust. It flows between layers of rocks. Magma also moves across layers of rocks. In time, the magma cools and becomes solid. The solid rock formed from magma can be seen in the eroded layers of the crust. Magma that flows between layers of rocks forms a <u>sill</u>. Magma that cuts across the layers forms a <u>dike</u>. The diagram shows the ways magma moves in the crust.

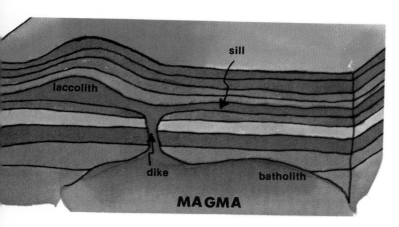

The Palisades along the Hudson River are made of solid magma. These rocks were formed inside the crust. Erosion wore away the surface that once covered them.

▶ **What is a sill?**

**Igneous rocks.** As you know, igneous rocks are formed from magma. Volcanism forms igneous rocks. Granite is one kind of igneous rock formed inside the crust of the earth. Large deposits of granite show that there was once volcanism in a region.

▶ **What do granite deposits tell you about a region?**

## WHAT YOU LEARNED

1. Volcanism is the movement of molten rock on or inside the earth's crust.
2. Folding, faulting, and volcanism build up the land on the earth's crust.
3. Domed mountains are formed from upward pressures of magma.

## SCIENCE WORDS

**volcanism** (VOL-ca-nism)
   movement of molten rock on or inside the earth's crust.

**domed** (DOHMD) **mountain**
   a mountain formed by magma pushing up the crust to form a dome shape

**sill**
   magma that flows in between the layers of rock in the earth's crust

**dike**
   magma that cuts across layers of rock in the earth's crust

## ANSWER THESE

1. Volcanism is the movement of
   **a.** solid rocks
   **b.** molten rocks
   **c.** plastic rocks

2. Domed mountains are produced by
   **a.** pools of magma
   **b.** water pressure
   **c.** earthquakes

3. Igneous rocks tell you that an area once had
   **a.** animals
   **b.** oceans
   **c.** volcanism

## NOW TRY THIS

Unscramble the following words.

GAMAM — hot molten rock
MISVOLANC — movement of molten rock
ONGEIUS — rock formed from molten magma
EMOD — type of mountain formed by the pressure of trapped magma

# What is a volcano?

cinders and gases

cone

crater

lava

A VOLCANO

magma

**A mountain is born.** Would you like to watch a mountain forming? A Mexican farmer saw it happen in 1943. First, the ground started shaking. A few weeks later, the farmer found cracks, called <u>fissures</u> (FISH-ers), in the earth. Soon, hot gases began to come out of these fissures. As the fissures widened, lava came out. Small pieces of solid lava, called <u>cinders</u> (SIN-ders), were thrown out. A <u>volcano</u> (vol-CAY-no) formed.

Cinders, lava, ashes, and rocks piled up around the opening, or <u>crater</u> (CRAY-ter), of the volcano. They formed a <u>volcanic</u> (vol-CAN-ic) <u>cone</u>. After several months, the volcanic cone was 450 meters high and five kilometers wide.

▶ **What is the opening of a volcano called?**

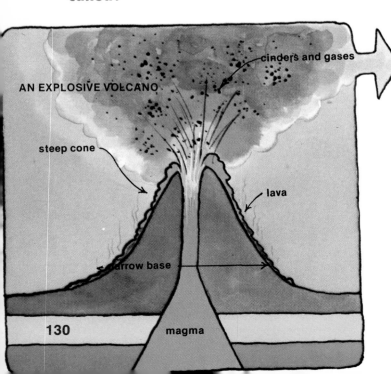

AN EXPLOSIVE VOLCANO

cinders and gases

steep cone

lava

narrow base

magma

130

**Types of volcanoes.** Not all volcanoes are like the one that formed in Mexico, called Paricutin. But all volcanoes form from pressures inside the earth. The pressure forces magma to the surface. The magma pushes through weak spots in the crust. If the pressure becomes very great, the rock layers on the surface crack. Rocks, lava, gases, and steam shoot up through the cracks. This is an <u>explosive</u> (eck-SPLO-siv) <u>volcano</u>. An explosive volcano has a narrow base. Its cone is steep. The Mexican volcano Paricutin is an example of an explosive volcano.

When lava flows out freely through the fissures, a <u>quiet</u> <u>volcano</u> is formed. A quiet volcano has a wide base. Its cone is not steep. The Hawaiian Islands are examples of quiet volcanoes.

▶ **What are two types of volcanoes?**

gases
steam →

A QUIET VOLCANO

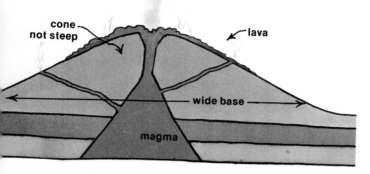

cone
not steep

← lava

← wide base →

magma

**Ring around the Pacific.** "The ring of fire" is the name given to the volcanoes that almost form a circle around the Pacific Ocean. The map shows the location of these volcanoes and many others.

Volcanoes are formed in areas where the earth's crust is weak. Earthquakes also take place where the crust is weak. Compare the earthquake regions shown on the map with the volcano regions. Are earthquakes and volcanoes usually found in the same areas?

▶ **What is "the ring of fire?"**

## WHAT YOU LEARNED

1. A volcano forms when pressure within the earth forces magma to the surface.
2. Volcanoes may be explosive or quiet.

## SCIENCE WORDS

**fissure** (FISH-er)
   a crack in the earth's crust
**cinders** (SIN-ders)
   solid pieces of lava that are thrown out of a volcano
**volcano** (vol-CAY-no)
   an opening in the earth's crust from which lava comes out
**crater** (CRAY-ter)
   a hole at the top of a volcano
**volcanic** (vol-CAN-ic) **cone**
   a mountain built up around the opening of a volcano
**explosive** (eck-SPLO-siv) **volcano**
   a volcano that shoots up through the surface with great force
**quiet volcano**
   a volcano formed when lava flows freely through the surface

## ANSWER THESE

1. What material forms a volcano?
2. What is a fissure?
3. What is a volcanic cone?
4. Name an explosive volcano.
5. Where can you find a quiet volcano?

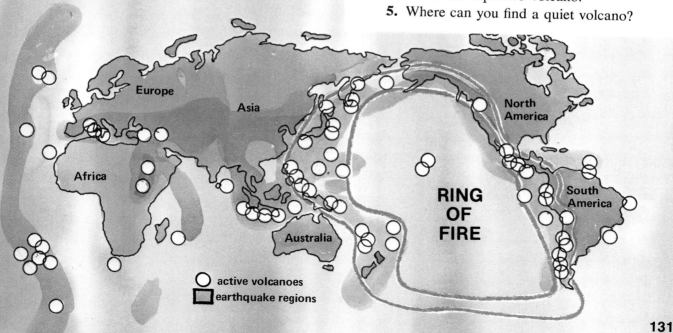

Europe

Asia

North America

Africa

RING
OF
FIRE

South America

Australia

○ active volcanoes
▢ earthquake regions

# How do we describe mountains?

Mt. Ranier in Washington State is an example of an inactive volcano.

**Differences in mountains.** The elevation (el-uh-VAY-shun) of a mountain is its distance above sea level. For a hill to be classed as a <u>mountain</u>, its elevation must be at least 600 meters higher than that of the land surrounding it.

Mountains look different. For example, some have gentle slopes. Others have slopes that are steep. Mountains look different because of differences in how they were formed. The appearance of a mountain tells something about how it was formed.

▶ **What is the elevation of a mountain?**

**Folded mountains.** The layers of rock in sedimentary rock start out lying flat. Pressures in the crust of the earth can cause these layers to bend. The layers then curve up in one place and down in another. That is, the layers become folded. (See page 110.) An upward fold is called an <u>anticline</u> (AN-tih-kline). A downward fold is called a <u>syncline</u> (SIN-kline). Anticlines can become the peaks of some mountains.

Mountains formed by the folding of rock layers are called folded mountains. The Appalachian (ap-uh-LAY-chee-un) Mountains in Pennsylvania are examples of folded mountains.

▶ **What do we call the upward and downward folds in a folded rock?**

**Fault-block mountains.** Recall that a crack can form at a weak spot in the earth's crust. Sometimes pressures cause the crust on one side of the crack to slip up past the crust on the other side. If the crust is pushed up enough, it forms a mountain. The place where the slipping took place will form one side of the mountain. This side will be steep. The other side will be gentle. Mountains formed in this way are called fault-block mountains. The Sierra Nevada Mountains in California are good examples of fault-block mountains.

▶ **Which part of a fault-block mountain has a steep slope?**

**Domed mountains and volcanic cones.** As discussed on page 116, the hot magma deep within the crust can push up on the land above. The rounded mountain that forms from this pressure is called a domed (DOHMD) mountain. Magma that pushes all the way to the surface forms volcanic cones. These volcanic cones are often large enough to be mountains.

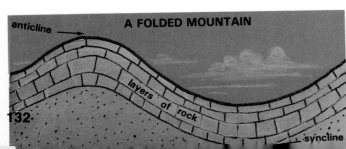

A FOLDED MOUNTAIN

anticline

layers of rock

syncline

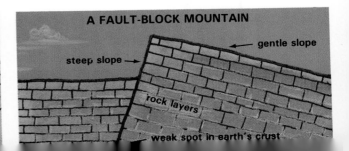

A FAULT-BLOCK MOUNTAIN

gentle slope

steep slope

rock layers

weak spot in earth's crust

The Rocky Mountains are complex mountains.

The Black Hills of South Dakota are domed mountains. Mount St. Helens in the state of Washington is a volcanic cone.

▶ **What two kinds of mountains are built by the movement of magma within the earth?**

**Complex mountains.** Most mountains are combinations of different types of mountains. For example, folding can form a mountain. Then a crack, or fault, can develop in the folded layers. A section on one side of the fault may slip up past the other section. The result is a mountain that is both a folded mountain and a fault mountain. Mountains that are combinations of two or more types of mountains are called complex (KOM-PLEKS) mountains.

The Rocky Mountains, the Blue Ridge Mountains, and the Laurentian Mountains of Canada are examples of complex mountains.

▶ **What are complex mountains?**

## WHAT YOU LEARNED

1. Mountains look different because of differences in how they were formed.
2. A folded mountain is formed when pressures in the crust of the earth cause sedimentary rock to become curved.
3. A fault-block mountain is formed when the crust on one side of a crack slips up past the crust on the other side.
4. A domed mountain is formed when hot magma deep within the crust pushes up on the land above.

## SCIENCE WORDS

**mountain**
  mound of land whose elevation is at least 600 meters higher than the surrounding land

**anticline** (AN-tih-kline)
  upward fold of rock layers

**syncline** (SIN-kline)
  downward fold of rock layers

## ANSWER THESE

1. Anticlines and synclines are found in
   **a.** folded mountains
   **b.** fault-block mountains
   **c.** domed mountains
2. In a folded rock layer, a syncline is
   **a.** an upward fold
   **b.** a downward fold
   **c.** a dome
3. If a mass of land is raised up alongside a fault in the earth's crust, the raised land can form a
   **a.** folded mountain
   **b.** fault-block mountain
   **c.** domed mountain

## NOW TRY THESE

Match each type of mountain described in Column I with the name of a mountain range given in Column II.

| Column I | Column II |
|---|---|
| 1. folded mountains | A. Sierra Nevada Mountains |
| 2. faulted mountains | B. Mt. St. Helens |
| 3. domed mountains | C. Rocky Mountains |
| 4. volcanic cone | D. Appalachian Mountains in Pennsylvania |
| 5. complex mountains | E. Black Hills of South Dakota |

## FINDING OUT MORE

**Distribution of mountains.** Mountain ranges are groups of mountains. They are found near the edges of continents. A group of mountain ranges forms a mountain belt. Two important belts, the Mediterranean and Pacific belts, seem to be located in earthquake zones.

# How do we describe plains and plateaus?

**Plains.** A <u>plain</u> is a large flat area whose elevation does not differ much from that of the surrounding land. Some plains in the United States spread out over several states. Plains can be horizontal or can slope gently. The elevation of some plains is near sea level. Other plains have elevations hundreds of meters above sea level. The Great Plains east of the Rocky Mountains have a high elevation. The Atlantic Coastal Plain has a low elevation.

▶ **How does the elevation of a plain compare to the elevation of the land around it?**

**How plains are formed.** Plains are made of rock layers. Plains can form in several ways. One way is for land of uneven elevation to be worn flat by erosion. Another way is for earth material to be deposited in a body of water. Then the water level may drop, or the land may be pushed up without folding. In either case, a flat area of dry land will remain. A plain can also be formed from lava pouring out of a volcano. The lava spreads out to form a large, flat area.

▶ **What must happen in order for land of uneven elevation to become a plain?**

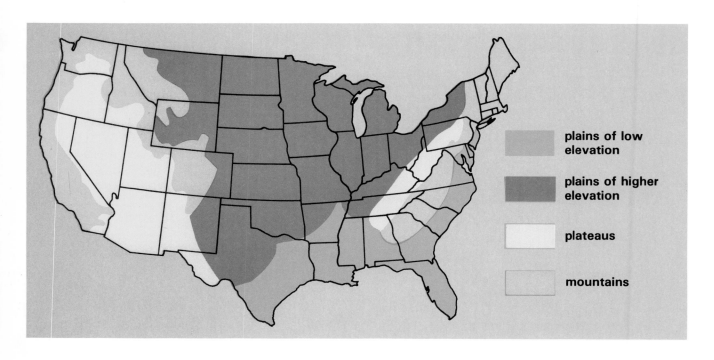

plains of low elevation

plains of higher elevation

plateaus

mountains

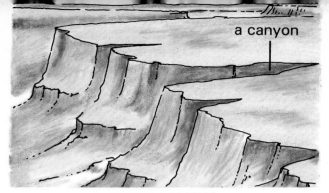

a canyon

## A PLATEAU

**Plateaus.** Plateaus (pla-TOHS) and plains are alike in some ways. Both are large, fairly flat landscapes. Both are made of rock layers. Here is how they differ. A plateau rises sharply above neighboring land on at least one side. A plain does not. A plateau often (but not always) has canyons running through it. A plain does not have canyons.

Some plateaus form when pressure within the crust raises a large section of land. The edge of this section is at a fault line. These plateaus are called <u>fault</u> <u>plateaus</u>. Plateaus can also form when lava flows out of a volcano and spreads over a large, raised area.

▶ **How are plateaus and plains alike?**

**Major landscape regions.** There are three main kinds of landscape regions. These are mountains, plateaus, and plains. The map shows where these regions are in the United States. Use the map to find what kind of region you live in.

▶ **What are the three main kinds of landscape regions?**

### WHAT YOU LEARNED

1. A plain is a large, flat area, horizontal or sloping gently, whose elevation does not differ much from that of the surrounding land.
2. A plateau is a large, flat area, horizontal or sloping gently, whose elevation on at least one side is sharply higher than the elevation of the surrounding land.
3. Deep canyons may run through plateaus but not plains.
4. The three major kinds of landscapes are mountains, plateaus, and plains.

### SCIENCE WORDS

**plain**
   large, flat area whose elevation differs little from that of the surrounding area

**plateau** (pla-TOH)
   large, flat area whose elevation on at least one side is sharply higher than that of the surrounding area

**fault plateau**
   a plateau formed when land on one side of a fault is raised up

### ANSWER THESE

1. The elevation of a plain
   a. can be near sea level or high above it
   b. is always near sea level
   c. is always high above sea level
2. Plains can form
   a. when uneven land is worn flat by erosion
   b. when land once under water is raised up
   c. both **a** and **b**
3. A plateau
   a. never has canyons running through it
   b. sometimes has canyons running through it
   c. always has canyons running through it
4. Mountains, plateaus, and plains are three kinds of
   a. landscape regions
   b. faults
   c. elevations

### FINDING OUT MORE

We saw in an earlier lesson that a river can be described as young, mature, or old. Mountains, plateaus, and plains can also be described by these words. For example, during its youth, a mountain has steep slopes. Its peaks are sharp and jagged. As the mountain becomes mature, weathering wears down the peaks. This makes them rounded. The slopes become less steep and more gentle. Still later, as the mountain becomes old, it becomes worn down, almost flat. While mountains are being worn down at one place, forces are raising the land at other places. While one mountain is dying, another is being born. Plains and plateaus also undergo changes as they age.

# What is the theory of continental drift?

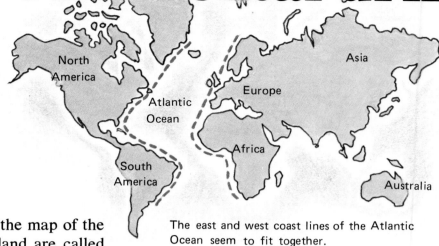

The east and west coast lines of the Atlantic Ocean seem to fit together.

**One large island.** Look at the map of the world. The large areas of land are called continents (KON-tuh-nents). Find North and South America, Africa, Europe, Asia, and Australia. Many scientists think that long ago there was only one continent. This piece of land had water all around it. Then the land broke into a number of pieces. The pieces slowly drifted apart. They became the continents we know today. Scientists believe the continents are still moving on the earth. The continents move only a few centimeters each year. The idea that continents move is called the theory of continental (con-tuh-NEN-tul) drift.

▶ **What do scientists think the continents are doing?**

**World's largest jigsaw puzzle.** On your map, find the Atlantic Ocean. Look at the shape of the coastlines of North and South America. Look across the ocean at the coastline of Europe and Africa. Notice that these two coastlines have the same shape. Both coastlines seem to fit together. Other places can be found that might have once fitted together. One reason for believing in continental drift comes from the shapes of land masses.

▶ **How are the coast lines on both sides of the Atlantic Ocean alike?**

**More clues for the puzzle.** Today, most scientists believe in continental drift. Here are some of their reasons.

Rocks along matching edges of continents have been studied. In many cases rocks found along one edge match those from the other. Even the sizes of diamonds in Brazil and West Africa are the same. Mountain ranges on different continents also seem to match. There is a mountain range in eastern Canada. It is similar to one in Norway and Sweden. These mountains could have once been part of the same range. The range would have split apart when the continents began moving.

Studies of plants and animals also support the theory. Scientists studied animals and plants in one area. They then studied organisms from a matching area in another continent. Many organisms living in one area also live in the other. Past forms of life have been studied, too. Remains of the same types of life have been found in matching places. Suppose that the continents were once joined. Organisms of the same type would have been carried apart when the land split.

▶ **How are diamonds in Brazil like those in West Africa?**

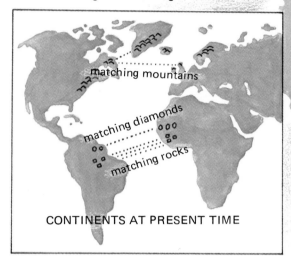

**Giant jigsaw puzzle.** The shapes of the coastlines are only one clue leading to the theory that the continents on either side of the Atlantic Ocean were once joined together in a single continent.

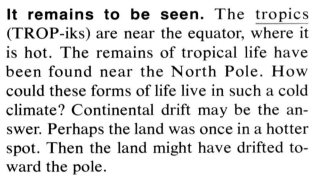

matching mountains

matching diamonds

matching rocks

CONTINENTS AT PRESENT TIME

**It remains to be seen.** The tropics (TROP-iks) are near the equator, where it is hot. The remains of tropical life have been found near the North Pole. How could these forms of life live in such a cold climate? Continental drift may be the answer. Perhaps the land was once in a hotter spot. Then the land might have drifted toward the pole.

▶ **Why do we believe that land now near the North Pole once had a warm climate?**

## WHAT YOU LEARNED

1. Most scientists today believe in the theory of continental drift.
2. The land on one side of the Atlantic Ocean looks as though it may have once been joined to the land on the other side.
3. Studies of rocks, plants, and animals from matching areas on different continents support the idea of continental drift.
4. Land near the North Pole may have drifted there from a warmer spot.

## SCIENCE WORDS

**continents** (KON-tuh-nents)
   very large areas of land
**theory of continental** (kon-tuh-NEN-tul) **drift**
   a theory that states that the continents have been moving and still are moving
**tropics** (TROP-iks)
   region near the equator where it is hot and damp

## ANSWER THESE

1. The eastern part of South America looks as if it could fit into the
   a. eastern part of Africa
   b. western part of Africa
   c. northern part of Africa
2. Evidence to prove the theory of continental drift came from
   a. a comparison of rocks and minerals
   b. caveman drawings
   c. watching the continents move
3. The plants and animals on continents separated by an ocean are
   a. sometimes very much alike
   b. never alike
   c. always alike

# What are crustal plates?

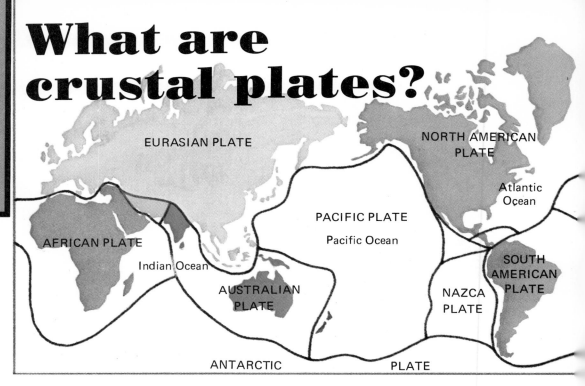

EURASIAN PLATE

NORTH AMERICAN PLATE

Atlantic Ocean

PACIFIC PLATE

Pacific Ocean

AFRICAN PLATE

Indian Ocean

SOUTH AMERICAN PLATE

AUSTRALIAN PLATE

NAZCA PLATE

ANTARCTIC          PLATE

**A major crack-up.** Scientists have a theory of why the continents move. It is called the theory of plate tectonics (tek-TON-iks). According to the theory, the earth's crust is like the shell of a cracked egg. The crust is cracked in many places. The cracks divide the crust into about 20 pieces. The pieces are called crustal (KRUS-tul) plates. The plates are made of solid rock. The continents and the floors of the oceans rest on the plates. The upper mantle lies below the plates. Scientists believe the earth material in the upper mantle is not completely solid. It is soft like putty or warm wax. It is able to flow like a liquid. The plates float on this soft material and move in it.

Suppose that a continent is resting on a certain plate. When the plate moves, the continent will move, too. The movements of the plates cause the continents to drift.

▶ **What kind of material is in the upper mantle?**

**Around she goes.** Arrange the equipment as shown in the picture. Fill the beaker with cold water. Place a blob of water-color paint into each loop. Then carefully lower

the four wire loops. Put a small flame under the middle of the beaker. See how the water moves the paint in the beaker. The arrows in the diagram show how the water moves. Water moving in this manner is called a convection (kon-VEK-shun) current. A convection current that flows around in a loop is called a convection cell.

▶ **What causes a convection current in water?**

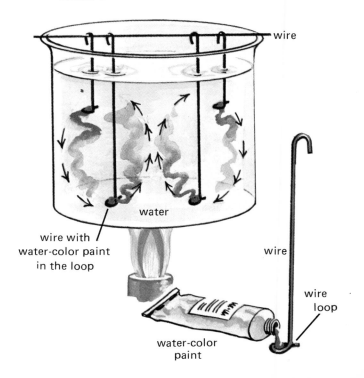

wire

water

wire with water-color paint in the loop

wire

wire loop

water-color paint

**They move, but why?** Scientists are not sure what causes the plates to move. There are a number of theories. According to one theory, there are convection cells within the mantle. Inside the earth there are hot spots. The liquid material in the mantle rises over these hot spots. Then the mantle material spreads out under the crust. As the mantle material moves, it carries the plates of the crust with it. One plate is carried in one direction. The other plate is carried in the other direction. Convection currents in the mantle cause some plates to move apart. They cause other plates to come together. Most scientists think that convection currents best explain how plates move.

▶ **What might cause convection currents in the mantle?**

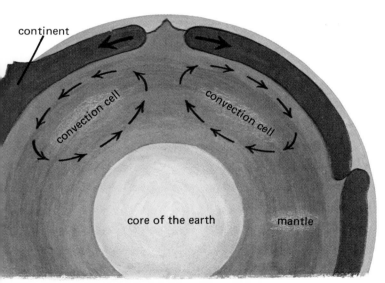

**One explanation for why the continents drift.** Convection cells in the mantle make crustal plates move.

## WHAT YOU LEARNED

1. The earth's crust is divided into about 20 pieces called crustal plates.
2. Scientists believe the earth material below the crust can flow like a liquid.

3. Crustal plates float on the liquid-like material in the upper mantle.
4. Some scientists believe that convection currents cause the earth material in the upper mantle to move.

## SCIENCE WORDS

**theory of plate tectonics** (tek-TON-iks)
a theory that states that the earth's crust is cracked to form about 20 large pieces

**crustal** (KRUS-tul) **plates**
the large pieces of the earth's crust

**convection** (kon-VEK-shun) **current**
the movement of material within a fluid caused by uneven temperature

**convection cell**
a convection current that flows around in a loop

## ANSWER THESE

1. The continents drift along on
   **a.** a large body of water
   **b.** themselves
   **c.** crustal plates
2. Scientists believe the material in the upper mantle is
   **a.** solid rock
   **b.** able to flow like a liquid
   **c.** mostly gases
3. Above the point where a flame is applied to the bottom of a container of water, the water will
   **a.** move sideways
   **b.** move down toward the flame
   **c.** rise
4. According to one theory, crustal plates move because of
   **a.** hot water inside the earth
   **b.** convection cells in the upper mantle
   **c.** pools of oil that help the plates to slide

## NOW TRY THIS

Unscramble the words in large print.

1. Plates move on material that flows in the earth's LEMTAN.
2. Some scientists believe that CRUNTERS in the mantle make the plates move.

# How does plate motion affect the earth's crust?

continent                     Mid-Atlantic Ridge                continent

Atlantic Ocean

earth's crust

The Mid-Atlantic Ridge is a tall mountain range that runs down the middle of the Atlantic Ocean. In only a few places does any part of it rise above the surface of the water.

**Mountains under the sea.** Some of the biggest mountains on the earth are under the oceans. The longest and highest mountain range on the earth runs down the middle of the Atlantic Ocean. It is called the Mid-Atlantic Ridge. Some of its peaks are 6000 meters above the ocean floor. There are mountain ranges like this in most of the oceans. Most of these mountain peaks are under water.

▶ **Where is the biggest mountain range on the earth?**

them. Magma rises up through the crack, forming a mid-ocean ridge. Some of the magma makes new ocean floor on both sides of the crack. As the plates move apart, the new ocean floor is carried with them. The ocean gets wider. This is called ocean-floor spreading.

▶ **What happens to the ocean floor where two plates are moving apart?**

Mid-Atlantic Ridge

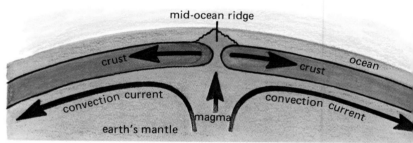
When plates move apart, magma rises from the mantle to fill the crack. The ocean floor spreads apart on either side of the crack.

**Filling the cracks.** The theory of plate tectonics explains how the mid-ocean ridges form. According to the theory, two plates are moving apart under the ocean. As they move apart, they leave a crack between

**Make me a trench.** Plates can also move toward each other. Then one plate is pushed down under the edge of the other. This forms a deep ditch or trench. As the edge is pushed down into the mantle, it melts. Magma may rise to the surface from the melting plate, and form volcanoes. Many volcanoes are found along the edges between plates. The ''ring of fire'' (page 131) is actually the outline of a large plate under the Pacific Ocean.

▶ **What happens to the edge of a plate that is forced down into the mantle?**

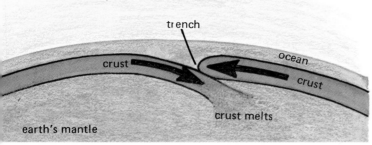

trench

crust

ocean

crust

crust melts

earth's mantle

When plates move toward each other, the edge of one plate is pushed down into the mantle. A deep trench is formed in the ocean where the two plates meet.

**Give a shake.** There is still another way plates can move. They can brush past each other. Faults are found where two plates brush past each other. A well-known fault is the San Andreas Fault in California. This fault is the edge between the Pacific Plate and the North American plate. Most of North America lies on the North American plate.

Sometimes plates lock together as they slide past each other. Pressure begins to build up. When the pressure becomes too great, the plates suddenly slip. An earthquake takes place as the plates suddenly slip. Earthquakes as well as volcanoes are found on the "ring of fire." Both occur at places where plates meet.

▶ How can the movement of crustal plates cause earthquakes?

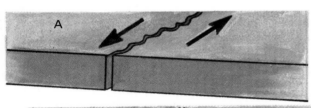

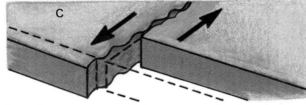

(A) Two plates may try to slide past each other but may lock together. (B) Strain develops where materials are locked together. (C) When the strain gets too great, the plates spring past each other, causing an earthquake.

## WHAT YOU LEARNED

1. Most of the oceans of the world have large underwater mountains.
2. These mid-ocean ridges are formed when two plates move apart and magma rises up through the crack.
3. Deep ditches or trenches are formed where one plate sinks down under the edge of another.
4. Earthquakes take place where plates brush past each other, lock together, and suddenly spring loose.

## SCIENCE WORDS

**Mid-Atlantic Ridge**
a large underwater mountain range running down the middle of the Atlantic Ocean
**ocean-floor spreading**
the widening of an ocean
**ocean trench**
a deep ditch in the ocean

## ANSWER THESE

1. The longest and highest mountain range on earth is
   **a.** in Asia
   **b.** in Alaska
   **c.** in the Atlantic Ocean
2. Magma rises up where the edges of two neighboring plates
   **a.** move apart  **b.** move toward each other
   **c.** brush past each other
3. A trench will form where the edges of two neighboring plates
   **a.** move apart  **b.** move toward each other
   **c.** brush past each other
4. Faults are found where the edges of two neighboring plates
   **a.** move apart  **b.** move toward each other
   **c.** brush past each other

## FINDING OUT MORE

Scientists are trying to find ways of preventing earthquakes. They would like to keep the edges of plates from locking together. They are looking for ways to make the rocks slide quietly past each other. One way being tried is to pump water into the crust along a fault. Water may lubricate (LOO-bruh-kate) the rocks and make it easier for them to slide.

**141**

*Do the following questions on a separate sheet of paper.*

**Fill in the Blank**    *Write down the statements in Column I. Where there is a blank line in each statement, write the word or phrase from Column II that best completes the meaning of the statement.*

| **Column I** | **Column II** |
|---|---|
| 1. The band of volcanoes around the Pacific is called _____. | syncline |
| 2. A deep ditch in the ocean is an _____. | ocean trench |
| 3. The widening of the oceans is due to_____. | the Ring of Fire |
| 4. The theory of tectonics tells us the earth's crust is divided into about 20_____. | fissure |
| | tremor |
| 5. Very large areas of land are called _____. | ocean floor spreading |
| 6. An upward fold of rock layers is called a(n)_____. | anticline |
| 7. A downward fold of rock layers is called a(n) _____. | surface wave |
| 8. A crack in the earth's crust is a(n) _____. | continents |
| 9. The earthquake shock that causes the most damage is the _____. | crustal plates |
| 10. A slight shaking of the earth's crust is a(n) _____. | |

*Do the following questions on a separate sheet of paper.*

**Multiple Choice**    *Write the letter of the choice that best completes the statement or answers the question.*

1. A seismograph measures
   a. the height of mountains
   b. the length of faults
   c. the movements of the earth's crust
2. A seismogram tells
   a. the direction of an earthquake
   b. where an earthquake occurred
   c. how far away the focus of an earthquake was
3. Sills and dikes form as a result of
   a. magma moving into cracks in the earth's crust
   b. earthquakes and tidal waves
   c. mountains being worn down
4. Volcanoes form in areas where
   a. the ground is very stable
   b. the earth's crust is weak
   c. there are lots of rivers

5. Fault-block mountains usually have
   a. one steep slope and one gentle slope
   b. only steep slopes
   c. only gentle slopes
6. A fault plateau is formed when land
   a. sinks below sea level
   b. is raised up on one side of a fault
   c. is shattered by many earthquakes
7. If the theory of continental drift is correct, then
   a. California and Europe were once attached
   b. Greenland and Australia were once attached
   c. Africa and South America were once attached
8. As magma rises along the Mid-Atlantic Ridge,
   a. the Atlantic gets wider
   b. the Atlantic gets narrower
   c. the width of the Atlantic remains the same

# UNIT 7

# The Record in the Rocks

## Unit Lessons

1. How can you learn about the earth's past?
2. What are fossils?
3. How are fossils formed?
4. What can we learn from fossils?
5. What is the geologic time scale?
6. What happens to the remains of living things?

## Goals and Objectives

After completing this unit, you should be able to:

- understand how the earth's age is determined from dating the oldest rocks.
- understand how rocks preserve a record of the earth's history.
- describe how traces of life are preserved in rocks.
- explain how fossils show that life has changed on earth.
- understand how rocks can help us date fossils, and fossils can help us date rocks.
- describe how coal, gas, and oil come from prehistoric swamps.

143

# How can you learn about the earth's past?

**A story in rocks.** History books tell you the story of the past 5000 years on earth. Scientists study rocks to find out what the earth was like more than 5000 years ago. Rocks do not have words like a book. But they help tell you about the earth's history. By studying rocks, scientists have found out the age of the earth. They believe that the earth is about 5 billion years old. They also believe that life on earth began about 3 billion years ago.

▶ **How old is the earth?**

**Rock dating.** Uranium is a heavy element. In time, it changes into lead. The time it takes to change into lead is known. By measuring the amount of uranium and lead in a rock, you can find out the age of the rock. Carbon is an element found in living things. It can help tell you the age of the remains of living things.

▶ **How can you find out the age of a rock?**

**Reading layers of rocks.** You know that erosion wears down the earth's crust. The eroded material is carried to another place. Sediments pile up layer upon layer. Where would you expect to find the oldest layer? Usually, the bottom layer is the oldest. The layers above were formed later. The newest layers are on top.

▶ **Which layer of sedimentary rock is usually the oldest?**

## WHAT YOU LEARNED

1. The earth is about 5 billion years old.
2. Uranium can be used to help find out the age of rocks.
3. Carbon can be used to help find out the age of the remains of living things.
4. The bottom layer of sedimentary rock is usually the oldest layer.

## ANSWER THESE

1. The oldest rocks found on the earth are
   a. 1 thousand years old
   b. 4 million years old
   c. 5 billion years old
2. In layers of rock, the oldest layer is usually found
   a. on top
   b. in the middle
   c. at the bottom
3. Carbon can be used to find the age of
   a. minerals
   b. igneous rocks
   c. remains of living things

## NOW TRY THESE

1. Find the word for an element that changes to lead.

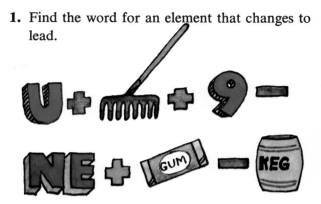

2. Find the word for an element used to find the age of remains of living things.

## PEOPLE IN SCIENCE

**Randolph Bromery**

Dr. Bromery is professor of geophysics and former chancellor at the University of Massachusetts. He began his career with the United States Geological Survey. As Project Chief for numerous programs, he has worked on magnetic and other surveys of the United States and Puerto Rico. Dr. Bromery has served on many advisory committees. He has been awarded a number of honorary degrees, and has received national and international awards for his achievements.

UNIT 7
**The records in the rocks**
**2**

# What are fossils?

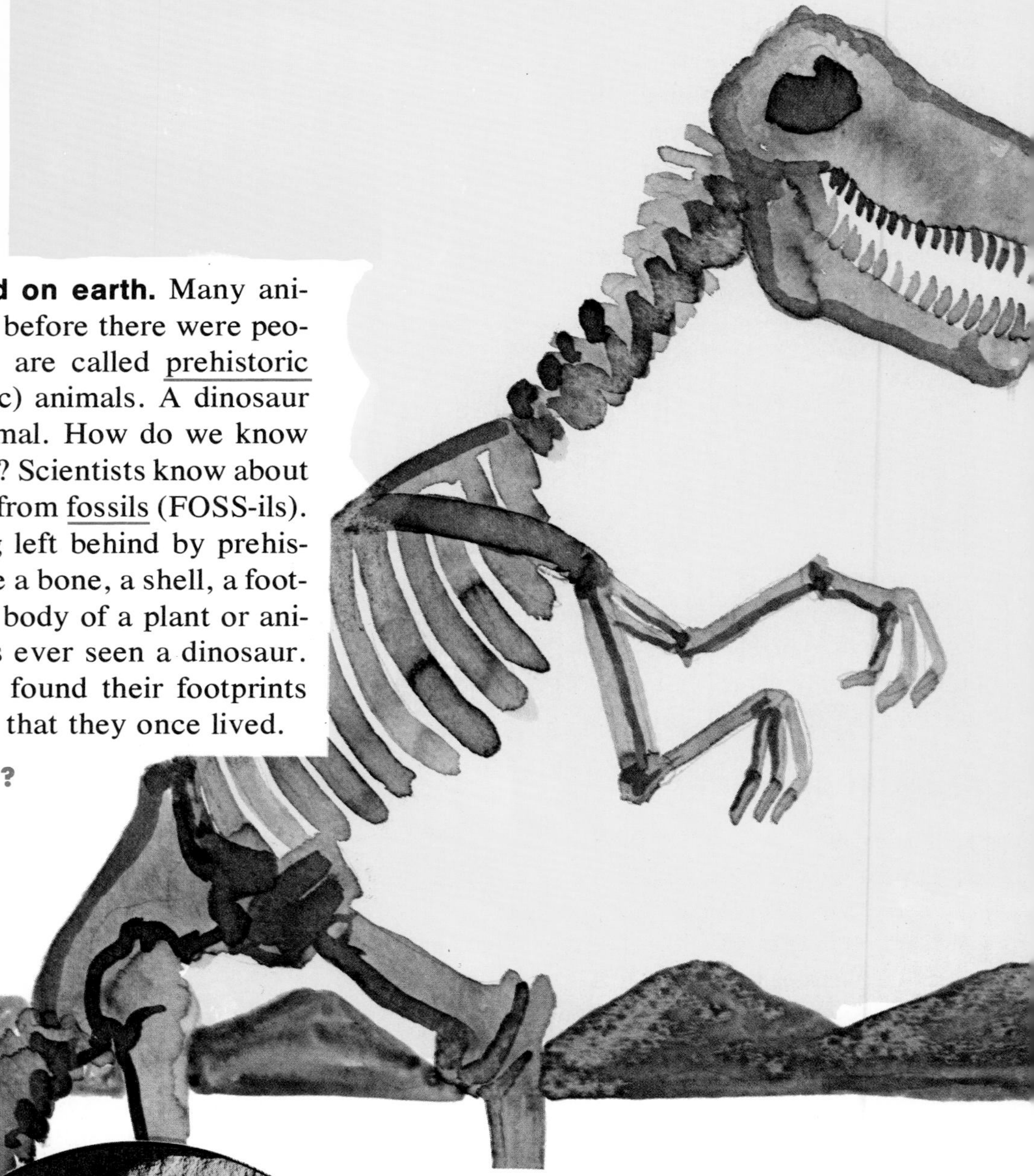

**Animals that lived on earth.** Many animals lived on earth before there were people. These animals are called prehistoric (PREE-his-TAHR-ic) animals. A dinosaur is a prehistoric animal. How do we know that dinosaurs lived? Scientists know about prehistoric animals from fossils (FOSS-ils). A fossil is anything left behind by prehistoric life. It could be a bone, a shell, a footprint, or the actual body of a plant or animal. No person has ever seen a dinosaur. But scientists have found their footprints and bones to prove that they once lived.

▶ **What is a fossil?**

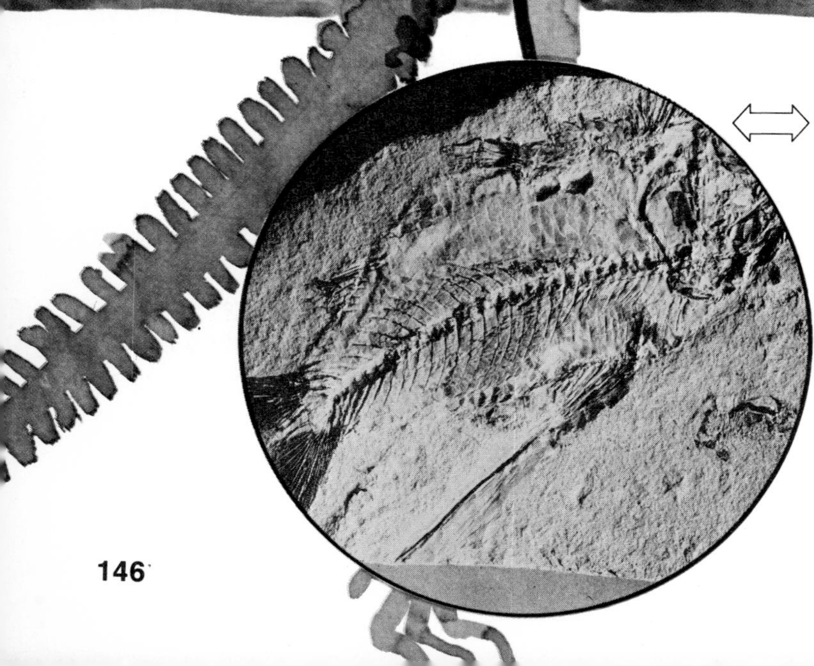

**Fossils in rocks.** Most fossils are found in sedimentary rocks that were once under water. An animal that lives in a shallow body of water dies. It sinks to the bottom and becomes covered with mud. The soft parts of the animal rot away. The hard parts become completely covered by sediments. In time, the sediments harden into sedimentary rock. A fossil forms inside the rock.

▶ **In what type of rock would you find most fossils?**

**Studying prehistoric life.** Ground water can get through sedimentary rock. The water may dissolve the bones or shells left by the animals. But the bones and shells sometimes leave an <u>impression</u> in the rock. The inside of the rock takes on the same shape as the material that was dissolved. Impressions can also be the tracks, tunnels, and trails left by prehistoric animals.

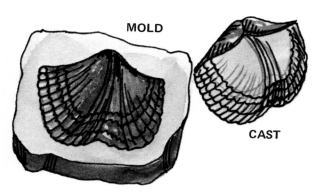

MOLD

CAST

When a fossil impression hardens, a <u>mold</u> forms. Sometimes a mold is filled with <u>min</u>eral deposits from the water. When the minerals harden, they form an exact copy of the bone or shell. This is called a <u>cast</u>. Scientists learn a lot about prehistoric life by studying impressions, molds, and casts.

▶ **How does a mold form?**

## WHAT YOU LEARNED

1. Fossils are the remains of prehistoric life.
2. Fossils form in sedimentary rocks.
3. Scientists study impressions, molds, and casts to find out about prehistoric life.

## SCIENCE WORDS

**prehistoric** (PREE-his-TAHR-ic)
    before the written history of man on earth
**fossil** (FOSS-il)
    anything left behind by prehistoric life
**impression**
    a shape left in something by an object
**mold**
    a hardened impression left by an object
**cast**
    a mold that has filled up with minerals

## ANSWER THESE

1. What kinds of fossils have been found?
2. How do we know that dinosaurs once lived?
3. Why are most fossils formed from the hard parts of animals?
4. Name three types of fossils.

## FINDING OUT MORE

Fossils sometimes turn into stone. To petrify (PET-tri-fy) means to turn into stone. Many of the hard parts of dead plants and animals have been petrified. Minerals dissolved in ground water replace the original parts of the plant or animal. The minerals harden and turn to stone. This forms an exact stone copy of the plant or animal. There is a forest of petrified trees in Arizona.

## DO THIS AT HOME

Try to make your own fossils. In nature, a fossil takes millions of years to form. Your "fossil" will form overnight.

Press a sea shell into a piece of clay. Remove the sea shell. Place the clay with the impression into a paper cup. Fill a second cup half-full of plaster of Paris. Add water to the plaster of Paris until it becomes thick and creamy. Now pour the plaster over the clay. The next day, remove the clay from the plaster. Is your homemade fossil a mold or a cast?

# How were some fossils formed?

**Fossils in ice.** There is always great excitement when a fossil is found. One of the most exciting finds was a woolly elephant called a mammoth (MAM-uth). It was found whole, with all its hair and skin. How was this possible? The mammoth was found in Siberia, Russia. It was preserved (pre-ZERVED), or kept as it was, in a huge chunk of ice. It still had some food in its mouth. It probably had fallen into some soft snow and could not get out. When it died, the freezing temperatures preserved it for thousands of years.

▶ **What is a mammoth?**

This is an artist's idea of how animals may have become trapped in tar pits millions of years ago.

**Fossils in tar pits.** There are pools of thick, sticky tar outside the city of Los Angeles, California. Tar for paving streets is taken from these pools. Hundreds of thousands of bones have been found in the tar. The bones belonged to extinct (eck-STINCT) animals. Extinct animals are animals that are no longer found alive on earth. The saber-toothed tiger is an extinct animal whose bones are found in the tar. Many, many years ago, animals walked into the tar pits. They became trapped in the pits and died. The tar preserved their bones.

▶ **What is an extinct animal?**

**Insect fossils.** A clear, sticky sap flows from pine trees. Long ago, some insects were trapped in the sap of these trees. When sap hardens, it is called <u>amber</u>. Even after the tree dies, the amber with the insects in it remains. There are many well-preserved fossils of insects found in amber.

▶ **What is amber?**

This insect fossil has been preserved in amber for millions of years.

## WHAT YOU LEARNED

1. The remains of animals and plants are found in ice, tar, and amber.

## SCIENCE WORDS

**mammoth** (MAM-uth)
an ancient woolly elephant
**preserve** (pre-ZERVE)
keep something as it is
**extinct** (eck-STINCT)
something that once lived on the earth but is no longer found alive
**saber-toothed tiger**
an extinct animal
**amber**
hardened pine sap

## ANSWER THESE

1. A mammoth was a
   a. dinosaur
   b. woolly elephant
   c. dog
2. A good method of preserving the soft remains of animals is
   a. freezing
   b. heating
   c. burying
3. Some of the animal bones found in pools of tar were those of
   a. ancient fish
   b. prehistoric clams
   c. saber-toothed tigers
4. Animals became trapped in tar pits because
   a. the tar is hot
   b. the smell of the tar killed them
   c. tar is thick and sticky
5. Insects that lived long ago were trapped and preserved in
   a. rocks
   b. amber
   c. lava

## PEOPLE IN SCIENCE

### Mary Nicol Leakey (1913-    )

Mary Leakey was born in London, England. She married Louis Leakey, the son of English missionaries who worked in Africa. Both she and her husband discovered many human fossils in Africa. Many of these fossils have helped us understand how early people were different from later people.

**149**

# What can we learn from fossils?

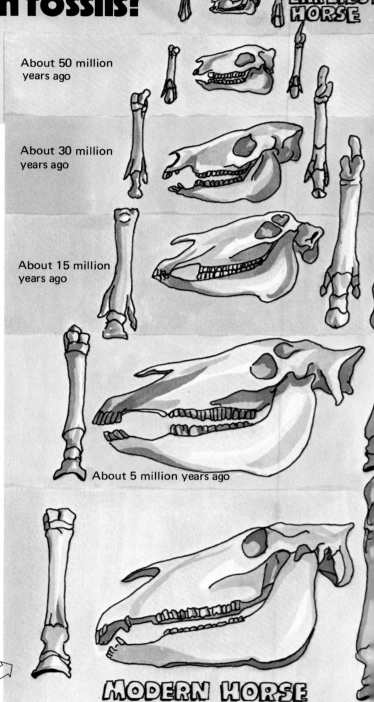

Fore Foot    Skull    Hind Foot

EARLIEST HORSE

About 50 million years ago

About 30 million years ago

About 15 million years ago

About 5 million years ago

MODERN HORSE

**The earth changes.** Scientific studies of the earth show that the crust is always changing. Erosion wears down rocks and crust movements build them up. Fossils tell us how the earth has changed through the ages. Fossils of sea animals have been found in desert regions. This shows that these regions were once sea bottoms.

▶ **What can fossils tell us about the earth?**

**Living things change.** Giant glaciers once spread over many regions of the world. As the glaciers moved into new regions, the temperature dropped in those regions. Some of the plants and animals of those regions could not adapt (a-DAPT), or adjust, to their changing environment. They became extinct. We know about these plants and animals because they left fossils. Many kinds of plants and animals that lived long ago are not living today. Many kinds of plants and animals living today were not living long ago. Fossils tell us the history of changes in living things.

▶ **What do fossils tell us about living things?**

**The changing horse.** Scientists have found fossils of a four-toed animal the size of a large cat. This animal lived about 60 million years ago. Later fossils show how this animal changed through the ages. There were changes in the animal's size, in its teeth, its legs, and its toes. The horse of today once looked like this smaller animal. Other fossils show that animals such as the elephant, the giraffe, and the camel also are related to animals that are now extinct.

▶ **How do scientists know that the horse has changed through the ages?**

150

**Life through the ages.** Scientists believe that life began in the ocean about 3000 million years ago. About 400 million years ago, some kinds of water animals became adapted to living on land and breathing air. Many new kinds of animals appeared on the land. Other kinds became extinct. About two million years ago, human beings appeared on the earth. Human beings are newer to the earth than nearly all other animals.

▶ **Where did life probably begin?**

## WHAT YOU LEARNED

1. Fossils show that living things have changed through the ages.
2. Many living things have become extinct.
3. Life probably began in the sea.

## SCIENCE WORD

**adapt** (a-DAPT)

change in order to adjust to changes in the environment.

## ANSWER THESE

1. What do fossils tell us about living things?
2. How has the horse changed through the ages?
3. When did human-like animals first appear on the earth?

## NOW TRY THIS

Do the puzzle to find the name of a clue to past life on earth.

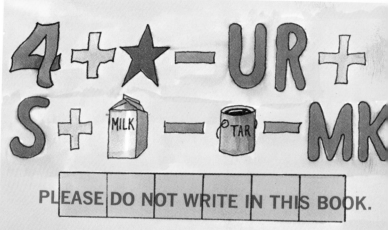

PLEASE DO NOT WRITE IN THIS BOOK.

The heads shown are based on four very old skulls found in Africa. The head on the left is the oldest. The one on the right is more recent. All four skulls used to make these heads are believed to be more than a million years old.

151

# What is the geologic time scale?

**Fossils date sedimentary rocks.** You learned that sedimentary rocks are formed layer upon layer. If sedimentary rocks have not been folded over or broken by faults, the oldest layers are at the bottom. The youngest layers are on top. Most sedimentary rocks contain fossils of plants and animals that lived long ago. Certain types of living things lived for a time and then all died out. For example, trilobites (TRY-lo-bites) were animals that lived in the oceans about 600 million years ago. Scientists have found fossils of trilobites in many sedimentary rocks. Whenever they do, they know that the rock layers containing the fossils must have been formed about 600 million years ago. Lower layers must then be older than that. Higher layers are younger. Fossils of things that lived during other ages have also been found. If scientists know the age of the fossil, they know the age of the rock layer containing the fossil.

▶ **What does knowing the age of a fossil tell you?**

**The geologic time scale.** By making many observations of rocks and fossils, scientists have been able to write a history of the earth. This history is called the geologic (jee-uh-LOJ-ik) time scale. The time scale begins when the earth was formed and goes on until the present. It divides that time into five eras (ER-uhs). Each era lasted for millions of years. The three most recent eras have been divided into smaller amounts of time called periods. The most recent era has time divided into even smaller units called epochs (EP-uks). The chart of the geologic time scale shows what kinds of things were living on earth at different times in the past.

▶ **How many eras are there in the geologic time scale?**

### WHAT YOU LEARNED

1. The age of a fossil tells the age of the sedimentary rock layer it was found in.
2. A history of the earth based on observations of rocks and fossils is called the geologic time scale.

Trilobite fossil

## THE GEOLOGIC TIME SCALE

| Era | Period | Epoch | Millions of years ago | Some things living at that time |
|---|---|---|---|---|
| **Cenozoic** "Age of Mammals" | Quaternary | Recent | .01 | Modern people and modern animals |
| | | Pleistocene | 2 | Early people living |
| | Tertiary | Pliocene | 12 | Many mammals; earliest people |
| | | Miocene | 26 | Grasses develop. |
| | | Oligocene | 37 | Modern mammals |
| | | Eocene | 53 | Pygamy ancestors of the modern horse |
| | | Paleocene | 65 | Modern birds |
| **Mesozoic** "Age of Reptiles" | Cretaceous | | 136 | Dinosaurs die out. |
| | Jurassic | | 190 | Giant dinosaurs living |
| | Triassic | | 225 | First mammals |
| **Paleozoic** | Permian | | 280 | Modern insects |
| | Carboniferous | | 345 | First reptiles |
| | Devonian | | 395 | First amphibians First land plants |
| | Silurian | | 430 | First land animals |
| | Ordovician | | 500 | First animals with backbones (fish) |
| | Cambrian | | 570 | Ocean animals without backbones |
| **Proterozoic** | | | | Life exists only in water (none on any land) |
| **Archeozoic** | | | 4,500 | |

## SCIENCE WORDS

**trilobites** (TRY-lo-bites)
   animals that lived in the oceans about 600 million years ago

**geologic** (jee-uh-LOJ-ik) **time scale**
   a history of the earth based on observations of rocks and fossils

**eras** (ER-uhs) intervals
   five periods of time that the geologic time scale is divided into

**periods**
   smaller intervals of time that some eras of the geologic time scale are divided into

**epochs** (EP-uks)
   still smaller intervals of time that recent periods of the geologic time scale are divided into

## ANSWER THESE

1. An animal that lived over 600 million years ago was the
   **a.** horse       **b.** trilobite       **c.** dinosaur

2. The oldest layers of sedimentary rock are
   **a.** on top
   **b.** in the middle
   **c.** on the bottom

3. The geologic time scale
   **a.** begins 1 million years ago
   **b.** is divided into five years
   **c.** is made up of minutes and hours

4. The length of an era is
   **a.** hundreds of years
   **b.** millions of years
   **c.** trillions of years

5. The most recent era of the geologic time scale is divided into
   **a.** epochs       **b.** years       **c.** periods

# What happens to the remains of living things?

**Forming charcoal.** Heat some wooden splints in a test tube. Hold a lighted splint to the mouth of the test tube. A gas is formed from the wooden splints. The gas burns. This gas is very much like natural gas, or gas that is found in the earth's crust. The material inside the test tube turns black. The black material is charcoal.

Charcoal is a form of the element carbon. Carbon is in all common fuels (FEWLS). Fuels are materials that give off heat when they are burned. A fuel may be a solid, a liquid, or a gas. Fuels that come from the remains of living things are called fossil fuels. Wood, coal, natural gas, and the liquid fuel petroleum (puh-TRO-lee-um) are common fossil fuels.

► **What is a fossil fuel?**

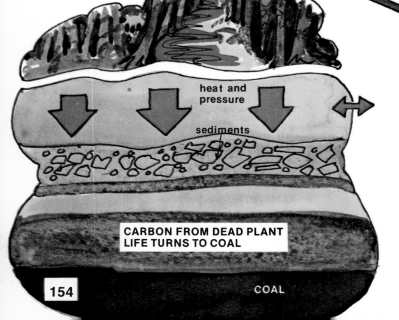

heat and pressure

sediments

**CARBON FROM DEAD PLANT LIFE TURNS TO COAL**

COAL

**Forming coal.** Coal was formed in swamps, or areas of shallow water where thick plant life grew. The plants died and were covered by water, mud, and sediments. Heat and pressure slowly caused chemical changes to take place. After many, many years, most of the elements in the plants combined with other elements. Carbon was left. Coal was formed.

► **Where was coal formed?**

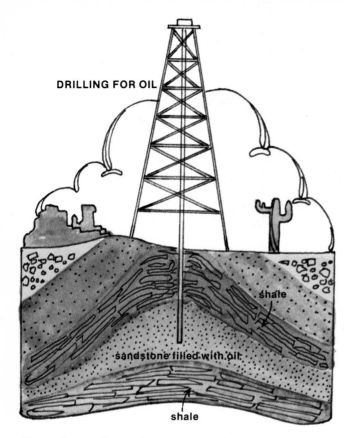
DRILLING FOR OIL

shale

sandstone filled with oil

shale

**Forming oil and gas.** Petroleum is formed within the crust of the earth. It is also called crude (CROOD) oil. Scientists think that the bodies of prehistoric sea animals and plants became trapped in sediments. After millions of years, heat and pressure changed them into crude oil and natural gas. Crude oil and natural gas are usually found together in the crust of the earth. To get the oil and gas, it is necessary to drill into the earth's crust.

▶ **What is crude oil?**

## WHAT YOU LEARNED

1. All common fuels contain carbon.
2. Heat and pressure changed prehistoric swamp plants to coal.
3. Petroleum and natural gas were formed from prehistoric sea plants and animals.

## SCIENCE WORDS

**natural gas**
   a gas found in the earth's crust
**fuel** (FEWL)
   a material that gives off heat when it is burned
**fossil fuel**
   a fuel that is formed from the remains of living things
**petroleum** (puh-TRO-lee-um)
   a liquid fossil fuel; crude oil
**swamp**
   an area of shallow water where a lot of plant life grows

## ANSWER THESE

1. What element is always found in common fuels?
2. What are some common fuels?
3. Why are petroleum and coal called fossil fuels?

## FINDING OUT MORE

Here are some more fossil clues to the earth's past.

| PLACE | CLUE | CONCLUSION |
|---|---|---|
| Antarctic | Coal found here | May once have been warm, with swamps and trees |
| Texas | Oil found here | May once have been covered by a shallow sea |

# UNIT 7 Review

*Do the following review questions on a separate sheet of paper.*

**Modified True/False**      *Write down each of the following statements, leaving a blank line between each line you write. Before the number for each statement, write T if the statement is true and F if the statement is false. For the false statements, cross out the word written in capital letters and write above it a word that will make the statement true.*

1. CHARCOAL is a liquid fossil fuel.
2. Heat and pressure turn SWAMPS into fossil fuel.
3. The amount of uranium and IRON in a rock can help date the rock.
4. An era is the SMALLEST unit of geologic time.
5. Fossils are found in SEDIMENTARY rocks.
6. Scientists have found fossils of many EXTINCT animals.
7. Scientists believe life began ON LAND.
8. Many insects have been preserved in AMBER.
9. A CAST is a hardened impression left by an object.
10. A plant or animal adapts to new conditions by REMAINING THE SAME.

**Multiple Choice**      *Write the letter of the choice that best completes the statement or answers the question.*

1. By measuring the amounts of lead and uranium in a rock,
   a. you can identify the rock
   b. you can tell where it came from
   c. you can tell the age of the rock
2. A fossil is
   a. anything left behind by prehistoric life
   b. a very old rock
   c. a very old animal
3. Fossils are usually found in
   a. a metamorphic rock
   b. igneous rock
   c. sedimentary rock
4. An extinct animal is a kind of animal
   a. found only in Siberia
   b. that once lived on earth, but no longer does
   c. that lives on earth today, but did not always
5. If an animal cannot adapt, it will probably
   a. live longer
   b. become extinct
   c. hibernate
6. Finding fossils, such as trilobites, can help
   a. locate uranium
   b. determine the age of sedimentary rocks
   c. find sedimentary rocks
7. Lower layers of rock are usually
   a. older than surface rocks
   b. younger than surface rocks
   c. the same age as surface rocks
8. Petroleum, gas, and charcoal are examples of
   a. fossil fuels
   b. extinct plants
   c. kinds of magma

156

# UNIT 8

# Water

## Unit Lessons

1. What makes water change its phase?
2. What is the water cycle?
3. How does water get into the ground?
4. What is hydrology?
5. What is hard water?
6. How is water purified?

## Goals and Objectives

After completing this unit, you should be able to:

- describe how water can exist as a gas, a liquid, or a solid.
- understand how water on earth evaporates, condenses and precipitates in a cycle.
- explain what happens to rainwater when it reaches the soil.
- understand the importance of studying new ways to find fresh water.
- name the elements found in hard water, and describe some ways of purifying water.

# UNIT 8
## Water
# 1

# What makes water change its phase?

**The phases of matter.** Matter is anything that takes up space and has mass. Matter can exist in three states, or phases. These phases are the solid phase, the liquid phase, and the gaseous (GAS-ee-us) phase. Water is one kind of matter. It is most familiar to us in the liquid phase. We drink it, wash in it, and swim in it. Water in the solid phase we call ice. Water in the gaseous phase we call steam or water vapor.

▶ **What do we call the three phases of water?**

**From solid to liquid.** In order for a block of ice to melt, it must absorb (ub-SORB), or take in, heat. The ice will absorb heat from warmer things that surround it. The surrounding things get cooler. The ice gets warmer and melts. This is what happens to soda pop in an ice chest. The soda is warmer than the ice. The soda gets cooler. The ice gets warmer and melts. Suppose the surrounding things are colder than the ice. Then the ice cannot melt. Ice cubes in a freezer do not melt because the surrounding area is just as cold.

▶ **What must happen to ice in order for it to melt?**

**From liquid to gas.** Heat energy must also be absorbed for liquid water to become gaseous water. Water in a tea kettle absorbs heat from the burner flame. After the water gets hot enough, it boils. During boiling, water in

the liquid phase becomes water in the gaseous phase.

▶ **What must happen to water in the liquid phase for it to become water in the gaseous phase?**

**Drying up.** Water in the liquid phase can change to the gaseous phase without boiling. That is what happens when a puddle dries in the sun. The water absorbs heat from the sunlight and changes to water vapor, a gas.

**After a rain**          **Two days later**

After a day or so of sunny weather, the water in most puddles will have been dried up by the evaporation of the water.

158

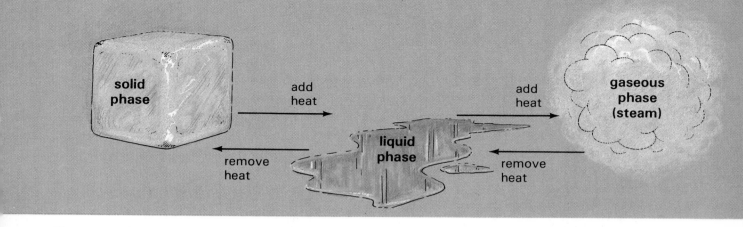

solid phase → add heat → liquid phase → add heat → gaseous phase (steam)

gaseous phase (steam) → remove heat → liquid phase → remove heat → solid phase

The changing of a liquid to a gas without boiling is called evaporation (eh-vap-uh-RAY-shun). When a liquid evaporates, it absorbs heat.

▶ **What is evaporation?**

**From gaseous phase to solid phase.** Ice absorbs heat to become water. Water absorbs heat to become gaseous water. Suppose the opposite change is to take place. We want to change the gaseous water back to solid water (ice). Then heat must be taken away rather than absorbed. Gaseous water must give up heat to become liquid water. Even more heat must be given up by the liquid water in order for it to become solid water.

▶ **What must happen for gaseous water to become liquid water?**

**WHAT YOU LEARNED**

1. The three phases of matter are the solid phase, the liquid phase, and the gaseous phase.
2. A solid must absorb heat in order to change to a liquid.
3. A liquid must absorb heat in order to change to a gas.
4. A gas must give up heat in order to change to a liquid.
5. A liquid must give up heat in order to change to a solid.

**SCIENCE WORDS**

**matter**
anything that takes up space and has mass

**phase**
a state that matter can exist in

**absorb** (ub-ZORB)
take in

**evaporation** (eh-vap-uh-RAY-shun)
the changing of a liquid to a gas wihtout boiling

**ANSWER THESE**

1. Ice is water in the (solid / liquid) phase.
2. In order for a block of ice to melt, it must (give up / absorb) heat.
3. In order for liquid water to become water vapor, it must (give up / absorb) heat.
4. Evaporation is the changing of a liquid to a (solid / gas).
5. In order for water vapor to become liquid water, it must (give up / absorb) heat.

**NOW TRY THIS**

Below is a list of words describing water in different phases. Write all the words on a piece of paper. After each word, write either solid, liquid, or gas to identify what phase of water each word refers to.

| | |
|---|---|
| rain | steam |
| snow | ice |
| water vapor | lake |
| ocean | fog |
| river | mist |
| cloud | puddle |

# What is the water cycle?

**Evaporation of water.** About 3/4 of the earth's surface is water in the oceans. Water from the ocean surface is constantly evaporating and changing to water vapor. Water is also evaporating from the surface of lakes and rivers and from the soil. The water vapor from evaporation becomes one of the gases in the air. Air always contains some water vapor.

▶ **What is constantly happening to water at the surface of the earth?**

**Condensation of water.** Water at the earth's surface absorbs heat and evaporates. It changes to water vapor. Water vapor is a gas in the air that cannot be seen. When air containing water vapor is cooled, the water vapor loses heat. If the water vapor gives up enough heat, it changes back to the liquid phase. It condenses (kon-DENS-es) into tiny water droplets. Condensation (kon-den-SAY-shun) is the changing of a gas to a liquid. After condensation, the tiny water droplets form clouds. Clouds are simply a collection of tiny water droplets.

▶ **What phase change happens to water when it forms clouds?**

**Back to earth.** The tiny water droplets that make up clouds are very small and light. They are kept up in the clouds by air currents. If these tiny droplets grow larger, they become too heavy to stay up. They fall to the earth as raindrops. If the air is very cold, water vapor may change to the solid phase and fall as snow or sleet. Any form of water that condenses out of the air and returns to the earth is called precipitation (pruh-sip-uh-TAY-shun). Rain and snow are the main kinds of precipitation.

▶ **What must happen to tiny water droplets before they can fall as raindrops?**

**The water cycle.** Water on the earth is constantly changing its phase. It changes from a liquid to a gas as it evaporates from the surface of the earth. It changes back to a liquid and forms clouds. Rain and other kinds of precipitation bring the water back to the surface of the earth. These changes happen over and over again. Changes that repeat themselves are called cycles (SY-kulz). The cycle of the seasons is the repeating each year of spring, summer, fall, and winter. The main part of the water cycle is the evaporation of water from the surface of the earth and the return of water to the earth as some kind of precipitation.

▶ **What are cycles?**

# THE WATER CYCLE

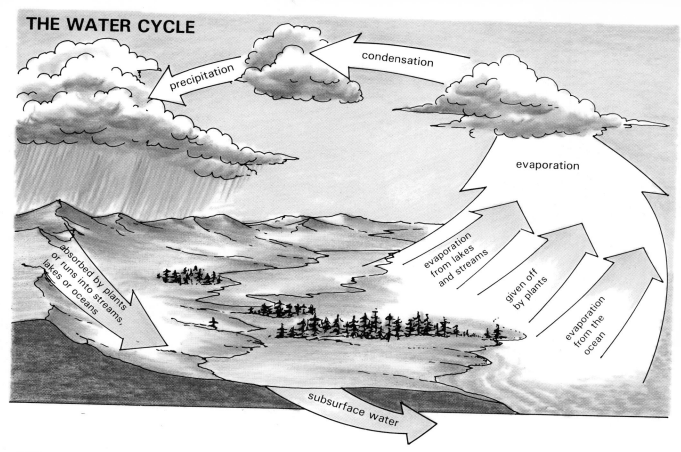

- precipitation
- condensation
- evaporation
- evaporation from lakes and streams
- given off by plants
- evaporation from the ocean
- absorbed by plants or runs into streams, lakes or oceans
- subsurface water

## WHAT YOU LEARNED

1. Water at the surface of the earth is constantly evaporating.
2. Condensation is the changing of a gas to a liquid.
3. Water vapor condenses to tiny water droplets, which collect to form clouds.
4. Precipitation is any form of water that condenses out of the air and returns to the earth.
5. The evaporation of water from the surface of the earth and the return of water to the earth as precipitation make up the water cycle.

## SCIENCE WORDS

**condense** (kon-DENS)
   change from a gas to a liquid

**condensation** (kon-den-SAY-shun)
   the changing of a gas to a liquid

**precipitation** (pruh-sip-uh-TAY-shun)
   any form of water that condenses out of the air and returns to the earth

**cycles** (SY-kulz)
   changes that repeat themselves

## ANSWER THESE

1. Name four places where the water evaporates from the earth into the air.
2. How are clouds formed from water vapor?
3. Explain the main part of the water cycle.

## NOW TRY THIS

Two kinds of precipitation.

1. – ail + – l

2. – ke + – p

# How does water get into the ground?

**Water in the ground.** Some water that falls to the earth may sink into the ground. The water that collects in the ground is known as <u>ground</u> <u>water</u>. Pour water on some soil. The water slowly disappears. Where did it go? It went down into the soil. Water sinks through spaces or <u>pores</u> in rocks and soil.

▶ What is ground water?

**What stops ground water?** How far down through the earth's crust does ground water sink? The water moves down until it comes to a rock that will not let the water go through. Then the water cannot go any lower. Shale is a sedimentary rock made of cemented mud and clay. The spaces in shale are so small that water cannot pass through them. Shale can stop water from moving deeper into the crust of the earth.

▶ What type of rock stops water from sinking into the crust?

**Rocks can hold water.** Pour water into a glass of gravel. The water moves down until it reaches the bottom of the glass. It can not go through the glass. It stops moving down. The glass begins to fill up with water.

The ground acts the same way. Water moves down until it hits a layer of rock it can't go through. This is like the bottom of the glass. The water then begins to fill up the pores and spaces in the rocks above this layer. When the pores in rocks are filled with water, we say the rocks are <u>saturated</u> (SACH-uh-ray-tid). The top of the saturated part of the rocks is called the <u>water</u> <u>table</u>.

▶ What is the water table?

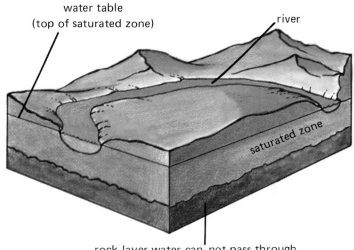

water table
(top of saturated zone)

river

saturated zone

rock layer water can not pass through

162

**Some water is held up.** All water does not move down to the saturated zone. Some water stays behind. It clings to the surface of the soil particles. Pour 50 milliliters of water through a funnel filled with sand. Catch the water that comes through the sand in a graduated cylinder. Less than 50 milliliters flowed into the cylinder. Some of the water stays back. It is held on the surface of the sand particles. The roots of most plants can't reach the water table. These plants get their moisture from water in the upper levels of the soil.

▶ What happens to some of the water that seeps down into the earth?

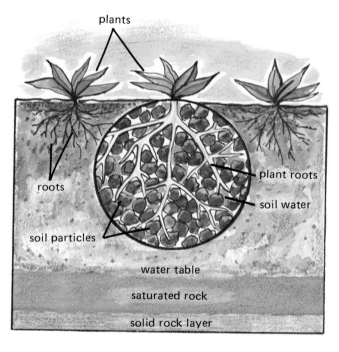

plants

plant roots

roots

soil water

soil particles

water table

saturated rock

solid rock layer

**Smaller can be bigger.** Cut a block of wood in half. The two pieces now have an extra surface where they were cut. The two pieces have more surface than the single piece had. If you cut the wood into smaller and smaller pieces, the total surface gets larger and larger. Soils made of smaller particles have more surface for holding water. The finer the texture of a soil, the more water it can hold.

▶ Do smaller-size particles hold more or less water?

# What is hydrology?

**The importance of water.** Only 3 percent of the water on the earth is fresh water. Three-fourths of this fresh water lies as ice and snow in the cold regions of the earth. This leaves for our use only a small amount of fresh liquid water.

An average person needs about 2½ liters of water each day. Some of this water can be in food. The rest must be in drinking water. A person can live without food for about a month. Without water, the person would die in about a week. Plants and animals that we use for food need water, too.

Water on the earth is so important that some scientists give all their attention to its study. These scientists are called hydrologists (hy-DRAHL-uh-jists). The study of water on land, in the oceans, and in the air is called hydrology (hy-DRAHL-uh-jee).

▶ Where can most of the world's fresh water be found?

**Hydrologists at work.** Every city, town, and farm must have its supply of fresh water. Hydrologists are concerned with how to supply people with the fresh water they need. Hydrologists may help decide the best place to build a dam. They may draw up plans for supplying a city with fresh water from an outlying area. They may help farmers bring in water to their crops.

▶ What concern is of great importance to hydrologists?

The Grand Coulee Dam, on the Columbia River in Washington State, provides irrigation water for an area larger than the State of Rhode Island.

An irrigated corn field in California

**Constant water supply, greater need.** The amount of water on earth does not change. We don't use up water. We simply make use of it for a while. We drink it, bathe in it, and water our plants with it. Finally, most of this water finds its way into the ocean. When it evaporates, it becomes pure again. Rain returns water to our reservoirs. Then we use it all over again.

The demand for fresh water is increasing. During the last 20 years, the amount of fresh water needed by people has about doubled. This makes it important not to waste water. As the demand for water increases, the work of the hydrologist will become even more important.

▶ **How has the demand for water changed over the last 20 years?**

## WHAT YOU LEARNED

1. Very little of the water on earth is fresh liquid water that we can use.
2. Hydrology is the study of water on land, in the oceans, and in the air.
3. Hydrologists are concerned with how to supply people with fresh water.
4. The amount of fresh water on the earth does not change, but the demand for it is increasing.

## SCIENCE WORDS

**hydrologist** (hy-DRAHL-uh-jist)
 a scientist who studies the water on the earth

**hydrology** (hy-DRAHL-uh-jee)
 the study of water on the earth

## ANSWER THESE

1. How much of the water found on earth is fresh water?
   a. 3%
   b. 50%
   c. 85%
2. The study of the earth's water is called
   a. geology
   b. waterology
   c. hydrology
3. The amount of water on the earth
   a. is constantly changing
   b. does not change
   c. will be used up soon

## FINDING OUT MORE

Take a look at the water cycle. Does the amount of water on earth change? Just as much water evaporates as falls back to the earth. The amount does not change. The number of people living on earth is increasing. More people need more fresh water. There is enough fresh water for everyone now. Polluting what we have, however, would soon create a shortage.

These fish were the victims of pollution.

165

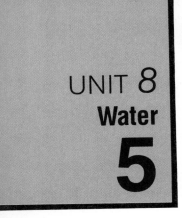

# What is hard water?

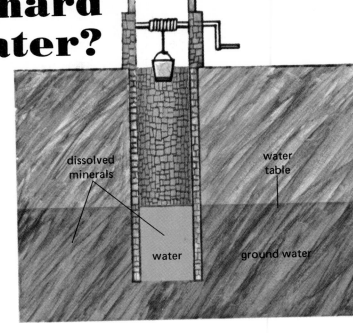

dissolved minerals

water table

water

ground water

**Ground water.** Ground water dissolves small amounts of minerals as it moves down through rocks and soil. Some of these dissolved minerals are compounds of calcium and magnesium. Water that contains dissolved compounds of calcium and magnesium is called <u>hard water</u>.

▶ **What is ground water?**

**Hard water.** Put some liquid soap into a test tube containing distilled water. Shake the test tube. The soap forms suds. Now dissolve a small amount of calcium chloride or magnesium chloride in another test tube containing distilled water. Pour a few drops of soap into this test tube and shake it. The soap does not form suds. The parts of the mineral in the dissolved water have com-

bined with the soap. This prevents the soap from forming suds.

The water in the test tube is hard water. Hard water contains calcium and magnesium salts. It is hard for soap to form suds in hard water. Much soap has to be used before suds will form. When we wash clothes in hard water, a large amount of soap has to be used. Much of the soap is wasted.

▶ **What does hard water contain?**

**AFTER SHAKING**

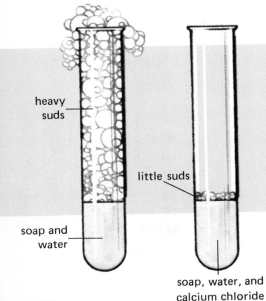

heavy suds

little suds

soap and water

soap, water, and calcium chloride

| CALCIUM AND MAGNESIUM SALTS | | | |
|---|---|---|---|
| SALT | CHEMICAL FORMULA | METALLIC PART | NON-METALLIC PART |
| Calcium chloride | $CaCl_2$ | $Ca^{+2}$ | $Cl^-$ |
| Magnesium chloride | $MgCl_2$ | $Mg^{+2}$ | $Cl^-$ |
| Calcium sulfate | $CaSO_4$ | $Ca^{+2}$ | $SO_4^{-2}$ |
| Magnesium sulfate | $MgSO_4$ | $Mg^{+2}$ | $SO_4^{-2}$ |
| Calcium bicarbonate | $Ca(HCO_3)_2$ | $Ca^{+2}$ | $HCO_3^-$ |
| Magnesium bicarbonate | $Mg(HCO_3)_2$ | $Mg^{+2}$ | $HCO_3^-$ |

$$Ca(HCO_3)_2 \xrightarrow{\text{heat}} CaCO_3 + H_2O + CO_2$$

$$\text{calcium bicarbonate} \xrightarrow{\text{heat}} \text{calcium carbonate} + \text{water} + \text{carbon dioxide}$$

## Changing bicarbonates to carbonates.

Dissolve some calcium bicarbonate in a beaker of water. Then heat the water to boiling. A white precipitate forms. The precipitate that forms in the beaker is calcium carbonate. The heat changed the calcium bicarbonate to calcium carbonate, water, and carbon dioxide. The carbon dioxide escapes into the air. The carbonate is left behind. Carbonate precipitates form inside hot water pipes that have hard water running through them. This rock-like precipitate can clog the pipes.

▶ **What can calcium carbonate do to hot water pipes?**

### WHAT YOU LEARNED

1. Hard water contains calcium and magnesium salts.
2. It is hard for soap to form suds in hard water.

### SCIENCE WORD

**hard water**
   water that contains calcium or magnesium salts

### ANSWER THESE

1. Water that seeps into the ground is called
   a. precipitation
   b. ground water
   c. carbonate

2. Water that contains calcium and magnesium salts is called
   a. ground water
   b. hard water
   c. precipitation

3. In order to change calcium bicarbonate to calcium carbonate, we must add
   a. heat
   b. carbon dioxide
   c. soap
4. When soap is added to hard water, the soap
   a. forms suds easily
   b. has a hard time forming suds
   c. changes to a carbonate

### FINDING OUT MORE

Water that contains iron bicarbonate is also hard water. Iron bicarbonate gives water a reddish color. This can stain clothing that is washed in the water. The iron bicarbonate causes rust spots, which are not easily removed. It also stains sinks and leaves a red ring around them. Special cleaning materials must be used to remove these stains.

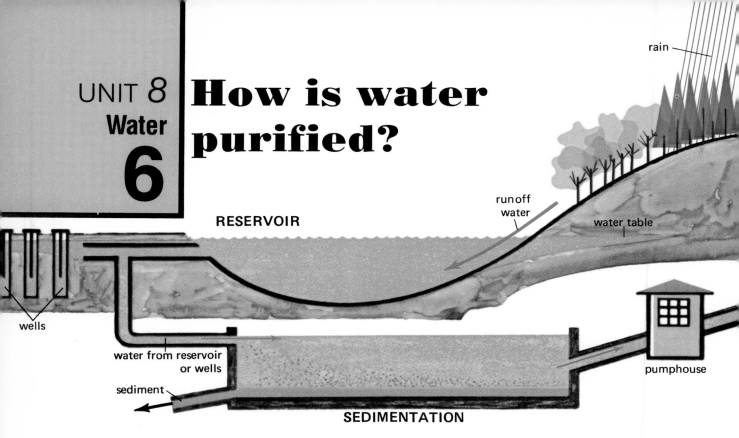

rain

runoff water

water table

**RESERVOIR**

wells

water from reservoir or wells

sediment

**SEDIMENTATION**

pumphouse

**Drinking water.** The water we drink comes from reservoirs and wells. Reservoirs are large bodies of water. They supply drinking water. Rain and melting snow collect in reservoirs. Pipelines bring water from reservoirs to our homes. A well is a hole dug down below the water table. Pumps lift water from wells to pipelines. Pipelines carry water to where it is needed.

▶ Where does our drinking water come from?

**Dissolved substances in water.** The earth contains many minerals that are soluble in water. As water flows through the earth, minerals dissolve in it. Water that enters reservoirs contains dissolved minerals. Dissolved minerals are also found in well water. They give water a taste.

▶ How do minerals get into the water we drink?

**Suspended materials in water.** As water flows over the ground, it picks up many insoluble particles. The faster the water flows, the more material it can carry. Sand, clay, dirt, bits of twigs, and microorganisms are picked up. This material becomes suspended in the water. It causes the water to be cloudy. Suspended materials can make reservoir water unfit to drink.

▶ What kinds of suspended materials are found in water?

**Purifying water.** There are many ways to purify drinking water. It can be treated in the following ways.

**Purifying Drinking Water**

1. Sedimentation (sed-uh-men-TAY-shun)—The water is allowed to stand for long periods of time. Heavy suspended particles settle to the bottom and are removed.

2. Coagulation (co-ag-yew-LAY-shun) —Chemicals are added that cause particles to clump together. These large

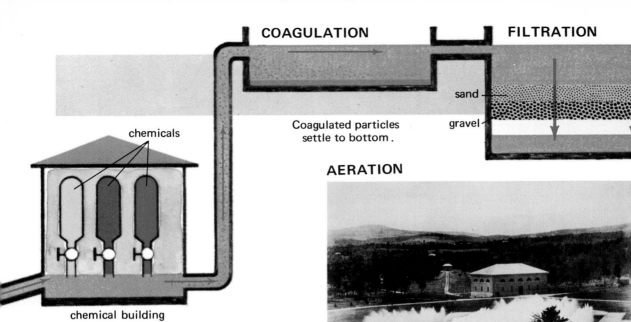

**COAGULATION**

Coagulated particles settle to bottom.

**FILTRATION**

sand

gravel

**AERATION**

chemicals

chemical building

chlorine

**CHLORINATION**

clumps of particles are heavy and settle faster than the smaller particles would.

3. Filtration (fil-TRAY-shun)—Water is passed through a filter to remove small particles.

4. Aeration (air-AY-shun)—Water is sprayed into the air. Oxygen from the air dissolves in the water. The oxygen kills some germs and gives water a fresher taste.

5. Chlorination (clor-uh-NAY-shun) —Chlorine is added to the water. Chlorine kills disease-causing microorganisms in the water.

▶ **What are 5 ways to purify drinking water?**

**WHAT YOU LEARNED**

1. Water contains many suspended materials.
2. Five ways to remove suspended particles from water are:
Sedimentation
Coagulation
Filtration
Aeration
Chlorination

**ANSWER THESE**

1. In order to purify water for drinking, we must remove
   a. dissolved substances only
   b. suspended substances only
   c. dissolved and suspended substances
2. The water we drink comes from
   a. wells only
   b. reservoirs only
   c. wells and reservoirs
3. Germs are killed during
   a. sedimentation
   b. chlorination
   c. filtration

**NOW TRY THIS**

Match the items in column B with the ways of purifying water from column A.

| A | B |
|---|---|
| Sedimentation | Adding chemicals that |
| Coagulation | make small particles |
| Filtration | clump together |
| Chlorination | Adding chlorine |
| Aeration | Standing |
| | Spraying into the air |
| | Passing through a filter |

# UNIT 8 Review

*Do the following questions on a separate sheet of paper.*

**Matching**   *Write down each of the statements in Column I, leaving one line of space after each statement. On the blank line following each statement, write the word or phrase from Column II that is described by that statement.*

### Column I

1. Studies the water on the earth.
2. The study of water on the earth.
3. Filled up.
4. Openings in rocks and soil.
5. Water that collects in soil and rocks.
6. Take in.
7. A state that matter can exist in.
8. Snow, sleet, rain.
9. Changes that repeat themselves.
10. Changing from a liquid to a vapor.

### Column II

pores
cycles
absorb
hydrologist
evaporation
hydrology
ground water
saturated
phase
precipitation

*Do the following questions on a separate sheet of paper.*

**Multiple Choice**   *Write the letter of the choice that best completes the statement or answers the question.*

1. In order for water to change its phase, it must
   a. give up heat
   b. absorb heat
   c. either give up or absorb heat
2. Condensation is the changing of
   a. a gas to a solid
   b. a gas to a liquid
   c. a liquid to a gas
3. Evaporation takes water from a liquid state
   a. to a gaseous state
   b. to a solid state
   c. to a boiling state
4. Saturated soil cannot
   a. lose any more water
   b. hold any more water
   c. contain any water at all
5. The water table is the top level
   a. of a lake or ocean
   b. that a river can rise to
   c. of saturated rock in the ground
6. A hydrologist might
   a. decide the best place for a dam
   b. figure out how to make rain
   c. look for petroleum
7. The amount of fresh water on earth is
   a. about the same as the salt water
   b. getting less all the time
   c. about 3% of all water
8. Hard water is water
   a. in the form of ice
   b. that is hard to find
   c. with dissolved compounds in it

170

# 9

# The Oceans

## Unit Lessons

1. How can we study the oceans?
2. How does the temperature of ocean water vary?
3. What changes the salinity of ocean water?
4. What does the ocean floor look like?
5. What materials make up ocean sediments?
6. What causes ocean currents?
7. What kinds of life are found in the ocean?
8. Where do we find life in the ocean?

## Goals and Objectives

After completing this unit. you should be able to:

- describe how echoes are used to map the ocean floor.
- explain why different areas of the ocean have different temperatures and salinities.
- describe a cross-section of an ocean floor.
- predict what kind of sediments would be found on different parts of the ocean floor.
- understand why we classify marine organisms as plankton. nekton. or benthos.

# How can we study the oceans?

Arctic Ocean

Atlantic Ocean

Pacific Ocean

Indian Ocean

Pacific Ocean

**The ocean connection.** Look at the oceans on the map. They cover nearly ¾ of the earth's surface. They are all connected. The Atlantic, Pacific, Indian, and Arctic oceans make up one large ocean. Scientists who study the oceans are called oceanographers (oh-shun-OG-ruh-furs). Oceanographers study the sediments on the ocean floor. They study ocean currents, and the temperature, composition, and depth of the water. They also study the animals and plants that live in the oceans.

▶ **What do we call a scientist who studies the oceans?**

**Laboratories in the sea.** Oceanographers study the ocean from special ships. The ships are called research vessels or floating laboratories. They travel over all the oceans. Scuba divers from these vessels go down into the water. They use oxygen from tanks to breathe. But they cannot go very deep, because the water pressure becomes too great. For deep diving, oceanographers use a bathyscaphe (BATH-ih-skaf). It is a special boat that can withstand large amounts of water pressure. The U.S. Navy bathyscaphe Trieste I went to the bottom in one of the deepest parts of the ocean. It reached a depth of 10 915 meters.

▶ **What is a bathyscaphe?**

**Echoes measure depth.** Echoes (EK-ohs) are sounds that bounce off objects. Echoes in oceans are measured with an echo sounder. The echo sounder sends a sound from the ocean's surface to the bottom. The sounder measures the time it takes the sound to reach the bottom and bounce back to the ship. Sound travels through water at 1500 meters per second. If an echo returns after two seconds, the sound must have traveled 3000 meters. This tells us that the ocean is 1500 meters deep at that place. It took the sound one second to travel 1500 meters to the bottom. It took the echo another second to travel 1500 meters back up to the ship. The echo sounder can be used to measure the ocean depth at many places. In this way it describes the shape of the ocean floor.

▶ **What instrument measures ocean depths?**

Trieste II, one of the deep-diving research boats of the United States Navy.

HOW SONAR IS USED

sound  echo  sound  echo

172

**Other instruments that go to sea.** Many different kinds of instruments are used to gather data about the ocean. Here is a list of some of these instruments and what each one does.

| SOME INSTRUMENTS USED TO STUDY THE OCEANS | |
| --- | --- |
| Instrument | What the Instrument Does |
| corer | a long, hollow tube that digs out layers of sediments lying under the oceans |
| dredge | a scoop or shovel that brings up samples of sediments from the bottom of the ocean |
| Nansen bottle | collects samples of ocean water from different depths |
| bathythermograph | records ocean water temperatures |
| deep water net | collects animals that live deep in the oceans |
| float | collects information on ocean currents |

▶ **Which instrument collects sea water samples?**

## WHAT YOU LEARNED

1. Oceanographers are scientists who study the oceans.
2. Oceanographers use special ships and instruments in their research.
3. One of the instruments uses echoes to measure ocean depths and to describe the shape of the ocean floor.
4. Other instruments gather data on ocean floor sediments, water temperature and composition, currents, and ocean life.

## SCIENCE WORDS

**oceanographer** (oh-shun-OG-ruh-fur)
a scientist who studies the oceans
**bathyscaphe** (BATH-ih-skaf)
a special boat that can dive very deep and withstand large amounts of pressure
**echo** (EK-oh)
a sound that bounces off an object
**echo sounder**
an instrument that uses echoes to measure ocean depths

## FINDING OUT MORE

You'll FLIP over this. A special research vessel is called FLIP. FLIP means Floating Instrument Platform. The platform is towed to the experiment area in a horizontal position. Then a part of the platform is flooded with sea water. The platform flips into a vertical position. Experiments are then conducted. When the work is completed, the sea water is pumped out. The vessel flips back to its horizontal position. It can then be towed to another area.

## ANSWER THESE

1. How many oceans are there on the earth?
   **a.** one   **b.** four   **c.** seven
2. A scuba diver cannot dive very deep because of
   **a.** his or her weight   **b.** lack of light
   **c.** water pressure
3. A boat that can withstand great amounts of water pressure is a
   **a.** research vessel   **b.** bathyscaphe
   **c.** scuba
4. The speed of sound in water is
   **a.** 1500 meters per second
   **b.** 10 915 meters per second
   **c.** 100 000 meters per second
5. A long, hollow tube that collects sediment layers from the ocean floor is a
   **a.** corer   **b.** dredge   **c.** Nansen bottle

## NOW TRY THESE

1. Match the instrument in column A with what it measures or collects in column B.

   | Column A | Column B |
   | --- | --- |
   | 1. corer | a. water composition |
   | 2. dredge | b. water temperature |
   | 3. Nansen bottle | c. layer of ocean-floor sediments |
   | 4. bathythermograph | |
   | 5. deep-water nets | d. ocean currents |
   | 6. floats | e. deep-water fish |
   | | f. minerals on the ocean floor |

2. An echo sounder sent a sound to the ocean bottom. The echo reached the instrument 6 seconds later. How deep was the ocean there?

# How does the temperature of ocean water vary?

**Water temperature in the mixed layer.**
Winds and waves keep the water in the ocean well mixed near the surface. This well-mixed water is called the <u>mixed layer.</u> The mixed layer goes from the surface to 100 meters deep in some places and up to 300 meters deep in other places.

Sunlight striking water is absorbed and warms the water. In very still water, only the top layer would be warmed by sunlight. The temperature would drop rapidly in the deeper parts. But the upper parts of the ocean are not still. They are mixed. The sun's heat is spread evenly through the mixed layer. Temperatures are about the same everywhere in the mixed layer.

▶ **Why is the temperature about the same throughout the mixed layer?**

**Water temperatures in deeper water.** The layer of water below the mixed layer is called the <u>thermocline</u> (THER-muh-kline). The thermocline goes down to a depth of about 900 meters. In the thermocline, the temperature drops sharply as the water gets deeper.

Below the thermocline is a zone of very cold water. In this zone the temperature of the water remains constant between 4°C and 0°C.

▶ **How does water temperature change in the thermocline?**

**Temperature change from the equator to the poles.** We have already seen that the temperature of the mixed layer does not

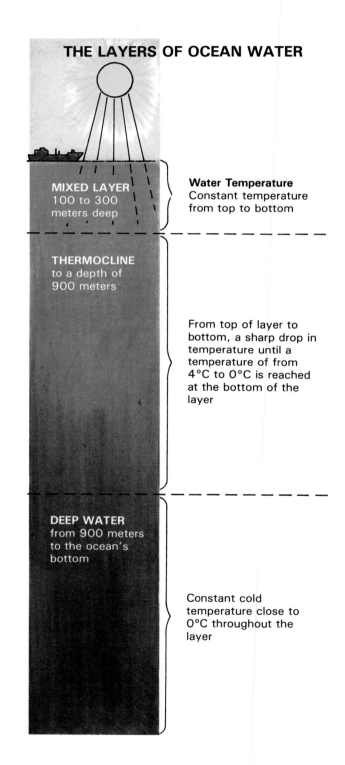

**THE LAYERS OF OCEAN WATER**

MIXED LAYER
100 to 300
meters deep

**Water Temperature**
Constant temperature
from top to bottom

THERMOCLINE
to a depth of
900 meters

From top of layer to
bottom, a sharp drop in
temperature until a
temperature of from
4°C to 0°C is reached
at the bottom of the
layer

DEEP WATER
from 900 meters
to the ocean's
bottom

Constant cold
temperature close to
0°C throughout the
layer

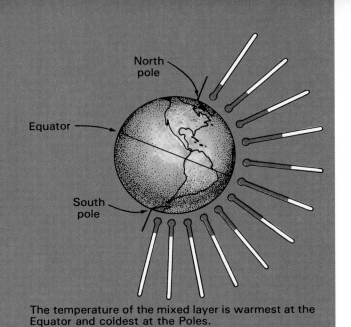

The temperature of the mixed layer is warmest at the Equator and coldest at the Poles.

change much with depth at any one spot in the ocean. But the mixed layer is warmer at a spot near the equator than at a spot near the North Pole or South Pole. Near the equator, its temperature is about 30°C. Near one of the poles, its temperature is about -2°C. This is very near the freezing point of salt water.

▶ **Where would water in the mixed layer be warmest?**

## Freezing temperature of ocean water.

Fresh water freezes at 0°C. Ocean water freezes at about -2°C. This difference is caused by the salt and other minerals dissolved in ocean water. Dissolving chemicals in water makes the freezing point of the water drop. The greater the amount of salt and dissolved minerals in ocean water, the lower its freezing point.

▶ **What effect do the salt and other dissolved minerals have on the freezing point of ocean water?**

## WHAT YOU LEARNED

1. Ocean water is well mixed in a layer next to the surface called the mixed layer.
2. Below any one point, the mixed layer shows little change in temperature with depth.

3. The temperature drops sharply with depth in the thermocline.
4. Below the thermocline, there is cold water that doesn't change temperature much as you go deeper in the water.
5. The mixed layer gets colder as you move north or south from the equator.
6. Ocean water freezes at a lower temperature than fresh water.

## SCIENCE WORDS

**mixed layer**
   a layer of water in the ocean next to the surface where the water is well mixed

**thermocline** (THER-muh-kline)
   a layer of water in the ocean below the mixed layer where the water temperature drops sharply with depth

## ANSWER THESE

1. As you move north or south of the equator, the surface temperature of ocean water
   a. increases
   b. decreases
   c. remains the same
2. As you go deeper in the thermocline, the temperature of the water
   a. increases
   b. decreases
   c. remains the same
3. The surface waters of the ocean are heated mostly by
   a. the sun
   b. the land
   c. currents
4. The mixed layer goes down from the surface to a depth of about
   a. 100 to 300 meters
   b. 200 to 900 meters
   c. 900 meters and greater
5. As more salt is added to water, its freezing point
   a. increases
   b. decreases
   c. remains the same

# What changes the salinity of ocean water?

**BEFORE BOILING**

1000g sea water

**AFTER BOILING**

33-37g salts

After 1000 g of sea water is completely boiled to dryness, 33 to 37 grams of solid salts will be left.

**Salt water.** The water in rivers, streams, and most lakes is called fresh water. The water in oceans and bays is called ocean water, sea water, or salt water. An important difference between fresh water and ocean water is the salt and other minerals dissolved in ocean water. Fresh water contains only a small amount of dissolved minerals. But salt water contains 33 to 37 grams of minerals in every 1000 grams of water.

▶ **What bodies of water contain salt water?**

**Salinity.** The amount of salt and other dissolved minerals in water is called its salinity (suh-LIN-uh-tee). Water with a large amount of minerals is said to have a high salinity. The salinity of ocean water differs slightly from place to place. Salinity affects things living in the ocean. Ocean plants and animals may be healthy in water of one salinity. If the salinity changes, they may die.

▶ **Why is the salinity of ocean water important for things living in the ocean?**

**Lowering salinity.** Salt water becomes less salty if fresh water is added to it. The fresh water dilutes (duh-LUTES) the salt water. Fresh water is added to ocean water when a river pours into a bay or ocean. At its mouth, the Mississippi River lowers the salinity of the salt water in the Gulf of Mexico. Icebergs and glaciers contain fresh water. When they melt, they lower the salinity of ocean water. Rain and snow contain no salt. They too lower the salinity of ocean water.

▶ **List three things that lower the salinity of ocean water.**

**Raising salinity.** Removing the water from salt water raises its salinity. Evaporation (eh-vap-uh-RAY-shun) removes the water from salt water. The salt and other minerals stay behind. Warm water evaporates more quickly than cool water. At the equator, where the water is warm, the water has a high salinity.

Freezing water also removes water from salt water. The fresh water becomes ice. The minerals stay in the unfrozen liquid. This makes the salinity of ocean water high at the North Pole and South Pole.

▶ **Where is the salinity of ocean water high?**

## EVENTS THAT LOWER THE SALINITY OF OCEAN WATER

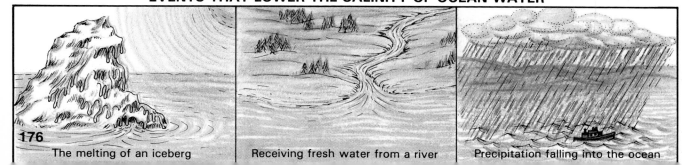

The melting of an iceberg | Receiving fresh water from a river | Precipitation falling into the ocean

# EVENTS THAT RAISE THE SALINITY OF OCEAN WATER

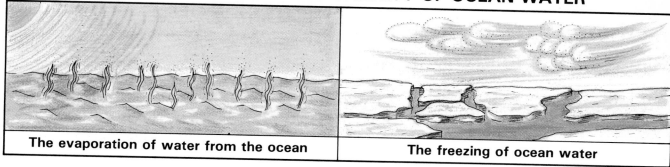

| The evaporation of water from the ocean | The freezing of ocean water |

**Other factors affect salinity.** Some sea animals need minerals to build their shells and skeletons. They get the minerals from ocean water. This lowers the salinity of the water. Clams, snails, oysters, and coral lower the salinity of the ocean water where they live.

▶ **Why do some sea animals remove minerals from the water of the ocean?**

## WHAT YOU LEARNED

1. Ocean water contains a large amount of dissolved minerals.
2. The salinity of ocean water is lower where rivers empty into oceans, where icebergs and glaciers melt, and where rain or snow is plentiful.
3. Salinity is higher where ocean water is warm and where ocean water freezes.
4. Some sea animals lower the salinity of ocean water.

## SCIENCE WORDS

**salinity** (suh-LIN-uh-tee)
  the amount of salt and other dissolved minerals in ocean water

**dilute** (duh-LUTE)
  to make a solution weaker

## ANSWER THESE

1. The salinity of ocean water is
   a. 33 to 37 grams minerals per 1000 grams water
   b. 100%
   c. 40 parts per thousand

2. The salinity of the ocean
   a. is the same all over
   b. varies slightly
   c. varies a great deal
3. Near the mouth of a large river, the salinity of the ocean
   a. is lower
   b. is higher
   c. remains the same
4. A melting iceberg tends to make the salinity of ocean water
   a. become lower
   b. become higher
   c. remain the same
5. Evaporation of ocean water tends to make the salinity of the water
   a. become lower
   b. become higher
   c. remain the same
6. Marine animals with shells tend to make the salinity of water
   a. become lower
   b. become higher
   c. remain the same

## NOW TRY THESE

Find the hidden words.
1. To make less salty

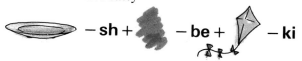

2. Amount of salt in the ocean

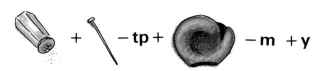

# What does the ocean floor look like?

continent   continental shelf

continental slope
continental rise
basin
seamount   guyot

**The ocean floor.** If you could pull a plug and drain the water, you could see the ocean floor. Oceanographers explore the ocean floor without actually seeing it. Using an echo sounder, they can "see" mountains, valleys, and deep canyons. The ocean floor looks very much like the land. But some of the mountains on the ocean floor are the highest on earth. Some of the canyons are the deepest.

▶ How is the ocean floor like the land?

**Shelves and slopes.** The edges of the continents extend into the oceans. At first, they slope gently downward under the water. This is called the continental (kontuh-NEN-til) shelf. In some places the shelf is very narrow. In other places the shelf extends more than 150 kilometers from the edge of the continent. Beyond the continental shelf is the continental slope. This part of the ocean floor is steeper than the continental shelf. At the bottom of the continental slope, the ocean floor flattens out. The region where this flattening takes place is called the continental rise. The continental rise ends at the ocean basin.

▶ What happens to the ocean floor at the end of the continental shelf?

**The ocean basin.** The ocean basin makes up most of the ocean floor. People once thought the ocean basin was smooth and flat. We now know this is not so. You have learned about the ranges of high mountains that run through the middle of the oceans.

These are called mid-ocean ridges. In some places the mid-ocean ridges show above the ocean surface. The islands of the Azores are peaks of the Mid-Atlantic Ridge.

You also know about the deep trenches near the edges of some continents. The deepest one is the Mariana Trench in the Pacific Ocean. It is more than 11 000 meters deep. Mount Everest is 8800 meters high. It is the highest mountain on the land. Mount Everest would fit into the Mariana Trench and still be more than 2000 meters below the ocean surface.

▶ Where is the deepest part of the ocean?

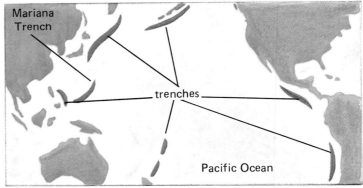

Mariana Trench

trenches

Pacific Ocean

Most ocean trenches are found in the Pacific Ocean. The deepest spot in any ocean, 11 033 meters deep, is in the Mariana Trench.

**Volcanoes in the ocean.** Besides the mid-ocean ridges, there are many other mountain peaks on the ocean floor. They are called seamounts (SEE-mounts). Most of them were once active volcanoes under the sea. Some seamounts have flattened tops. These are called guyots (GEE-ohs).

Scientists believe that a guyot was once a volcano that reached above sea level. The top of the volcano was then eroded away. Later, the ocean floor sank into the mantle, and the mountain top dropped below sea level. The Hawaiian Islands are the peaks of volcanoes that still show above the ocean surface.

▶ What are seamounts?

## WHAT YOU LEARNED

1. The ocean floor has mountains, valleys, and deep canyons.
2. The edge of a continent slopes gently under the ocean surface to form the continental shelf.
3. The continental slope is a steeper slope that connects the continental shelf with the ocean basin.
4. Ridges and trenches are found on the ocean basin.
5. There are many mountain peaks on the ocean basin. Some of them rise above the water's surface to form islands.

## SCIENCE WORDS

**continental** (kon-tuh-NEN-til) **shelf**
the edge of the continent that slopes gently under the ocean water

**continental slope**
the part of the ocean floor between the continental shelf and the ocean basin

**ridges**
ranges of mountains on the ocean basin

**trenches**
very deep canyons in the ocean basin

**seamount** (SEE-mount)
a mountain peak that rises from the ocean floor but does not show above the ocean surface

**guyot** (GEE-oh)
a seamount with a flat top

## ANSWER THESE

1. The ocean floor
   a. is smooth
   b. has mountains and deep canyons
   c. has only high mountains

2. The gently sloping edge of a continent is called
   a. a seamount
   b. an ocean basin
   c. the continental shelf
3. Compared to mountains on the continents, ocean mountains are usually
   a. taller
   b. shorter
   c. about the same height
4. An example of an ocean-floor volcano is
   a. one of the Hawaiian Islands
   b. Mt. Everest
   c. the Azores

## FINDING OUT MORE

**Magnetic stripes.** Oceanographers have found that some rocks of the ocean floor are magnetized. The magnetism in the rocks seems to follow a pattern. Stripes of magnetized rock run parallel to the mid-ocean ridges. In one stripe, the rocks are magnetized in one direction. In the next stripe, they are magnetized in the opposite direction. The pattern of stripes is the same on both sides of the mid-ocean ridges. This is a strong reason for believing that the ocean floor is spreading outward from the ridges. The ridges are formed from lava flowing up from the mantle. As the lava hardens to rock, it is magnetized in a certain direction. The magnetized rock then moves away from the ridge on both sides, carrying its magnetism with it.

**A section of the ocean floor.** The rocks lying within each stripe are magnetized in the directions shown by the arrows. The pattern (marked A in the drawing) to one side of the ridge is the same as the pattern (B) on the other side.

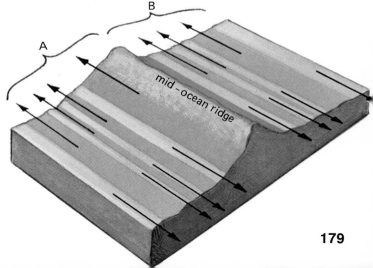

# What materials make up ocean sediments?

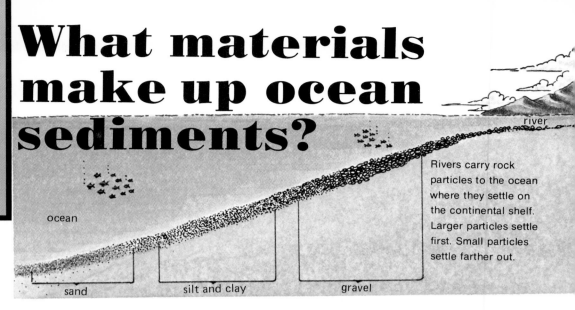

ocean

sand

silt and clay

gravel

river

Rivers carry rock particles to the ocean where they settle on the continental shelf. Larger particles settle first. Small particles settle farther out.

**Sediments on the ocean floor.** Materials that fall and collect on the ocean floor are called ocean sediments. Some ocean sediments come from rocks eroded from the land. Some are the remains of living things. Dust and ashes from volcanoes also sink to the ocean floor to form sediments. Objects from outer space, such as meteorites, sometimes land in the ocean and fall to the ocean floor. They too are part of the ocean sediments.

▶ **What materials make up the sediments of the ocean floor?**

**Eroded rock sediments.** Most of the sediments on the continental shelf are eroded rock particles. Rivers carry rock particles of all sizes to the ocean. These particles settle down on the continental shelf. Waves and wind also erode the rocks along the ocean shores. These particles become part of the sediments on the continental shelf. The eroded rock sediments gradually spread out over the shelf. When they reach the edge of the shelf, they may slide down the continental slope. But sediments eroded from the land usually do not go past the continental slope. Very little of these sediments are found on the ocean basin.

▶ **Where do most of the sediments on the continental shelf come from?**

**Sediments on the ocean basin.** Most of the ocean basins are covered by thick layers of sediments. Some of this material was eroded from the land. For example, very fine particles of clay are carried to the ocean by rivers. These particles can drift for thousands of kilometers before settling to the ocean floor. Winds may carry volcanic ash far out over the ocean. The ash particles then drop into the ocean and sink to the bottom. Even some large rock particles are found on the ocean basins. Glaciers carry these rock particles to the ocean shore. Icebergs break off the glaciers and float far out to sea. When the icebergs melt, the rock particles sink to the ocean floor.

But most of the ocean basin sediments do not come from the land. They come from living things in the ocean. These sediments are called oozes.

▶ **Where do most of the ocean basin sediments come from?**

**Formation of oozes.** There are many minerals dissolved in the ocean water. Certain tiny living things in the ocean use these minerals to make their shells and skeletons. These living things are made of only a single cell. They are too small to be seen without a microscope. But there are very large numbers of them in the ocean. As they die, their shells and skeletons sink to the ocean bottom. This material forms most of the oozes of the ocean basins.

▶ **What material forms most of the oozes of the ocean basins?**

**Microscopic organisms of the sea.** The remains of tiny organisms like these are an important part of ocean basin sediments, or oozes.

## WHAT YOU LEARNED

1. The ocean sediments are made up of eroded rocks, volcanic ash, meteorites, and remains of living things.
2. Most eroded rock sediments are found on the continental shelf and slope.
3. Ocean basin sediment is mostly made of ooze.
4. Ooze forms from the shells and skeletons of microscopic life.

## SCIENCE WORD

**ooze**
    ocean basin sediments formed from the shells and skeletons of microscopic life

## ANSWER THESE

1. Materials that fall and collect on the ocean floor are called
    a. sediments
    b. basins
    c. bedrock
2. Most material eroded from land collects on the
    a. ocean basin
    b. ocean ridges
    c. continental shelf and slope
3. Volcanic ash may be carried far into the ocean by
    a. glaciers
    b. winds
    c. sea life
4. Ocean basin sediment is called
    a. bedrock
    b. mud
    c. ooze
5. Ooze is formed from
    a. microscopic living things
    b. glaciers
    c. volcanic dust

## NOW TRY THESE

1. Materials that fall and collect on the ocean floor

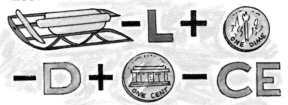

2. Material that makes up the ocean basin sediment

## FINDING OUT MORE

In many places the continental slope has deep canyons. They look like the canyons cut by rivers on land. Scientists are not sure how these canyons were carved into the ocean floor. They believe it may have been done by a kind of landslide under the sea. According to this theory, sediments collect near the edge of the continental shelf. From time to time, these sediments slide down the continental slope. They cause a swift current of water to flow down the slope like a river. These currents gradually erode the slope and form the canyons. Large oil companies are drilling for oil in some of the canyons off the eastern coast of the United States.

# What causes ocean currents?

**A current story.** Have you ever heard of people throwing bottles containing messages into the ocean? Some time later the bottles are found in a distant place. How did they get there? They were carried by an <u>ocean</u> <u>current</u> (KUR-ent). Ocean currents are rivers of water. They flow through the waters around them. Some currents in the ocean flow along the surface. Some move along the ocean bottom. Currents can also move up and down within the ocean.

▶ **What are ocean currents?**

## Note in bottle ends 19-year trip

MELBOURNE, Australia–A bottle that was thrown into the sea 19 years ago with a message in English, French, and Spanish and traveled an estimated 20,000 miles was found this week on a lonely beach on the south coast of Australia. The ship's officer who threw it overboard while on an expedition to Antarctica had asked the finder to return it.

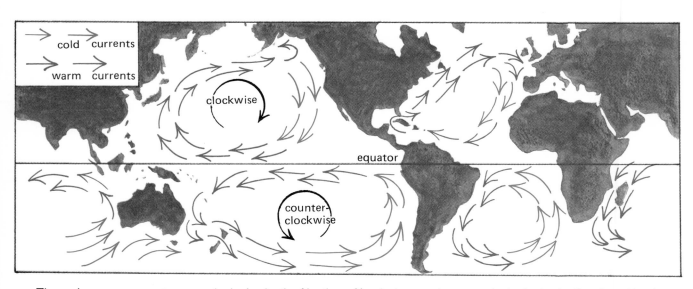

The main ocean currents move clockwise in the Northern Hemisphere and counterclockwise in the Southern Hemisphere. In some places they change direction because of the shape of the continents.

**Causes of ocean motion.** Blow gently across the surface of a pan filled with water. See how the current of water moves straight across the pan. Winds are the force causing most surface currents. Winds near the equator blow mainly from east to west.

This causes ocean currents to flow from east to west near the equator. At latitudes of about 40°, winds blow mainly from west to east. The main ocean currents also flow from west to east at these latitudes.

The ocean currents do not flow in straight paths. Continents and large islands make them change direction. The turning of the earth also has an effect. It makes the currents curve to the right in the Northern Hemisphere. It makes them curve to the left in the Southern Hemisphere. All these things cause the main ocean currents to go around in circles. They go around clockwise in the Northern Hemisphere and counterclockwise in the Southern Hemisphere. The map shows some of the main ocean currents.

▶ **What is the cause of most surface currents in the ocean?**

**Hot and cold running currents.** Currents flowing from regions near the equator are warm currents. They bring warm water to cooler regions. These warm currents tend to warm the air over nearby land areas. Currents coming from regions near the poles bring cold waters to warmer regions. These cold currents cool the surrounding areas. Look at the map showing the major ocean currents. See if you can find the cold currents and the warm currents.

▶ **Where do warm currents come from?**

**Other ocean currents.** Differences in temperature can also cause water to move. Cold water is denser than warm water. Cold water around the polar regions sinks to the ocean bottom. Water is warmed around the equator. This water rises upward to the surface. Cold and warm water produce currents that move up and down.

They are called density currents. Different amounts of salt in water also cause density currents. More salt makes water denser. Saltier water sinks. Less salty water rises.

▶ **What causes density currents?**

**WHAT YOU LEARNED**

1. Ocean currents are rivers of water that flow through the ocean.
2. Winds are the force causing most surface currents.
3. Continents and the turning of the earth cause surface currents to flow in circular paths.
4. Cold currents come from polar regions, while warm currents come from areas near the equator.
5. Differences in temperature and the amount of salt in water cause density currents.

**SCIENCE WORDS**

**ocean currents** (KUR-ents)
  rivers of water flowing through the ocean
**density currents**
  currents of water that move up and down in the ocean

**ANSWER THESE**

1. Most surface currents are caused by
   a. the turning of the earth
   b. winds
   c. density differences
2. The ocean currents curve because of
   a. the turning of the earth
   b. temperature differences
   c. density differences
3. Most cold currents come from the
   a. polar regions
   b. regions around the equator
   c. surface of the ocean
4. Currents that move up and down can be caused by
   a. the turning of the earth
   b. winds
   c. temperature differences

# What kinds of life are found in the ocean?

**NEKTON**

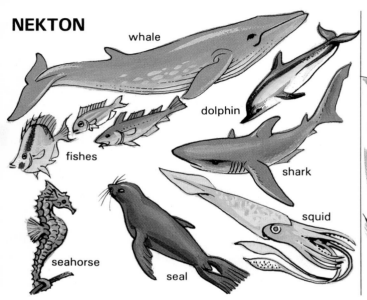

whale

dolphin

fishes

shark

squid

seahorse

seal

**BENTHOS**

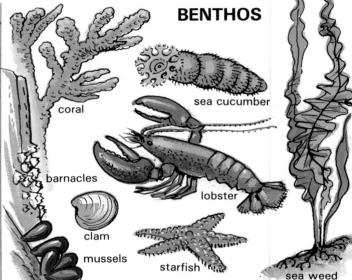

coral

sea cucumber

barnacles

lobster

clam

mussels

starfish

sea weed

**Who lives there?** The ocean is the home of many living things, or organisms (OR-gun-isms). They are called marine (muh-REEN) organisms. They have needs similar to those of plants and animals living on land. Marine organisms are able to find what they need in the waters of the ocean. They are able to find food, oxygen, and the right temperature so they can grow and reproduce.

▶ **What do we call living things that live in ocean waters?**

**Food of the sea.** Plants make their own food. They use the energy of sunlight to make food from carbon dioxide and water. Most of the plants in the sea are one-celled plants called diatoms (DY-uh-tums). Diatoms can be seen only with the aid of a microscope. They float by the billions near the surface of

the ocean. Very small organisms floating in the ocean are called plankton (PLANK-tun). Diatoms are one kind of plankton. Other kinds of plankton are tiny animals. The plankton are a source of food for many marine animals. Some marine animals eat plankton. Others eat animals that have eaten plankton.

▶ **What are plankton?**

**Free-swimming sea animals.** Plankton are moved by the motion of ocean waters. Nekton (NEK-tun) are animals that live in water and can swim by themselves. Adult fish, whales, seals, dolphins, and squid are all nekton. These animals can swim in different parts of the ocean. They are able to look for and find their food. Whales, seals, and dolphins are not fish. They are mammals that breathe

**184**

air just as we do. Free-swimming animals usually swim in groups called schools.

▶ **What are nekton?**

**Life on the ocean floor.** Plants and animals that live on the ocean floor are called benthos (BEN-thos). Some benthos attach themselves to the ocean floor. They stay in that spot until they die. Mussels, barnacles, and coral remain attached to one spot. Some animals bury themselves in sand, mud, or shells. Others creep and crawl along the bottom. Starfish, crabs, and scallops are examples of animals that move about. Some benthos live in shallow water along a coast. Others are found in deep ocean waters. Sea urchins, sea cucumbers, and brittle stars are a few of the deep-water animals.

▶ **What are benthos?**

## WHAT YOU LEARNED

1. Plankton are tiny floating plants and animals.
2. Diatoms are plant plankton that make most of the food for ocean life.
3. Plankton are the first source of food for many marine animals.
4. Nekton are free-swimming sea animals.
5. Benthos are plants and animals that live on the ocean floor.

## SCIENCE WORDS

**organism** (OR-gun-izm)
   a living thing

**marine** (muh-REEN)
   living in the ocean

**plankton** (PLANK-tun)
   tiny, floating marine organisms

**diatoms** (DY-uh-tums)
   plant plankton

**nekton** (NEK-tun)
   free-swimming sea animals

**benthos** (BEN-thos)
   plants and animals that live on the ocean floor

## ANSWER THESE

1. Organisms that live in the ocean are called
   a. marine
   b. submarine
   c. porcine
2. Tiny plants floating in the ocean are
   a. sea cucumbers
   b. diatoms
   c. seaweed
3. A first source of food for many marine organisms is
   a. nekton
   b. benthos
   c. plankton
4. Some examples of nekton are
   a. crabs and scallops
   b. whales and seals
   c. squid and sea cucumbers
5. Benthos are organisms that
   a. live on the ocean floor
   b. are free-swimming
   c. are one celled

## NOW TRY THIS

Find the names of sea animals and plants hidden in the letter square. Read up, down, across, and backwards.

| K | P | L | A | M | M | A | M | W |
|---|---|---|---|---|---|---|---|---|
| S | L | M | O | T | A | I | D | H |
| O | A | S | B | Z | C | L | O | A |
| H | N | Q | C | O | R | A | L | L |
| T | K | U | D | Y | A | E | P | E |
| N | T | I | G | V | B | S | H | X |
| E | O | D | F | I | S | H | I | R |
| B | N | E | K | T | O | N | N | W |

## DO THIS AT HOME

Make a salt-water acquarium. A 10-gallon tank is a good size to use. Make sure it is made for salt water. Use salt water from the ocean, or make your own salt water. An aquarium dealer can supply you with the salt mixture and other materials you will need. You will need to keep an air filter going in the water at all times. Place plants, rocks, and sea animals in your aquarium.

# Where do we find life in the ocean?

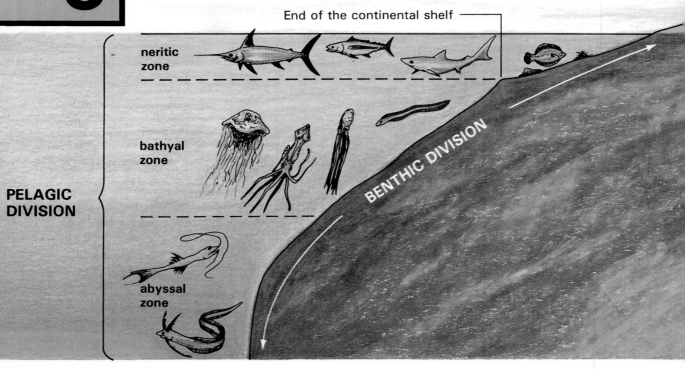

End of the continental shelf

neritic zone

bathyal zone

PELAGIC DIVISION

BENTHIC DIVISION

abyssal zone

**Dividing the marine environment.** Everything around you is called your environment (en-VY-run-ment). Sea plants and animals live in a marine environment. Oceanographers have divided the marine (muh-REEN) environment into two parts.
— The waters of the ocean are called the pelagic (puh-LAJ-ik) division.
— The entire ocean floor is called the benthic (BEN-thik) division.

▶ What are the two divisions of the marine environment?

**Life in the pelagic division.** Plants need sunlight to make food. Sunlight does not go very deep into the ocean. So most plants are found in the upper parts of this division. The upper part of the pelagic division is called the neritic (nuh-RIT-ik) zone. It extends from the shore down to the end of the continental shelf. Here there are many plankton and fish. Many forms of seaweed are found in this region.

▶ What is the upper part of the pelagic division called?

**Deeper ocean water.** Below the neritic zone lies the bathyal (BATH-ee-ul) zone. Plant life is scarce in this region. Sharks, squid, and octopuses live in this region. Below this region is the abyssal (uh-BIS-ul) zone. The abyssal zone is the deepest zone in the ocean. There is no light, and the temperature is just above freezing. Animals here live on food that sinks from upper regions. Animals that live in the abyssal zone must be able to live under high water pressures. These animals are usually small with large, sharp teeth. Some glow in the dark.

▶ What is the deepest zone in the ocean?

**Life in the benthic division.** Near the shoreline, the water above the benthic division is shallow. The water moves constantly because of the waves and undertow. The area of the benthic division near the shoreline is called the splash zone. At times, such as at low tide, the splash zone may be dry. Life here is very hard. Plants and animals must be able to live under the force of the waves. Barnacles, mussels, and some seaweeds are able to attach themselves to rocks. Other animals dig into the wat sand. Clams, crabs, and marine worms are examples of such animals.

▶ In what zone do clams, crabs, and marine worms live?

## WHAT YOU LEARNED

1. Your environment is everything around you.
2. The marine environment is divided into the pelagic and benthic regions.
3. The pelagic region includes all the waters of the ocean.
4. The benthic region includes the entire ocean floor.
5. The pelagic region includes the neritic, bathyal, and abyssal zones.
6. The benthic region includes the splash zone.

## SCIENCE WORDS

**environment** (en-VY-run-ment)
    everything around you

**pelagic** (puh-LAJ-ik) **division**
    the waters of the ocean

**benthic** (BEN-thik) **division**
    the entire ocean floor

**neritic** (nuh-RIT-ik) **zone**
    the ocean region from the shore to the end of the continental shelf

**bathyal** (BATH-ee-ul) **zone**
    the ocean region below the neritic zone

**abyssal** (uh-BIS-ul) **zone**
    the deepest zone in the ocean

**splash zone**
    the area where the waves crash onto the shore

## ANSWER THESE

1. Everything around an organism is called its
    **a.** environment
    **b.** home
    **c.** background
2. The marine environment that includes the ocean waters is the
    **a.** benthic region
    **b.** pelagic region
    **c.** splash zone
3. Plants and animals are most abundant in the
    **a.** neritic zone
    **b.** bathyal zone
    **c.** abyssal zone
4. The deepest zone in the ocean is the
    **a.** bathyal zone
    **b.** abyssal zone
    **c.** splash zone

## NOW TRY THIS

Tell which zone — bathyal, abyssal, splash, or neritic — the following describe.
1. Sometimes dry
2. Absolutely no light
3. Scarce plant life
4. Temperature just above freezing
5. Very high pressures
6. Clams, crabs, and marine worms live here.
7. Shark, squid, and octopus found here
8. Plankton and fish plentiful
9. Barnacles and mussels attach themselves to rock here
10. Plant life is scarce here

## FINDING OUT MORE

**Seaweed.** Diatoms are the smallest plants of the sea. Seaweed is a larger kind of marine plant. Many forms of seaweed float. Other forms attach themselves to rocks. Seaweed can be green, red, or brown. Large types of seaweed are called kelp.

# 9 Review

Do the following questions on a separate sheet of paper.

**Fill in the Blank**     *Write down the statements in Column I. Where there is a blank line in each statement, write the word or phrase from Column II that best completes the meaning of the statement.*

| Column I | Column II |
|---|---|
| 1. A sound that bounces off an object is a(n) _____ . | salinity |
| 2. The surface layer of the ocean is warmed by the _____ . | benthos |
| 3. Ocean water freezes at _____ . | echo |
| 4. At the equator the water has a high _____ . | continental shelf |
| 5. The edge of the continent that extends into the ocean is the _____ . | $-2°c$ |
| 6. Oozes are made of the sunken shells of tiny _____ . | diatoms |
| 7. Ocean currents tend to curve to the right in the _____ . | sun |
| 8. Ocean water is warmed near the _____ . | equator |
| 9. Many sea plants are one-celled plants called _____ | marine organisms |
| 10. Animals and plants that live on the ocean floor are called _____ . | northern hemisphere |

Do the following questions on a separate sheet of paper.

**Multiple Choice**     *Write the letter of the choice that best completes the statement or answers the question.*

1. The surface water of the ocean is mixed by
   a. rain falling on it
   b. wind and waves
   c. fish swimming through it
2. The layer of water below the mixed layer is called
   a. the thermocline
   b. the unmixed layer
   c. the middle layer
3. The salinity of water is a measure of
   a. the temperature of the water
   b. the depth of the water
   c. the amount of salt and dissolved minerals in it
4. Seamounts and guyots are examples of
   a. ocean ridges
   b. ocean trenches
   c. ocean volcanoes

5. Materials that fall and collect on the ocean floor are called
   a. ocean sediments
   b. sea floor sludge
   c. ocean mud
6. Rivers of water flowing through the ocean are called
   a. tides
   b. ocean currents
   c. migrations
7. Diatoms and plankton are kinds of
   a. tiny marine plants and animals
   b. large spiny fish
   c. sea mammals
8. An echo can be used to
   a. tell the depth of the ocean floor
   b. tell a ship its location at night
   c. locate gold on the ocean floor

# UNIT 10° The Atmosphere

## Unit Lessons

1. What is air?
2. What do we know about the gases in air?
3. What are the layers of the atmosphere?
4. How does the earth get its heat?
5. How is the atmosphere heated?
6. How does heat move in the air?
7. Which warms up faster, land or water?
8. What is air pressure?
9. How much pressure does air have?
10. How is air pressure measured?
11. Why does air pressure change?
12. How does air pressure change around the earth?
13. How are winds formed?
14. Which way does a wind blow?
15. What causes local winds?
16. How do we measure winds?

## Goals and Objectives

After completing this unit, you should be able to:

- understand that air is a mixture of gases.
- describe the layers of the atmosphere.
- understand how the atmosphere warms the earth by conducting radiant energy.
- explain how convection currents move heat through air and water.
- explain how air pressure is the result of molecules hitting a surface.
- differentiate between air currents and winds.
- explain how differences in air presure direct winds.

# What is air?

**Air takes up space.** Take a plastic sandwich bag. Open it wide. What do you see inside? It may look empty, but it is not. Close the bag by bringing the top edges together. Then twist them. Does the bag flatten out? Air in the bag keeps the bag from becoming flat. The bag is filled with air. Air takes up space.

▶ Why does air in a tightly closed bag keep the bag from flattening out?

**Air is a mixture of gases.** Air cannot be seen. It has no color. Air also has no taste or smell. Air is a colorless, odorless, and tasteless mixture of gases. Air is made up mostly of nitrogen and oxygen. It also has small amounts of argon, carbon dioxide, and other gases.

▶ What is air?

AIR: nitrogen 78%
oxygen 21%
argon 0.94%
carbon dioxide 0.04%
helium, neon, krypton, xenon 0.02%

1.

2.

**Weighing air?** Weigh an empty balloon. Blow up the balloon. Weigh it again. The balloon weighs more when it is filled with air. Air has weight.

▶ Why does a balloon weigh more when it is blown up than it does when it is empty?

## WHAT YOU LEARNED

1. Air is a mixture of gases.

2. Air is made up of about 78% nitrogen, 21% oxygen, and small amounts of argon, carbon dioxide, and other gases.

3. Air is colorless, odorless, and tasteless.

4. Air takes up space and has weight.

## ANSWER THESE

1. Describe air.
2. How can air be weighed?
3. Match each gas with its percent in air:

| carbon dioxide | argon | nitrogen | oxygen |
|---|---|---|---|
| 78% | 21% | .94% | .04% |

## FINDING OUT MORE

Fit a two-holed rubber stopper tightly in a jar. Place a funnel in one of the holes. Hold your finger tightly over the other hole. Fill the funnel with water. Why doesn't the water go into the jar? There is air in the jar. Air takes up space. Take your finger away from the opening. Water from the funnel now enters the jar. It pushes the air from inside the jar out through the other opening of the stopper.

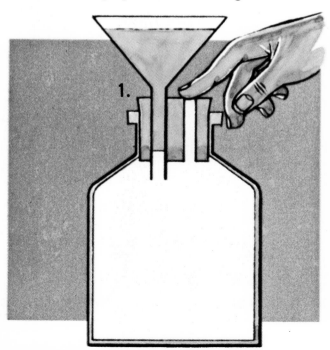

1.

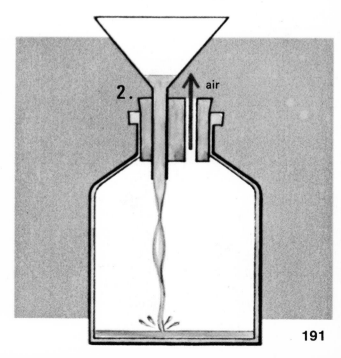

2. air

191

# What do we know about the gases in air?

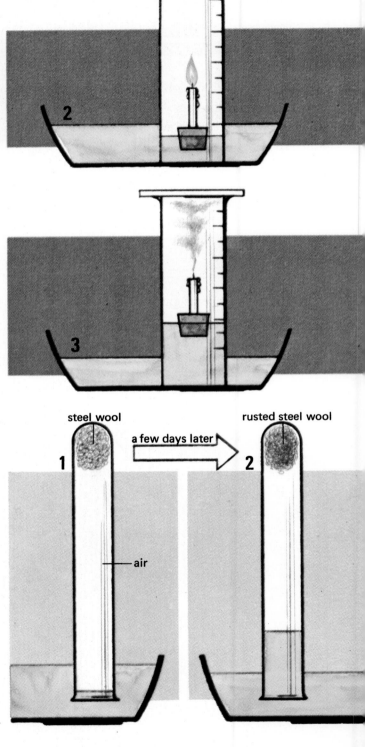

**Oxygen is needed for burning.** Attach a candle to a cork. Float the cork in a dish of water. Light the candle. Place a 100-ml graduated cylinder upside down over the candle and the cork. After a short time the candle goes out. Water rises up into the cylinder. Why does this happen? A burning candle combines with oxygen in the air. When there is no oxygen left in the air, the candle stops burning. The water rises to take the place of the oxygen.

► **What gas does a candle need in order to burn?**

**Twenty percent of the air is oxygen.** Push some steel wool down to the bottom of a test tube. Place the open test tube upside down in a dish of water. Does any water enter the test tube? The air in the test tube keeps the water out. After a few days, the steel wool rusts. When steel rusts, it combines with oxygen. Water rises in the test tube. The water rises about 20 percent, or one-fifth, of the way up. Twenty percent, or one-fifth, of the air in the test tube was oxygen.

► **How much of the air is oxygen?**

steel wool

a few days later

rusted steel wool

air

**Carbon dioxide is found in the air.**
Carbon dioxide turns limewater milky. Blow into limewater. The limewater turns milky. The air we breathe out contains much carbon dioxide. Place a piece of burning paper into the mouth of a test tube containing limewater. Shake the test tube. The limewater turns milky. Burning produces carbon dioxide. Breathing and burning add carbon dioxide to the air.

▶ How can you show that you exhale carbon dioxide?

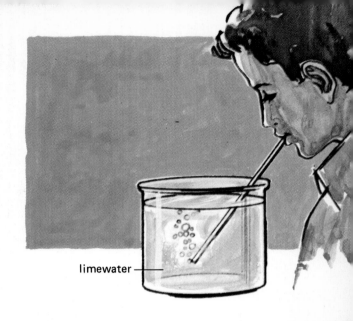

limewater

**Nitrogen.** All living things need nitrogen. But most types of living things cannot use nitrogen gas from the air. Bacteria (bac-TEER-ee-uh) are tiny living organisms found in the soil, water, and air. Some bacteria can change the nitrogen gas from the air into nitrogen compounds. Plants get the nitrogen they need from the nitrogen compounds produced by bacteria. Animals get the nitrogen they need by eating plants.

▶ How do animals get nitrogen?

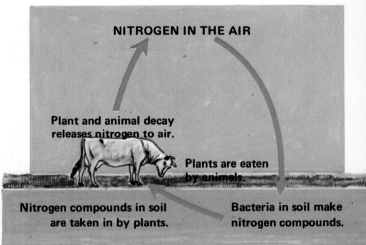

NITROGEN IN THE AIR

Plant and animal decay releases nitrogen to air.

Plants are eaten by animals.

Nitrogen compounds in soil are taken in by plants.

Bacteria in soil make nitrogen compounds.

**WHAT YOU LEARNED**

1. Oxygen is needed for burning.
2. One-fifth, or 20 percent, of the air is oxygen.
3. Breathing and burning add carbon dioxide to the air.
4. Bacteria help living things get nitrogen.

**SCIENCE WORD**

bacteria (bac-TEER-ee-uh)
    tiny organisms found in soil, water, and air

**ANSWER THESE**

1. Why does a covered fire go out?
2. In a closed jar, how much of the air is used by rusting steel wool?
3. How do plants get nitrogen?

**NOW TRY THESE**

1. Experiments done that are not so rare Prove that oxygen is 1/5 of the _____.
2. A solution called limewater should be tried To test for a gas called _____ _____.
3. From the air some bacteria take again and again A gas that plants need called _____.
4. Breathing and burning, a fact we can't hide, Add a gas to the air called _____ _____.

**FINDING OUT MORE**

Carbon dioxide is heavier than air. If this gas is poured onto a flame, the flame goes out. The carbon dioxide surrounds the flame and keeps oxygen away. Carbon dioxide is used to put out fires. Many fire extinguishers work by releasing carbon dioxide.

# What are the layers of the atmosphere?

IONOSPHERE

ions found here

ozone found here

40 kilometers

STRATOSPHERE

TROPOPAUSE

8-18 kilometers

TROPOSPHERE
weather occurs here

EARTH

**Layers of the atmosphere.** Scientists think of the atmosphere as made up of layers. The troposphere (TROPE-uh-sfeer) is the layer closest to the earth. The stratosphere (STRAT-uh-sfeer) is the layer on top of the troposphere. The ionosphere (eye-ON-uh-sfeer) is one of the layers above the stratosphere.

▶ **Name three layers of the atmosphere.**

**The troposphere.** The troposphere is the lowest layer of the atmosphere. It goes up to about 8 kilometers over the cold regions around the poles. It goes up to about 18 kilometers over the warm regions around the equator. Winds occur in the troposphere. Most of the water vapor in the atmosphere is found here. This water vapor forms clouds. Rain, snow, and ice form in this layer. All weather takes place in the troposphere.

▶ **In which layer of the atmosphere does weather occur?**

**The tropopause.** The higher you go into the troposphere, the colder it gets. At a certain height it stops getting colder. This is where the troposphere ends. The top of the troposphere is called the tropopause (TROPE-uh-pawz).

▶ **What is the tropopause?**

**The stratosphere.** The stratosphere is the second layer of the atmosphere. It is about 40 kilometers thick. In the stratosphere the temperature of the air hardly changes. Airplanes travel in this layer. The stratosphere

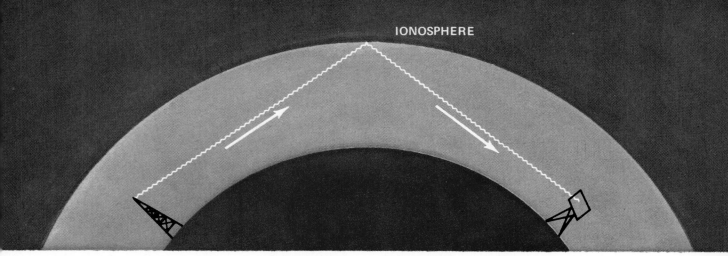

is calm compared to the stormy troposphere below. The stratosphere contains a special form of oxygen called <u>ozone</u> (OH-zone). Ozone stops most of the sun's ultraviolet light from reaching the earth. Small amounts of ultraviolet light are needed by living things. Large amounts are harmful.

▶ **Why do many airplanes travel in the stratosphere?**

**The ionosphere.** The ionosphere is one of the top layers of the earth's atmosphere. Charged particles called <u>ions</u> (EYE-ons) are found in this layer. Radio waves sent from the earth are reflected back by this layer of ions. The diagram shows how we send radio signals around the earth.

▶ **What kinds of particles are found in the ionosphere?**

## WHAT YOU LEARNED

1. The troposphere is the lowest layer of the atmosphere. Weather occurs in this layer.
2. The stratosphere is the second layer of the atmosphere. The temperature of the air remains about the same all through the stratosphere.
3. The ionosphere contains charged particles called ions. The ionosphere reflects radio waves.

## SCIENCE WORDS

**troposphere** (TROPE-uh-sfeer)
the lowest layer of the atmosphere, where weather occurs

**stratosphere** (STRAT-uh-sfeer)
the second layer of the atmosphere, where the temperature does not change much and where there is much ozone

**ionosphere** (eye-ON-uh-sfeer)
an upper layer of the atmosphere that has ions and reflects radio waves

**tropopause** (TROPE-uh-pawz)
the top of the troposphere, where the troposphere ends

**ozone** (OH-zone)
a form of oxygen that stops ultraviolet light rays

**ion** (EYE-on)
a charged particle

## ANSWER THESE

1. Which part of the atmosphere has storms?
2. In which layer of the atmosphere do we find ozone?
3. How does the ionosphere help us send radio messages around the earth?

## NOW TRY THIS

On a sheet of paper, name the sphere that
1. has rain clouds _____sphere
2. is a fairly calm region _____sphere
3. has a layer of ions _____sphere
4. has a great deal of ozone _____sphere
5. stops ultraviolet rays _____sphere
6. has weather _____sphere
7. reflects radio signals _____sphere
8. has an even temperature _____sphere
9. ends at the tropopause _____sphere
10. begins at the tropopause _____sphere

# How does the earth get its heat?

**The sun gives off radiation.** Go out into the sunlight and feel it warming your skin. Sunlight is a kind of energy called <u>radiant</u> (RAY-dee-unt) <u>energy</u>. Radiant energy can travel across millions of kilometers of empty space. Giving off radiant energy is called <u>radiation</u> (RAY-dee-AY-shun).

▶ **What kind of energy can travel through empty space?**

**Radiation from the sun heats the earth.** Place a magnifying glass in the path of the sun's light. Move the glass until the light forms a small bright spot on a piece of paper. Soon the paper starts to burn. Heat is needed to make paper start to burn. Where did the heat come from? It came from the radiant energy in the sunlight. Most of the earth's energy comes from radiation from the sun.

▶ **How does the earth get most of its energy?**

**Radiant energy can be absorbed.** Wrap two ice cubes of the same size with cloth. Wrap one ice cube with dark-colored cloth and the other with light-colored cloth. Both pieces of cloth should be of the same material and the same size. Place both wrapped ice cubes in sunlight for about 15 minutes. Which cube melts faster? The ice cube wrapped in dark cloth melts faster than the one wrapped in light cloth. Dark-colored surfaces <u>absorb</u> (ab-SORB) light. When light is absorbed, it is changed into

heat. Light-colored surfaces reflect light. Objects that reflect light remain cooler than objects that absorb light.

▶ **Why do dark-colored surfaces heat up faster than light-colored surfaces?**

**Energy from the sun.** Most of the sun's energy goes out into space. Only a very small amount of the sun's total energy hits the earth. Some of the sun's radiant energy

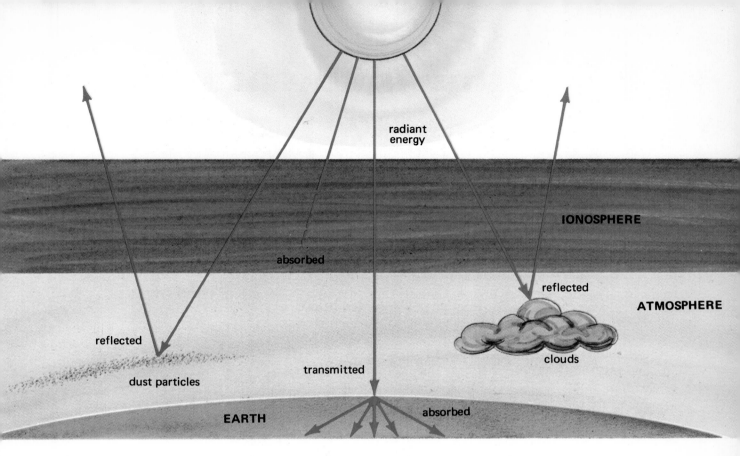

radiant energy

IONOSPHERE

absorbed

reflected

ATMOSPHERE

reflected

clouds

dust particles

transmitted

EARTH

absorbed

that reaches the earth is absorbed by the ionosphere. Clouds, dust particles, and water droplets in the atmosphere also absorb or reflect some of the sun's energy. Energy that is reflected goes back into outer space. About half of the energy that reaches our planet is <u>transmitted</u> (trans-MITT-ed) by the atmosphere. This means it passes through the atmosphere. Energy that is transmitted by the atmosphere is absorbed at the earth's surface. The absorbed energy is changed into heat. The earth becomes warmer.

▶ **What happens to the sun's energy when it is absorbed by the earth?**

## WHAT YOU LEARNED

1. Most of the earth's energy comes from the sun.
2. Radiant energy that reaches the earth's atmosphere may be reflected, absorbed, or transmitted.
3. When sunlight is absorbed, it is changed to heat.

## SCIENCE WORDS

**radiant** (RAY-dee-unt) **energy**
 energy that can travel through empty space
**radiation** (RAY-dee-AY-shun)
 giving off radiant energy
**absorb** (ab-SORB)
 take in
**transmit** (trans-MIT)
 allow to pass through

## ANSWER THESE

1. How does the earth get most of its heat?
2. In the summer, why is it more comfortable to wear light-colored clothes than dark-colored clothes?
3. Why is a cloudy day usually cooler than a sunny day?

## NOW TRY THIS

Find the word. It means the kind of energy given off by the sun.

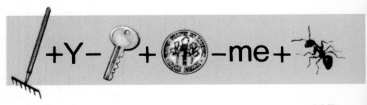

+Y– + + –me+

# How is the atmosphere heated?

**CONDUCTION**

heat

**Conduction.** Hold one end of a metal strip in a flame. Soon the strip becomes too hot to hold. In the area near the flame, the molecules begin to move faster. They bump into slower-moving molecules around them, and make them move faster. In this way heat moves through the metal strip. The heat moves from an area of higher temperature to an area of lower temperature. This kind of movement of heat is called <u>conduction</u> (con-DUCK-shun). Heat moves through solids by conduction.

▶ **How does heat move through solids?**

**Conduction in the atmosphere.** The sunlight absorbed by the earth is changed to heat. This warms the earth. The air touching the warmed earth is heated by conduction. The lower layer of the atmosphere is warmed by conduction.

▶ **What part of the atmosphere is heated by conduction?**

**The earth heats the atmosphere by radiation.** The earth absorbs radiant energy from the sun and becomes warm. The warm earth gives off radiation. This radiation is absorbed by the atmosphere and is changed into heat. The atmosphere is warmed by radiation from the earth.

▶ **How is the atmosphere warmed by radiation?**

Earth also radiates heat to the atmosphere.

Conduction heats the atmosphere

Earth absorbs sunlight and heats up.

## Short waves and long waves.

Radiation travels through space in waves. Most of the sun's radiation is short-wave radiation. Short-wave radiation is transmitted by the atmosphere and absorbed by the earth. The earth warms up and radiates energy back to the atmosphere. The earth's radiation is long-wave radiation. Long-wave radiation from the earth is absorbed by the atmosphere and helps to warm it.

► What kind of radiation is absorbed by the atmosphere?

### WHAT YOU LEARNED

1. Conduction is the movement of heat between objects that are in contact.
2. The atmosphere is heated by conduction and radiation.

### SCIENCE WORD

**conduction** (con-DUCK-shun)
   a method of moving heat by contact

### ANSWER THESE

1. What is conduction?
2. How does conduction heat air over the earth?
3. What happens to most of the sunlight that strikes the earth?

### NOW TRY THIS

Unscramble the words in capital letters.
1. Radiation is changed into heat when the radiation is EBABDRSO.
2. The earth ISTAREAD heat into the atmosphere.
3. The air is heated by TUNIOCDONC and radiation from the earth.

### FINDING OUT MORE

Heat energy always moves from a warmer object to a cooler one. The diagram shows two cups made of a material called styrofoam. One cup is filled with boiling water. The other is filled with cold water. The cups are covered. A piece of metal goes from the hot water to the cold water. After a short time the hot water cools down and the cold water warms up. The heat moves along the metal from the hot water to the cold water.

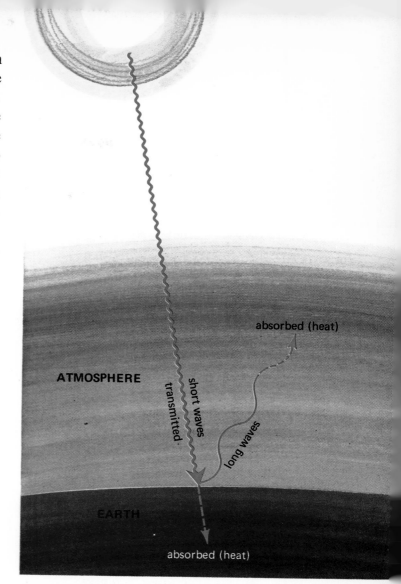

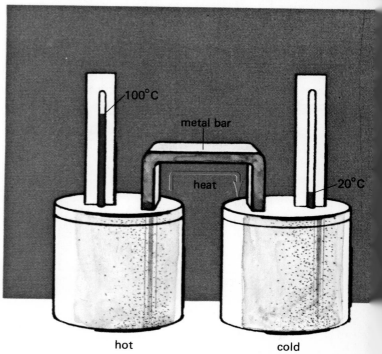

# How does heat move in the air?

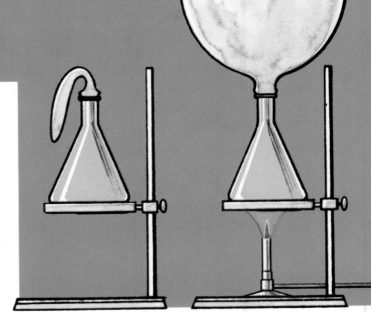

**Heated air expands.** Fit a balloon over the mouth of a flask. Heat the flask. What happens to the balloon? The heated air in the flask expands. It fills the balloon and causes the balloon to expand. When air is heated, it expands.

▶ What happens to air when it is heated?

**Warm air rises.** Look at the drawing. The candle heats the air above it. The warm air expands and becomes lighter. Warm air is lighter than cool air. The surrounding air is cooler and heavier. It sinks down and pushes the warm air up. This up and down movement of air is called convection (con-VEK-shun). Convection currents move heat through air and other gases.

Hold a pinwheel over an electric hotplate. The pinwheel starts to turn. The hotplate heats the air over it. Cooler air pushes this warmer air upward. The air moving upward turns the pinwheel.

▶ How does heat move through a gas?

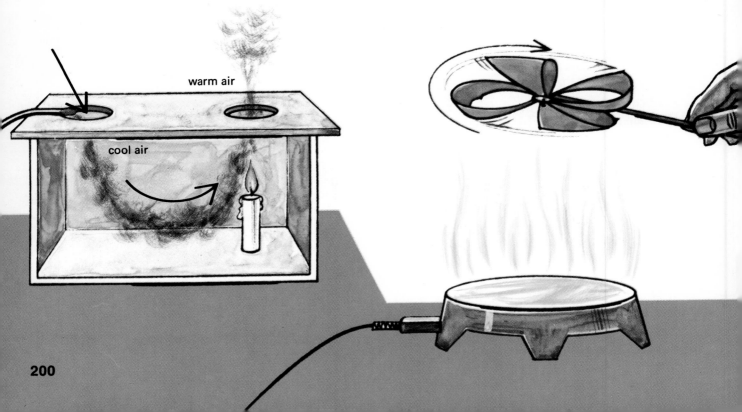

warm air

cool air

## WHAT YOU LEARNED

1. Heated air expands and becomes lighter.
2. Cold air forces warm air to rise.
3. Convection currents move heat through the air.

## SCIENCE WORD

**convection** (con-VEK-shun) **current**
  the upward movement of warm air and downward movement of cool air

## ANSWER THESE

1. Air that is heated
   a. expands
   b. sinks
   c. becomes heavier
2. Warm air
   a. sinks
   b. becomes heavier
   c. rises
3. The air over a flame becomes
   a. heavier
   b. cooler
   c. lighter

## DO THIS AT HOME

Take two small paper bags of the same size. Hang them upside down with string on the ends of a long stick. Balance the stick. Place a lamp under one of the bags. After a while, what happens to this bag? Why does the bag rise? Hot air can be used to fill large balloons for travel by air.

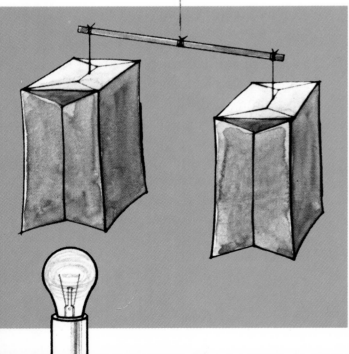

## NOW TRY THIS

Heat moves by convection, conduction, and radiation. Each diagram shows one of these types of movement. See if you can label each diagram.

1.

2.

3.

# Which warms up faster, land or water?

**Radiant energy heats both sand and water.** Place a container of sand and a container of water the same distance from a lighted bulb. After 20 minutes, both the sand and the water have become warmer. Radiant energy from the lamp warms both materials. But the sand gets warmer than the water.

▶ What happens to sand and water under a lighted bulb?

sand          water

**Sand heats faster than water.** During a summer day at the beach, the sand gets much hotter than the water. Both get the same amount of sunlight. But the sand heats up faster than the water. All parts of the land heat up faster than the water.

▶ During the day, why is the sand warmer than the ocean?

**Land cools faster than water.** Look at the experiment with the sand and water. What happens when the lamp is turned off? Both materials cool. The sand cools faster than the water. After the sun goes down, the sand and water at the beach begin to cool. At night the water at the beach is warmer than the sand. Land cools faster than water. Water heats up slowly and cools off slowly.

▶ Why is the beach cooler than the ocean at night?

**Heat spreads through water.** Radiation from the sun is absorbed at the surface of the land. All the heat stays near the surface. The surface gets hot. Radiation goes deeper into water. Some of the energy is absorbed near the surface. Some is absorbed farther down. This spreads the heat through the water. The surface of the water does not get as hot as the surface of the land. Convection currents also help to spread the heat through the water.

▶ What part of the land is heated most by the sun's radiation?

## WHAT YOU LEARNED

1. Land heats up faster than water.
2. Land cools off faster than water.

## ANSWER THESE

1. Radiation goes deeper into (land/water).
2. Heat is absorbed in land
   a. entirely at the surface
   b. only below the surface
   c. mostly below the surface
3. Convection currents move heat through
   a. solid land
   b. loose sand
   c. water
4. The land is warmer than the water
   a. at midnight
   b. at noon
   c. at sunrise
5. The land is cooler than the water
   a. at midnight
   b. at noon
   c. at sunset

## NOW TRY THIS

**Across**
3. Energy from the sun.
5. Does water cool faster than land?
6. Does land heat faster than water?

**Down**
1. Cools slowly at night.
2. Heats quickly by day.
4. Is land heated by convection?

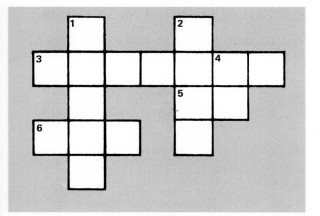

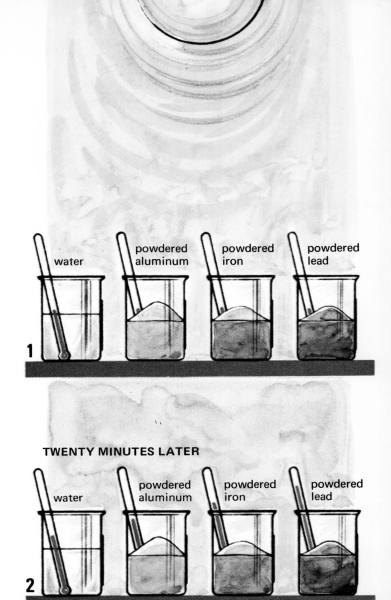

**TWENTY MINUTES LATER**

## FINDING OUT MORE

Heat is needed to raise temperatures. Each substance needs a different amount of heat to raise its temperature one degree. The same amount of sunlight heats all the materials in the flasks. After 20 minutes, each substance has become warmer. But the lead gets warmer than the iron. The iron gets warmer than the aluminum. The aluminum gets warmer than the water. Water needs more heat than aluminum to raise its temperature the same amount. Aluminum needs more heat than iron. Iron needs more heat than lead. Lead heats faster than the other materials because it needs less heat for each degree of temperature rise.

# What is air pressure?

A jar of India ink, a bar of butter, and a flashlight "D" cell all weigh about 1 newton.

**Measuring weight.** Place a book on the palm of your hand. You can feel the weight of the book pressing down on your hand. Weight is a force. Scientists measure weight and other forces in units called newtons (NOO-tuns). The picture shows some things that have a weight of about 1 newton. A 1-kilogram mass has a weight of about 10 newtons.

▶ **What is the unit of force that scientists use?**

**Weight and pressure.** When you hold a book up with your hand, you feel the whole weight of the book. But the force of the book's weight is spread out over your hand. The book may weigh 10 newtons. Your hand may have an area of 100 square centimeters. The force on each square centimeter will then be 10 newtons divided by 100 square centimeters, or 0.1 newton per square centimeter. The amount of force on a unit of area is called pressure (PRESH-er). The pressure of the book on your hand

is 0.1 newton per square centimeter. Scientists measure pressure in units called pascals (pass-KALS). A pressure of 1 pascal equals 1 newton per square meter. Its abbreviation is Pa.

▶ **How much pressure equals 1 pascal?**

**Water exerts pressure.** When you swim underwater, you can feel the pressure of the water on your ears. The deeper you go, the greater the pressure. The weight of the water above you causes this pressure.

▶ **What causes water to have pressure?**

**Air exerts pressure.** Scientists have weighed air. One liter of air weighs about 0.01 newton at sea level. This is about the weight of an ordinary paper clip. But we live at the bottom of a great ocean of air. The weight of all the air above us causes pressure on the earth's surface. Air pressure pushes downward on all objects.

▶ **What causes the air to have pressure?**

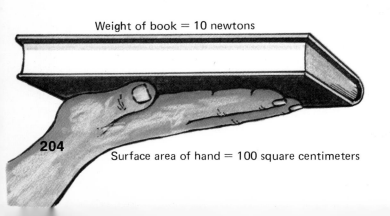

Weight of book = 10 newtons

Surface area of hand = 100 square centimeters

204

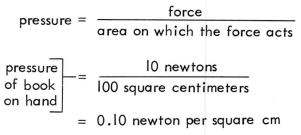

$$\text{pressure} = \frac{\text{force}}{\text{area on which the force acts}}$$

$$\left.\begin{array}{l}\text{pressure}\\\text{of book}\\\text{on hand}\end{array}\right\} = \frac{10 \text{ newtons}}{100 \text{ square centimeters}}$$

$$= 0.10 \text{ newton per square cm}$$

**Air exerts pressure upward.** Place a piece of cardboard on top of a glass filled with water. (Do the next step over a sink or basin.) Holding the cardboard tightly on the glass, turn the glass upside down. Take your hand away from the cardboard. The cardboard does not fall. The water does not spill out of the glass. Why? Air pressure pushing upward keeps the cardboard and water from falling. Air pressure pushes upward.

▶ **What helps the cardboard keep the water from falling out of a glass?**

**Air exerts pressure sideways.** Place a piece of cardboard on top of a glass filled with water. Hold the glass with the cardboard sideways. The water and cardboard remain in place. Air pushing sideways holds the cardboard in place. Air pressure pushes sideways. Try turning the glass in other directions. The cardboard remains in place. Air pressure pushes in all directions.

▶ **In what directions does air pressure push?**

### WHAT YOU LEARNED

1. Scientists measure weight and other forces in units called newtons.
2. The amount of force on a unit of area is called pressure.
3. Scientists measure pressure in units called pascals.
4. The weight of all the air above objects produces air pressure.
5. Air pressure pushes in all directions.

### SCIENCE WORDS

**newton** (NOO-tun)
   a unit scientists use to measure weights and other forces
**pressure** (PRESH-er)
   the amount of force pushing on each unit of area
**pascal** (pass-KAL)
   a unit scientists use to measure pressures

### ANSWER THESE

1. The newton is a unit of
   **a.** pressure
   **b.** distance
   **c.** force
2. The pascal is a unit of
   **a.** pressure
   **b.** distance
   **c.** force
3. As you go deeper under water, the water pressure
   **a.** increases
   **b.** decreases
   **c.** remains the same
4. At sea level, the weight of a liter of air is
   **a.** about the weight of a paper clip
   **b.** nothing
   **c.** about the weight of a golf ball
5. Air pressure pushes
   **a.** only upward
   **b.** only downward
   **c.** in all directions

### NOW TRY THIS

Find the words.

### DO THIS AT HOME

Air pressure can force a hard-boiled egg into a milk bottle. Take the shell off a hard-boiled egg. Place a small piece of paper in the top of a milk bottle. Light the paper. Push the paper into the bottle. Place the egg (small end down) in the top of the bottle. In a few seconds, the egg slides into the bottle. The burning paper used up some of the oxygen in the bottle. The air pressure is lower inside of the bottle than outside because some of the air has been used up. The greater air pressure outside pushed the egg into the bottle.

# How much pressure does air have?

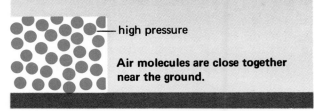

Air molecules are far apart high in the atmosphere.

— low pressure

— high pressure

Air molecules are close together near the ground.

When air molecules hit a surface, they cause pressure.

**Pressure squeezes the air.** The molecules of a gas are far apart. Pressure on a gas squeezes the molecules closer together. The greater the pressure, the closer the molecules get. The atmosphere is hundreds of kilometers thick. The weight of all this air causes a large pressure near the ground. The air molecules are close together near the ground. Near the top of the atmosphere, there is very little weight of air pressing down. The pressure there is low. The air molecules are far apart.

▶ Where are the air molecules closest together?

**Molecules of air cause pressure.** The molecules of air are always moving. As they move, they hit the surfaces of objects. The force of the molecules hitting a surface causes pressure. The greater the number of molecules that hit each unit of area, the greater the pressure. The air molecules are closest together near the earth's surface. Many molecules hit each unit of area each second. At sea level, the air pressure is about 100 000 pascals, or 100 kilopascals. This is abbreviated 100 kPa. This pressure is equal to 100 000 newtons per square meter, or 10 newtons per square centimeter. The force of air pressure at sea level is 10 newtons on every square centimeter.

▶ What is the air pressure at sea level?

**Air pressure can crush a tin can.** Boil a little water in a gallon can. When steam

comes out of the can, replace the cap. Let the can cool. The can is crushed. When the water boils, steam fills the can. The molecules of steam push most of the air molecules out of the can. When the steam cools, it changes back into water. There are only a few air molecules left in the can. The air pressure inside the can is much less than the air pressure outside the can. The air outside pushes in the sides of the can. Air pressure causes the can to crumple.

▶ What causes a can to crumple when the air pressure inside the can is reduced?

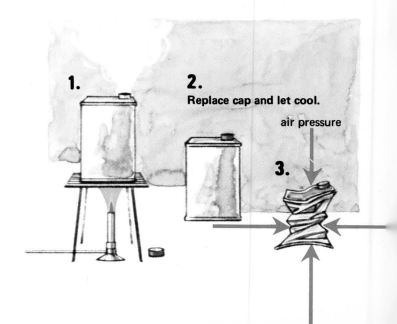

1.

2.
Replace cap and let cool.

air pressure

3.

**The Magdeburg hemispheres.** In 1654, Otto von Guericke performed an interesting experiment. Von Guericke was the mayor of a small German town called Magdeburg. He made a hollow metal sphere that had two halves, or hemispheres. The two hemispheres fitted tightly together. The only opening was through a valve in one of the hemispheres. Air was pumped out of the sphere through the valve. Few air molecules remained inside. The air pressure inside the sphere was very low. The greater outside air pressure held the hemispheres together. Sixteen horses could not pull the hemispheres apart. Then the valve was opened to let air into the sphere. The two hemispheres came apart easily.

▶ **What held the Magdeburg hemispheres tightly together?**

## WHAT YOU LEARNED

1. Air pressure is caused by molecules hitting a surface.

2. At sea level, air pressure is about 100 kilopascals.

3. Air pressure decreases as you go higher up into the atmosphere.

## ANSWER THESE

1. What do the Magdeburg hemispheres show?

2. At sea level, what is the air pressure per square centimeter?

3. Why is air pressure greater in a valley than on top of a mountain?

## NOW TRY THESE

1. Place a straw in a glass of water. Put your finger over the top end of the straw. Take the straw out of the water. The water in the straw stays there as long as your finger is over the top. It falls when you remove your finger. What keeps the water in the straw? Why does the water fall when you take your finger away?

2. Wet two plates of glass. Place them together. Now try to pull them apart. What holds them together?

207

# How is air pressure measured?

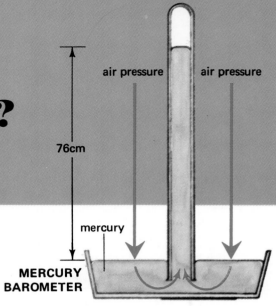

air pressure     air pressure

76cm

mercury

**MERCURY BAROMETER**

**Air pressure can hold up a column of water.** Put a glass in a tank of water. Turn the glass upside down. Slowly lift the glass. Water stays in the glass as long as the mouth is under the surface of the water. Air pressure pushes down on the surface of the water in the tank. This pressure is transmitted in all directions. It is transmitted upward into the glass. Air pressure is holding up a column of water in the glass. At sea level, air pressure can hold up a column of water 1000 cm high.

▶ How high a column of water can air pressure hold up at sea level?

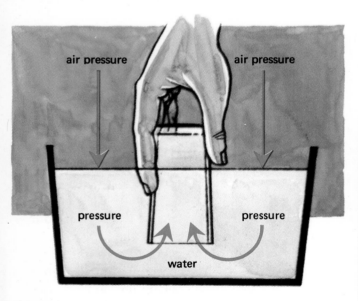

air pressure     air pressure

pressure     pressure

water

**Mercury barometers.** The Italian scientist Torricelli (tor-uh-CHEL-ee) studied air pressure using mercury instead of water. Mercury is a liquid. But mercury is 13.6 times more dense than water. At sea level,

air pressure can hold up a column of mercury only 76 cm high. The air pressure is not always exactly the same. When the air pressure increases, it pushes down harder on the mercury. The mercury in the tube moves up. When the air pressure on the mercury decreases, the mercury in the tube moves down. Torricelli studied how air pressure changed the level of mercury in a tube. An instrument used to measure air pressure is called a barometer (buh-ROM-uh-ter). A barometer that uses mercury is a mercury barometer.

▶ What instrument is used to measure air pressure?

**Aneroid barometers.** Another kind of barometer is the aneroid (AN-uh-royd) barometer. It uses no liquid. An aneroid barometer is made with a metal can. The top of the can is very thin. It can bend in or out. A pointer is connected to the top of the can. When the air pressure increases, the top of the can is pressed in. This makes the pointer move one way. When the air pressure decreases, the top of the can moves out. This makes the pointer move the other way.

▶ What kind of barometer does not use a liquid?

## WHAT YOU LEARNED

1. Air pressure can hold up a column of water 1000 cm high.
2. Air pressure can hold up a column of mercury 76 cm high.
3. Air pressure is measured with a barometer.

## SCIENCE WORDS

**mercury barometer** (buh-ROM-uh-ter)
an instrument that uses a column of mercury to measure air pressure

**aneroid** (AN-uh-royd) **barometer**
an instrument that measures air pressure, but uses no liquid

## ANSWER THESE

1. The scientist who first used mercury to make a barometer was
   a. Newton
   b. Einstein
   c. Torricelli
2. At sea level, air pressure holds up a column of mercury
   a. 76 cm high
   b. 1000 cm high
   c. 1 cm high
3. At sea level, air pressure holds up a column of water
   a. 76 cm high
   b. 1000 cm high
   c. 76 meters high

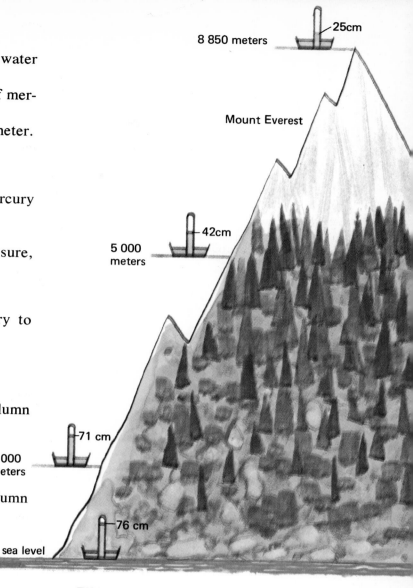

8 850 meters — 25cm

Mount Everest

5 000 meters — 42cm

1 000 meters — 71 cm

sea level — 76 cm

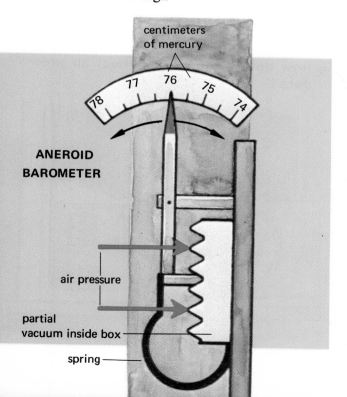

centimeters of mercury

78  77  76  75  74

**ANEROID BAROMETER**

air pressure

partial vacuum inside box

spring

## FINDING OUT MORE

A barometer can be used to measure altitude, or height above sea level. A barometer that is used to measure altitude is called an altimeter (al-TIM-uh-ter). At sea level, air pressure can hold up a 76-cm column of mercury. As you go up in the atmosphere, air pressure decreases. The mercury column drops. At 1 000 meters above sea level, air pressure will support a column of mercury only 71 cm high. At 5 000 meters the mercury column is about 42 cm high. Mount Everest, which is 8850 meters high, is the highest point on earth. Here the mercury column is only about 25 cm high. At 25 000 meters, the air pressure is less than 2 cm of mercury. There is not enough air to hold up a plane, and there is not enough oxygen for fuel to burn.

209

# Why does air pressure change?

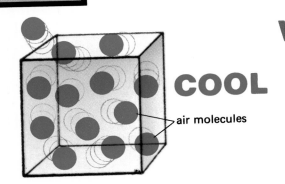

COOL

air molecules

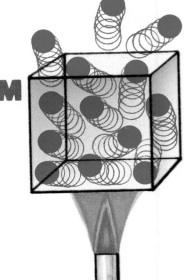

WARM

**Warm air is lighter than cool air.** Heat makes the molecules of a material move faster. As the molecules move faster, they spread farther apart. Think of an open box of air being heated. The molecules of air in the box spread farther apart. Some of the molecules have to move out of the box. Now there are fewer molecules of air in the box. The weight of the air in the box is less. A box of warm air weighs less than the same box with cooler air.

▶ Which has more molecules, a box of warm air or the same box with cool air?

**Warm air has less pressure than cool air.** In the summer, the air is warmer than in the winter. The warm air has fewer molecules than the cool air. Warm air weighs less than cool air. In the summer, the air pressure is usually less than in the winter. In warm regions of the earth, the air pressure is less than in cold regions.

▶ How does temperature affect air pressure?

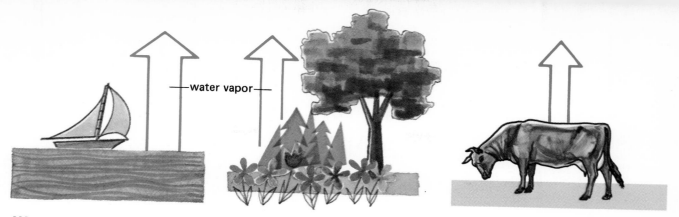

water vapor

**Water vapor in the air.** Water evaporates from lakes, rivers, and oceans. All living things give off water vapor. Molecules of water go into the air from all these things. Water molecules in the air are called <u>water vapor</u> (VAY-per). The molecules of water vapor take the place of some of the molecules of air. Water molecules weigh less than most air molecules. Air with water vapor in it weighs less than dry air. It exerts less pressure. The pressure of dry air is greater than the pressure of moist air.

▶ How does water vapor affect air pressure?

## WHAT YOU LEARNED

1. Heat causes air molecules to move apart.
2. Cool air weighs more than warm air.
3. Air pressure is greater in cool air than in warm air.
4. Air pressure is greater in dry air than in moist air.

## SCIENCE WORD

**water vapor** (VAY-per)
  molecules of water in the air

## ANSWER THESE

1. Molecules move faster in (warm/cool) air.
2. Air will take up more space when it is (cool/warm).
3. Air will be heavier when it is (cool/warm).
4. Pressure is greater in (cool/warm) air.
5. Air weighs less when it is (moist/dry).
6. Pressure is greater in (moist/dry) air.

## NOW TRY THESE

Unscramble the words in capital letters.
1. Heated air has less SERPURSE than cold air.
2. Cool air is IVAHERE than warm air.
3. Air pressure becomes SELS if water vapor is added.
4. As you go higher, air pressure SEC-RADEES.

## FINDING OUT MORE

Air pressure decreases as you go higher into the atmosphere. Mountain climbers have trouble breathing at great heights. Airplanes that fly at great heights must keep their cabins tightly closed. Air for the cabins must be kept at the pressure near the normal amount at sea level. We say these cabins are pressurized (PRESH-ur-ized).

# How does air pressure change around the earth?

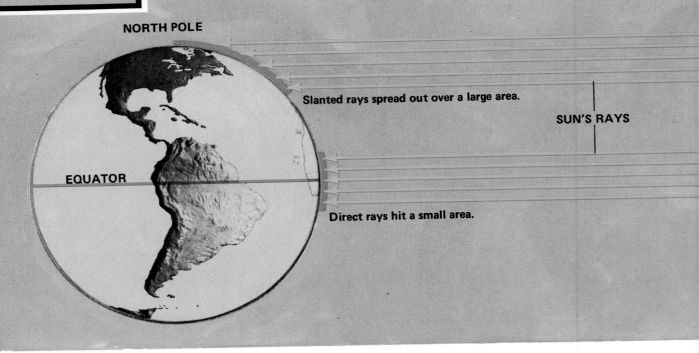

NORTH POLE

Slanted rays spread out over a large area.

SUN'S RAYS

EQUATOR

Direct rays hit a small area.

**Sunlight at the equator.** Around the equator the sun's rays are direct. The area around the equator gets a large amount of energy from the sun. The earth's surface at the equator is very warm.

▶ Where on earth are the sun's rays direct?

**It's cold at the poles.** At the poles of the earth the sun's rays hit the surface at a slant. The slanted rays spread out over a large area. The area near the poles gets much less energy from the sun than the same area near the equator. The earth's surface near the poles is cold.

▶ Why does the earth's surface get less energy from sunlight at the poles than at the equator?

**Air pressure at the equator.** The air at the equator is warmed by the earth's surface. The air expands and becomes lighter. Its pressure decreases. The air near the equator has low pressure. The regions around the equator are low-pressure regions.

▶ Why is the air pressure low near the equator?

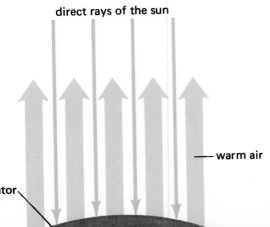

direct rays of the sun

warm air

low-pressure region around the equator

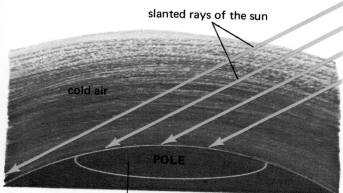

slanted rays of the sun

cold air

POLE

high-pressure region around the earth's pole

**Air pressure at the poles.** The earth's surface near the poles is cold. The air over the poles is also cold. Cold air is heavier than warm air. The pressure of cold air is greater. The regions around the poles are high-pressure regions.

▶ **Why is the air pressure high near the poles?**

## WHAT YOU LEARNED

1. Light rays that are direct give more heat than rays that hit on a slant.
2. The equator is a low-pressure region.
3. The poles are high-pressure regions.

## ANSWER THESE

1. The equator is hot because
   a. it gets all the sun's rays
   b. the sun's rays are direct on this area
   c. the sun's rays hit on a slant in this area

2. The equator is a low-pressure region because
   a. the air above it is warm
   b. the air above it is heavy
   c. the air above it is cool

3. At the poles,
   a. the sun's rays are direct
   b. the sun's rays hit on a slant
   c. there is no sunlight

## NOW TRY THIS

**Down**
1. Direct rays give more heat than _____ ones.
2. The sun supplies the earth with light and _____.
3. Slanted rays hit the earth's _____.
**Across**
4. Direct rays of the sun strike the _____.

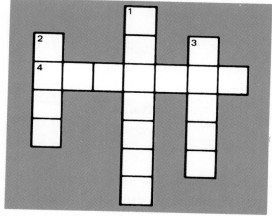

## FINDING OUT MORE

Did you ever stand in front of an open refrigerator when you were not wearing shoes or socks? How did your feet feel? They felt cool. There is cold air in the refrigerator. Cold air is heavy and it moves down. When you opened the door, the cold air from inside the refrigerator moved out and down.

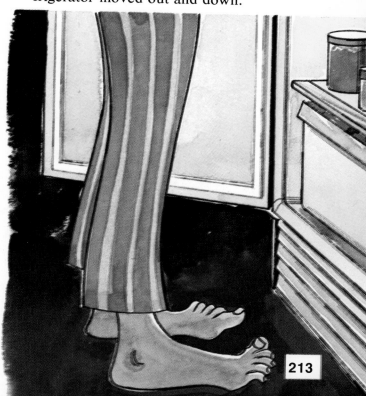

# How are winds formed?

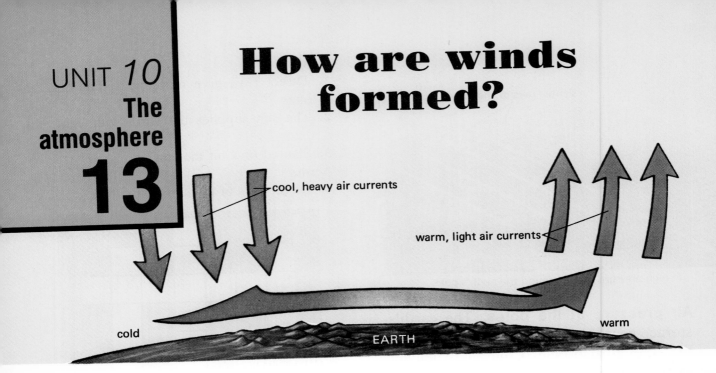

cool, heavy air currents

warm, light air currents

cold

EARTH

warm

**Air currents.** The sun does not heat all parts of the earth equally. Some areas of the earth are warmed more than others. The air over the warmer regions is heated and expands. The air over cooler regions is heavier, and sinks downward. Cool air moves in under the warm air. It pushes the warm air up. These up-and-down movements of the air are called <u>air currents</u> (CUR-rents).

▶ **What are air currents?**

**Winds.** Cool air moves in under warm air. The cool air moves along the surface of the earth toward the warmer air. <u>Horizontal</u> (hor-uh-ZONT-ul) <u>movements</u> of air over the earth are called <u>winds</u>. Winds form as cool, heavy air moves toward warm, light air.

▶ **What are winds?**

**Winds and air pressure.** Differences in air pressure cause winds. Regions of cold, heavy air have high pressure. We call these regions "highs." Regions of warm, light air have low pressure. We call these regions "lows." Air moves from regions of high pressure to regions of low pressure. Winds form when air moves. The speed of the wind depends on the difference in pressure.

▶ **What causes winds to form?**

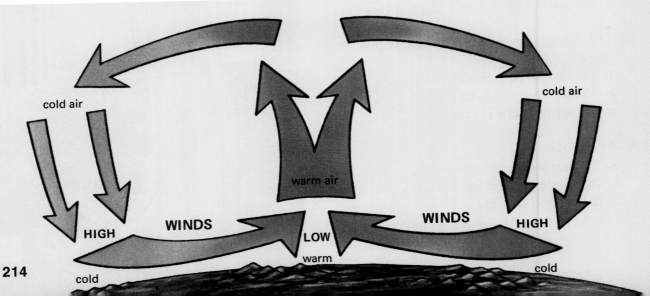

cold air

cold air

warm air

HIGH

WINDS

LOW

WINDS

HIGH

cold

warm

cold

BOSTON 750 mm
NEW YORK 760 mm
PHILADELPHIA 765 mm
CHICAGO 770 mm

## WHAT YOU LEARNED

1. Unequal heating of the earth causes air currents and winds.
2. Air currents are up-and-down movements of air.
3. Winds are horizontal movements of air.
4. Air moving from high-pressure regions to low-pressure regions causes winds.

## SCIENCE WORDS

**air currents** (CUR-rents)
 up-and-down movements of air
**horizontal** (hor-uh-ZONT-ul) **movement**
 moving across the surface of the earth
**winds**
 horizontal movements of air

## ANSWER THESE

1. Up-and-down movements of air are called
   a. currents
   b. winds
   c. waves
2. Horizontal movements of air are called
   a. currents
   b. winds
   c. waves
3. Air moves from
   a. highs to lows
   b. lows to highs
   c. warm regions to cooler regions
4. The sun heats different parts of the earth (equally/unequally).

## NOW TRY THIS

The numbers on the map are the air pressures for different cities. Remember that air moves from a high-pressure region to a low-pressure region. Now answer the following questions:

1. Will the wind move from Chicago to New York or from New York to Chicago?
2. Will the wind move from New York to Boston or from Boston to New York?
3. Will the wind move from Philadelphia to New York or from New York to Philadelphia?

## FINDING OUT MORE

During World War II, American bomber pilots discovered regions in the upper atmosphere with very strong winds. Scientists have found that these strong winds weave back and forth through the atmosphere, like a stream on the land. These air streams in the upper atmosphere are called jet streams. They are between 6 000 and 12 000 meters up in the atmosphere. The speed of the winds in the jet stream may be as high as 500 kilometers per hour. In the Northern Hemisphere, the jet stream flows from west to east. Airplanes flying in the jet stream gain speed from it when going from west to east, but lose speed going the other way. Flight times from California to New York are shorter than from New York to California because of the jet stream.

# Which way does a wind blow?

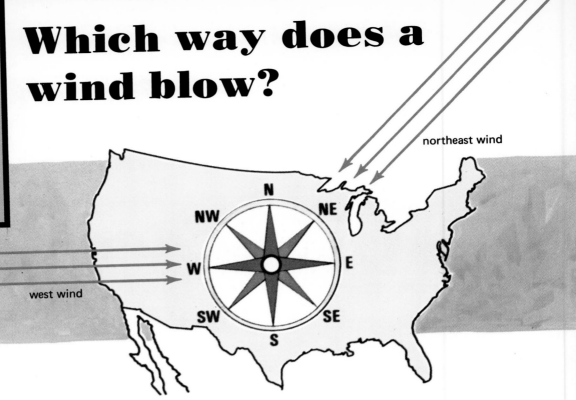

northeast wind

west wind

**Naming winds.** The direction a wind comes from gives the wind its name. If a wind comes from the north, it is called a north wind. If a wind comes from the south, it is called a south wind. What do we call a wind from the north and east? It is called a northeast wind.

▶ How are winds named?

**Winds blow in different directions.** Winds blow from regions of high pressure to regions of low pressure. The equator is a low-pressure region. North and south of the equator there are high-pressure regions. Winds blow from these regions toward the equator. There are different pressure regions between the equator and the poles. Some are high-pressure regions. Some are low-pressure regions. Winds blow from high-pressure regions toward nearby low-pressure regions. This causes different regions of winds. The diagram shows the directions of the winds that blow around our planet.

▶ Which way do winds blow in different regions of the earth?

**Winds curve.** Winds do not move in straight lines. Winds curve as they move from high-pressure to low-pressure regions. Winds moving toward the equator curve to the west. Winds moving toward the poles curve to the east. Winds curve because the earth spins, or <u>rotates</u> (ROH-tates), like a top.

▶ Why do winds curve?

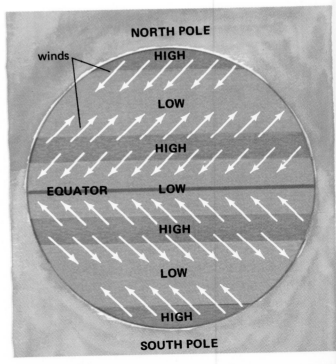

NORTH POLE
HIGH
winds
LOW
HIGH
EQUATOR
LOW
HIGH
LOW
HIGH
SOUTH POLE

## WHAT YOU LEARNED

1. The direction a wind comes from gives the wind its name.
2. Winds blow from high-pressure regions to low-pressure regions.
3. The earth's rotation causes winds to curve.

## SCIENCE WORD

**rotate** (ROH-tate)
 spin like a top

## ANSWER THESE

1. A west wind comes from the
   a. north
   b. south
   c. east
   d. west
2. Winds curve because the earth _____.
3. Winds moving toward the equator curve to the _____.
4. Winds moving toward the poles curve to the _____.

## NOW TRY THIS

Draw a diagram of the earth. Place the highs and lows in the proper places. Using arrows, show the directions of the different winds. The

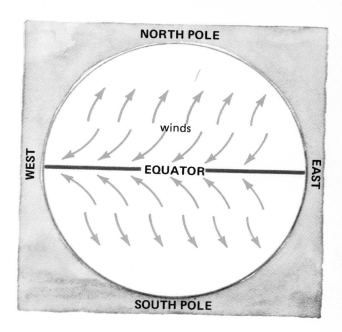

winds blowing toward the equator from the north and east are called northeasterly winds. Those blowing from the south and east are called the southeasterlies. On the diagram write the names of the other winds.

## FINDING OUT MORE

Winds are known by many names. Northeast and southeast winds blow in toward the equator. They are called the trade winds. Long ago, sailboats carried supplies across the ocean. The northeast and southeast trade winds moved these trading ships across the ocean.

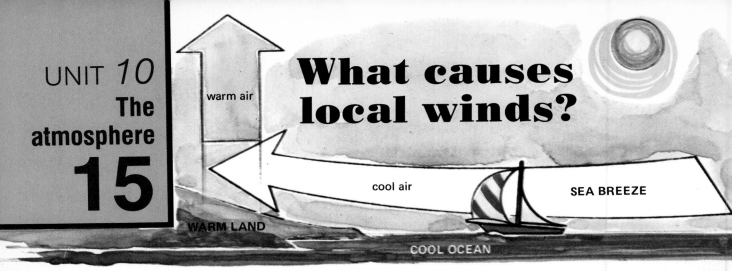

# What causes local winds?

warm air

cool air

SEA BREEZE

WARM LAND

COOL OCEAN

warm air

LAND BREEZE

cool air

COOL LAND

WARM OCEAN

**Sea breezes.** A gentle wind is called a breeze. A breeze coming from the ocean toward the land is called a sea breeze. Like a wind, a breeze is named after the direction it comes from. A sea breeze comes from the sea. Why is there often a sea breeze on a sunny summer day? The sun heats both the land and the water. But the land heats faster than water. The air over the land becomes warmer and lighter. The cooler, heavier air over the water moves in toward the land. The warm light air over the land is pushed upward.

▶ What is a sea breeze?

**Land breezes.** During the night, the land cools faster than the water. The air over the land becomes cooler than the air over the water. Heavier air over the land moves toward the water. The warmer, lighter air over the water is pushed upward. The movement of air from the land toward the water is called a land breeze.

▶ What is a land breeze?

**Monsoons.** Land and sea breezes are local winds. They only happen near large bodies of water. Larger winds can overpower them. Portions of some continents have winds that change direction with the season. In the summer, the continent remains warm, both day and night. The winds move from the ocean toward the land all summer. In the winter, the land gets very cold. The winds blow out toward the ocean all winter. Winds that change direction from season to season are called monsoons (mon-SOONS).

▶ What are monsoons?

**Mountain and valley breezes.** Mountain regions also have local winds. Air moves downhill at night and uphill during the day.

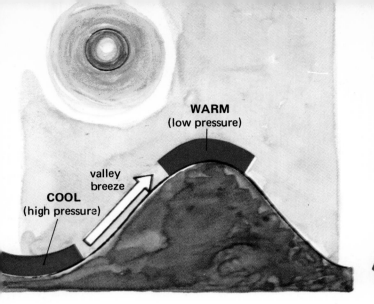

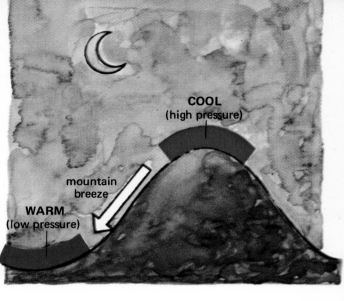

During the day, the air on top of hills is warmer than the air in the valleys. Warm air has low pressure. Air in the valley is cooler and has high pressure. Air moves from the high pressure of the valley to the low pressure of the mountaintop. This is a valley breeze. At night the valleys are warmer than the hilltops. The heavier mountain air flows downhill. This is a mountain breeze.

▶ **What is a mountain breeze?**

## WHAT YOU LEARNED

1. Unequal heating of land and water causes land and sea breezes.
2. Winds that change direction from season to season are called monsoons.
3. Differences in temperature between mountains and valleys cause mountain and valley breezes.

## SCIENCE WORDS

**breeze**
  a light wind
**monsoon** (mon-SOON)
  wind that changes direction with the seasons

## ANSWER THESE

1. On a sunny summer day at the beach, cooler air over the water produces a
   a. land breeze
   b. sea breeze
   c. mountain breeze

2. A summer night at the beach produces a land breeze because
   a. the air over the ocean is warmer
   b. the air over the ocean is cooler
   c. the ocean is calm
3. At night, cool mountain air
   a. stops the wind
   b. blows uphill
   c. blows downhill
4. Winds that change direction with the seasons are called
   a. valley breezes
   b. summer, winter winds
   c. monsoons

## NOW TRY THESE

Find the words.

1. Seasonal winds

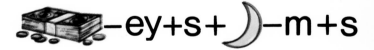

2. Type of breeze

3. Another type of breeze

# How do we measure winds?

**Finding the direction of winds.** It is important to know the direction the wind is coming from. A <u>weather</u> <u>vane</u> shows the direction a wind is coming from. Many weather vanes are shaped like arrows. When the wind blows, the arrow turns and points into the wind.

▶ What does a weather vane do?

**Measuring wind speed.** An <u>anemometer</u> (an-uh-MOM-uh-ter) is an instrument used for measuring wind speed. The photograph of the anemometer shows that it is made of cups turned on their sides and attached to rods. Wind pushes the cups and causes the anemometer to turn. The stronger the wind, the faster the cups turn. Some anemometers have a meter attached to them. This meter is like the speedometer in a car. It show how fast the wind is moving.

▶ What does an anemometer measure?

**Weather balloons.** Weather balloons are also used to measure wind speed and direction high in the air. The balloons are filled with helium. Helium is lighter than air. Balloons filled with helium rise in air. Weather balloons are filled with helium and released. Wind high in the air moves the balloon. Scientists measure how fast the balloon moves. This shows the speed of the wind. The direction the balloon moves shows the direction of the wind.

▶ What can weather balloons tell us about winds?

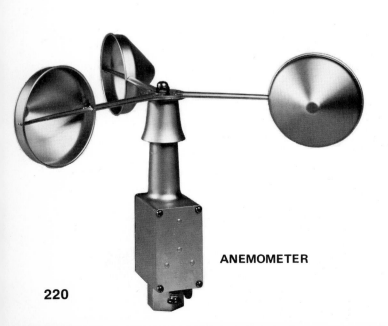

**ANEMOMETER**

| KIND OF WIND | WIND SPEED (km per hr) | OBSERVATIONS |
|---|---|---|
| calm | 0 | Smoke goes straight up. |
| light to gentle breeze | 1-19 | Leaves and twigs are in constant motion. Flags wave. |
| moderate to fresh breeze | 20-38 | Small trees sway. Papers are blown around. |
| strong breeze | 39-57 | Hard to walk against the wind. Umbrellas are hard to open. |
| gale | 58-77 | Branches are broken from trees. TV antennas, store windows break. |
| strong gale | 78-115 | Trees are uprooted. |
| hurricane | above 115 | Great damage is done to buildings. |

## WHAT YOU LEARNED

1. A weather vane shows wind direction.
2. An anemometer measures wind speed.
3. A weather balloon can show wind speed and wind direction.

## SCIENCE WORDS

**weather vane**
  instrument used to measure wind direction
**anemometer** (an-uh-MOM-uh-ter)
  instrument used to measure wind speed

## ANSWER THESE

1. A weather vane points north. The wind is coming from the
   a. north
   b. south
   c. west
2. An anemometer turns fast. The wind is
   a. calm
   b. gentle
   c. strong
3. A weather balloon moves south at a speed of 10 km/hr. The winds are from the
   a. north at 10 km/hr
   b. south at 10 km/hr
   c. north at 5 km/hr
4. Weather balloons are filled with helium so that they
   a. will be cheap
   b. will float in air
   c. will move very fast

## FINDING OUT MORE

You can measure wind speed without an anemometer. Wind speed can be measured by looking at things that are moved by winds. The chart shows you how to do this. The chart is not as exact as an anemometer.

## DO THIS AT HOME

Make a weather vane. Cut out two cardboard arrows like the one in the picture. Make them the same size. Put glue on the tails and heads of the arrows. Glue the two arrows together. Clip a ballpoint pen cover in the middle between the two arrows. Place the pen cover on a pencil point. Move the cover back and forth until the arrow balances. Use your weather vane to find wind direction. Use the wind chart to find wind speed. Compare your observations with the newspaper weather reports.

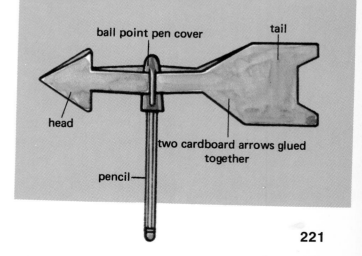

# UNIT 10 Review

Do the following questions on a separate sheet of paper.

**Matching**   Write down each of the statements in Column I, leaving one line of space after each statement. On the blank line following each statement, write the word or phrase from Column II that is described by that statement.

### Column I

1. Measures wind speed.
2. Spin like a top.
3. Molecules of water in air.
4. Amount of force per unit area.
5. Movement of heat by contact.
6. Allow to pass through.
7. The process of giving off radiant energy.
8. A charged particle.
9. Main ingredient in air.
10. A mixture of gases.

### Column II

nitrogen
water vapor
air
anemometer
rotate
ion
pressure
conduction
transmit
radiation

Do the following questions on a separate sheet of paper.

**Multiple Choice**   Write the letter of the choice that best completes the statement or answers the question.

1. A form of oxygen that stops ultraviolet waves is called
   a. ozone
   b. argon
   c. neon
2. Sunlight is a kind of energy called
   a. conducted energy
   b. star heat
   c. radiant energy
3. A convection current is the upward movement of warm air and the
   a. downward movement of cool air
   b. upward movement of cool air
   c. lack of movement of cool air
4. The pascal is a unit scientists use to measure
   a. pressure
   b. heat
   c. radiant energy

5. A barometer is an instrument used to measure
   a. solar radiation
   b. warm air currents
   c. air pressure
6. The air pressure at the earth's poles is
   a. greater than at the equator
   b. less than at the equator
   c. the same as at the equator
7. A region of cold, heavy air is called a
   a. low
   b. current
   c. high
8. A monsoon is a wind that changes direction with
   a. every rotation of the earth
   b. each full moon
   c. the passage of the seasons

# UNIT 11

# Weather and Climate

## Unit Lessons

1. How does water get into the atmosphere?
2. What is humidity?
3. What is relative humidity?
4. How can we measure relative humidity?
5. How does water come out of the air?
6. Why does it rain?
7. How do we identify clouds?
8. How does weather affect us?
9. How do we get our weather?
10. What happens when air masses meet?
11. What is a station model?
12. How do we read a weather map?
13. What factors determine climate?
14. How can we classify climates?

## Goals and Objectives

After completing this unit, you should be able to:
- understand how water vapor exists in the air as humidity.
- explain how a psychrometer determines relative humidity.
- describe how clouds form and why precipitation occurs.
- distinguish between cirrus, cumulus, and stratus clouds.
- categorize air masses and explain what happens along fronts.
- read a weather map.
- classify climates, and understand the factors determining the climate of a region.

# How does water get into the atmosphere?

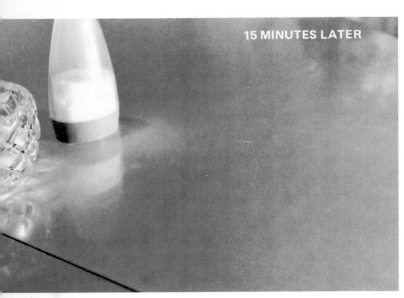

15 MINUTES LATER

**Water in the atmosphere.** On a warm day, droplets of water may form on the outside of a cold can of soda. Where does this water come from? It comes from the atmosphere. There is always some water in the atmosphere. The water may be in the form of a gas. This is called water vapor. Water is also found in the atmosphere as clouds and fog. Clouds and fog are made of tiny droplets of water.

▶ **What is water called when it is in the air as a gas?**

**Evaporation.** Wipe a damp cloth across a table top. The table top is wet. After a few minutes, the table top dries. What happened to the water? The water evaporated. It changed from a liquid to a gas. Evaporation (eh-vap-uh-RAY-shun) is the changing of a liquid to a gas.

▶ **What is evaporation?**

**Water vapor.** Where does water vapor come from? Water vapor in the air comes mostly from the oceans. Every day millions of tons of water evaporate from the surface of the oceans. Water also evaporates from puddles, lakes, rivers, and from wet soil.

Living things add water to the air. Blow on a cold mirror. Moisture forms on the mirror. Breathing adds moisture to the air. Cover the leaves and stems of a plant with a plastic bag. Place the plant in the sun. After a short time the inside of the bag becomes covered with moisture. The water came from the plant. Plants give off water to the atmosphere by a process called transpiration (trans-puh-RAY-shun).

▶ **Where does most of the water in the atmosphere come from?**

moisture

## WHAT YOU LEARNED

1. There is water in the atmosphere.
2. Evaporation is the changing of a liquid to a gas.
3. Most of the water vapor in the air comes from the evaporation of ocean water.
4. Living things add water to the air.

## SCIENCE WORDS

**evaporation** (eh-vap-uh-RAY-shun)
   changing from a liquid to a gas
**transpiration** (trans-puh-RAY-shun)
   the process by which plants give off water vapor to the atmosphere

## ANSWER THESE

1. Water that exists as a gas in the air is called
   a. rain
   b. water vapor
   c. clouds
2. When water evaporates, it changes from
   a. a liquid to a gas
   b. a gas to a liquid
   c. a cloud to rain
3. Most water vapor found in the air comes from
   a. rivers
   b. puddles
   c. oceans
4. Animals give off water by
   a. breathing
   b. using a mirror
   c. transpiration

## NOW TRY THESE

Find the words.
1. What water does to get into the air.

2. Supplies most of the water to the atmosphere.

o + ⏰ − 🔒 + 👂 − r + n

## FINDING OUT MORE

Molecules in a liquid are always moving. Some are moving faster than others. Some of the fast-moving molecules near the surface escape from the liquid. They go off into the air. They form a gas. That is how evaporation takes place.

When a liquid is heated, its molecules move faster. More of them escape from the surface. Evaporation takes place more rapidly. Water in a pan over a radiator evaporates much faster than water in a pan on a table. Evaporation from the oceans occurs most rapidly around the equator, where the water is heated by the direct rays of the sun.

# What is humidity?

**Humidity.** The weather reporter says, "The humidity was high today." What is humidity (hyoo-MID-uh-tee)? Humidity is the amount of water vapor in the air. A high humidity means that there is a lot of water vapor in the air. A low humidity means there is little water vapor in the air.

▶ What is humidity?

**Capacity.** How much water can a 100-ml beaker hold? If the beaker is filled to the top, it holds 100 ml. Its capacity (kuh-PASS-uh-tee) is 100 ml. The capacity of the beaker is the amount of material it can hold.

▶ What is meant by the capacity of a beaker?

**The capacity of the air can change.** A 100-ml beaker can hold 100 ml of water. Its capacity to hold water is always the same. The air has a capacity for holding water, too. But the capacity of the air can change. Warm air can hold more water vapor than cold air. The capacity of the air for holding water vapor changes with temperature.

▶ What affects the capacity of air to hold water?

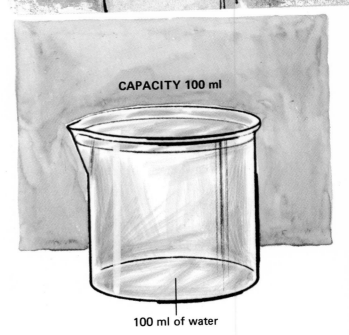

**CAPACITY 100 ml**

100 ml of water

226

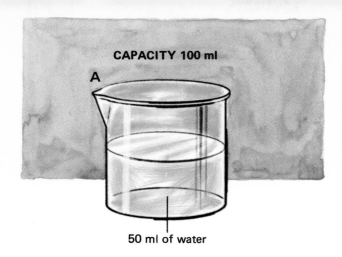

CAPACITY 100 ml

A

50 ml of water

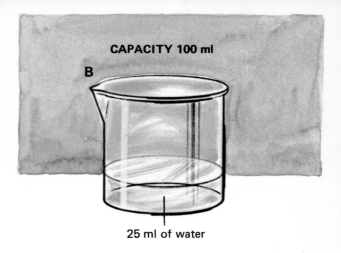

CAPACITY 100 ml

B

25 ml of water

**Absolute humidity.** How much water is there in beaker A? How much water is in beaker B? Beaker A has 50 ml of water. Beaker B has 25 ml of water. Both beakers can hold up to 100 ml of water. They are not filled to their capacity. Air can also hold different amounts of water. Air may not be filled to its capacity. The actual amount of water in the air is called the <u>absolute</u> (ab-suh-LOOT) <u>humidity</u>.

▶ What is absolute humidity?

## WHAT YOU LEARNED

1. Humidity is the amount of water vapor in the air.
2. Capacity is the amount of material something can hold.
3. Warm air has a greater capacity to hold water vapor than cold air.
4. Absolute humidity is the actual amount of water vapor found in the air.

## SCIENCE WORDS

**humidity** (hyoo-MID-uh-tee)
  amount of water vapor in the air
**capacity** (kuh-PASS-uh-tee)
  the amount of material something can hold
**absolute** (ab-suh-LOOT) **humidity**
  the actual amount of water vapor in the air

## ANSWER THESE

1. The amount of water vapor found in the air is its
  **a.** temperature
  **b.** pressure
  **c.** humidity

2. The amount of water vapor the air can hold is its
  **a.** pressure
  **b.** capacity
  **c.** evaporation
3. Absolute humidity is
  **a.** the actual amount of water vapor in the air
  **b.** the amount of water vapor the air can hold
  **c.** moisture that can evaporate into the air
4. As the temperature of air increases, its capacity to hold water vapor
  **a.** increases
  **b.** decreases
  **c.** remains the same

## DO THIS AT HOME

A hygrometer (hy-GROM-uh-ter) is an instrument used to measure humidity. Cobalt chloride is a chemical that is blue when dry. It turns pink when it is wet. Dip a strip of cloth or paper toweling in a solution of cobalt chloride. Let it dry. Hang the strip up. If the strip stays blue, the air is dry. If the strip turns pink, the air is moist.

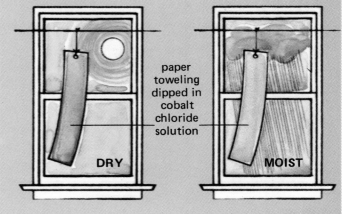

paper toweling dipped in cobalt chloride solution

DRY

MOIST

**Saturation.** Place a sponge in a pan of water. The sponge soaks up water. Soon the sponge is filled with water. It cannot hold any more. It is <u>saturated</u> (SACH-uh-ray-tid). It is filled to its capacity. Air can be compared to a sponge. Air that is filled to its capacity with water vapor is saturated. It cannot hold any more water.

▶ **What does it mean when we say that air is saturated?**

**Relative humidity.** A sponge that is filled to its capacity is saturated. It contains all the water it can hold. It is 100 percent full. When air is filled to its capacity with water vapor, it is 100 percent full. Air is not always filled to its capacity. It may be filled to only half its capacity. It is then only 50 percent full. The amount of moisture in the air compared to its capacity is called <u>relative</u> (REL-uh-tiv) <u>humidity</u>. The relative

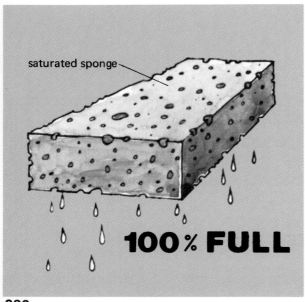

saturated sponge

**100% FULL**

**saturated
air**

**100% FULL**

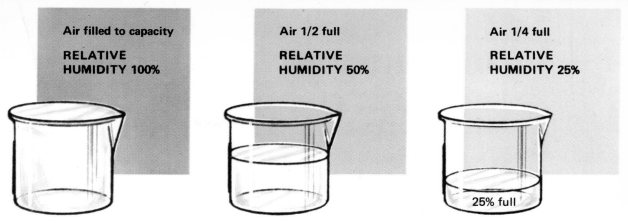

Air filled to capacity
**RELATIVE HUMIDITY 100%**

Air 1/2 full
**RELATIVE HUMIDITY 50%**

Air 1/4 full
**RELATIVE HUMIDITY 25%**

25% full

Relative humidity measures the amount of moisture in the air compared to its capacity.

humidity of air filled to its capacity is 100 percent. The relative humidity of air filled to half its capacity is 50 percent. The relative humidity of air filled to one-fourth its capacity is 25%.

▶ **What is the relative humidity of air if it is filled to one-half its capacity?**

## WHAT YOU LEARNED

1. Air filled to its capacity is saturated.
2. Relative humidity is the amount of moisture in the air compared to its capacity.

## SCIENCE WORDS

**saturated** (SATCH-uh-rate-ed)
 filled to capacity
**relative** (REL-uh-tiv) **humidity**
 amount of moisture in the air compared to its capacity

## ANSWER THESE

1. No more water can enter air that is
 a. saturated
 b. hot
 c. cold
2. The relative humidity of saturated air is
 a. 25 percent
 b. 50 percent
 c. 100 percent
3. Air with a relative humidity of 25 percent has
 a. all the water it can hold
 b. half the water it can hold
 c. one-fourth the water it can hold
4. Relative humidity is given in
 a. degrees
 b. percent
 c. grams

## NOW TRY THESE

Unscramble the words in capital letters.

1. If the relative humidity is 100 percent, air is filled to its PACITACY.
2. A relative humidity of 50 percent tells us the air has FALH the moisture it can hold.
3. Relative humidity is stated as a ERTNCEP.

## FINDING OUT MORE

In some cities the temperature may reach 25°C. In other cities the temperature may go over 30°C. People living in the hotter city may feel more comfortable than those in the cooler city. How is this possible? High relative humidity makes people uncomfortable. A temperature of 35°C with very low humidity may be quite comfortable. But a temperature of 25°C with high relative humidity can be uncomfortable. An air conditioner must do more than just cool the air. It must remove some of the water in the air, too.

**NEW YORK**      **LAS VEGAS**

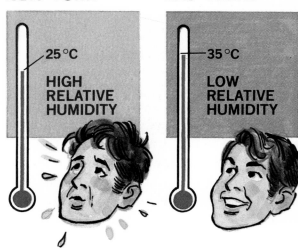

25°C
HIGH RELATIVE HUMIDITY

35°C
LOW RELATIVE HUMIDITY

# How can we measure relative humidity?

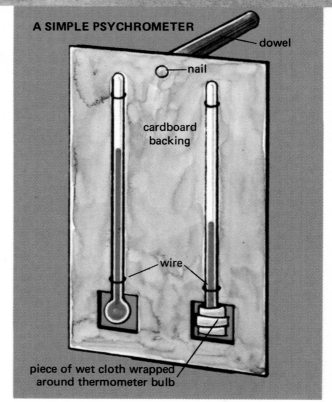

**A SIMPLE PSYCHROMETER**
— dowel
— nail
cardboard backing
wire
piece of wet cloth wrapped around thermometer bulb

**Evaporation and cooling.** Rub a little alcohol on your arm. As the alcohol evaporates, your arm feels cooler. After you come out of the water on a hot day, you feel cooler. The water evaporating from your skin cools you. When water or alcohol evaporates, it removes heat. It cools the surface it is evaporating from. Evaporation has a cooling effect.

▶ **What happens as water evaporates from the skin?**

**Evaporation and relative humidity.** Air that is nearly saturated with water is called humid (HEW-mid). Water evaporates faster into dry air than into humid air. Water is always coming out of your skin through your sweat glands. Evaporation of this moisture from your skin keeps you cool. The faster it evaporates, the cooler you feel. You feel cooler on a hot dry day than on a hot humid day.

▶ **Why are you cooler on a hot dry day than on a hot humid day?**

**Psychrometers.** A psychrometer (sy-CROM-uh-ter) is used to find relative humidity. Make a psychrometer like the one shown in the drawing. Wrap the bulb of one thermometer with a piece of wet cloth. Spin the psychrometer for one minute. After one minute, read both thermometers. The dry thermometer measures

the temperature of the air. Evaporation of water from the cloth cooled the wet thermometer. Its reading is lower than the dry thermometer. The wet thermometer is cooled more when the relative humidity is low than when it is high. The difference between the temperatures of the two thermometers can tell the relative humidity.

▶ **What happens to the reading of the wet thermometer when you spin the psychrometer?**

230

| | TEMPERATURE OF AIR FROM DRY THERMOMETER (°C) | | | | | | | | |
|---|---|---|---|---|---|---|---|---|---|
| | −5 | 0 | 5 | 10 | 15 | 20 | 25 | 30 | 35 |
| 1 | 75 | 81 | 86 | 88 | 90 | 91 | 92 | 93 | 94 |
| 2 | 52 | 64 | 72 | 77 | 80 | 83 | 85 | 86 | 87 |
| 3 | 29 | 46 | 58 | 66 | 70 | 74 | 77 | 79 | 81 |
| 4 | 6 | 29 | 46 | 55 | 62 | 66 | 70 | 73 | 75 |
| 5 | | 13 | 32 | 44 | 53 | 59 | 63 | 67 | 70 |
| 6 | | | 20 | 34 | 44 | 51 | 57 | 61 | 64 |
| 7 | | | 6 | 24 | 36 | 44 | 50 | 55 | 59 |
| 8 | | | | 15 | 28 | 37 | 45 | 50 | 54 |
| 9 | | | | 6 | 21 | 31 | 39 | 44 | 49 |
| 10 | | | | | 13 | 24 | 33 | 39 | 44 |

DIFFERENCE BETWEEN DRY AND WET THERMOMETERS (°C)

RELATIVE HUMIDITY (%)

**Finding the relative humidity.** Spin the psychrometer for one minute. Quickly read the wet thermometer. Write down its temperature. Write down the temperature of the dry thermometer. Write down the difference between the two temperatures. Now you can use the chart to find the relative humidity. Suppose the dry thermometer reads 25°C and the wet one reads 18°C. The difference is 7°. Find 25° along the top of the chart. Find 7° down the left side. Look down from the 25° and across from the 7°. Where the two rows meet, you see the number 50. This means the relative humidity is 50 percent.

▶ Which thermometer reading is listed along the top of the relative humidity chart?

**WHAT YOU LEARNED**
1. Evaporation has a cooling effect.
2. Water can evaporate faster into dry air than into humid air.
3. A psychrometer is used to find the relative humidity of the air.

**SCIENCE WORD**
**psychrometer** (sy-CROM-uh-ter) an instrument used to find relative humidity

**ANSWER THESE**
1. Water evaporates faster into
   a. cool air
   b. humid air
   c. dry air

2. A psychrometer is used to find
   a. air temperature
   b. wind speed
   c. relative humidity

3. If evaporation takes place quickly, the wet bulb of a psychrometer will be
   a. cooler
   b. warmer
   c. wetter

4. A psychrometer has
   a. two wet thermometers
   b. two dry thermometers
   c. one wet and one dry thermometer

**NOW TRY THIS**
Use the chart to find the relative humidity when the temperature readings from the psychrometer are:

| wet bulb | dry bulb |
|---|---|
| 12°C | 20°C |
| 33°C | 35°C |
| 22°C | 30°C |

# How does water come out of the air?

**Water from the atmosphere.** Have you ever noticed how the insides of windows get steamed up on a cold day? Where does the moisture come from? It comes from the air by <u>condensation</u> (con-den-SAY-shun). Condensation is the opposite of evaporation. Condensation is the changing of a gas to a liquid. Condensation of water vapor may take place when air is cooled. On a cold day, the outside air cools the windows. Inside the room, the cold windows cool the air near them. Water vapor in the air condenses (cun-DEN-ses) to water on the cold glass.

▶ **What is condensation?**

**What causes condensation?** You have learned that warm air can hold more water vapor than cool air. As the air cools, it can hold less and less water vapor. If the temperature drops enough, the air becomes saturated. Its relative humidity is 100 percent. If saturated air is cooled, some of the water vapor in it condenses. The water vapor changes to water. Condensation takes place when saturated air is cooled.

▶ **When does water vapor in the air condense?**

**The dew point.** If air is cooled enough, condensation takes place. The temperature at which this begins to happen is called the dew point. At night the ground cools fast. It cools the air near it. The temperature of

the air may drop below the dew point. Then condensation will take place. Drops of water will form on grass and bushes. Drops of water will form on the outside of a parked car. This water that condenses out of the air is called <u>dew</u>.

▶ **What is the dew point?**

**Frost.** The freezing point of water is 0°C. When the humidity is low, the dew point is below the freezing point of water. If the air temperature drops to the dew point, water vapor will come out of the air. But it will change to ice, not water. Ice that forms this way is called <u>frost</u>.

▶ **When does frost form?**

## WHAT YOU LEARNED

1. Condensation is the changing of a gas to a liquid.
2. When saturated air is cooled, condensation takes place.
3. The dew point is the temperature at which water vapor condenses.
4. When the dew point is below the freezing point of water, frost forms.

## SCIENCE WORDS

**condensation** (con-den-SAY-shun)
   changing from a gas to a liquid
**dew**
   water that condenses on cold surfaces
**dew point**
   temperature at which water vapor condenses
**frost**
   ice that forms by condensation below the freezing point

## ANSWER THESE

1. Condensation is the opposite of
   a. evaporation
   b. humidity
   c. temperature
2. Condensation takes place as the air is
   a. heated
   b. cooled
   c. moved
3. The temperature at which water vapor condenses is known as the
   a. humidity
   b. evaporation rate
   c. dew point
4. Condensation that occurs at temperatures below 0°C produces
   a. dew
   b. steam
   c. frost

## NOW TRY THESE

1. What is formed when water vapor changes into water.

2. What is formed when water vapor changes into ice.

## DO THIS AT HOME

Find the dew point of your room. Fill a tin can about two-thirds full with water and ice. Place a thermometer in the water. Stir the water and the ice. Observe the outside of the can. As soon as condensation appears on the can, read the thermometer. This is the dew point of the air in your room.

# Why does it rain?

**How clouds form.** From space the earth seems to be covered by a blanket of clouds. What are clouds? How are they formed? Condensation may occur in the atmosphere above the earth. When this happens, clouds form. Water droplets and ice form around dust and other particles in the air. Clouds are made up of billions and billions of tiny water droplets and ice crystals. Air currents keep them from falling to the earth.

▶ **How are clouds formed?**

**What is fog?** Condensation may occur near the ground. When this happens, fog forms. Fog is a cloud that forms near the ground. The ground cools quickly on a clear night. It cools the layer of air that lies above it. The air may be cooled to the dew point. If it is, the water vapor in the air condenses and forms fog.

▶ **How does fog form?**

Fog over the Golden Gate Bridge.

**Rain and snow.** Droplets of water and crystals of ice that make up clouds are very small. They are kept up in the air by air currents. The droplets of water are always moving. They hit into each other. When they hit, they join together. They become bigger and heavier. If the droplets of water become too heavy, they fall as rain. Snow forms when crystals of ice grow larger and become too heavy to remain in the cloud. Rain and snow are called forms of precipitation (pruh-sip-uh-TAY-shun).

▶ When does rain fall from a cloud?

**Sleet and hail.** Sleet and hail are other forms of precipitation. Rain falls through layers of air. If rain falls through a cold layer of air, the drops may freeze. Rain that freezes as it falls is called sleet. Hail also forms from raindrops that freeze. Hail forms when frozen drops rise and fall many times through warm and cold layers of air.

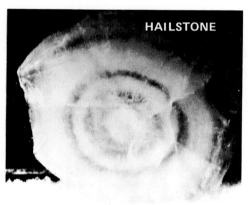
HAILSTONE

Each time the hailstones move up and down through the warm and cold layers, they get bigger and bigger. Hailstones as large as golf balls may form before they finally fall to the ground.

▶ How is sleet different from hail?

## WHAT YOU LEARNED
1. Clouds form when water vapor condenses around particles in the air.
2. A cloud is made up of billions and billions of tiny water droplets or ice crystals.
3. Fog is a cloud that forms near the ground.

4. Precipitation occurs when water droplets and ice crystals become heavy and fall to the ground.
5. Rain, snow, sleet, and hail are forms of precipitation.

## SCIENCE WORD
**precipitation** (pruh-sip-uh-TAY-shun) falling of water or ice formed by condensation

## ANSWER THESE
1. What is a cloud?
2. What is the difference between a cloud and fog?
3. List four kinds of precipitation.
4. How is rain different from snow?

## WHAT'S HAPPENING
Factories send out tons and tons of smoke into the air. This smoke can mix with fog. A combination of smoke and fog is called smog. Smog may cause your eyes to tear. Smog makes it hard to breathe. Smog is very dangerous for people with heart or lung diseases. It can make their conditions worse.

## DO THIS AT HOME
Precipitation can be measured in millimeters. A rain gauge (GAJE) is used to measure precipitation. You can make a simple rain gauge using a wide-mouthed jar and a ruler. Stand the ruler inside the jar. Place the jar in an open area when the rain begins. When the rain stops, you can measure the amount of rain that has fallen.

A SIMPLE RAIN GAUGE

CIRRUS CLOUDS

# How do we identify clouds?

**The shape of clouds.** Do all clouds look alike? No. Some are big and puffy. Some are thin and feathery. Clouds form in different ways. The way a cloud forms gives it its shape.

▶ What gives clouds their shape?

**Cirrus clouds.** Cirrus (SIR-us) clouds look light and feathery. They are made up of ice crystals. They form at heights above 10 000 meters.

▶ What do cirrus clouds look like?

**Cumulus clouds.** Cumulus (KYU-myu-lus) clouds are big and puffy. They form from rising currents of warm air. As they form, they build up to great heights. The base of a cumulus cloud is usually flat.

▶ What do cumulus clouds look like?

**Stratus clouds.** Stratus (STRAT-us) clouds form a sheet across the sky. They spread out layer upon layer, covering the sky. Stratus clouds usually form at low heights. Fog is a stratus cloud on the ground.

▶ What do stratus clouds look like?

CUMULUS CLOUDS

STRATUS CLOUDS

236

## WHAT YOU LEARNED

1. Clouds are identified by their shapes.
2. Clouds get their shape from the way they form.
3. Three types of clouds are cirrus, cumulus, and stratus.

## SCIENCE WORDS

**cirrus** (SIR-us) **clouds**
light and feathery clouds
**cumulus** (KYU-myu-lus) **clouds**
big and puffy clouds
**stratus** (STRAT-us) **clouds**
clouds that form a sheet across the sky

## ANSWER THESE

1. Clouds made up of ice crystals are
   a. cirrus
   b. cumulus
   c. stratus

2. Clouds formed in layers are
   a. cirrus
   b. cumulus
   c. stratus

3. Clouds that have flat bases and that build upwards are
   a. cirrus
   b. cumulus
   c. stratus

## NOW TRY THIS

Find the names of some clouds.

1.
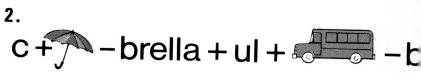
s + 🚂 – in + tus

2.

c + ☂ – brella + ul + 🚌 – b

3.
○ – cle + 📏 – ler + s

## FINDING OUT MORE

Many clouds are combinations of cirrus, cumulus, and stratus clouds. Cirrus and stratus clouds combine to form cirrostratus (sir-oh-STRAT-us) clouds. Stratocumulus (strat-oh-KYU-myu-lus) clouds are combined stratus and cumulus clouds. Clouds from which rain falls are called nimbus (NIM-bus) clouds. Thunderstorms come from cumulonimbus (kyu-myu-lo-NIM-bus) clouds.

STRATOCUMULUS CLOUDS

CUMULONIMBUS CLOUDS

237

# How does weather affect us?

**Describing the weather.** What's today's weather? What is it like outside? Is it cold? Is it windy? Is it rainy? Weather is what happens in the troposphere. The following things are usually given in a weather report:

| | |
|---|---|
| air pressure | wind speed |
| air temperature | wind direction |
| precipitation | relative humidity |
| appearance of the sky | |

▶ **What things are given in a weather report?**

**Who wants to know about the weather?** Everyone is interested in the weather. Large cities need to know about weather. Snowstorms can tie up a city. Power failures may result. Food cannot be delivered. People cannot get to work. Weather predictions help us to prepare for bad weather.

Farmers and ranchers are interested in weather reports. Frost can destroy crops. Cold and snow can kill animals. Weather reports warn farmers and ranchers of bad weather. A prediction of rain is good news for areas where the danger of forest fires is high. Airlines also need weather information to plan flight routes and takeoffs and landings. Weather is important to all of us.

▶ **Why are farmers interested in weather reports?**

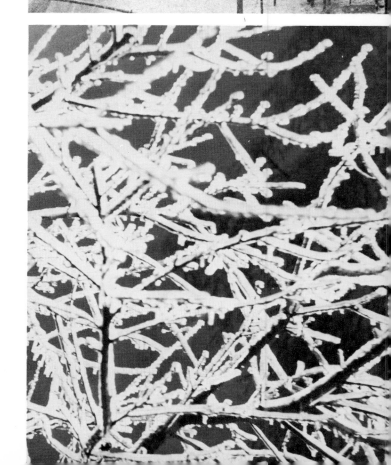

**Who makes the weather report?** Look at a newspaper weather report. Where does the newspaper get this report? The National Weather Service in Washington, D.C., sends out weather reports. Weather stations in all parts of the country make observations. Each one is called a station report. The station reports are sent to the head office in Washington. This central bureau puts all the information together. They then send out a complete report for the entire country.

▶ **What is the job of the National Weather Service?**

## WHAT YOU LEARNED

Weather is described in terms of air temperature, air pressure, precipitation, wind speed and direction, humidity, and appearance of the sky.

## ANSWER THESE

1. Weather takes place in the
   a. hydrosphere
   b. troposphere
   c. lithosphere

2. Where the danger of forest fire is high, a helpful weather prediction would be for
   a. sunshine
   b. cloudiness
   c. rain

3. Weather reports are prepared by
   a. The National Weather Service
   b. The Treasury Department
   c. The Secret Service

## NOW TRY THIS

In column A there are some measurements from a weather report. Match each measurement with what it could be measuring in column B.

| A | B |
|---|---|
| 1. 22°C | a. air pressure |
| 2. 30 km per hour | b. wind speed |
| 3. 46% | c. wind direction |
| 4. 764 mm of mercury | d. relative humidity |
| 5. Northwest | e. air temperature |

## DO THIS AT HOME

Weather predictions, or forecasts, are not always correct. Collect weather forecasts from a newspaper. Compare them with the actual weather each day. Do this for two weeks. Make a chart comparing the forecasts with the actual weather conditions. How accurate are the weather forecasts?

# How do we get our weather?

**Weather changes.** It may be cloudy one day, rainy the next day, and clear the day after that. How does weather form? Why does it change? To help answer these questions we must learn about air masses. An <u>air mass</u> is a large column of air that collects over the region. It may remain over the same region for some time. An air mass may cover an area more than 1000 kilometers across.

▶ What is an air mass?

**Land conditions affect an air mass.** An air mass is affected by the region it covers. Air masses that form over land are dry. Air masses that form over water are moist. Air masses formed over warm regions are warm. Air masses formed over cold regions are cold.

▶ How does a land area affect an air mass covering it?

**Cold air masses.** Canada is north of the United States. It has very cold winters. Air masses that form over Canada in the winter are cold and dry. They are called continental (cont-in-ENT-ul) polar air masses. They are called continental because they form over land. They are called <u>polar</u> because they are cold. Air masses that form over oceans are moist. They are called <u>maritime</u> (MAR-uh-time) air masses. If they are moist and cold, they are called maritime polar air masses.

▶ What is a cold, moist air mass called?

**Warm air masses.** Warm air masses are formed near the equator. They are called <u>tropical</u> (TROP-uh-kul) air masses. If they form over water near the equator they are wet and warm. They are called maritime tropical air masses. Maritime tropical air

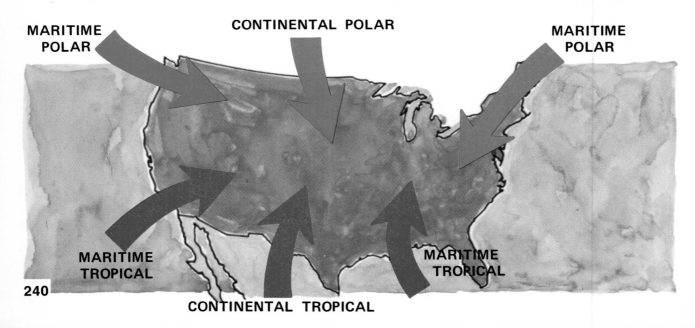

MARITIME
POLAR

CONTINENTAL POLAR

MARITIME
POLAR

MARITIME
TROPICAL

MARITIME
TROPICAL

CONTINENTAL TROPICAL

masses form over the Caribbean Sea and over the Gulf of Mexico. Continental tropical air masses are warm and dry. They form over land areas close to the equator. Air masses move away from the regions where they form. As they move, they bring different kinds of weather with them.

▶ What is a warm, moist air mass called?

## WHAT YOU LEARNED

1. An air mass is a large column of air that covers a region. It may remain there for some time.
2. Air masses get their heat and moisture from the regions they cover.
3. Weather is formed by the movement of large air masses.

## SCIENCE WORDS

**air mass**
a large volume of air that covers a region
**maritime** (MAR-uh-time)
having to do with the sea
**polar**
having to do with the areas around the North and South Poles
**tropical** (TROP-uh-kul)
having to do with the warm regions around the equator

## ANSWER THESE

1. Air that covers a large region is called
   a. a cloud
   b. an air mass
   c. a storm

2. Polar continental air masses form over
   a. Canada
   b. the Caribbean
   c. the Gulf of Mexico

3. Polar maritime air masses form over
   a. Canada
   b. the Gulf of Mexico
   c. the North Atlantic Ocean

4. Tropical maritime air masses form over
   a. Canada
   b. the North Pacific Ocean
   c. the Caribbean Sea

## NOW TRY THIS

Here is a chart that lists some important types of air masses that affect weather over the United States. See if you can fill in the two blank columns.

| TYPE OF AIR MASS | KIND OF WEATHER IT BRINGS (warm, cold; moist, dry) | WHERE FORMED (over land, over water; at the poles, at the equator) |
| --- | --- | --- |
| CONTINENTAL POLAR | | |
| MARITIME POLAR | | |
| CONTINENTAL TROPICAL | | |
| MARITIME TROPICAL | | |

# What happens when air masses meet?

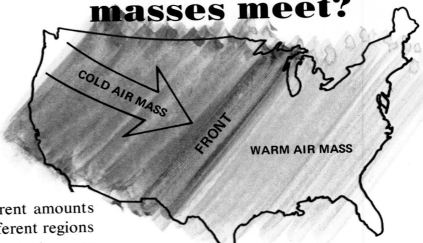

COLD AIR MASS

FRONT

WARM AIR MASS

**Fronts.** Air masses get different amounts of heat and moisture over different regions of the earth. Air masses move east across the United States. Different air masses meet along the way. Air masses usually don't mix. The surface between the different masses is called a <u>front.</u> The front can cover hundreds of kilometers. The forward edge of a cold air mass is called a cold front. The forward edge of a warm air mass is called a warm front. Fronts bring changes in weather.

▶ **What is a front?**

**Cold fronts.** What happens as a cold front moves through a region? Cold air is denser than warm air. It pushes down under warm air. It forms a steep slope. As the cold front approaches, the warm air over the region is forced upward. The upward movements cause gusty winds. As the warm air moves upward, it expands and cools quickly. Big puffy clouds are produced by the cooling. This is followed by heavy precipitation. As the cold front moves through, the precipitation stops. The air over the ground becomes clear and cooler. The cold front has passed. A cold air mass has now moved in.

▶ **What happens when warm air is forced upwards?**

**Warm fronts.** What happens when a warm front moves through a region? Warm air moves more slowly than cold air. Warm air

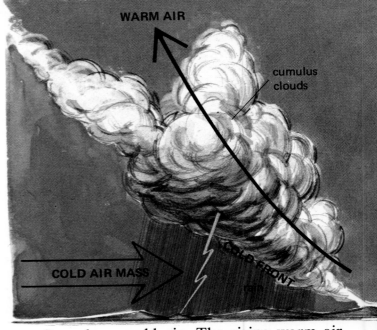

WARM AIR

cumulus clouds

COLD AIR MASS

COLD FRONT

rain

rises above cold air. The rising warm air forms a gentle slope. This is a warm front. The warm air slowly moves up and over the cold air. As it rises, it cools off. Very high, feathery clouds form. As the warm front moves closer, more clouds appear. They are piled up layer upon layer. Each layer is closer to the ground. Long, steady precipitation follows. Slow clearing and rising temperatures show the warm front has passed. A warm air mass has moved in.

**What happens when a warm front moves in?**

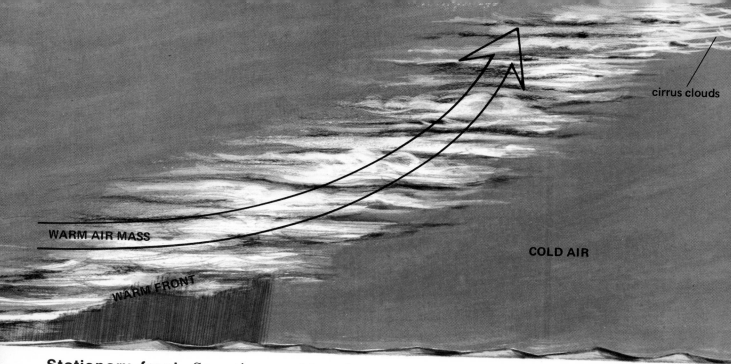

WARM AIR MASS

COLD AIR

cirrus clouds

WARM FRONT

**Stationary front.** Sometimes cold and warm air masses stay in one place for a while. They do not move. They remain stationary (STAY-shun-er-ee). A stationary front brings very little change in the weather.

▶ **What is a stationary front?**

## WHAT YOU LEARNED

1. A front is the surface between two air masses.
2. A cold front is the forward edge of a cold air mass.
3. A warm front is the forward edge of a warm air mass.
4. The movement of cold and warm fronts produces changes in weather.

## SCIENCE WORDS

**front**
   surface between two air masses
**stationary** (STAY-shun-er-ee)
   not moving
**stationary front**
   front that does not move

## ANSWER THESE

1. Air masses usually move (east/west) across the United States.
2. A front forms
   **a.** inside an air mass
   **b.** around an air mass
   **c.** between two air masses
3. Fronts bring _____ in the weather.
4. A cold air mass forces warm air to move
   **a.** downward
   **b.** upward
   **c.** to the side
5. A cold front produces
   **a.** big, puffy clouds
   **b.** light, feathery clouds
   **c.** no clouds
6. After a cold front has passed, the weather is usually
   **a.** clear and cool
   **b.** rainy and warm
   **c.** cloudy and warm
7. A warm front produces
   **a.** strong, gusty winds
   **b.** high, feathery clouds
   **c.** no change in the clouds

## NOW TRY THIS

Copy these sentences and fill in the blanks.
1. Big puffy clouds, gusty winds, and heavy rains occur when a _____ front moves through a region.
2. Light feathery clouds and then a long period of rain occur when a _____ front moves through a region.
3. With a _____ front, the weather remains unchanged.

# What is a station model?

**Station models.** A weather scientist is called a meteorologist (meet-ee-uh-ROL-uh-jist). In the United States, meteorologists are using English units for weather reports. This book uses the same units to help you understand weather reports.

How does the meteorologist make a record of weather data? A short, fast way is needed to list the many weather facts. A secretary uses shorthand to take notes. A chemist uses symbols to write formulas. The meteorologist also uses symbols. Each weather factor has a different symbol. The meteorologist uses these symbols to make a station model. A station model shows the weather conditions at a particular weather station. A station model uses symbols instead of words to describe the weather.

▶ **What is a station model?**

**Reading station models.** Let's learn how to read a station model. Each station is marked by a circle. The amount of shading in the circle tells how much cloudiness there is.

clear    cloudy

partly cloudy    rain    snow

**SYMBOLS USED TO INDICATE WIND SPEED** (in miles per hour)

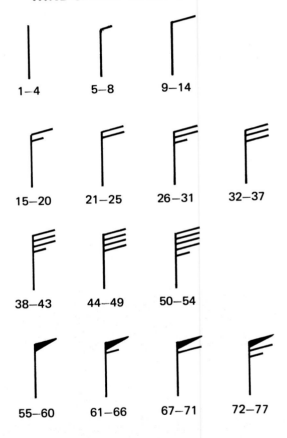

1–4    5–8    9–14

15–20    21–25    26–31    32–37

38–43    44–49    50–54

55–60    61–66    67–71    72–77

Wind direction is shown by an arrow pointing into the station circle. It points as if it were carried by the wind. Wind speed is shown by little lines or "feathers" on the wind arrow. The number and length of the feathers show the wind speed.

▶ **How is wind speed shown on a station model?**

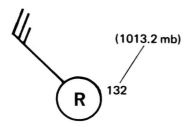

At this station there is a northwest wind blowing at 26 to 31 miles per hour. It is raining. The air pressure is 1013.2 millibars. (To find the air pressure, we put a 10 in front of the 132, and a decimal point in front of the 2.)

**Air pressure.** Air pressure can be measured in many units. Meteorologists in the U.S. measure air pressure in units called millibars (MILL-uh-bars). One millibar equals 0.1 kilopascal. Air pressure at the ground is usually around 1000 millibars (1000 mb). A station model shows the air pressure to tenths of a millibar. The number in the upper right-hand corner of the station model is the last 3 figures in the millibar reading. To find the complete reading, put a 9 or a 10 in front of the 3 figures, and put a decimal point in front of the last figure.

▶ What unit is used by meteorologists to measure air pressure?

## WHAT YOU LEARNED

1. A meteorologist uses a station model to record weather information.
2. A station model uses symbols to show different weather factors.

## SCIENCE WORDS

**meteorologist** (meet-ee-uh-ROL-uh-jist)
a weather scientist
**station model**
a record of weather information at a weather station
**millibar** (MILL-uh-bar)
a unit of measurement for air pressure

## ANSWER THESE

Look at the symbol.

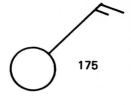

1. The air pressure is
   a. 17.5 mb
   b. 175 mb
   c. 1017.5 mb

2. The wind is from the
   a. NW
   b. SE
   c. NE

3. The wind speed is
   a. 4 mph
   b. 16 mph
   c. 175 mph

4. The sky is
   a. cloudy
   b. clear
   c. partly cloudy

## DO THIS AT HOME

Draw a station model for your area using a local weather report.

## FINDING OUT MORE

Temperature, dew point, and rainfall are among the many factors given on a station model. Look at the station model. Identify each factor and its place around the circle.

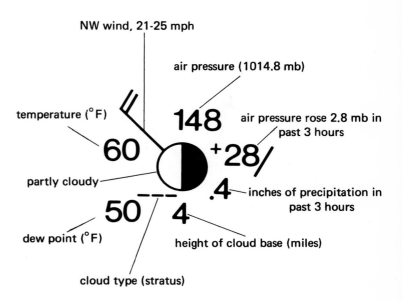

# How do we read a weather map?

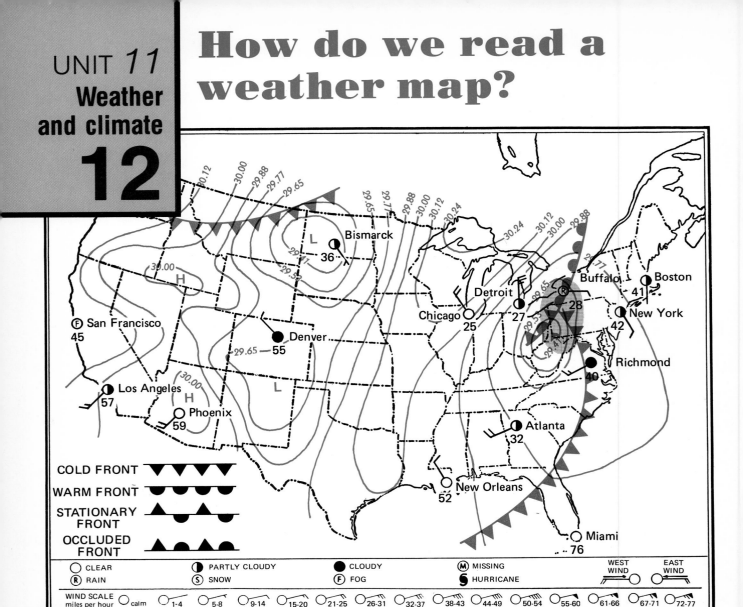

COLD FRONT ▼▼▼
WARM FRONT ●●●
STATIONARY FRONT ●▲●▲
OCCLUDED FRONT ▲●▲●

○ CLEAR    ◐ PARTLY CLOUDY    ● CLOUDY    Ⓜ MISSING    WEST WIND    EAST WIND
Ⓡ RAIN    Ⓢ SNOW    Ⓕ FOG    ❺ HURRICANE

WIND SCALE miles per hour ○ calm ○ 1-4 ○ 5-8 ○ 9-14 ○ 15-20 ○ 21-25 ○ 26-31 ○ 32-37 ○ 38-43 ○ 44-49 ○ 50-54 ○ 55-60 ○ 61-66 ○ 67-71 ○ 72-77

**Weather maps.** Look at the weather map of the United States. Station models list weather conditions at different places. These records are taken at the same time each day. You can easily compare the weather at Buffalo with the weather at Detroit or San Francisco. A weather map shows weather conditions for many places at the same time.

▶ **What do weather maps show?**

**Where can you find a weather map?** Weather maps appear in many daily news-papers. A key on the map helps you to read the station models. The lines on the map are called <u>isobars</u> (EYE-suh-bars). They connect points of equal air pressure. Places on the same line have the same air pressure. Areas of high pressure are called highs. They are shown by an "H." Areas of low pressure are called lows. They are shown by an "L." Symbols are used to show fronts. Precipitation is shown as shading on a weather map.

▶ **What are isobars?**

| WEATHER FACTOR | HIGH | LOW |
|---|---|---|
| temperature of air | usually cool | usually warm |
| winds | move out from the center | move in toward the center |
| condition of the sky | clear | cloudy; some precipitation |

**The weather in highs and lows.** The weather in high-pressure and low-pressure regions is different. The chart compares the different weather factors within highs and lows. Highs and lows move from west to east across the United States. As they pass through each region, they bring changes in the weather.

▶ **What type of weather does a low bring?**

## WHAT YOU LEARNED

1. Weather maps show weather conditions for different places at the same time.
2. Isobars are lines connecting points of equal pressure on a weather map.
3. Highs and lows bring different weather.

## SCIENCE WORD

**isobar** (EYE-suh-bar)
line drawn on a weather map connecting points of equal air pressure

## ANSWER THESE

1. Isobars show
   a. temperature
   b. humidity
   c. air pressure

2. In a high, winds
   a. are never present
   b. move out from the center
   c. move in to the center
3. The weather of a low is usually
   a. cool and clear
   b. warm and rainy
   c. cool and windy
4. On a weather map, precipitation is shown by
   a. shading
   b. colors
   c. circles

## NOW TRY THIS

Using the weather map in this lesson, find a city that is

   a. on a cold front
   b. on a warm front
   c. inside a high
   d. inside a low
   e. having clear skies
   f. having rain
   g. cloudy
   h. having the highest temperature
   i. having the lowest temperature

## DO THIS AT HOME

Cut out a weather map from a newspaper. Collect them for four days in a row. Paste them in your notebook and study them to see if (1) the highs and lows move in a particular direction, and (2) you can use them to predict tomorrow's weather.

# What factors determine climate?

AVERAGE JULY TEMPERATURES
AT DIFFERENT LATITUDES

above 26°C

between 16° and 26° C

between 4° and 16° C

below 4°C

**Day by day, or year by year.** In many regions of the United States, the winters are much colder than the summers. People who live in those regions expect this. They plan for it. They know that this pattern of weather is part of their <u>climate</u> (KLY-mut). Climate is the average weather during the year. Temperature and rainfall are important factors of climate.

▶ **What are two factors of climate?**

**Latitude affects climate.** The latitude of a region is its distance from the equator in degrees. The climate of a region depends partly on its latitude. The sun's rays fall most directly on regions near the equator. These regions have a warmer climate than places far from the equator. The closer a region is to the equator, the warmer its climate is.

▶ **How does latitude affect climate?**

**Altitude affects climate.** The air is warmer at sea level than at high altitudes. Land areas at sea level are also warmer than areas at high altitudes. As you move up from sea level, the climate becomes colder. Even near the equator, the tops of mountains have snow all year long.

▶ **How does altitude affect climate?**

**Bodies of water affect climate.** Water heats up and cools off more slowly than land does. In winter, ocean water is warmer than the land. In summer, the

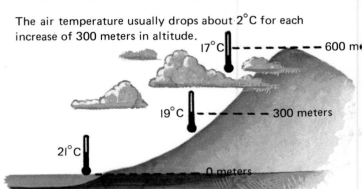

The air temperature usually drops about 2°C for each increase of 300 meters in altitude.

17°C — — — — 600 m

19°C — — — 300 meters

21°C

0 meters

ocean water is cooler than the land. Therefore, land areas near the ocean are warmed in winter and cooled in summer. The temperatures of these areas do not change as much during the year as in regions far inland. Regions far inland may have very cold winters and hot summers.

Ocean currents also affect the average temperature. Warm ocean currents warm nearby land areas. Look at the map. Note that England is farther north than many parts of Canada. But the Gulf Stream gives England a mild climate.

▶ **How do the winters of inland regions compare with those near the ocean?**

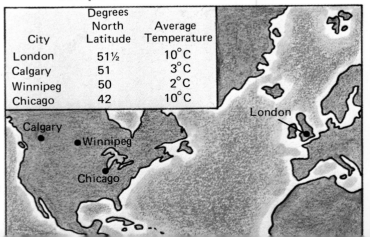

| City | Degrees North Latitude | Average Temperature |
|------|------------------------|---------------------|
| London | 51½ | 10°C |
| Calgary | 51 | 3°C |
| Winnipeg | 50 | 2°C |
| Chicago | 42 | 10°C |

Of the four cities shown on the map, London has one of the warmest average temperatures even though it is the farthest north.

## Winds around the world affect climate.

Winds can bring cold or warm air to a region. Winds blowing south from Canada cool the northern United States. Winds blowing north from Mexico warm the southwestern United States. Winds coming from the ocean bring moisture. Winds coming from a land area are usually dry.

▶ **When do winds bring moisture to a region?**

**Mountains affect climate.** Winds blowing from the ocean may strike a mountain range. This is called the windward (WIND-werd) side of the mountain. The air is forced up the windward side of the mountain. The air cools as it rises. Moisture condenses from the cool air. Rain falls on the windward side of the mountain. The air moves over the mountain and down the other side. This is called the leeward (LEE-werd) side. The air warms up as it comes down the leeward side. It is warm and very dry. It hardly ever rains on the leeward side. Many deserts are found on the leeward side of mountains.

▶ **Which side of a mountain usually receives the most rainfall?**

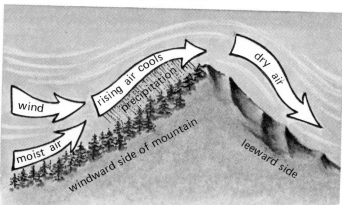

Moist air becomes cooler as it rises, causing the moisture in the air to condense and precipitate. Dry air blows down the leeward side.

### WHAT YOU LEARNED

1. Climate is the average weather over the year.
2. Temperature and rainfall are important factors of climate.

3. The climate of an area is affected by
   a. latitude
   b. altitude
   c. ocean currents
   d. distance from a large body of water
   e. winds
   f. mountain ranges

### SCIENCE WORD

**climate** (KLY-mut)
   the average weather of an area during the year

### ANSWER THESE

1. In general, as the distance of an area from the equator increases, its climate
   **a.** becomes colder   **b.** becomes warmer
   **c.** remains the same
2. In general, as the altitude of an area increases, its climate
   **a.** becomes colder   **b.** becomes warmer
   **c.** remains the same
3. In the winter the warmest areas usually are found
   **a.** at the seashores   **b.** inland
   **c.** on mountain tops
4. The Gulf Stream tends to make the climate of nearby areas
   **a.** cooler   **b.** drier   **c.** warmer
5. The leeward side of a mountain tends to be
   **a.** rainy   **b.** dry   **c.** cold

### NOW TRY THIS

Pick two words, one from Group A and one from Group B, to describe the climate of each of the 4 locations listed below.
   **Group A words:** hot, mild, cold
   **Group B words:** wet, dry

### Locations

1. Sea level at the equator, with winds blowing from the ocean.
2. Halfway between the equator and the North Pole, with the Gulf Stream flowing nearby.
3. In a valley on the leeward side of a mountain close to the equator.
4. Near the top of a high mountain, on the windward side, far from the equator.

# How can we classify climates?

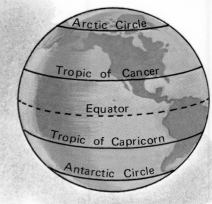

low latitudes

middle latitudes

high latitudes

**CLIMATE ZONES ON EARTH**

**The temperature zones.** The first step in classifying climates is to group them by average temperature. We can do this by dividing the earth into zones. Regions at sea level near the equator are hot all year. This is called a tropical (TROP-uh-kul) or low-latitude climate. Regions near the poles are cold all year long. They have a polar (POH-ler) or high-latitude climate. Regions in between have temperatures that change from cold in winter to warm in summer. This is called a middle-latitude climate.

▶ **What are the three temperature zones of climate?**

**Temperature ups and downs.** The average temperature during the year is important in classifying climate. But the amount of temperature change during the year is also important. Eureka, California, and Omaha, Nebraska, have the same average temperature of about 10°C. But the temperature in Eureka does not change much during the year. The warmest summer month averages about 13°C. The coldest

winter month averages about 8°C. In Omaha, the average temperature goes from about 25°C in summer to about −6°C in winter. The temperature range for Eureka is only 5°C. For Omaha, it is 31°C. Eureka and Omaha have different climates.

▶ **Why is temperature range important in classifying climates?**

**Climate and rainfall.** Plant growth is affected by the amount of rainfall during the year. If plants get more rainfall than they need, the climate is called humid (HYOO-mid). If they get just enough rainfall, the climate is called subhumid (SUB-hyoo-mid). In some places, the plants get a little less rainfall than they could use. More plants would grow if there were more rainfall. This kind of climate is called semiarid (SEM-ee-A-rid). Then there are places that get much less rainfall than the plants need. Very few plants can grow there at all. This kind of climate is called arid (A-rid).

▶ **Which kind of climate has more rainfall than the plants need?**

**It's the combination that counts.** Different climates are described by their combination of temperature and rainfall. A tropical climate can be hot and humid, or it can be hot and arid. These are two kinds of tropical climate. A middle-latitude climate can have many different combinations of

The yearly average temperature of these two cities is about the same, but Omaha has cold winters and warm summers, while Eureka's temperature doesn't change much from winter to summer.

Eureka, California

Omaha, Nebraska

temperature and rainfall. For example, it might have warm, wet summers and mild, dry winters. The chart lists some of the types of climate. Which climate best describes where you live?

▶ **Which type of climate is hot and humid all the time?**

## WHAT YOU LEARNED

1. Climates are classified according to temperature and amount of precipitation.
2. Climates are divided into tropical or low-latitude climates, polar or high-latitude climates, and middle-latitude climates.
3. Climates are classified by the amount of rainfall as humid, subhumid, semiarid, and arid climates.

## SCIENCE WORDS

**tropical** (TROP-uh-kul)
near the equator

**polar** (POH-ler)
near the poles

**middle-latitude**
between the low latitudes near the equator and the high latitudes near the poles

**humid** (HYOO-mid) **climate**
a climate in which plants get more rainfall than they need

**subhumid** (SUB-hyoo-mid) **climate**
a climate in which plants get just enough rainfall

**semiarid** (SEM-ee-A-rid) **climate**
a climate in which plants get less rainfall than they need

**arid** (A-rid) **climate**
a climate in which plants get much less rainfall than they need

## ANSWER THESE

1. Climates can be classified according to the
   a. number of people living there
   b. average temperature
   c. average wind speed
2. A hot climate is usually found in the
   a. low latitudes
   b. middle latitudes
   c. high latitudes
3. A humid climate is usually
   a. hot    b. dry    c. wet
4. Plants can't get enough moisture in a climate that is
   a. subhumid    b. humid    c. arid

## NOW TRY THIS

Match the description of the climate with the name given to that type of climate.

1. Tropical rain forest
2. Tropical desert
3. Tundra
4. Mediterranean
5. Marine
6. Humid continental
7. Humid subtropical

a. very cold winters
b. mild rainy summers, cool winters
c. dry summers, mild moist winters
d. hot and arid
e. hot and rainy all the time
f. long rainy summers, short mild winters
g. humid hot summers, wet cold winters

| CLIMATES IN DIFFERENT TEMPERATURE ZONES | | | |
|---|---|---|---|
| Temperature zone | Name of climate | Description | Places with these climates |
| low latitude | tropical rain forest | hot and humid all the time | Amazon, Congo, and Philippines |
| | savanna (grasslands) | hot rainy summer, warm dry winter | Bolivia and Venezuela |
| | steppe (grassy plains) | hot, semiarid | parts of central Mexico |
| | tropical desert | hot and arid | Sahara Desert in Africa |
| middle latitude | Mediterranean | mild moist winters, dry summers | southern California |
| | humid subtropical | summers long and rainy, winters short and mild | southeastern U.S. |
| | humid continental | humid hot summers, wet cold winters (four seasons) | northern and central U.S. |
| | marine | mild rainy summers, cool winters | Pacific Northwest |
| | steppe (prairies) | hot summers, cold winters, light rainfall | Great Plains |
| | deserts | hot and dry | Southwest U.S. |
| high latitude | tundra | winters bitterly cold, short summers | northern Canada and Greenland |
| | taiga | long cold winters, short warm summers | Alaska |

# UNIT 11 Review

*Do the following review questions on a separate sheet of paper.*

**Modified True/False**    *Write down each of the following statements, leaving a blank line between each line you write. Before the number for each statement, write T if the statement is true and F if the statement is false. For the false statements, cross out the word written in capital letters and write above it a word that will make the statement true.*

1. A tropical climate is usually found at LOW altitudes.
2. Places that get much rainfall have an ARID climate.
3. Air temperature usually RISES as you go up a mountain.
4. A HYDROLOGIST is a weather scientist.
5. A front that does not move is a STATIONARY front.
6. A cloud formed in layers is a CUMULUS cloud.
7. The temperature at which water condenses is the DEW POINT.
8. TEMPERATURE is the amount of moisture in the air compared to its capacity.
9. HUMIDITY is the amount of water vapor in the air.
10. Changing from a liquid to a gas is called TRANSPIRATION.

**Multiple Choice**    *Write the letter of the choice that best completes the statement or answers the question.*

1. Humidity is a measure of
   a. rainfall each year
   b. water vapor in the air
   c. cloud capacity
2. Something that is saturated is
   a. filled to capacity
   b. filled with holes
   c. unable to absorb gases
3. The changing of a gas to a liquid is called
   a. humidity
   b. transpiration
   c. condensation
4. Big puffy clouds are called
   a. cirrus
   b. cumulus
   c. stratus

5. The term maritime means
   a. having to do with the sea
   b. sunset at the north pole
   c. having to do with hurricanes
6. The surface between two air masses is
   a. front
   b. wall
   c. cloud bank
7. An isobar is a line on a weather map connecting points
   a. of equal humidity
   b. of equal temperature
   c. of equal air temperature
8. A climate in which plants get somewhat less rainfall than they need is called
   a. tropical
   b. Middle-latitude
   c. semi-arid

# UNIT 12

# Natural Resources

## Unit Lessons

1. What are the earth's resources?
2. What are our main energy sources?
3. What will be our future energy resources?
4. What causes air pollution?
5. What causes water pollution?
6. How can we prevent pollution?

## Goals and Objectives

After completing this unit, you should be able to:
- distinguish between renewable and nonrenewable resources.
- understand how fossil fuels supply us with energy.
- describe methods of conservation and new sources of energy.
- explain how water and air pollution upset the balance of nature.
- describe methods we can use to end pollution.

# What are the earth's resources?

**Natural resources.** The earth is like a large storeroom. We rely on the earth for the materials needed for life. Much of our food, clothes, and shelter comes from plants grown on land. The rocks in the ground supply us with metals to build machinery. The fuel to run machines and heat homes comes from the earth. These materials are natural resources. Without these natural resources we could not live.

▶ What are natural resources?

**Renewable resources.** The water, air, soil, and forests are renewable (ree-NEW-uh-bull) resources. They can be replaced after we use them. The water cycle allows us to use water over and over again. Forests are replanted after they are cut down. Fertilizers put chemicals back into the soil. This soil can then be used to grow crops again. The air too is used over and over again.

▶ What are renewable resources?

**Nonrenewable resources.** Some materials cannot be replaced after they are used. A mineral is such a resource. A mineral removed from one place in the ground is gone. Another spot must be found for more of that mineral. Materials that cannot be replaced are called nonrenewable (non-ree-NEW-uh-bull) re-sources. Oil, gas, and coal are also nonrenewable minerals. We are using these nonrenewable resources in large amounts. Will we ever run out of them? If we do, what then?

▶ What are nonrenewable resources?

**Conservation.** The number of people living on the earth is becoming larger. More people need more land to live on. More land is needed to grow greater amounts of food. Larger amounts of pure water and air are needed. With more people on earth, greater demands are made on all our resources. Will

Good fertilizer will help this land grow a new crop.

Strip mining coal in Colorado

there be enough resources for the future? We must look for new things to take the place of nonrenewable materials. Resources that are renewable must be used carefully. <u>Conservation</u> (kon-ser-VAY-shun) is a way to make our natural resources last longer. When we conserve things, we use as little of them as possible.

▶ **What happens to our natural resources as the number of people on earth becomes larger?**

## WHAT YOU LEARNED

1. The earth supplies natural resources needed for life.
2. Renewable resources can be replaced after they are used.
3. Nonrenewable resources cannot be replaced after they are used.
4. Conservation is the using of natural resources as little as possible in order to make them last longer.

## SCIENCE WORDS

**natural resources**
    materials from the earth that are needed for life

**renewable** (ree-NEW-uh-bull) **resources**
    natural resources that can be replaced after they are used

**nonrenewable** (non-ree-NEW-uh-bull) **resources**
    natural resources that cannot be replaced after they are used

**conservation** (kon-ser-VAY-shun)
    using as little of natural resources as possible in order to make them last longer

## ANSWER THESE

1. What are some of our natural resources?
2. What are some of our renewable resources?
3. What are some of our nonrenewable resources?
4. Why is an increase in the number of people on earth a danger to our natural resources?
5. How can we prevent the loss of our natural resources?

## NOW TRY THESE

1. For each material below, tell whether it is a renewable or nonrenewable natural resource.
    **a.** soil    **b.** natural gas    **c.** oil
    **d.** trees    **e.** coal    **f.** water
2. What are some ways you can help to conserve natural resources?

## FINDING OUT MORE

**Recycling.** Is everything you throw away garbage? Can some of the materials be used again? Many items thrown out can be used. Some companies are paying for used metals. Copper, lead, and aluminum are some metals being reused. Paper and bottles too are being saved and collected. These materials are being recycled (ree-SY-kuld). Recycling helps in two ways. It conserves our renewable and nonrenewable resources. It also reduces the amount of garbage that has to be taken care of.

# What are our main energy resources?

**Energy from fossil fuels.** Recall that coal, oil, and natural gas are fossil fuels. It took many years for the fossil fuels to be made. They formed from plants and animals that lived millions of years ago. The fossil fuels supply us with most of the energy we use. They run cars, trucks, and machines. They heat buildings and make much of the electricity we use. But they are nonrenewable resources. As we remove them from the ground, a smaller amount of them is left. We are beginning to run out of the fossil fuels.

While fossil fuels have served us well, they have also caused problems. When burnt, they

Air pollution is often a side effect of burning fossil fuels.

produce harmful gases. These gases pollute the air.

▶ Which three fuels supply us with most of the energy we use?

**Energy from falling water.** Water running downhill has kinetic (ki-NET-ik) energy, the energy of motion. Water at the top of a waterfall or stored behind a dam has potential (puh-TEN-shul) energy. When this water falls to a lower level, its potential energy changes to kinetic energy. The kinetic energy of moving water can be used to produce electricity, or electrical energy. The moving water turns the blades of a turbine (TUR-byne), and the turbine drives an electric generator (JEN-uh-ray-ter).

A place where moving water makes electricity is called a hydroelectric (HY-droh-ih-LEK-trik) plant. Hydroelectric plants do not pollute the air. Their source of energy, moving water, is a renewable resource.

▶ What kind of energy is changed into electricity at a hydroelectric plant?

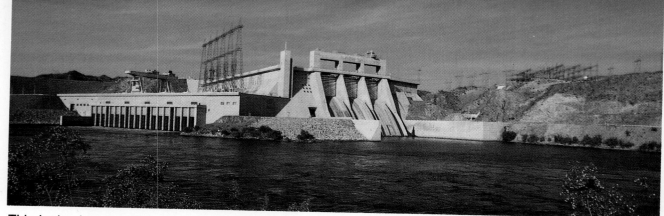

This hydroelectric plant in Arizona furnishes electricity for thousands of homes.

**Energy from the wind.** The energy from moving air is another renewable resource. Windmills have been used for years. Farmers

A windmill can supply some of the electricity used in a house.

use windmills to pump water and grind grain. Today more and more people are using windmills to make electricity.

Windmills do not pollute the air, but there is a major problem with them. What happens on a windless day? Some people use their windmill to charge up storage batteries on windy days. On days when the wind is weak, they use the electricity in the batteries.

▶ **What are windmills being used for today?**

## WHAT YOU LEARNED

1. Most of the energy we use comes from fossil fuels.
2. The energy of motion is called kinetic energy.
3. Stored energy is called potential energy.
4. The kinetic energy of moving water and of wind can be used to produce electricity.

## SCIENCE WORDS

**kinetic** (ki-NET-ik) **energy**
the energy of motion

**potential** (puh-TEN-shul) **energy**
stored energy

**hydroelectric** (HY-droh-ih-LEK-trik) **plant**
a place where moving water is used to produce electricity

## ANSWER THESE

1. Most of the energy we use comes from
   a. kinetic fuels
   b. fossil fuels
   c. the wind
2. Water running downhill has
   a. kinetic energy
   b. potential energy
   c. turbine energy
3. Water at the top of a waterfall has
   a. kinetic energy
   b. potential energy
   c. turbine energy
4. Hydroelectric plants and windmills are used to produce
   a. steam energy
   b. nuclear energy
   c. electricity

## NOW TRY THESE

Unscramble the words.
1. Coal, oil, and natural gas are SISOLF fuels.
2. Moving water is a BAWELEREN resource.
3. DINLWLMIS are used to produce electricity from the wind.

# What will be our future energy resources

This worker is putting insulation under the roof in a house.

**Conserving energy.** We are using up our fossil fuels. We have already had shortages of oil and natural gas. These shortages are likely to happen again. We can avoid these shortages by conserving what we have and by looking for other sources of energy. Less driving and more "car pooling" save gasoline. Insulating the house and lowering the heat save gas or oil. Turning out the lights when we leave the room saves electricity.

▶ **What are some ways of conserving energy?**

**Geothermal and tidal energy.** Another source of energy is the heat inside the earth. This heat within the crust is called <u>geothermal</u> (jee-oh-THER-mul) <u>energy</u>. Geothermal energy causes ground water to boil and change to steam. Sometimes this boiling water and steam shoot out of the ground at regular times. This action is called a <u>geyser</u> (GUY-ser). There are a number of <u>places</u> around the world where geothermal energy is used to make electricity.

The boiling water in this erupting geyser is evidence of geothermal energy.

Still another source of energy is the tides. The energy of moving water of the tides is called <u>tidal</u> (TY-dul) <u>energy</u>. Tidal energy can be used to make electricity. But it can only be used in certain places. These places must be near a shoreline where there are very high and low tides.

▶ **What is geothermal energy?**

**Solar energy.** Energy from sunlight, or solar energy, is another source of energy. It can help replace the energy from fossil fuels. Solar energy is being used today to supply heat to some homes. On the roofs of thes houses you can see the units that are used to collect the energy of the sun.

Solar energy can also be used to make electricity. This is done with special <u>solar cells</u>. These cells change sunlight into electricity.

Solar energy is part of the solution to our energy problem. Sunlight is all around us. It does not pollute our surroundings. However, solar energy is a good source of energy only in places with lots of sunlight. Scientists are looking for ways to store the sun's energy. Then, energy stored on sunny days can be used on cloudy days.

▶ **What are solar cells used for?**

The solar cells on the roof of this house help supply hot water to the house.

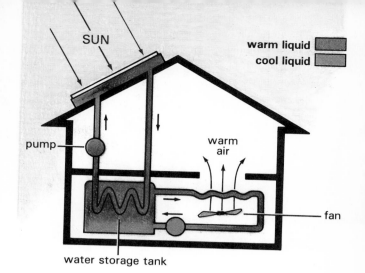

warm liquid
cool liquid

pump

SUN

warm air

fan

water storage tank

**Nuclear energy.** Conserving energy is only part of the answer to our energy problems. We must also use new sources of energy to take the place of the fossil fuels. Nuclear energy from the splitting of atoms is one possible source. It is already being used to produce electricity.

Nuclear energy has some serious drawbacks. Deadly radiation is produced in the reactors. There must be thick shields to keep the radiation from entering the environment. Dangerous radioactive wastes are also produced. Finding a safe place to get rid of them is a real problem. Finally, uranium and other nuclear fuels are nonrenewable resources. With time, we will run out of them, too.

▶ **What are some problems of using nuclear energy?**

## WHAT YOU LEARNED

1. We must begin to conserve energy and find new sources of it because we are using up our fossil fuels.
2. Some new and important sources of energy include nuclear, solar, geothermal, and tidal energy.

## SCIENCE WORDS

**nuclear energy**
    energy from the splitting of atoms

**solar energy**
    energy from sunlight

**solar cells**
    devices that change sunlight into electricity

**geothermal** (jee-oh-THER-mul) **energy**
    heat within the crust of the earth

**geyser** (GUY-ser)
    the shooting out of the ground of boiling water and steam produced by geothermal energy

**tidal energy**
    energy of the moving water of the tides

## ANSWER THESE

1. Nuclear energy is produced by
    a. the burning of oil
    b. the heat within the earth's crust
    c. the splitting of atoms
2. One of the problems with nuclear energy is
    a. nuclear fuels are renewable resources
    b. some places have too little sunlight
    c. dangerous wastes are produced
3. Cells that change sunlight into electricity are
    a. solar cells
    b. geothermal cells
    c. nuclear cells
4. Geothermal energy is produced by
    a. the moving water of tides
    b. heat within the earth's crust
    c. solar cells
5. Tidal energy can be used to produce electricity only in places near a shoreline and with
    a. high and low tides
    b. many geysers
    c. a sunny climate

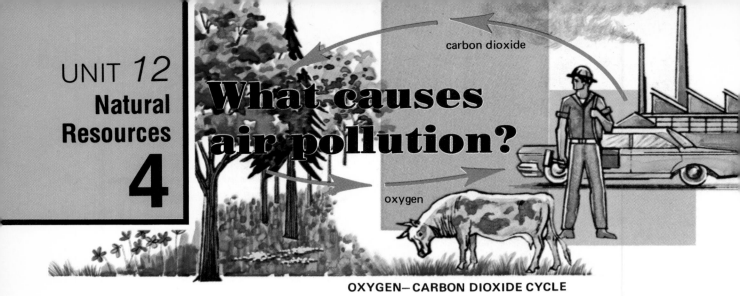

# What causes air pollution?

carbon dioxide

oxygen

**OXYGEN— CARBON DIOXIDE CYCLE**

**The air we breathe.** Air is mainly nitrogen and oxygen. When we breathe in, we remove some oxygen from the air. When we breathe out, we add carbon dioxide to the air. Why don't we use up the oxygen in the air? Green plants change carbon dioxide back into oxygen. This is called the oxygen-carbon dioxide cycle.

The balance of oxygen and carbon dioxide in the air has changed very little over millions of years. But now we may be upsetting this balance. Fuels use oxygen to burn. When they burn, they release carbon dioxide into the air. Can the green plants on the earth change all that carbon dioxide back to oxygen? We are not sure they can.

▶ **How do green plants help in the oxygen-carbon dioxide cycle?**

**Dirty air.** Coal and oil are needed to run our factories. Fuel oil is used to heat our homes. Gasoline is burned to make our cars, trucks, and buses run. Fuels are burned to help produce electricity. When these fuels are burned, they release smoke and other chemicals into the air. The unwanted smoke and chemicals are pollutants (puh-LOOT-ents). They make the air dirty. Some of these pollutants are harmful. They may cause sickness in humans. They sometimes make the air unfit to breathe. Smog is a mixture of smoke, fog, and chemicals. Smog can be harmful to people and other living things.

▶ **What are pollutants?**

One cause of air pollution is factories that release smoke and chemicals into the air when they burn fuels.

When fog combines with smoke and chemicals in the air, it produces the dirty gray air called smog. These two pictures of New York City were taken only one day apart.

**Carbon dioxide in the air.** When fuels burn, they use oxygen from the air. They give off carbon dioxide. Scientists think that too much carbon dioxide in the air can cause changes in the earth's climate. They think it might cause another ice age.

▶ **How does carbon dioxide get into the air?**

## WHAT YOU LEARNED

1. The burning of fuels releases pollutants into the air.
2. Pollutants may be harmful to humans and other living things.

## SCIENCE WORDS

**pollutant** (puh-LOOT-ent)
material that makes the environment dirty
**smog**
a mixture of smoke, fog, and chemicals

## ANSWER THESE

1. Green plants help put _____ back into the air.
2. When fuels burn they
   a. put oxygen into the air
   b. take carbon dioxide out of the air
   c. give off carbon dioxide
3. The air we breathe is mainly
   a. oxygen and carbon dioxide
   b. oxygen and nitrogen
   c. carbon dioxide and nitrogen

## DO THIS AT HOME

The following experiment will enable you to see some of the pollutants found in the air.
1. Take a glass slide. Coat one side with a thin layer of Vaseline.
2. Leave the slide on a window ledge overnight.
3. Examine the slide with a magnifying lens or a microscope.
4. The particles you see stuck to the Vaseline are smoke particles and dust.

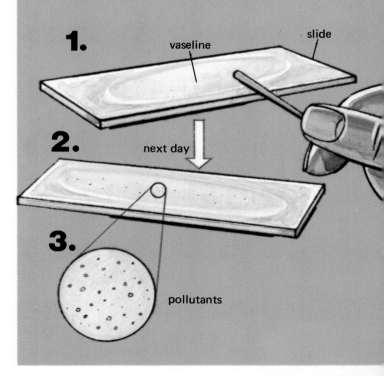

1.
vaseline    slide
2.
next day
3.
pollutants

# What causes water pollution?

**Water, water, everywhere . . . . .** More than three-fourths of the earth's surface is covered with water. Most of this water is salt water. Salt water is unfit for drinking. Our supplies of fresh water are limited. Cities build huge <u>reservoirs</u> (REZ-er-vwahrs) to collect and store fresh water. Reservoirs are human-made lakes. Wells drilled into the water table provide a supply of drinking water. <u>Aqueducts</u> (AK-wuh-ducts) carry water from the mountains to the cities. Even with all this effort, there may not be enough fresh water to meet the world's needs in the future.

▶ **How much of the earth's surface is covered with water?**

When a lake or river becomes heavily polluted, animals may no longer be able to live in it. This river in Ohio became so dirty that fish died by the thousands.

**. . . and not a drop to drink.** Many of our lakes and rivers were important sources of fresh water. But people used them as dumping grounds for wastes and sewage. This has caused them to become polluted. The water is unfit for drinking. Many lakes and rivers are so polluted that fish cannot live in their waters. Once a lake becomes polluted, it takes many years for it to become pure again. Our Great Lakes are dying because of the many wastes that have been dumped into them.

▶ **Why have many lakes and rivers become polluted?**

This picture shows liquid wastes from a factory polluting a canal in New York City. These wastes made it impossible for fish to live in the canal.

**Water pollution.** Some pollutants are dissolved materials. Other pollutants are suspended particles. The dissolved pollutants can come from sewage emptied into the water. Suspended particles can come from factories emptying wastes into the waters. Boats and ships pollute the water with oil and gasoline.

▶ How may factories pollute water?

**The death of a lake.** Some pollutants are chemicals that aid the growth of green plants. They act like <u>fertilizers</u> (FURT-uh-lie-zers). These pollutants can cause the rapid growth of <u>algae</u> (AL-gee) in a lake. Algae are simple plants. While they are alive, they produce oxygen. But when they die, they decay. This uses up the oxygen in the water. As a result, most of the other living things in the lake die. Many <u>pesticides</u> (PES-tuh-sides) also end up in lakes. As they build up, they cause harm to fish and other forms of life.

▶ How can the growth of algae affect a lake?

**WHAT YOU LEARNED**

1. Water pollutants may be dissolved materials or suspended particles.
2. People are the major cause of pollution.

**SCIENCE WORDS**

**reservoir** (REZ-er-vwahr)
a large body of water used to supply drinking water
**aqueduct** (AK-wuh-duct)
a means of sending water from one place to another
**fertilizer** (FURT-uh-lie-zer)
a chemical used to help plants grow
**algae** (AL-gee)
microscopic green plants
**pesticide** (PES-tuh-side)
a chemical used to destroy pests, such as rats, mice, and harmful insects

Green algae are growing rapidly in this lake. The decay of this algae will use up the oxygen in the lake.

**ANSWER THESE**

1. Pollutants can be _____ materials or _____ particles.
2. Polluted lakes
   a. can never be cleaned
   b. clean themselves quickly
   c. take many years to become pure again
3. Cities collect and store water in
   a. aqueducts
   b. rivers
   c. reservoirs

**FINDING OUT MORE**

There are other forms of pollution besides air and water pollution. Thermal pollution is caused by pouring large amounts of heated water into rivers. Power plants often cause thermal pollution this way. The warm water can cause the death of many fish. Loud noises can cause damage to the human ear. Unpleasant or dangerous sounds are called noise pollution. Cities are trying to reduce unnecessary sounds. Environmental pollution is the spoiling of our environment.

# How can we prevent pollution?

Oil spills have killed many birds.

**Are we in trouble?** Some people say that pollution can destroy all life on the earth. Is the problem of pollution that serious? Can we do anything about it? People have always had pollution problems. In the Middle Ages, cities were filthy places. People used to throw their garbage out the window. It would rot in the streets. Now garbage is collected. Streets are cleaned regularly. Pollution of cities is much less than in those times. But much more can be done and needs to be done. Many governments have new laws to reduce pollution and to prevent it. These laws can work if everyone cooperates.

▶ **Is pollution a new problem?**

**The world's largest garbage dump.** Cities produce large amounts of sewage. Most of these wastes have been going into rivers. The rivers then carried it into the ocean. The ocean is very large. The wastes seemed to disappear in it. But now we know this isn't so. Raw sewage is harmful to water life. Today, cities send their wastes through sewage treatment plants. The sewage is changed to harmless materials before it is dumped into rivers or oceans. Factories also produce harmful chemical wastes. Factories used to dump these wastes into the rivers and oceans. Now they, too, must find other ways of getting rid of wastes. Oil pollution of the ocean is another serious problem. Ways

must be found to reduce spills and leakage of oil into the ocean. Quick ways to clean up oil spills must also be found.

▶ **How are cities helping to prevent water pollution?**

**Tuna on rye, hold the mercury.** Mercury is a very dangerous poison. A few years ago, scientists found mercury in tuna fish. The mercury came from factory wastes dumped into the water. Chemical sprays that are used to kill insects and weeds are called pesticides (PES-tuh-sides). Pesticides contain chemicals that are poisonous to humans. Animals may take in these poisonous chemicals with their food and water. Some of these poisons may collect in the bodies of animals that we use as food. New laws bar the use of these chemicals in pesticides. The laws protect our food supplies against further pollution.

▶ **How did mercury get into our food supplies?**

264

Pesticides are needed that kill bugs but do not harm pets, plants, or people.

**Preventing air pollution.** Automobiles and factories cause most of our air pollution. Lead was added to gasoline to make car engines run smoother. New automobiles use only lead-free gasoline. This prevents dangerous lead from entering the air and polluting it. New cars have many anti-pollution devices (duh-VISE-es) built into them. Automobile exhaust systems remove many kinds of pollutants before they enter the air. Factory smokestacks use electrical devices to remove the soot. Some fuels used in factories contained sulfur. When these fuels were burned, the sulfur polluted the air. These fuels are no longer allowed to be used.

▶ **What kind of gasoline helps prevent pollution?**

The lead compounds from gasoline exhausts were seriously polluting the air. New cars are made to operate on unleaded gas.

## WHAT YOU LEARNED

1. Pollution can be prevented in many ways.
2. Not allowing factories and cities to dump pollutants into our waters helps to prevent water pollution.
3. Banning pesticides helps to prevent pollution of our food supplies.
4. Air pollution can be prevented by getting rid of automobile and factory pollutants.

## SCIENCE WORDS

**sewage treatment plant**
   a place where raw sewage is changed into less harmful substances
**pesticides** (PES-tuh-sides)
   chemicals that kill insects and weeds
**anti-pollution device** (duh-VISE)
   something that helps to stop pollution

## ANSWER THESE

1. Cities are helping to prevent water pollution by
   a. building sewage treatment plants
   b. saving their garbage
   c. dumping garbage directly into the ocean
2. Many animals are accidentally being poisoned by the use of
   a. pesticides
   b. poor diets
   c. the wrong kinds of foods
3. Most air pollution is caused by
   a. people and airplanes
   b. automobiles and factories
   c. boats and trains
4. A pollutant added to gasoline is
   a. carbon monoxide
   b. oil
   c. lead
5. Some fuels that are no longer used contained
   a. carbon
   b. oil
   c. sulfur

## FINDING OUT MORE

Do you use aerosol sprays? Most people use them for many different purposes. Billions of spray cans and bottles are made every year. A few years ago scientists found that the fluorocarbon gas used in aerosol sprays was damaging the atmosphere. The gas was harmless in the lower atmosphere. But when it reached high altitudes, it destroyed the ozone in the air. Ozone is a kind of oxygen present in the upper atmosphere. It absorbs dangerous ultraviolet rays from the sun. To prevent the loss of ozone in the upper air, the government has banned the use of fluorocarbons in sprays.

# UNIT 12 Review

*Do the following questions on a separate sheet of paper.*

**Matching**     *Write down each of the statements in Column I, leaving one line of space after each statement. On the blank line following each statement, write the word or phrase from Column II that is described by that statement.*

### Column I

1. Chemical that kills insects and weeds.
2. Microscopic green plants.
3. Chemical that helps plants grow.
4. Mixture of smoke, fog, chemicals.
5. Energy from the splitting of atoms.
6. Energy from sunlight.
7. Heat within the crust of the earth.
8. The energy of motion.
9. Stored energy.
10. Saving our natural resources.

### Column II

pesticide
kinetic energy
nuclear energy
conservation
potential energy
algae
fertilizer
solar energy
smog
geothermal energy

*Do the following questions on a separate sheet of paper.*

**Multiple Choice**     *Write the letter of the choice that best completes the statement or answers the question.*

1. A natural resource is a material from the earth that is
   a. not needed for life
   b. needed for life
   c. manufactured
2. A nonrenewable resource is a natural resource that cannot
   a. be used by human beings
   b. be replaced after it is used
   c. be found by human beings
3. A problem with burning fossil fuels is that often they
   a. give off no energy
   b. consume energy
   c. give off harmful gases
4. One drawback to nuclear energy is
   a. the radioactive waste
   b. it has never worked
   c. it produces little energy

5. A material that makes the environment dirty is
   a. fog
   b. a pollutant
   c. nitrogen
6. An aqueduct carries water from
   a. the mountains to the cities
   b. a river to the oceans
   c. the atmosphere to the hydrosphere
7. Algae can harm lakes when it decays, because
   a. it blocks sunlight
   b. it swells and takes up more room
   c. it uses up the oxygen
8. Mercury is a poison that has been found in
   a. tuna fish
   b. hamburger
   c. fried chicken

## Unit Lessons

1. Why study about the stars and outer space?
2. What are the tools of astronomy?
3. How does a refracting telescope work?
4. How are mirrors used in telescopes?
5. How do we study light from the stars?
6. What unit of distance do astronomers use?
7. What are constellations?

## Goals and Objectives

After completing this unit, you should be able to:

- describe how an astronomer uses a spectroscope and a radio telescope.
- explain how convex lenses are used in a refracting telescope.
- explain how a concave mirror collects light from distant stars.
- describe distances to stars on astronomical units and light-years.
- recognize several constellations.

# Why study about the stars and outer space?

UNIT *13*
Astronomy
**1**

**Can you describe the size and shape of an orange?** You can easily examine an orange by holding it in your hand. How can you describe the size and shape of the earth? How large is our planet compared to others?

Astronomy (uh-STRON-uh-mee) is the study of heavenly bodies. Heavenly bodies include the stars and planets. Astronomy has helped us figure out the size and shape of the earth. It helps us find the distance between the earth and other heavenly bodies. It enables us to compare the size of the earth with the size of other heavenly bodies.

▶ **What is astronomy?**

**The Space Age began in 1957.** The first human-made satellite (SAT-uh-lite) traveled into space in 1957. It was launched by the Russians. Space scientists proved that space travel was possible. Space science also helps us learn more about scientific laws.

▶ **When did the Space Age begin?**

**What time is it?** Look at a clock. It was probably set by the radio. The radio station gets its time from the Naval Observatory. This is called radio time. Radio time is determined by the stars. Days and years are measurements of time. Time is measured by the movement of the earth in space.

▶ **What are some measurements of time?**

268

**SOS.** A radio message is received by a ship's captain. Another ship is in trouble. "What is your location?" the captain asks. The other ship's <u>navigator</u> (NAV-ih-gate-er) uses his knowledge of astronomy. He uses the stars to figure out where the ship is. Ships and airplanes can use the stars for figuring out where they are and where they are going.

▶ How does a ship's navigator determine where his ship is located?

## WHAT YOU LEARNED

1. Astronomy helps us learn more about our planet.
2. Space science helps us learn more about scientific laws.
3. Time and navigation make use of astronomy.

## SCIENCE WORDS

**astronomy** (uh-STRON-uh-mee)
the study of the stars and other heavenly bodies

**satellite** (SAT-uh-lite)
a body that moves around a larger one in space

**navigator** (NAV-ih-gate-er)
a person who is trained to guide a ship or airplane from one place to another

## ANSWER THESE

True or False?
1. We can't find the size and shape of the earth because we live on it.
2. The first satellite proved that space travel was possible.
3. Satellites help us learn more about scientific laws.
4. Time is measured by the movement of the stars.
5. Location on the earth can be found by looking at the moon.

## NOW TRY THESE

Find the science words.
1. The study of heavenly bodies.

2. An object that travels around a body in space.

## FINDING OUT MORE

Pictures taken from satellites are sent back to earth. They show the earth and its covering of clouds. Weather can be predicted from these pictures. Radio waves are bounced off satellites. This helps communication (cuh-MYOO-ni-KAY-shun). A satellite was sent into space in 1972. It did some experiments made up by junior and senior high school students. Could you think of an experiment for a satellite?

**UNIT 13**
**Astronomy**
**2**

# What are the tools of astronomy?

**How many stars can you see?** In some places, you can see thousands of stars on a clear night. How many stars can an <u>astronomer</u> (uh-STRON-uh-mer) see? He or she can see millions of stars. Astronomers have many tools to help them. One of these tools is the <u>telescope</u> (TEL-uh-scope).

▶ **What is one of the astronomer's tools?**

**Reaching for the stars.** A large object that is far away looks small. A telescope makes far-away objects look bigger. Bodies far off in space do not seem to be very bright. Most far-away stars are too dim to be seen with the eye alone. Telescopes make many of these stars appear brighter. There are different kinds of telescopes. Most telescopes use lenses. Some use mirrors as well as lenses.

▶ **How does a telescope help us see far-away objects?**

**Seeing stars by day.** Are there stars in the sky during the day? Yes. But we can't see them because of the sun's light. The sun is a star. It is the closest star to earth. The bright light of the sun hides the light from other stars. We cannot see stars on cloudy or rainy nights. The clouds hide the light from the stars. An ordinary telescope cannot help us see stars on cloudy nights.

Astronomers can use another kind of telescope. It can find stars during the day, or when the sky is covered with clouds. It is called a radio telescope. A radio telescope does not depend on light from the stars. It has an <u>antenna</u> (an-TEN-uh) shaped like a very large dish. The antenna catches the energy of radio waves sent out by the stars. The astronomer "listens" to the stars with a radio telescope.

▶ **Why is a radio telescope sometimes used instead of an ordinary telescope?**

This U.S. Navy radio telescope catches radio waves from the stars in its dish-shaped antenna.

270

**The spectroscope.** Another tool of the astronomer is the <u>spectroscope</u> (SPEC-truh-scope). The spectroscope breaks up light from stars. It helps an astronomer study the light from stars. The spectroscope can tell us what stars are made of. It can also tell the temperature, age, and size of stars.

▶ **What can we learn about stars with a spectroscope?**

## WHAT YOU LEARNED

1. Telescopes make stars appear larger and brighter.
2. A radio telescope catches radio waves from stars.
3. A spectroscope is used to study light from stars.

## SCIENCE WORDS

**astronomer** (uh-STRON-uh-mer)
a person who studies astronomy
**telescope** (TEL-uh-scope)
a tool used to study distant objects
**antenna** (an-TEN-uh)
a tool used to receive radio waves
**spectroscope** (SPEC-truh-scope)
a tool used to break up light so it can be studied

## ANSWER THESE

1. Telescopes make distant objects appear
   a. brighter and smaller
   b. brighter and larger
   c. farther away
2. A dish-shaped antenna is part of a
   a. microscope
   b. radio telescope
   c. spectroscope
3. A spectroscope studies
   a. light
   b. heat
   c. radio waves
4. The number of stars an astronomer can see with a telescope is
   a. hundreds
   b. thousands
   c. millions

## NOW TRY THIS

**Down**
1. Astronomers study the _____.
3. A spectroscope is used to study _____ from distant stars.
4. An instrument that breaks up light from stars.

**Across**
2. An instrument that enables us to see distant stars.
5. Stars can't be seen on a _____ night.
6. _____ telescopes can be used on rainy or cloudy nights.
7. The closest star to the earth.
8. Telescopes make distant objects look _____.

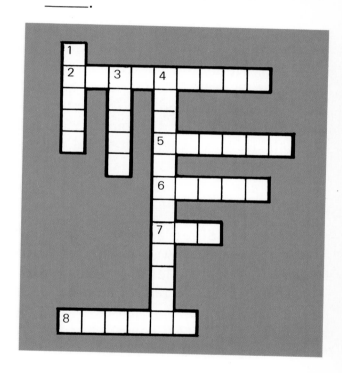

## WHAT'S HAPPENING

Astronomers work in observatories (ub-ZERV-uh-tor-ees). Telescopes and other instruments are used in these buildings. Observatories are built on mountain tops, away from cities. This is done to get away from the bright lights of the city. Today, air pollution makes observing the heavens difficult. Satellites are sent into space with tools of astronomy. Observations are made in space, and information is sent back to earth. Satellites get above the earth's air pollution.

# How does a refracting telescope work?

**Moon gazing.** Have you ever looked at the moon through a telescope? The telescope makes the moon appear much larger. You can see many things on the moon that you can't see with your eyes alone. The first person to get a close-up look at the moon was an Italian scientist, Galileo (gal-ih-LEE-oh). He used a telescope to look at the moon in 1609. The telescope had just been invented. Galileo was the first to see that the surface of the moon was not smooth. He saw craters, hills, and valleys on the moon.

▶ **What does a telescope show about the surface of the moon?**

**What was Galileo's telescope like?** Galileo's telescope was a tube with two lenses inside. A lens <u>refracts</u> (ree-FRACTS) light. To refract is to bend. A telescope that uses only lenses is called a <u>refracting</u> (ree-FRACT-ing) <u>telescope</u>. A simple refracting telescope uses two <u>convex</u> (CON-vex) <u>lenses</u>. A convex lens is thicker in the middle than at the edges.

▶ **What is a refracting telescope?**

**Lenses working together.** The lens at the far end of the tube is called the <u>objective</u> (ob-JEC-tiv) <u>lens</u>. It collects light and brings it to a <u>focus</u> (FOH-cus). It forms an image, or picture, of a distant object. The lens at the other end of the tube is called the <u>eyepiece</u> <u>lens</u>. The eyepiece lens acts like a magnifying glass. It makes the image formed by the objective lens larger.

▶ **What does the eyepiece lens of the telescope do?**

**Make a simple telescope.** Look at a distant object through a convex lens. Move the lens back and forth slowly. Stop when you see the image of the object clearly in the lens. The image will be upside down, and smaller than the object. Without moving the first lens, place a second lens close to your eye. Move the second lens back and forth slowly. Stop when you can see

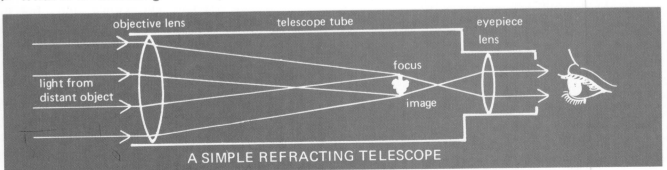

A SIMPLE REFRACTING TELESCOPE

the object clearly through both lenses. The object now appears much larger. You have made a simple telescope.

▶ **How many lenses must you use to make a simple telescope?**

MAKING A SIMPLE TELESCOPE

objective lens

eyepiece lens

## WHAT YOU LEARNED

1. A refracting telescope uses only lenses to make objects appear larger and brighter.
2. The objective lens collects light and brings it to a focus.
3. The eyepiece lens enlarges the image formed by the objective lens.

## SCIENCE WORDS

**refract** (ree-FRACT)
   to bend
**refracting** (ree-FRACT-ing) **telescope**
   a telescope that uses only lenses
**convex** (CON-vex) **lens**
   a lens that is thicker in the middle than at the edges

**objective** (ob-JEC-tiv) **lens**
   a lens that collects light and brings it to a focus
**focus** (FOH-cus)
   a point where light rays are brought together
**eyepiece lens**
   a lens that acts like a magnifying glass

## ANSWER THESE

1. The important parts of a refracting telescope are the
   a. lenses
   b. mirrors
   c. objects
2. The image formed by the objective lens is
   a. right side up and smaller than the object
   b. upside down and larger than the object
   c. upside down and smaller than the object
3. The eyepiece lens
   a. stops light
   b. brightens the image
   c. enlarges the image
4. The first man to discover that the moon had hills and valleys was
   a. Columbus
   b. Newton
   c. Galileo

## NOW TRY THESE

Complete the rhymes on a separate sheet of paper.
1. When a ray of light goes through a lens, we know how it has acted;
   For when the light goes through the lens, we know it is _____.
2. To the naked eye a distant star is completely out of sight;
   But we can use a telescope to collect the star's dim _____.

## FINDING OUT MORE

A large objective lens collects more light than a smaller one. An astronomer can see more through a telescope with a larger lens. The largest refracting telescope has an objective lens that is 100 centimeters across. Its tube is 19 meters long. This telescope is located at the Yerkes observatory in Williams Bay, Wisconsin.

# How are mirrors used in telescopes?

**Different kinds of telescopes.** You learned that a refracting telescope uses a lens to collect light. Another kind of telescope uses a mirror to collect light. This kind of telescope is called a <u>reflecting</u> (rih-FLEC-ting) <u>telescope</u>.

▶ What kind of telescope uses a mirror to collect light?

**What kind of mirror is used in a telescope?** The mirror used in a reflecting telescope is curved inward. This kind of mirror is called a <u>concave</u> (CON-cave) <u>mirror</u>. Concave mirrors are sometimes used for shaving or putting on makeup. Light rays are brought to a focus by a concave mirror. In a telescope, the mirror collects light from distant stars and brings it to a focus.

▶ What kind of mirror is used in a reflecting telescope?

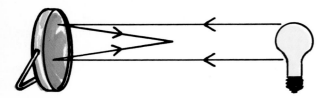

**How does a reflecting telescope work?** Isaac Newton made the first reflecting telescope in 1671. He used a concave mirror to form an image. He used a convex lens as an eyepiece to magnify the image. The concave mirror was only 2½ centimeters across. Newton could not look at the image inside the tube. His head would block the light. So he used a flat mirror to reflect the image to one side. The diagram shows how the mirrors and the lens were arranged. Reflecting telescopes usually have their eyepiece lens at the side. A camera can be attached to the eyepiece to take pictures of the images. The pictures can then be studied.

▶ Where is the eyepiece lens of a reflecting telescope usually placed?

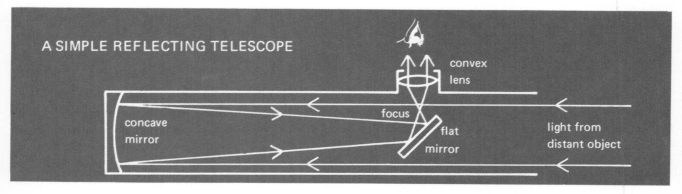

A SIMPLE REFLECTING TELESCOPE

concave mirror

focus

convex lens

flat mirror

light from distant object

274

## We've come a long way since Newton.

Today's reflecting telescopes are very large. One of the largest is the Hale telescope located at Mt. Palomar in California. Its mirror is 5 meters across. The telescope is so big the astronomer does not have to be at the side. He or she works inside the telescope, high up near the top where the image is formed. The light the astromer blocks is so small that it does not matter.

▶ Where does the astronomer work when using a very large reflecting telescope?

### WHAT YOU LEARNED

A reflecting telescope uses a concave mirror to collect light.

### SCIENCE WORDS

**reflecting** (rih-FLEC-ting) **telescope**
a telescope that uses a mirror to collect light
**concave** (CON-cave) **mirror**
a mirror that is curved inward

### ANSWER THESE

1. Reflecting telescopes use
   a. only mirrors
   b. only lenses
   c. both lenses and mirrors

2. A concave mirror is
   a. flat
   b. curved inward
   c. curved outward

3. The mirror in a reflecting telescope is
   a. flat
   b. convex
   c. concave

4. The mirror in a reflecting telescope
   a. collects and focuses light
   b. breaks up light
   c. spreads light out

5. The eyepiece of a reflecting telescope is a
   a. concave mirror
   b. convex lens
   c. convex mirror

6. The reflecting telescope was invented by
   a. Newton
   b. Hale
   c. Galileo

7. One of the largest reflecting telescopes is the
   a. Yerkes
   b. Newton
   c. Hale

### NOW TRY THIS

Match the words in column A with those in column B.

| A | B |
|---|---|
| 1. refracting telescope | a. light-collecting mirror |
| 2. reflecting telescope | b. enlarges image |
| 3. point of light | c. 5-meter mirror |
| 4. Hale telescope | d. light-collecting lens |
| 5. eyepiece lens | e. focus |

### FINDING OUT MORE

Make a simple reflecting telescope. Put a lighted candle at one end of a table. Place a concave shaving mirror at the other end. Tilt the mirror toward a wall. You will be able to project the image of the flame onto the wall. Move the mirror toward or away from the candle until there is a sharp image on the wall. Look at the image with a magnifying glass. Observe the tip of the flame. You can make the image of the flame's tip bigger by moving the magnifying glass back and forth.

# How do we study light from the stars?

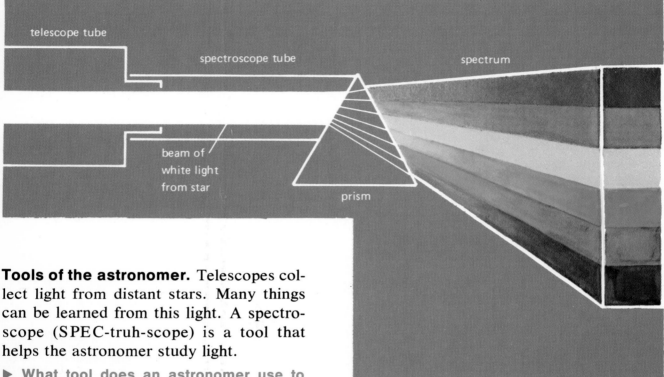

telescope tube

spectroscope tube

spectrum

beam of
white light
from star

prism

**Tools of the astronomer.** Telescopes collect light from distant stars. Many things can be learned from this light. A spectroscope (SPEC-truh-scope) is a tool that helps the astronomer study light.

▶ **What tool does an astronomer use to study light from stars?**

**Colors from a spectroscope.** A prism separates white light into the colors that make it up. These colors are called the light's spectrum (SPEC-trum). Some spectroscopes use prisms. A tube in the spectroscope directs light into the prism. When the light passes through the prism, it is broken up into a spectrum. The spectroscope can be attached to a telescope. The telescope collects light. The spectroscope breaks up the light into the colors of the spectrum. The spectrum is studied to give information about the stars.

▶ **What does a prism do?**

**Identifying elements in stars.** Heat some sodium chloride in a flame. The flame turns yellow. Sodium gives the flame its yellow color. Heat some copper chloride in a flame. The flame turns green. Copper gives the flame its green color. When an element

SODIUM SPECTRUM

SOLAR SPECTRUM

is heated to a high temperature, it gives off colors. These colors are the spectrum of the element. Each element has a different spectrum. Stars are very hot. Each element in a star gives off its own spectrum. The spectrum of the star can be studied to see which elements made the spectrum. In this way, the spectroscope helps identify the elements in the star.

▶ **When do elements give off a spectrum of colors?**

**A spectroscope does more.** Other things can be learned from a star's spectrum. Scientists can find out how hot a star is from its spectrum. They can also tell the size of the star and how old it is. The spectroscope helps us learn about the movements of stars, too.

▶ **What are some things scientists can tell from a star's spectrum?**

**ANSWER THESE**

1. A spectroscope can be used to study
   a. prisms
   b. light
   c. sound

2. Light is broken into a spectrum by a
   a. telescope
   b. lens
   c. prism
3. In astronomy, spectroscopes are often used together with
   a. telescopes
   b. periscopes
   c. microscopes
4. The spectrum of a star seen through a spectroscope helps to find
   a. the elements in the star
   b. the color of the star
   c. the name of the star

**NOW TRY THESE**

Unscramble the mixed-up words.
1. A MIRSP is found inside a spectroscope.
2. A spectroscope helps study GLITH.
3. Elements have different SMURPTECS.
4. A spectrum of a star can often tell us the METPRETRUEA, ZISE, and GEA of that star.

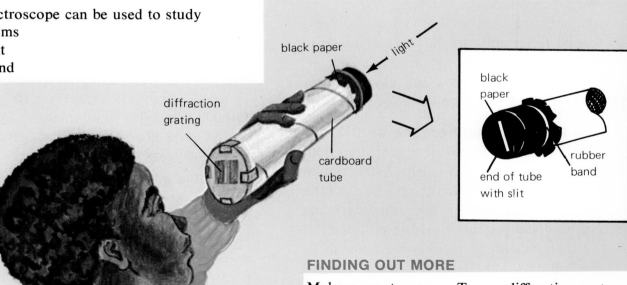

**FINDING OUT MORE**

Make a spectroscope. Tape a diffraction grating (dih-FRAC-shun grate-ing) to one end of a cardboard tube. A diffraction grating acts like a prism. It is a piece of plastic with thousands of lines scratched on its surface. The lines break up light into a spectrum. Cover the other end of the tube with a piece of black paper. Make a thin slit in the paper. Look at a bright light through the tube. Slowly turn the tube until you see a spectrum.

277

# UNIT 13
## Astronomy
# 6

# What unit of distance do astronomers use?

**A long throw.** How far is it from home plate to first base? You could use a tape measure to find out. But how would you measure the distances to the stars? It is not easy. Scientists have to put many facts together to figure out how far away the stars are. They have found that the stars are billions upon billions of kilometers away. The distances are so large that astronomers use special large units to measure distance in space.

▶ **Why do astronomers use special units to measure distance in space?**

**How far is the sun from the earth?** The sun is about 150 million (150 000 000) kilometers away from earth. Astronomers have a name for this distance. They call the distance between the sun and the earth one astronomical (astruh-NOM-ih-cul) unit, or 1 AU. One astronomical unit equals about 150 million kilometers. The sun is one astronomical unit away from the earth. Astronomical units are easier to work with than millions of kilometers.

▶ **What is one astronomical unit?**

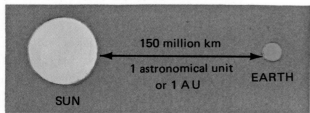

SUN
150 million km
1 astronomical unit
or 1 AU
EARTH

**How fast does light travel?** Light travels about 300 000 kilometers in one second. Something moving as fast as light could travel around the earth more than seven times in one second. The distance light can travel in one year is called a light-year. A light-year is nearly 10 trillion (10 000 000 000 000) kilometers. Distances to the stars are so large that astronomers use light-years to measure them.

▶ **What is a light-year?**

## HOW FAR DOES LIGHT TRAVEL WITH TIME?
### (all figures in kilometers)

| Time | Distance |
| --- | --- |
| 1 second | 300 000 |
| 1 minute | 18 000 000 |
| 1 hour | 1 080 000 000 |
| 1 day | 25 920 000 000 |
| 1 year | 9 460 800 000 000 |

**How close are some stars?** The star closest to the earth is the sun. Proxima Centauri (PROX-ih-muh sen-TOR-ee) is the next closest star. It is 4⅓ light-years away from earth. The North Star, Polaris (poh-LAR-is), is about 300 light-years away. It takes about 300 years for light from the North Star to reach us. It takes only about 8⅓ minutes for light from the sun to reach us.

▶ **How long does it take for light from the North Star to reach us?**

## WHAT YOU LEARNED

1. Stars are billions upon billions of kilometers from the earth.
2. One astronomical unit (1 AU) is about 150 million kilometers.
3. A light-year is the distance light can travel in one year.
4. Distances to the stars are measured in light-years.

## SCIENCE WORDS

**astronomical** (astruh-NOM-ih-cul) **unit**
  a unit of distance that astronomers use; it is about 150 million kilometers
**light-year**
  the distance light can travel in one year; one light-year equals about 10 trillion kilometers

## ANSWER THESE

1. How many astronomical units away is the sun from the earth?
   a. 1
   b. 150
   c. 150 million
2. A light-year is a measurement of
   a. brightness
   b. distance
   c. time
3. How many years does it take for light to reach the earth from Proxima Centauri?
   a. 1
   b. 4⅓
   c. 300

## NOW TRY THESE

1. The sun's nine planets are listed in the chart below. Their distances from the sun are shown in astronomical units. On a separate sheet of paper, arrange the planets in order of their distances from the sun. Put the closest planet first.

| Planet | Distance in AU |
|---|---|
| Earth | 1.0 |
| Jupiter | 5.2 |
| Mercury | 0.4 |
| Uranus | 19.2 |
| Saturn | 9.5 |
| Venus | 0.7 |
| Neptune | 30.1 |
| Mars | 1.5 |
| Pluto | 39.4 |

2. The sun is about eight light-minutes away from the earth. Pluto is about five light-hours from the earth. Which is closer to us?

## FINDING OUT MORE

Hold your thumb up close to your face. Look at it first with one eye, then the other. Your thumb seems to move against the background of the room. Now move your thumb farther away. It still seems to move when you look with one eye at a time, but not as much. Nearby stars seem to move against a background of distant stars. Astronomers call this parallax (PAR-uh-lax). Parallax can be used to find distances to the closer stars.

# What are constellations?

What's your sign—Aquarius, Leo, Pisces? The signs used in a horoscope have the names of <u>constellations</u> (con-stuh-LAY-shuns). Constellations are groups of stars that seem to form patterns in the sky. People in ancient times imagined that they saw animals and people in these patterns. They gave names to the patterns and made up stories about them. Today the constellations help us locate stars in the sky.

▶ **What are constellations?**

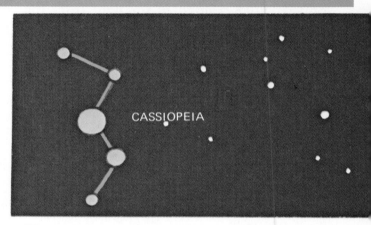
CASSIOPEIA

**The big bear.** One constellation that is easy to find is Ursa (ER-suh) Major. Its name means "big bear." Ancient people saw the shape of a large bear in Ursa Major. The Big Dipper is a smaller constellation that is a part of Ursa Major. The Big Dipper has seven stars. Three stars form the handle of the dipper, and four stars form the bowl. The stars in the Big Dipper are bright. They are easily found in the northern sky.

▶ **Where is the Big Dipper located?**

**The little bear.** Ursa Minor is another constellation found in the northern sky. Ursa Minor means "little bear." It is also called the Little Dipper. The Little Dipper is not as bright as the Big Dipper. But it, too, is made up of seven stars. The first star in the handle of the Little Dipper is Polaris. Cassiopeia (cass-ee-uh-PEE-uh) is another constellation found in the northern sky. It has five bright stars in the shape of a W.

▶ **What constellation is shaped like a W?**

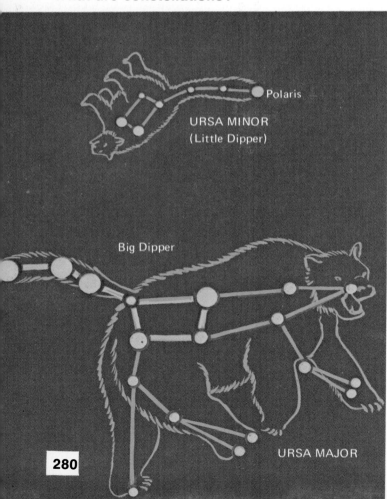
Polaris
URSA MINOR
(Little Dipper)
Big Dipper
URSA MAJOR

Betelgeuse

ORION

Rigel

**ANSWER THESE**

**ANSWER THESE**

1. Aquarius, Leo, and Pisces are all
   a. big stars
   b. constellations
   c. spaceships
2. A giant red star is
   a. Polaris
   b. Aquarius
   c. Betelgeuse
3. Orion is seen during our
   a. winter
   b. summer
   c. daytime
4. Polaris is in
   a. Orion
   b. the Big Dipper
   c. the Little Dipper
5. A constellation found in the southern sky is
   a. Orion
   b. Ursa Major
   c. Ursa Minor

**The hunter.** Orion (uh-RYE-un) "the hunter" is a constellation in the southern sky. Orion appears during our winter. Betelgeuse (BEET-ul-jooz) is a giant red star in this constellation. Rigel (RYE-jul) is a very hot white star in Orion. Look toward the south for this constellation some winter night. When you find it, compare Rigel and Betelgeuse. Note their different colors.

▶ **When can we see Orion?**

**WHAT YOU LEARNED**

1. Constellations are groups of stars that form patterns in the sky.
2. Constellations help us locate stars in the sky.

**SCIENCE WORD**

**constellation** (con-stuh-LAY-shun)
  a group of stars that forms a pattern in the sky

**NOW TRY THESE**

Unscramble the words in capital letters.

1. Northern constellation: GIB PIPRED
2. Southern constellation: NOOIR
3. Bright white star: LIGER
4. Constellation shaped like a W: SAPCESIOIA

# UNIT 13 Review

*Do the following questions on a separate sheet of paper.*

**Fill in the Blank**      *Write down the statements in Column I. Where there is a blank line in each statement, write the word or phrase from Column II that best completes the meaning of the statement.*

| Column I | Column II |
|---|---|
| | Newton |
| 1. Orion is also called _____. | the spectrum |
| 2. Rigel is a very hot, white star in _____. | Galileo |
| 3. Light travels 300,000 km in one _____. | The Hunter |
| 4. The nearest star, besides the sun, is _____. | navigator |
| 5. A prism divides white light into _____. | Orion |
| 6. The first person to use a reflecting telescope was _____. | location |
| 7. The first person to study the moon with a telescope was _____: | second |
| 8. A light-year is the distance light travels in one _____. | Proxima Centauri |
| 9. A person who guides a ship is called a _____. | year |
| 10. A navigator uses the stars to determine his or her _____. | |

*Do the following questions on a separate sheet of paper.*

**Multiple Choice**      *Write the letter of the choice that best completes the statement or answers the question.*

1. A body in space that moves around a larger body is called
   a. a rocket
   b. a navigator
   c. a satellite

2. An astronomer can find stars day or night with a
   a. magnifying glass
   b. mirror
   c. radio telescope

3. Light from distant objects enters a refracting telescope through
   a. the objective lens
   b. the eyepiece
   c. the focus

4. A reflecting telescope collects starlight with a
   a. concave mirror
   b. convex mirror
   c. convex lens

5. A concave mirror is a mirror that is
   a. curved inward
   b. curved outward
   c. not curved

6. White light is made up of
   a. clear radiation
   b. hot gases
   c. a spectrum of colors

7. One astronomical unit, 150 million km, is
   a. the distance from the earth to the moon
   b. the distance from the earth to the sun
   c. the distance from the sun to the nearest star

8. Constellations help us
   a. locate stars in the sky
   b. determine distances to the stars
   c. tell time

# UNIT 14

# Stars

## Goals and Objectives

After completing this unit, you should be able to:

- understand that the magnitude of a star depends its distance from us.
- describe a star by its position on the H-R diagram.
- describe some unusual stars, such as cepheid or binary stars.
- look at a picture of a galaxy and classify it as spiral, elliptical, or irregular.
- describe our view of the Milky Way.

# What can we learn from a star's light?

**Star light, star bright . . .** Stars are made up of hot gases. The gases in stars are so hot that they give off light. Some stars appear brighter than others. We say that stars that appear brighter have a greater apparent magnitude (MAG-nih-tood). Apparent magnitude is a measure of the brightness a star appears to have.

▶ What is meant by the apparent magnitude of a star?

**How bright you are.** Does a dim star give off less light than a bright one? Not always. A star may appear dim because it is very far away. Compare the light from two flashlights that are exactly alike, but at different distances from you. The flashlight that is farther away appears dimmer. Two stars may both give off the same amount of light. They may have the same real brightness. But if one star is farther away from the earth, it appears dimmer. Its apparent magnitude is less.

▶ How is a star's apparent magnitude affected by distance from the earth?

**Turn on the heat.** Hold a needle in a Bunsen burner flame. Notice how the needle turns red as it gets hot. As it gets hotter, it glows brighter. Take the needle out of the flame. As the needle cools, its glow becomes dimmer. Stars act in the same way. The hotter a star is, the brighter it is.

▶ How does temperature affect the brightness of a star?

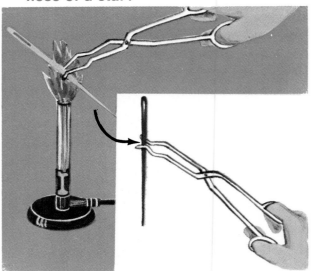

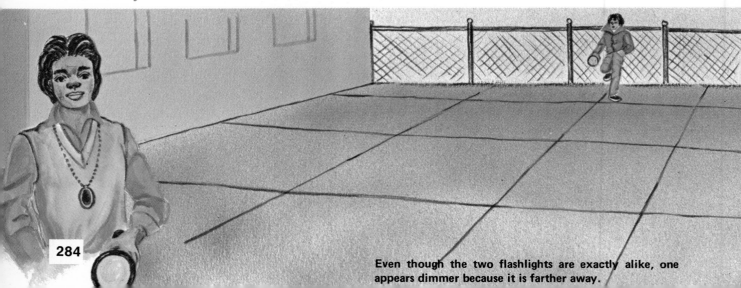

Even though the two flashlights are exactly alike, one appears dimmer because it is farther away.

**Bigger and brighter.** Compare the brightness of a large light bulb with a small one. The larger bulb usually gives off more light. A large star usually gives off more light than a smaller one. The larger a star is, the brighter it is.

▶ How does a star's size affect its brightness?

## WHAT YOU LEARNED

1. Stars are made of hot gases that give off light.
2. The magnitude of a star is a measure of how bright it appears to be.
3. The distance of a star from the earth affects its magnitude, or the brightness it appears to have.
4. The brightness of a star depends upon its temperature and size.

## SCIENCE WORD

**magnitude** (MAG-nih-tood)
a measure of the brightness a star appears to have

## ANSWER THESE

1. Stars are made up of
   a. rocks and minerals
   b. hot gases
   c. burning liquids
2. Magnitude is a measure of a star's
   a. brightness
   b. weight
   c. age
3. Two stars that give off the same amount of light are at different distances from you. The more distant star appears
   a. brighter
   b. dimmer
   c. the same as the closer one
4. As a star gets hotter, it
   a. gets brighter
   b. gets dimmer
   c. keeps the same brightness

## NOW TRY THESE

1. Two stars have the same size and temperature. Explain why one of the stars might appear brighter.
2. Two stars of the same size are about the same distance from the earth. Explain why one star might appear brighter.
3. Two stars of the same temperature are about the same distance from the earth. Explain why one of the stars might appear brighter.

## PEOPLE IN SCIENCE

### Charlotte Moore Sitterly (1898-   )

Dr. Charlotte Moore Sitterly was born in a small town in Pennsylvania. After attending the public schools, Dr. Sitterly majored in mathematics and astronomy at Swarthmore College. She earned her Ph.D. degree in astronomy at the University of California. Part of Dr. Sitterly's research has been a study of the light coming from the sun and stars. As a result of these studies, we now know how much of certain chemical elements there are in the sun and stars. For her distinguished work, Dr. Sitterly has earned many honors.

285

# How are stars classified?

**Temperature and color.** Look at the stars on a clear night. A close look shows that they have different colors. Some appear blue-white. Others look yellow. Still others appear orange or red. The color of a star is determined by its temperature. White stars are hotter than red stars. Blue stars are hotter than white stars. The chart shows how the color of a star is related to its temperature.

▶ What determines the color of a star?

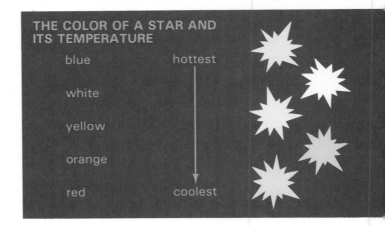

THE COLOR OF A STAR AND ITS TEMPERATURE

blue — hottest

white

yellow

orange

red — coolest

**H-R diagram.** Two astronomers, Ejnar Hertzsprung and Henry Russell, made an interesting chart. This chart is called a Hertzsprung-Russell diagram, or an H-R diagram. A point can be placed in the chart that stands for each star. The place where the point goes depends on the color of the star and on the amount of light it really gives off. The amount of light that a star really gives off is called its absolute magnitude (AB-suh-loot MAG-nuh-tood).

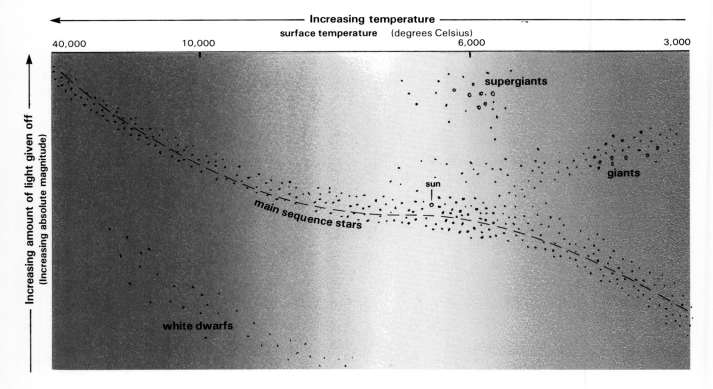

Increasing temperature

surface temperature (degrees Celsius)

40,000  10,000  6,000  3,000

Increasing amount of light given off (Increasing absolute magnitude)

supergiants

sun

giants

main sequence stars

white dwarfs

Suppose that a star has a blue color and a large absolute magnitude. The point for this star would go upper left in the chart. A red star with a small absolute magnitude has a point in the lower right. The points for most stars fall near a line that runs from upper left to lower right. Stars that fall near this line are called <u>main sequence</u> (SEE-kwens) stars. Our sun is a main sequence star.

▶ **Where would the point for a blue star with a large absolute magnitude fall on an H-R diagram?**

**Outside the main sequence.** Some stars do not fall within the main sequence group. For example, some stars are very bright, but are fairly cool. They have yellow, orange, or red colors. Because they are not very hot, they would give off little light if they were of average size. But they are very large. Their large size makes them give off a large amount of light. They have large absolute magnitudes. These stars are called <u>giant</u> stars. Their points are found in the upper right part of an H-R diagram.

Other stars that fall outside the main sequence are hot (blue and white), but very small. Their points fall in the lower part of an H-R diagram. These are the stars called <u>white dwarfs</u>.

Still another group of stars outside the main sequence are the <u>supergiants</u>. These are even larger than the giants. Their points fall in the upper part of an H-R diagram.

▶ **What kind of a star can be not very hot, yet give off a large amount of light?**

## WHAT YOU LEARNED

1. Stars have different colors.
2. The color of a star is determined by how hot it is.
3. In an H-R diagram, points standing for stars are arranged according to the colors and absolute magnitudes of the stars.
4. Stars can be main sequence stars, giant stars, white dwarfs, and supergiants.

## SCIENCE WORDS

**absolute magnitude** (AB-suh-lo[...]
  the amount of light a star [...]

**H-R diagram**
  a chart that describes the c[...]
  the amount of light they give off

**main sequence** (SEE-kwens) **stars**
  most of the stars we see, which fall along one line in an H-R diagram

**giant stars**
  very bright, large stars that are fairly cool

**white dwarfs**
  hot, very small stars

**supergiants**
  very large stars

## ANSWER THESE

1. The amount of light a star really gives off is its
   a. apparent magnitude
   b. H-R number
   c. absolute magnitude
2. The hottest star would probably appear
   a. blue
   b. yellow
   c. red
3. A star in the lower right part of an H-R diagram is
   a. blue with a large absolute magnitude
   b. blue with a small absolute magnitude
   c. red with a small absolute magnitude
4. Very bright, large stars that are not very hot are called
   a. main sequence stars
   b. giant stars
   c. white dwarfs

## NOW TRY THESE

Using the H-R diagram, answer the following questions.

1. In the main sequence stars, which color star is the brightest?
   a. red
   b. yellow
   c. white
2. Which stars are hotter, white dwarfs or supergiants?

# What is the life history of stars?

**Life of a star.** Stars are not living, yet they have a life history. They are formed, live for some time, and then die. From beginning to end takes billions of years. As time passes, a star changes its mass into energy. This energy is given off to outer space as light. The mass cannot last forever. In time, most of the mass is used up, and the star dies. Astronomers can describe what happens during each period in the life of a star.

▶ **How does a star produce its light?**

**A star is born.** Many parts of the heavens contain clouds of dust and gas. Stars form when material in one of these clouds is pulled together by the force of gravity. On earth, gravity is what pulls things downward when you let go of them. In outer space, there is no up or down. Gravity pulls things together from all directions. As dust and gas are pulled together in outer space, they become squeezed. This squeezing produces great heat. In several million years, the star begins to glow. Finally, it becomes hot enough for the hydrogen in the star to become the fuel in a nuclear reaction. As this kind of fuel, hydrogen produces very large amounts of energy. The star shines with a steady light.

▶ **What materials form a star?**

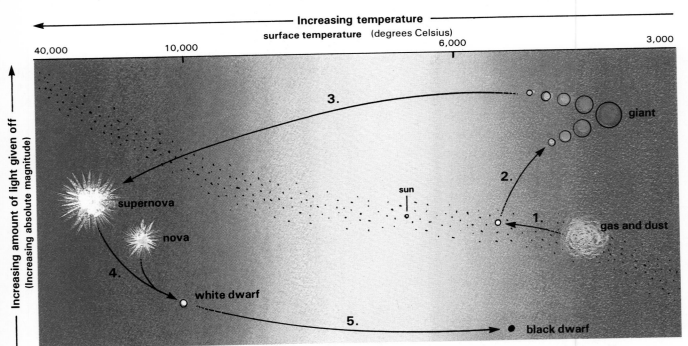

**The life cycle of a star.** 1. Clouds of dust and gas contract to form a star on the main sequence. 2. The star expands and becomes a giant. 3. The giant may explode to become a nova or supernova. 4. The nova or supernova shrinks to become a white dwarf. 5. The white dwarf becomes a small, cold body—a black dwarf.

**A star lives.** The hydrogen in a star gets used up as time passes. The center of the star shrinks. As the star shrinks, its temperature increases. Next, elements other than hydrogen become the fuel for nuclear reactions. The star expands again and becomes cooler. In doing so, it becomes a red giant or a supergiant.

▶ **What happens to a star's temperature as it expands?**

**A star dies.** Astronomers can see fewer red giants than main sequence stars. This is because stars remain red giants for a relatively short time. Stars are main sequence stars much longer. A red giant loses mass near its surface. As this happens, the star begins to shrink. The star may then explode off its outer layer and become many times brighter. This very bright star is called a nova (NOH-vuh). Some stars blow up with a very, very large force. This produces a body of very, very great brightness. Such stars are supernovas (SUE-per-NOH-vuhs). In the end, a star uses up almost all its energy. It shrinks to become a white dwarf. Finally, it becomes a small, cold, dark body called a black dwarf.

▶ **How does a nova form?**

## WHAT YOU LEARNED

1. Stars are made as gravity pulls together the dust and gas in clouds in outer space.
2. After its hydrogen is used up, a main sequence star expands and becomes cooler to form a red giant or supergiant.
3. A red giant shrinks and may explode off its outer layer to become a very bright nova or supernova.
4. When all of a star's energy is used up, it becomes a small, dark, cold body called a black dwarf.

## SCIENCE WORDS

**red giant (supergiant)**
    the form a main sequence star takes for a short time after its hydrogen is used up

**nova** (NOH-vuh)
    a very bright star formed when a red giant explodes off its outer layer

**supernova** (SUE-per-NOH-vuh)
    a star of very great brightness formed when a red giant blows up with a very great force

**black dwarf**
    a small, cold, dark body formed when a star uses up all its energy

## ANSWER THESE

1. As time passes, stars change their mass into
    **a.** energy
    **b.** color
    **c.** heat
2. Stars are formed from
    **a.** minerals
    **b.** dust and gas
    **c.** metals and nonmetals
3. The element used in nuclear reactions in main sequence stars to produce a steady light is
    **a.** helium
    **b.** uranium
    **c.** hydrogen
4. As a star expands to become a red giant, its temperature
    **a.** increases
    **b.** decreases
    **c.** stays the same
5. The extremely bright body formed when a star explodes with a very large force is a
    **a.** red giant
    **b.** supernova
    **c.** black dwarf

## NOW TRY THESE

1. Pulls dust and gas together to form stars

1.
   – pes + — olin + — ca + y

2. Bright star formed by the explosion of a red giant

2.
   – se + — cae + a

289

# What other kinds of stars have been observed?

THE BIG DIPPER

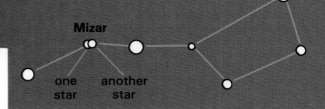

Mizar

one
star

another
star

**Variable stars.** Main sequence stars are fairly stable and send out a steady light. Our sun is a main sequence star whose brightness does not change to any extent. Some stars are not stable. They change in brightness to a great extent. Stars that show a large change in brightness are called variable (VAIR-ee-uh-bul) stars. There are several kinds of variable stars.

▶ **What are variable stars?**

**Pulsars, quasars, and black holes.** Pulsars (PUHL-sahrs) are small stars that give off little or no light. Instead, they send out radio waves. These radio waves are sent out at regular intervals. Pulsars are believed to be made of very densely packed particles called neutrons (NEW-trahns). One teaspoon of the matter in a pulsar has a mass of about 100 billion kilograms.

Quasars (KWAY-sahrs) are a large group of far away stars that send out very large amounts of energy in the form of radio waves and light.

A black hole is a star whose matter fell inward into a very small space. It has a strong pull of gravity. The pull is so strong that nothing can escape from it — not even light.

▶ **What is a pulsar?**

**Binary stars.** The second star in the handle of the Big Dipper is called Mizar (MY-zar). On a clear night, find the Big Dipper. Look carefully at Mizar. You can see two close stars

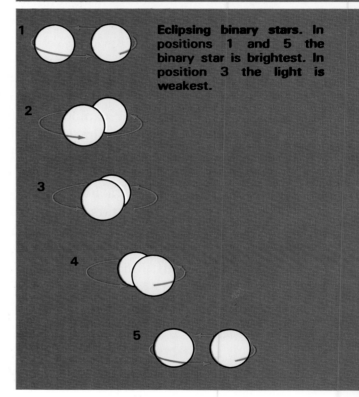

1

2

3

4

5

**Eclipsing binary stars.** In positions 1 and 5 the binary star is brightest. In position 3 the light is weakest.

instead of one. These stars are moving around each other. Two stars that move around each other are called a binary star or double star. When one star moves behind the other, the light of only one star can be seen. Then the binary star appears less bright. When one star blocks the light of the other, it is called an eclipsing (ih-KLIP-sing) binary star. Eclipsing binary stars repeat this difference in brightness in a regular pattern.

▶ **When will the light from a binary star appear dimmer?**

# A CEPHEID OR PULSATING STAR

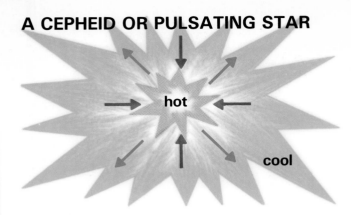

**Some other variable stars.** Red giants and supergiants are variable stars. As they change in size, they change in brightness.

Pulsating (PUHL-sayt-ing) stars, or cepheids (SEEF-ee-ids), change in size in a regular manner. They expand, shrink, expand, shrink, and so forth. As they change size, their brightness changes. When they expand, they get cooler and dimmer. When they contract, they get hotter and brighter.

▶ What happens to the brightness of a cepheid as it contracts?

## WHAT YOU LEARNED

1. Pulsars and quasars are stars that send out radio waves as well as light.
2. Black holes are stars whose matter fell inward into a very small space.
3. Binary stars are two stars that move around each other.
4. Pulsating stars, or cepheids, change in size and brightness in a regular manner.

## SCIENCE WORDS

**variable** (VAIR-ee-uh-bul) **star**
    a star that shows a large change in brightness

**pulsar** (PUHL-sahr)
    a small star that gives off little light but sends out radio waves

**neutrons** (NEW-trahns)
    densely packed particles that make up pulsars

**quasar** (KWAY-sahr)
    a large group of faraway stars that send out energy in the form of radio waves and light

**black hole**
    a star whose matter fell inward into a very small space

**binary star**
    two stars that move around each other

**Mizar** (MY-zar)
    the binary star in the handle of the Big Dipper

**eclipsing** (ih-KLIP-sing) **binary star**
    a binary star having one star that blocks the light of the other

**pulsating** (PUHL-sayt-ing) **star**, or **cepheid** (SEEF-ee-id)
    a variable star that changes in size and brightness in a regular manner

## ANSWER THESE

1. Stars that show a large change in brightness are
    **a.** main sequence stars
    **b.** variable stars
    **c.** regular stars
2. A variable star that sends out radio waves is
    **a.** a pulsar
    **b.** a black hole
    **c.** Mizar
3. A black hole
    **a.** has great brightness
    **b.** has a strong gravity pull
    **c.** is made up of neutrons
4. A binary star appears less bright when
    **a.** it expands
    **b.** gravity pulls it inward
    **c.** one star blocks the other
5. As a cepheid contracts in size, it becomes (hotter/cooler) and (brighter/dimmer).

## FINDING OUT MORE

**Star clusters.** Sometimes we find more than two stars revolving together. Groups or families of stars revolving together are called star clusters. The Pleiades is a group of stars moving in a giant circle together. Some stars are much closer together. They form a globe-shaped cloud. A globular cluster consists of a million stars together.

**291**

# What are galaxies?

A spiral galaxy

**Fuzzy objects in space.** We can see so many stars in the sky it would be hard to count them. The stars appear as small points of light. Among these points of light, you may see some fuzzy spots. Some of these fuzzy spots are nebulas (NEB-yoo-luhz). A nebula is a large cloud of gas and dust. The matter in nebulas is not hot. Nebulas only reflect the light that comes to them from stars.

The other fuzzy spots are galaxies (GAL-uhk-sees). In a galaxy there are a huge number of stars. Many galaxies can be seen with the help of a telescope. Only three can be seen from earth with the unaided eye. Although each of these three contains millions and millions of stars, each is so far away that it appears to be a single blurry spot of light.

▶ **What kinds of heavenly bodies are seen as fuzzy spots?**

**Types of galaxies.** All the stars are part of one galaxy or another. The sun and its planets are part of the galaxy called the Milky Way. In fact, all the single stars you can see with the unaided eye are part of this galaxy. But astronomers have photographed millions of galaxies through telescopes. These photos show that galaxies have different shapes. Based on shape, galaxies can be put into one of three groups. These groups are spiral (SPY-rul) galaxies, elliptical (ih-LIP-tih-kul) galaxies, and irregular (ih-REG-yoo-ler) galaxies.

▶ **On what basis may galaxies be grouped?**

**Spirals, ellipticals, irregulars.** Spiral galaxies are shaped like a pancake with a mound at the center. Two or more spiral arms branch out from the center. Three out of four galaxies are spiral galaxies.

Some elliptical galaxies are almost round, like a ball. Others look like a ball that has been flattened some. The stars in an elliptical galaxy are much older than those in the other types. Elliptical galaxies are much smaller than spiral galaxies.

Irregular galaxies have no definite shape. This is because the stars are arranged in no special order. Irregular galaxies are smaller and fainter than the other types. Also, there are fewer of them.

▶ **In what way is the shape of an irregular galaxy different from the shapes of the others?**

**292**

An elliptical galaxy

Nebula in the constellation Orion

## WHAT YOU LEARNED

1. Nebulas and galaxies are seen as fuzzy spots in space.
2. A galaxy contains a huge number of stars.
3. Galaxies can be put into one of three groups based on shape: spiral, elliptical, and irregular.

## SCIENCE WORDS

**nebula** (NEB-yoo-luh)
a large cloud of gas and dust that reflects light

**galaxy** (GAL-uhk-see)
a group of many stars

**spiral** (SPY-rul) **galaxy**
a group of stars that is shaped like a pancake with arms branching out from the center

**elliptical** (ih-LIP-tih-kul) **galaxy**
a small group of stars shaped like a round or flattened ball

**irregular** (ih-REG-yoo-ler) **galaxy**
a small group of stars with no definite shape

## ANSWER THESE

1. A galaxy is formed of
    a. a large cloud of gas and dust
    b. a huge number of stars
    c. a pattern of radio waves
2. Galaxies shaped with two or more arms branching out from the center are called
    a. elliptical galaxies
    b. spiral galaxies
    c. irregular galaxies
3. Galaxies shaped like round or flattened balls are called
    a. elliptical galaxies
    b. spiral galaxies
    c. irregular galaxies
4. Galaxies with no definite shape are called
    a. elliptical galaxies
    b. spiral galaxies
    c. irregular galaxies

## NOW TRY THESE

1. Draw diagrams of spiral, elliptical, and irregular galaxies.
2. Nebulas and galaxies are both seen as fuzzy spots in the sky. Explain how they arre different from one another.

## FINDING OUT MORE

| Type of Galaxy | Name | Location |
|---|---|---|
| Spiral | Milky Way | Passing through constellations of Sagittarius, Cygnus, Cassiopeia, Perseus, Auriga, and Orion |
| | Andromeda | In the constellation Andromeda |
| | Whirlpool M 51 | In the constellation Canes Venatici (hunting dogs) |
| Elliptical | NGC 205 | In the constellation Andromeda |
| | NGC 221 | In the constellation Andromeda |
| | NGC 3193 | In the constellation Leo |
| Irregular | Large Magellanic Cloud | In the constellation Dorado (the goldfish) |
| | Small Magellanic Cloud | In the constellation Tucana (the toucan) |
| | NGC 5195 | In the constellation Canes Venatici |

# What is the Milky Way?

**Stars, stars, everywhere.** All the stars we can see, the moon, and all the sun's planets (including the earth), are all part of the Milky Way. The Milky Way is a spiral galaxy.

About 20 billion stars make up the spiral arms. About 80 billion make up the center, which is called the nucleus (NEW-klee-us). The distance across the flat part is 80,000

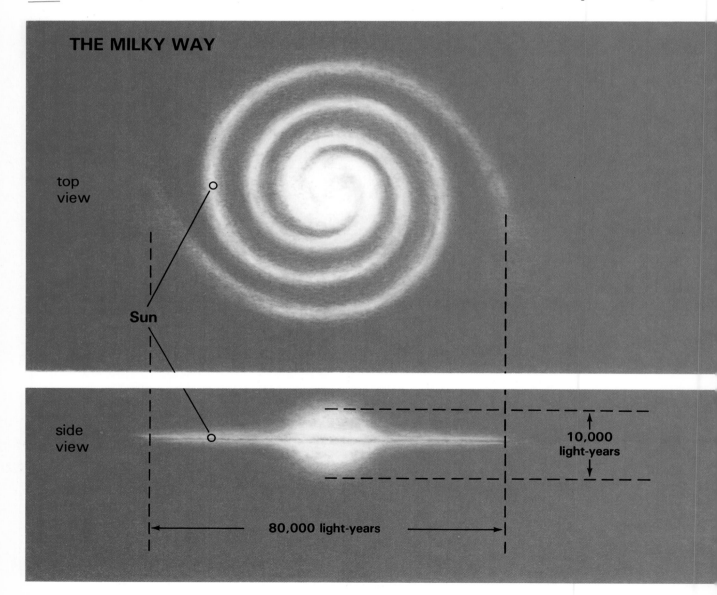

**THE MILKY WAY**

top view

Sun

side view

10,000 light-years

80,000 light-years

light-years. Across the thickest part of the nucleus is a distance of 10,000 light-years. Our sun is 2/3 of the distance from the center to the outer edge.

▶ **Which stars and planets make up the Milky Way?**

**Looking at the Milky Way.** When we look at faraway galaxies, we look in one direction. But we cannot see the entire Milky Way at a single glance. This is because the earth is inside the Milky Way galaxy. To see it, we must look in all directions. We are like a player on a basketball court. To see the people in the stands, the player must look all around, not just this way or that way. When we look toward the nucleus, we see the Milky Way as a milky-looking strip of stars. The best time to see the Milky Way is on a dark, moonless night away from street lights.

▶ **Why must we look in more than one direction to see the Milky Way?**

## WHAT YOU LEARNED

1. The earth and all the stars we can see are part of the Milky Way.
2. The Milky Way is a spiral galaxy.
3. Because the earth is inside the Milky Way, we must look in all directions to see it.

## SCIENCE WORDS

**Milky Way galaxy**
  a spiral galaxy containing the moon, the sun and all its planets, and all the stars we can see with the unaided eye

**nucleus** (NEW-klee-us)
  the center of the Milky Way galaxy, made up of about 80 billion stars

## ANSWER THESE

1. The Milky Way is
   a. a spiral galaxy
   b. an elliptical galaxy
   c. an irregular galaxy
2. Our sun is located in the Milky Way
   a. in a spiral arm
   b. toward the outer edge of the nucleus
   c. in the center of the nucleus
3. Humans have to look in all directions to see the Milky Way because
   a. the earth is inside the galaxy
   b. the galaxy is milky-looking
   c. the galaxy is far away
4. The best time to see the Milky Way is
   a. on a hot, sunny day
   b. at twilight during the winter
   c. on a dark, moonless night

## NOW TRY THESE

1. Explain why our galaxy is called the Milky Way.
2. Would you be able to see the Milky Way in one glance if you lived in another part of the earth, say, China? Explain your answer.

## FINDING OUT MORE

**How far are other galaxies?** The large and small Magellanic clouds are the closest galaxies to us. They are between 150,000 and 160,000 light-years away. They are irregular galaxies. Both can be seen without the aid of a telescope. The Great Spiral of Andromeda is 2 million light-years away. It is much larger than our galaxy. It can also be seen without a telescope.

# UNIT 14 Review

Do the following questions on a separate sheet of paper.

**Matching**    Write down each of the statements in Column I, leaving one line of space after each statement. On the blank line following each statement, write the word or phrase from Column II that is described by that statement.

### Column I

1. Our galaxy.
2. Center of the Milky Way.
3. What pulsars are believed to be made of.
4. Force that pulls things together.
5. Small, cold, dark body.
6. Very bright star resulting from an explosion.
7. Hot, very small star.
8. Very large star.
9. A star that changes in size and brightness.
10. A group of many stars.

### Column II

nova

supergiant

galaxy

Milky Way

cepheid

nucleus

neutrons

gravity

black dwarf

white dwarf

Do the following questions on a separate sheet of paper.

**Multiple Choice**    Write the letter of the choice that best completes the statement or answers the question.

1. The larger and nearer a star is,
   a. the dimmer it appears
   b. the brighter it appears
   c. the cooler it is
2. The color of a star is determined by its
   a. constellation
   b. galaxy
   c. temperature
3. Gravity causes stars to form from
   a. bits of heavy metals
   b. clouds of gas and dust
   c. particles of light
4. The reaction that produces heat and light in stars is a
   a. nuclear reaction
   b. chemical reaction
   c. physical reaction
5. Two stars that move around each other are called
   a. twins
   b. a pair
   c. a binary star
6. A star that shows large changes in brightness is called a
   a. black hole
   b. variable star
   c. neutron star
7. Galaxies are classified according to their
   a. color
   b. distance
   c. shape
8. A nebula is a cloud of
   a. bright stars
   b. dark stars
   c. dust and gas

296

# 15

# The Sun and Its Family

## Unit Lessons

1. How does the sun affect the earth?
2. What is the moon?
3. What are the motions of the moon?
4. How does the moon change its appearance?
5. How does a lunar eclipse occur?
6. How does a solar eclipse occur?
7. Where does the sun get its energy?
8. What are some features of the sun?
9. What is the sun's upper atmosphere like?
10. What do we know about the inner planets?
11. What do we know about the outer planets?
12. What else do we know about the solar system?

## Goals and Objectives

After completing this unit, you should be able to:

- understand how all life on earth depends on energy from the sun.
- describe the moon and its motions.
- explain the difference between a lunar eclipse and a solar eclipse.
- describe the features of the sun and the nuclear reaction that produces its energy.
- understand in what ways the earth is like and unlike the other planets in the solar system.

# How does the sun affect the earth?

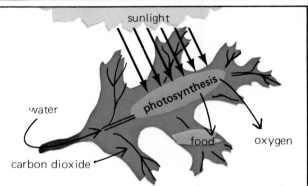

**Our life-giving star.** If the sun stopped shining, what would happen on earth? Life on earth would come to an end. The sun's energy comes to us as heat and light. This energy causes water on the earth to evaporate and rise into the air. The water then falls again as rain. Rain helps plants to grow. Plants need the energy of sunlight to make food. Plants would die without rain and sunlight. People and other animals could not survive without plants. The sun is the most important source of the earth's energy.

▶ **What would happen if the sun stopped shining?**

**The food factory.** You learned that green plants make their own food. The plants take in carbon dioxide and water. Sunlight supplies the energy needed by a plant to make food. Food-making in plants is called <u>photosynthesis</u> (foh-toh-SIN-thuh-sis). During photosynthesis, oxygen is given off by plants.

▶ **What do plants use sunlight for?**

**Fade-out.** Have you ever seen a sheet of yellow plastic covering the inside of a clothing store window? The energy in sunlight can cause the colors in clothing to fade. The yellow plastic helps keep out some of the energy from the sunlight. Some medicine bottles are colored brown. The brown color prevents sunlight from causing chemical changes in the medicine.

▶ **How can sunlight affect clothing?**

**Danger—too much sun!** The earth receives only one two-billionths of the sun's energy. Our atmosphere filters out much of this energy. But the rays that come through can be harmful. Sunlight tans the skin. Too much sunlight can burn the skin. Some kinds of skin cancer may be caused by over-exposure to sunlight. The direct rays of the sun can damage the eyes. Care should always be taken to prevent over-exposure to sunlight.

▶ What is one way sunlight can harm us?

## WHAT YOU LEARNED

1. The sun is the most important source of the earth's energy.
2. Green plants need sunlight for photosynthesis.
3. Sunlight can be both helpful and harmful to people.
4. Sunlight can make things fade or change chemically.

## SCIENCE WORD

**photosynthesis** (foh-toh-SIN-thuh-sis)
the use of sunlight by plants to make food

## ANSWER THESE

1. The most important source of energy for the earth is
   a. volcanoes
   b. fire
   c. the sun
2. A gas given off during photosynthesis is
   a. oxygen
   b. carbon dioxide
   c. air
3. Sunlight helps plants make
   a. food
   b. water
   c. seeds
4. Medicine bottles are colored brown to
   a. look pretty
   b. hide what's inside
   c. prevent the medicine from changing

## NOW TRY THIS

Complete the rhymes on a separate sheet of paper.
1. The sun tans the skin of you and me,
   But it must be used very _____;
   For there is a valuable lesson to learn,
   That too much sun can make skin _____.
2. Sunlight helps make the food we eat,
   And also supplies us with light and _____.

## FINDING OUT MORE

Coal and oil are the earth's chief fuels. Fuels supply us with energy. Coal and oil come from the remains of ancient plants and animals. Those plants and animals needed sunlight to live. It is hard to find anything on earth that does not depend on sunlight.

# What is the moon?

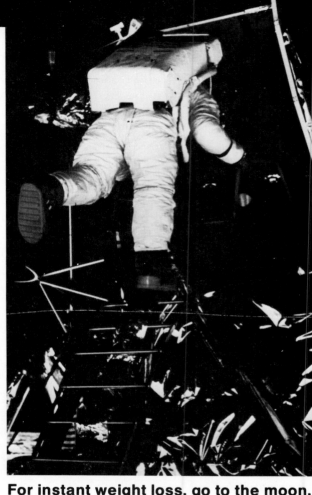

**"That's one small step for a man, one giant leap for mankind."** These were the words spoken as the first man stepped onto the surface of the moon. On July 20, 1969, American astronauts walked on the moon's rocky surface. They had traveled the 380,000 kilometers from earth to the moon in five days. They were the first men to reach the moon. The moon is the earth's only natural <u>satellite</u> (SAT-uh-lite). A satellite is a body that moves around a larger one in space.

▶ What is the earth's only natural satellite?

**Green cheese?** What do we find on the moon's surface? There are steep mountains, wide plains, and deep holes called <u>craters</u> (CRAY-ters). To Galileo, the plains looked like seas. We know that there is no water on the moon. Astronauts have studied the moon's surface and brought back rock samples. These rocks are like volcanic rocks found on earth.

▶ What is on the moon's surface?

**For instant weight loss, go to the moon.** The moon is much smaller than the earth. It is about 3,200 kilometers in diameter. Gravity on the moon is only 1/6 as strong as gravity on earth. This means that your weight on the moon would be 1/6 of your weight on earth. It also means that you could jump 6 times higher on the moon than on earth. Think how high you could throw a ball on the moon.

▶ How big is the moon?

**How do astronauts survive on the moon?** There is no atmosphere on the moon. There is no air to breathe. Parts of the moon get very hot. Other parts get very cold. Temperatures may get as high as

120°C, or as low as −153°C. Astronauts must wear space suits to survive on the moon.

▶ Why do astronauts wear space suits on the moon?

## WHAT YOU LEARNED

1. The moon is the earth's only natural satellite.
2. The moon is about 380,000 kilometers from earth.
3. The moon's surface has steep mountains, wide plains, and deep holes called craters.
4. The moon's gravity is 1/6 as strong as the earth's gravity.
5. There is no air on the moon.

## SCIENCE WORDS

**satellite** (SAT-uh-lite)
a body that moves around a larger one in space

**crater** (CRAY-ter)
a bowl-shaped hole

20 kg

120 kg

## ANSWER THESE

1. The moon is a
   a. planet
   b. satellite
   c. star
2. How long did the space trip from the earth to the moon take?
   a. 5 hours
   b. 1 day
   c. 5 days
3. Moon rocks are similar to
   a. volcanic rock on earth
   b. layered rocks on earth
   c. soft rocks on earth
4. Compared to the earth's gravity, the moon's gravity is
   a. 1/2 as much
   b. 1/4 as much
   c. 1/6 as much

## NOW TRY THESE

1. How much would a 60-kilogram person weigh on the moon?
2. Explain why a pinwheel would not work on the moon.
3. If you could jump 60 centimeters high on earth, how high could you jump on the moon?

## FINDING OUT MORE

The astronauts left their footprints on the moon. Columbus left his footprints when he explored the New World. But the footprints of Columbus lasted only a short time. Wind and rain soon wiped them out. The footprints left on the moon's surface may remain unchanged for millions of years. With no atmosphere on the moon, there is no wind or rain to disturb the surface.

# What are the motions of the moon?

**The sun shines by its own light.** The moon does not give off its own light. How are we able to see it? The moon reflects light from the sun. Sunlight strikes the moon and is reflected to earth. We see the moon by reflected light.

▶ How do we see the moon?

**Turn, turn, turn.** The moon rotates (ROH-tates). It spins like a top around its axis (AK-sis). The axis is an imaginary line that runs through the moon, from pole to pole. The spinning motion of a body around its axis is called rotation (roh-TAY-shun). The earth rotates, planets rotate, even the sun rotates. It takes the moon 27⅓ days to make one complete rotation around its axis.

▶ How long does it take the moon to make one complete rotation?

**Round and round it goes.** The moon moves around the earth in an oval-shaped path. The motion of a body traveling around another body is called revolution (reh-vuh-LOO-shun). The moon takes 27⅓ days to revolve (rih-VOLV) once around the earth.

▶ How long does it take the moon to revolve once around the earth?

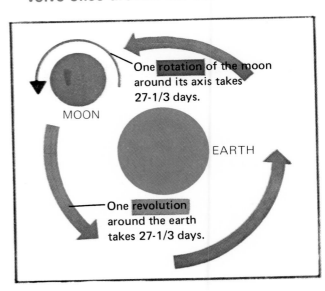

One rotation of the moon around its axis takes 27-1/3 days.

MOON

EARTH

One revolution around the earth takes 27-1/3 days.

**The hidden side.** One rotation of the moon takes the same time as one revolution. As the moon revolves around the earth, the same side of the moon always faces us. The diagram on the next page explains why this happens.

The moon moves through a quarter of its revolution from A to B. It also makes a quarter turn. Sections 1 and 2 keep facing the earth. The moon moves another quarter revolution from B to C. It makes

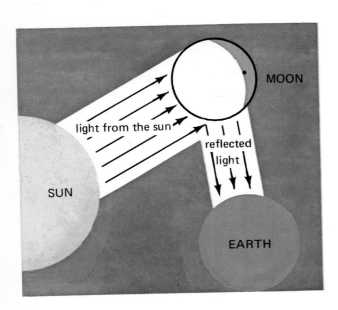

light from the sun

reflected light

SUN

MOON

EARTH

another quarter turn along the way, and sections 1 and 2 still face earth. From C to D is another quarter revolution. Again the moon makes a quarter turn, and sections 1 and 2 still face the earth. And so on back to A. The same side of the moon is always turned toward the earth. It was not until spaceships traveled to the moon that we were able to see the other side.

▶ **Why can't we see all sides of the moon?**

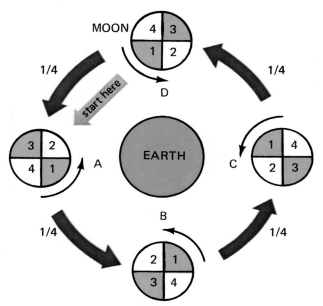

## WHAT YOU LEARNED

1. The moon shines by reflecting the sun's light.
2. The moon takes 27⅓ days to make one rotation and one revolution.
3. The same side of the moon always faces the earth.

## SCIENCE WORDS

**rotate** (ROH-tate)
  spin around an axis
**rotation** (roh-TAY-shun)
  spinning around an axis
**axis** (AK-sis)
  an imaginary line around which something spins
**revolution** (reh-vuh-LOO-shun)
  The motion of a body traveling around another body
**revolve** (rih-VOLV)
  move around another body

## ANSWER THESE

1. The moon shines by
   a. its own light
   b. reflected light
   c. refracted light
2. The time it takes for the moon to rotate once is
   a. 27⅓ days
   b. 24 hours
   c. 30 days
3. One revolution of the moon around the earth takes
   a. 1 day
   b. 1 year
   c. 27⅓ days
4. Only one side of the moon ever faces the earth because
   a. there is not enough light on the other side
   b. the earth turns too slowly
   c. revolution and rotation of the moon take the same amount of time

## NOW TRY THESE

Solve the puzzles to find the science words.

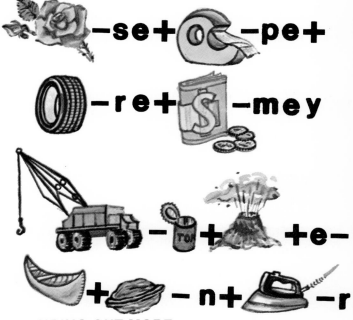

## FINDING OUT MORE

The Russians were the first to photograph the other side of the moon. An unmanned satellite traveled around the moon. It took pictures. These pictures showed the surface of the other side of the moon. The pictures showed that the two sides of the moon are not the same.

303

# How does the moon change its appearance?

**A change of face.** How does the moon change its appearance during the month? Sometimes the moon looks big and round. Other times it looks like just a thin slice. The moon does not change its shape. It is always round. The moon's shape appears to change because of the way the moon reflects sunlight to earth.

▶ What is the moon's shape?

**The moon shines by the sun's light.** The side of the moon facing the sun is always bright. The other side is dark. As the moon travels around the earth, the side facing us may be bright. Then we see the full moon. When the side facing us is dark, we don't see the moon at all. At other times we see parts of the moon. The changes we see in the shape of the moon are called <u>phases</u> (FAY-ziz). The phases of the moon depend upon the positions of the sun, moon, and earth.

▶ What do we call the changes we see in the moon's shape?

**Phases of the moon.** During the new moon phase, we cannot see the moon. The side of the moon facing the earth is dark. As the moon moves around the earth, a small part of the side facing us becomes bright. We call this the new <u>crescent</u> (CRESS-ent) <u>phase.</u>

When the moon has traveled a quarter of the way around the earth, we see the first quarter phase. At the first quarter phase, half of the side facing the earth is bright. As the moon continues to move, more and more of the side facing earth becomes bright. This is the new <u>gibbous</u> (GIB-bus) <u>phase.</u> Finally the moon completes half of its trip around the earth. The entire surface facing the earth is bright. This is called a full moon.

▶ How much of the moon can we see during the new moon phase?

**Moving on.** After the full moon, we begin to see less of the moon's surface. This is the old gibbous phase. At the last quarter

OLD CRESCENT
Can be seen in east
before sunrise

NEW CRESCENT
Can be seen in west
after sunset

SOME OF THE PHASES OF THE MOON

phase, we see only half of the moon's face. Less and less of the side turned to us is bright. Finally we see just a thin slice of the moon during the old crescent phase. After 29½ days, the moon is again at the new moon phase. It takes 29½ days for the moon to go through all of its phases. This is a little longer than the time for one revolution of the moon around the earth. The earth's motion around the sun causes this difference.

▶ **How long does it take for the moon to go through all of its phases?**

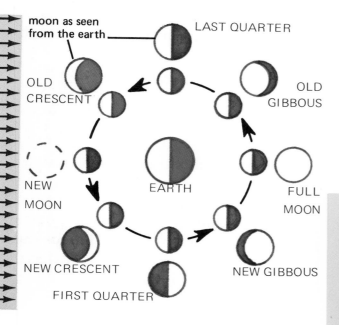

light from the sun

moon as seen from the earth —

LAST QUARTER

OLD CRESCENT

OLD GIBBOUS

NEW MOON

EARTH

FULL MOON

NEW CRESCENT

NEW GIBBOUS

FIRST QUARTER

## WHAT YOU LEARNED

1. The phases of the moon depend upon the positions of the sun, moon, and earth.
2. The phases of the moon change as the moon moves around the earth.

## SCIENCE WORDS

**phases** (FAY-ziz)
   changes we see in the moon's shape
**crescent** (CRESS-ent) **phase**
   a phase of the moon in which we see less than half of the moon's face
**gibbous** (GIB-bus) **phase**
   a phase of the moon in which we see more than half of the moon's face

## ANSWER THESE

1. The moon's actual shape
   a. changes
   b. never changes
   c. is unknown
2. The side of the moon facing the sun is bright
   a. all of the time
   b. some of the time
   c. only when it is facing the earth
3. The phases of the moon depend on the position of the
   a. earth only
   b. earth and moon only
   c. earth, moon, and sun
4. The moon goes through all of its phases once in
   a. 27⅓ days
   b. 29½ days
   c. 1 year

## NOW TRY THIS

For each statement in column A, find the name of the phase in column B that matches.

| A | B |
|---|---|
| 1. Phase seen just before new moon | a. new moon |
| 2. Phase seen just after full moon | b. new crescent |
| 3. Moon cannot be seen | c. first quarter |
| 4. Entire face of moon can be seen | d. new gibbous |
| 5. Phase seen just after new moon | e. full moon |
| 6. Phase seen just before full moon | f. old gibbous |
| 7. First time a half-face is seen | g. last quarter |
| 8. Second time a half-face is seen | h. old crescent |

## DO THIS AT HOME

Observe the moon over the next 30 days. Draw the phases you see each clear night. The moon rises about an hour later each night. You may have to stay up late to see some of the phases. The new crescent moon sets soon after sunset. Sometimes you can see it in the late afternoon. The old crescent moon rises a short while before sunrise. Sometimes you can see it in the early morning. Note the date for each phase. How could you use the phases of the moon to make a calendar?

# How does a lunar eclipse occur?

**The shadow forms.** Turn on a lamp in a darkened room. Your body blocks some of the light from the lamp. A shadow forms behind you. The sun is a bright light in space. Light from the sun is blocked by the earth, the moon, and other bodies in space. These bodies make shadows in space.

▶ How does the earth form a shadow in space?

Your shadow has two parts. The black part is the umbra. The gray part is the penumbra.

**Look closely at a shadow.** The center of the shadow is very dark. This part is called the umbra (UM-bruh). There is a lighter shadow around the umbra. It is called the penumbra (peh-NUM-bruh). Shadows of the earth and the moon also have an umbra and a penumbra.

▶ What do we call the darker part of a shadow?

**Moving into the earth's shadow.** As the moon revolves around the earth, it usually passes above or below the earth's shadow. Sometimes the moon moves into the earth's umbra. Sunlight is blocked from reaching the moon. The moon's surface darkens. An eclipse (uh-CLIPS) of the moon occurs. It is called a lunar (LOO-ner) eclipse. A lunar eclipse can occur only at the full moon phase.

▶ How does a lunar eclipse occur?

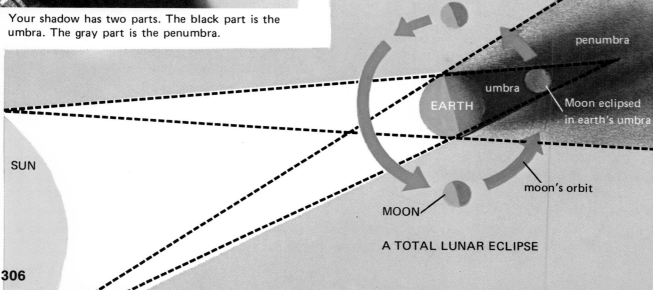

SUN

EARTH

penumbra

umbra

Moon eclipsed
in earth's umbra

moon's orbit

MOON

A TOTAL LUNAR ECLIPSE

**Total or partial.** The moon may move entirely into the earth's umbra. Then the moon's entire face darkens. This is a total lunar eclipse. Sometimes only part of the moon moves into the earth's umbra. Then only that part of the moon is darkened. A partial eclipse occurs. The earth's penumbra darkens the moon only slightly. We hardly notice it when the moon is in the earth's penumbra.

▶ What causes a partial lunar eclipse?

## WHAT YOU LEARNED

1. A lunar eclipse occurs when the moon moves into the earth's umbra.
2. A total lunar eclipse occurs when the moon is entirely within the earth's umbra.
3. A partial lunar eclipse occurs when only part of the moon is in the earth's umbra.

## SCIENCE WORDS

**umbra** (UM-bruh)
  the dark part of a shadow
**penumbra** (peh-NUM-bruh)
  the lighter shadow around an umbra
**eclipse** (uh-CLIPS)
  what happens when one body in space blocks the sun's light from reaching another body
**lunar** (LOO-ner) **eclipse**
  an eclipse of the moon

## ANSWER THESE

1. A shadow forms when an object
   a. is transparent
   b. blocks light
   c. is in motion
2. The darker part of a shadow is the
   a. blind spot
   b. umbra
   c. penumbra
3. The umbra is
   a. darker than the penumbra
   b. lighter than the penumbra
   c. the same as the penumbra
4. A lunar eclipse occurs when the moon moves into
   a. the sun's umbra
   b. its own umbra
   c. the earth's umbra

## NOW TRY THESE

Use the lunar eclipse diagram to help you answer these questions.
1. What is the phase of the moon during a lunar eclipse?
2. Why can a lunar eclipse be seen only at night?
3. What is the difference between a total lunar eclipse and a partial lunar eclipse?
4. Why doesn't a lunar eclipse occur when the moon passes above or below the earth's shadow?

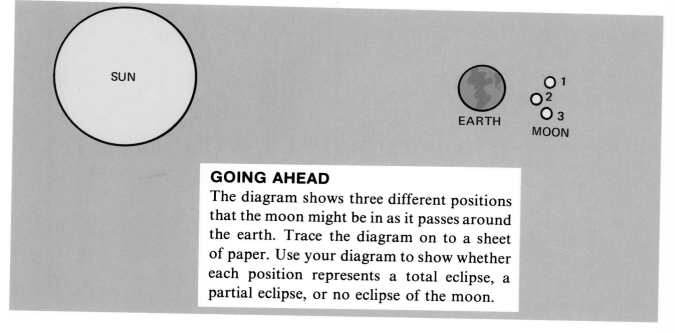

**GOING AHEAD**
The diagram shows three different positions that the moon might be in as it passes around the earth. Trace the diagram on to a sheet of paper. Use your diagram to show whether each position represents a total eclipse, a partial eclipse, or no eclipse of the moon.

# How does a solar eclipse occur?

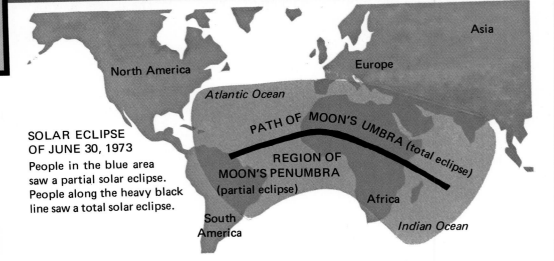

SOLAR ECLIPSE
OF JUNE 30, 1973
People in the blue area
saw a partial solar eclipse.
People along the heavy black
line saw a total solar eclipse.

PATH OF MOON'S UMBRA (total eclipse)

REGION OF
MOON'S PENUMBRA
(partial eclipse)

North America

Atlantic Ocean

Asia

Europe

Africa

South
America

Indian Ocean

SOLAR ECLIPSE

**A very special day.** On June 30, 1973, thousands of scientists set up telescopes and other instruments in Africa. They aimed them into the daytime sky. From certain parts of Africa they knew they could see a total eclipse of the sun, or total solar (SOH-ler) eclipse. We don't often get a chance to watch a total solar eclipse. When it occurs, it can be seen from only a very small area on the earth. This total solar eclipse lasted just seven minutes and four seconds. But it was the second longest in history.

▶ **How long did the solar eclipse of 1973 last?**

**What happened?** During a solar eclipse, a large black circle moves across the sun's face. It is the moon that makes the large black circle. If the moon blocks out the sun's entire face, a total solar eclipse occurs. If only part of the sun's face is darkened, a partial (PAR-shul) solar eclipse occurs.

▶ **What blocks out the sun's face during a total solar eclipse?**

**When does a solar eclipse occur?** The moon casts a shadow in space. The moon's shadow has an umbra and a penumbra. The shadow is long enough to reach the earth. But usually the shadow passes above or below the earth. Sometimes the shadow of the moon falls upon the earth. This happens when the moon is on a line between the earth and the sun. Then there is a solar eclipse.

▶ **When does a solar eclipse occur?**

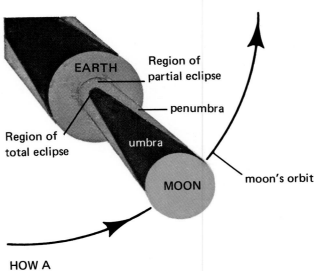

EARTH

Region of
partial eclipse

penumbra

Region of
total eclipse

umbra

MOON

moon's orbit

HOW A
SOLAR ECLIPSE
OCCURS

SUN

## When do we see a total solar eclipse?

Where the moon's umbra touches the earth, people see a total solar eclipse. The umbra is small. It is only about 270 kilometers across. Only those within the umbra can see a total solar eclipse. The penumbra is about 6500 kilometers wide. People who are in the penumbra see a partial eclipse. The penumbra region is much larger than the umbra region. Partial solar eclipses are seen much more often than total eclipses.

▶ **Which kind of solar eclipse is seen more often?**

### WHAT YOU LEARNED

1. A solar eclipse occurs when the moon's shadow falls on the earth.
2. Where the moon's umbra touches the earth, a total solar eclipse is seen.
3. Where the moon's penumbra touches the earth, a partial solar eclipse is seen.

### SCIENCE WORDS

**total solar** (SOH-ler) **eclipse**
   an eclipse of the sun in which the sun's entire face is darkened

**partial** (PAR-shul) **solar eclipse**
   an eclipse of the sun in which only part of the sun's face is darkened

### ANSWER THESE

1. A total solar eclipse is seen within the
   a. earth's umbra
   b. moon's penumbra
   c. moon's umbra
2. A partial solar eclipse is seen within the
   a. earth's umbra
   b. moon's penumbra
   c. moon's umbra
3. A larger region of the earth is covered by the
   a. sun's umbra
   b. moon's umbra
   c. moon's penumbra

4. A total solar eclipse can last about
   a. two hours
   b. seven days
   c. seven minutes

### NOW TRY THIS

**Down**
1. Partial solar eclipse can be seen in this region.
2. Eclipse that is seen when the moon's shadow falls on the earth.
3. Supplies the earth and moon with light.

**Across**
4. Eclipse that is seen when the moon moves into the earth's umbra.
5. Total solar eclipse can be seen in this region.

### WHAT'S HAPPENING

The sun's upper atmosphere is called the corona. Normally, the brightness of the sun keeps us from seeing the corona. During a solar eclipse, most of the sun's light is blocked out. The corona can be seen and studied. It looks like a halo around the sun. Scientists use special instruments to view a solar eclipse. Looking directly at a solar eclipse could damage the eyes.

# Where does the sun get its energy?

EARTH

**How big is the sun?** The sun is 1 400 000 kilometers in diameter. Compared to other stars, the sun is medium-sized. The earth's diameter is about 13 000 kilometers. More than 100 earths could fit in a line along the sun's diameter. It would take over a million earths to fill the entire space taken up by the sun.

▶ How big is the sun?

**Color me yellow.** The sun is a yellow star. The color of a star tells us its temperature. Yellow stars have a surface temperature of about 6000°C. The sun's temperature is about 6000°C at the surface. The inside of the sun is hotter. Astronomers believe that the inside temperature of the sun is over 13 million degrees Celsius (13 000 000°C).

▶ What is the surface temperature of the sun?

**No simple chemical reaction here.** You learned that burning is a chemical reaction. In a chemical reaction, atoms combine by exchanging or sharing electrons. When things on earth burn, they combine with oxygen to produce heat and light. This does not happen on the sun. The sun produces its heat and light by a nuclear (NOO-clee-er) reaction. In a nuclear reaction, atomic nuclei are changed. Atomic nuclei combine in the sun's interior. This kind of nuclear reaction is called thermonuclear fusion (ther-moh-NOO-clee-er FYOO-zhun).

▶ What kind of reaction produces heat and light on the sun?

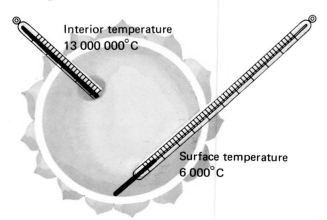

Interior temperature 13 000 000°C

Surface temperature 6 000°C

**What is the sun made of?** The sun is about 80% hydrogen and 18% helium. The other 2% is made up of other elements. Deep inside the sun, hydrogen nuclei fuse (FYOOZ), or combine, to form nuclei of helium. In this reaction, 4 hydrogen nuclei fuse to form 1 helium nucleus. The mass of the helium nucleus is less than that of the 4 hydrogen nuclei all together. The missing mass is matter that has changed into energy.

▶ **What elements make up most of the sun?**

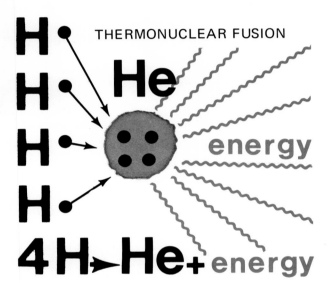

THERMONUCLEAR FUSION

$4H \rightarrow He + energy$

## WHAT YOU LEARNED

1. The sun is a medium-sized, yellow star.
2. The sun gets its energy from thermonuclear fusion.
3. Inside the sun, hydrogen nuclei combine to form nuclei of helium.

## SCIENCE WORDS

**nuclear** (NOO-clee-er) **reaction**
 a reaction in which the nuclei of atoms change

**thermonuclear fusion** (ther-moh-NOO-clee-er FYOO-zhun)
 a reaction in which the nuclei of atoms combine

**fuse** (FYOOZ)
 combine

## ANSWER THESE

1. Compared to other stars, the sun is
 a. small
 b. medium-sized
 c. large
2. The surface temperature of a yellow star is about
 a. 600°C
 b. 6 000°C
 c. 60 000°C
3. In the sun, hydrogen nuclei combine to form
 a. helium
 b. salts
 c. water
4. The mass lost in thermonuclear fusion is changed into
 a. helium
 b. nuclei
 c. energy

## NOW TRY THESE

Write the correct words on a separate sheet of paper.
1. Color of the sun.
2. Most of the sun is this element.
3. Heat and light are forms of _____.
4. A reaction that takes place in the sun.

## PEOPLE IN SCIENCE

**Albert Einstein** (1879-1955)
Albert Einstein was born in Germany and lived many years in the United States. He was a scientist who helped explain how the sun produces its energy. Einstein said that small amounts of matter could be changed to large amounts of energy. Einstein's work helped develop the use of atomic energy on earth.

**UNIT 15**
**The sun and its family**
**8**

# What are some features of the sun?

**The sun's atmosphere.** Unlike the earth, no part of the sun is a liquid or solid. It is too hot for there to be any liquids or solids in the sun. The sun is simply a large ball of hot gases. Beyond the sun itself is an atmosphere. Of course, it, too, is made of gases. The atmosphere has three layers. The layer closest to the sun is the photosphere (FOH-tuh-sfere). The photosphere is about 550 kilometers thick. The gases in this layer are so hot that they glow and can be seen.

▶ Why are there no solids or liquids in the sun?

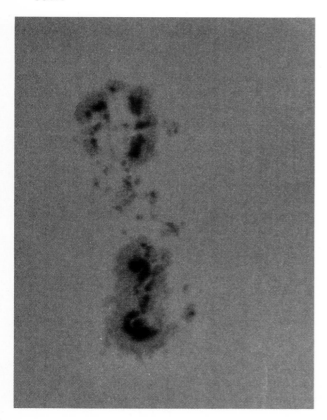

**Sunspots.** There are spots on the surface of the sun that are cooler than the surrounding areas. The gases in these cooler areas do not shine as brightly. These areas appear dark, and are called sunspots. All sunspots appear to move across the surface of the sun in the same direction. This motion of the sunspots is the result of the spinning of the sun about an axis.

Sunspots may last for a day or remain for several months. A sunspot may break up to form several sunspots. These new sunspots are called a sunspot group.

▶ Why do sunspots appear to all move in the same direction?

**Solar flares.** Energy sometimes becomes stored in the outer part of the atmosphere of the sun. This takes place above an area where there has been a sunspot group for some time. If the energy is released suddenly, a solar flare is produced. A solar flare appears as a patch

312

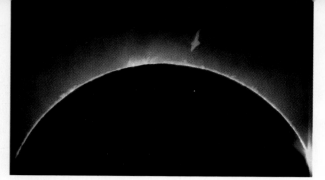

A solar flare

of sun of very great brightness. Flares do not last for more than about an hour. They may last for only a few minutes. Solar flares send out not only light and heat but also particles found in atoms. Streams of these particles are called cosmic (KAHZ-mik) rays. When cosmic rays reach earth from a large flare, they cause static on the radio.

▶ How may solar flares affect the earth?

## WHAT YOU LEARNED

1. The sun is a large ball of hot gases.
2. The atmosphere of the sun contains three layers, the closest one to the sun called the photosphere.
3. Sunspots are cooler, dark spots on the surface of the sun that appear to move in the same direction.
4. Solar flares send out light, heat, and cosmic rays.

## SCIENCE WORDS

**photosphere** (FOH-tuh-sfere)
the innermost layer of the sun's atmosphere

**sunspot**
a dark, cooler area of the sun's surface that appears to move

**sunspot group**
several sunspots in an area formed by the break-up of one sunspot

**solar flare**
the release of energy from the outer part of the sun's atmosphere above a sunspot group

**cosmic** (KAHZ-mik) **rays**
streams of particles found in atoms, which are released from solar flares

## ANSWER THESE

1. The sun does not contain any solids or liquids because
   **a.** it is too cold
   **b.** it is too hot
   **c.** it moves too quickly
2. The innermost layer of the sun's atmosphere is the
   **a.** stratosphere
   **b.** ionosphere
   **c.** photosphere
3. Sunspots appear to move as a result of
   **a.** the sun spinning on its axis
   **b.** cosmic rays
   **c.** solar flares
4. When energy above a sunspot group is released, it produces
   **a.** another sunspot
   **b.** a photosphere
   **c.** a solar flare
5. When cosmic rays reach the earth, they
   **a.** help plants to grow
   **b.** cause static on radios
   **c.** form a sunspot group

## FINDING OUT MORE

**Now you see them, now you don't.** The number of sunspots seems to vary. There are periods when over 100 sunspots are visible. Sometimes there are no visible sunspots. The interval of time between many and few sunspots follows a pattern. Large numbers of sunspots seem to appear every 11 years.

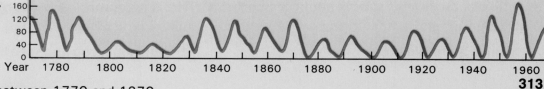

Relative number of sunspots

Sunspot activity between 1770 and 1970

# What is the sun's upper atmosphere like?

Corona
Chromosphere
Photosphere

**THREE LAYERS MAKING UP THE ATMOSPHERE OF THE SUN.**

**The chromosphere.** The chromosphere (KROH-muh-sfere) is the layer of the sun's atmosphere next to the photosphere. It gives off a red glow that is so weak it can only be seen under special conditions. One such condition is a solar eclipse. The glow of the chromosphere can also be seen with special telescopes. The chromosphere goes out thousands of kilometers from the photosphere.

▶ Why can you not usually see the red glow of the chromosphere?

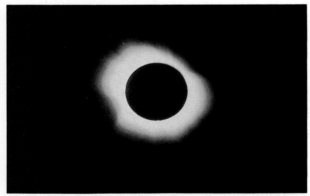

The sun's chromosphere is visible during a solar eclipse.

**Prominences.** Flames of gas shooting out from the chromosphere produce a spectacular view. These flamelike clouds of gas are called prominences (PROM-uh-nuns-ez). These flames shoot up away from the chromosphere for thousands of kilometers. Then, they flow back into the sun. Prominences are best seen during a solar eclipse.

▶ What is a prominence?

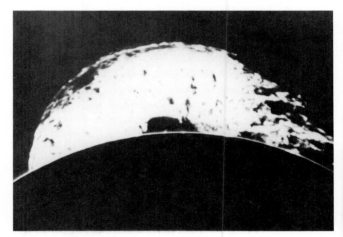

A solar prominence

**A crown of light.** Only a small path across the earth goes into total darkness during a solar eclipse. People wanting to be in this path may have to travel a long way to get to it. But the trip is worth it because only in this path does the corona become visible. Then the corona forms a crown of light that surrounds the sun. (*Corona* comes from a Latin word meaning crown.) The corona is the layer of the sun's atmosphere farthest from the sun. The temperature in the corona is more than one million degrees Celsius.

▶ What must you do to see the sun's corona?

## WHAT YOU LEARNED

1. The chromosphere is the layer of the sun's atmosphere next to the photosphere.
2. The chromosphere gives off a weak, red glow that can be seen only under special conditions.
3. Flamelike clouds of gas that shoot out from the chromosphere are called prominences.
4. The corona is the layer of the sun's atmosphere farthest from the sun.

## SCIENCE WORDS

**chromosphere** (KROH-muh-sfere)
   the weak, red layer of the sun's atmosphere next to the photosphere

**prominence** (PROM-uh-nuns)
   a flamelike cloud of gas that shoots up from the chromosphere

**corona**
   the layer of the sun's atmosphere farthest from the sun

## ANSWER THESE

1. The layer of the sun's atmosphere next to the photosphere is the
   a. corona
   b. chromosphere
   c. solarsphere
2. The chromosphere can best be seen
   a. on a dark, moonless night
   b. during a solar eclipse
   c. at noontime on a sunny day
3. A flamelike cloud of gas shooting out from the chromosphere is a
   a. prominnce
   b. solar flare
   c. sunspot
4. The layer of the sun's atmosphere farthest away from the sun is the
   a. photosphere
   b. chromosphere
   c. corona
5. The corona becomes visible only during
   a. a solar eclipse
   b. a solar flare
   c. a prominence

## NOW TRY THIS

**Across**

1. Layer of the sun's atmosphere next to the photosphere
2. The chromosphere can be seen during a solar _____ .
3. Kind of glow given off by the chromosphere

**Down**

4. The outermost layer of the sun's atmosphere
5. The layer of the sun's atmosphere next to the sun
6. Color of the chromosphere

## FINDING OUT MORE

**Viewing the sun.** The sun's light is too bright for direct viewing. Special instruments are needed to study the sun. One such solar telescope is located at Kitt Peak, Arizona. It is 800 meters long and built into the ground. The telescope is made so that the amount of the sun's light and heat entering the telescope can be carefully controlled.

Solar telescope at Kitt Peak, Arizona

# What do we know about the inner planets?

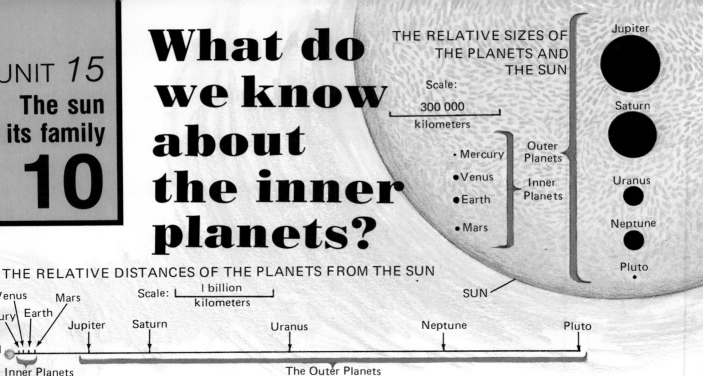

THE RELATIVE SIZES OF THE PLANETS AND THE SUN

Scale: |— 300 000 —| kilometers

· Mercury        Outer Planets
●Venus          Inner Planets
●Earth
· Mars

Jupiter

Saturn

Uranus

Neptune

Pluto

SUN

THE RELATIVE DISTANCES OF THE PLANETS FROM THE SUN

Scale: |— 1 billion —| kilometers

Venus   Mars
Mercury  Earth
Jupiter   Saturn   Uranus   Neptune   Pluto

SUN

The Inner Planets          The Outer Planets

**A spaced out family.** The sun has a family of nine <u>planets</u> (PLAN-ets). The earth is one of these planets. It is one of the smaller planets. Jupiter (JOO-puh-ter) is the largest planet. All the planets go around the sun in the same direction. But they go around at different speeds. Most of the planets have moons, or satellites. The pictures give some facts about each planet.

▶ **Which are the four planets closest to the sun?**

**Wanderers in the sky.** The stars do not change their places. The stars of the Big Dipper always form the same pattern. The planets look like stars. But each night they change their positions among the stars. They seem to wander about in the sky. That is because they are moving around the sun. The word planet comes from a Greek word that means wanderer.

▶ **Why do the planets change their positions among the stars?**

**Seeing planets.** Five of the planets can be seen without a telescope. They are Mercury (MURK-yoor-ee), Venus (VEE-nus), Mars, Jupiter, and Saturn (SAT-urn). Jupiter and Saturn are very far away. But we can see them because they are so large. Mercury is hard to see because it is small and close to the sun. Sometimes it is low in the west just after sunset. At other times it is low in the east just before sunrise. The weather and viewing conditions must be very good to see it at all.

▶ **Which planets can be seen without a telescope?**

**What are the inner planets like?** Unmanned <u>space</u> <u>probes</u> are giving us much new information about the planets. These devices travel close to the planets. They take pictures and make observations on command from the earth. They send the results back to the earth by radio signals.

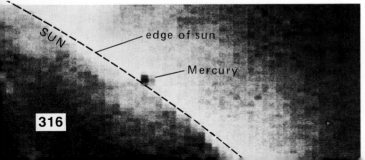

SUN
edge of sun
Mercury

**Mercury just after passing in front of the sun.** This picture was taken in a special way by a camera in space. The picture was broken up into tiny square dots before being sent to the earth.

Space probes showed that Mercury's surface has craters like those on the moon. Venus is covered with heavy clouds. Its surface is very hot. Its atmosphere is mainly carbon dioxide, and it has winds blowing at high speeds.

▶ **How do we know what the surface of Mercury looks like?**

**Exploring Mars.** Besides the earth, the planet we know most about is Mars. That is because unmanned space probes have circled Mars for months and years at a time. Two landers have been put down on the surface of Mars. Many years ago, astronomers saw lines on Mars that looked like canals. They believed there might be intelligent life on Mars. So far, the landers have found no signs of life of any kind.

The surface of Mars has many craters and is covered with loose rocks. There are huge volcanoes that are now dead. Mars has a thin atmosphere that is mostly carbon dioxide. Winds up to 500 kilometers per hour sometimes raise giant dust storms that cover the whole planet. There are canyons and grooves in the surface that look like dried-up river beds. Scientists think that only erosion by running water could have made them. But there is no liquid water on Mars. It is much too cold. The north pole of Mars is covered by ice. Could Mars

Looking down on Nix Olympica, a mountain on Mars far larger than any on earth. The distance across at the base is 550 kilometers. The mountain's height is estimated to be 25 kilometers.

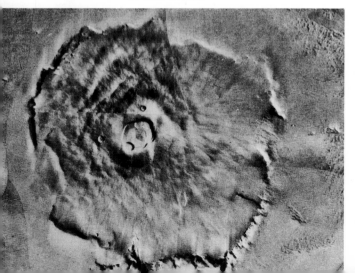

have once been warm enough to have rain and rivers? We don't know. There are now more questions about Mars than answers.

▶ **Why do scientists think that erosion occurred on Mars?**

## WHAT YOU LEARNED

1. The sun has nine planets, including the earth.
2. The planets move around the sun in the same direction, but at different speeds.
3. The planets are always changing their positions among the stars.
4. Mercury, Venus, Mars, Jupiter, and Saturn can be seen without a telescope.
5. Space probes have given us much new information about the inner planets.

## SCIENCE WORDS

**planet** (PLAN-et)
a large body that moves around the sun

**space probe**
an unmanned device sent close to the planets to make observations

## ANSWER THESE

1. Besides the earth, the sun has
   **a.** 8 planets   **b.** 9 planets   **c.** 10 planets
2. The largest planet is
   **a.** the earth   **b.** Pluto   **c.** Jupiter
3. The planets change their positions among the stars because
   **a.** all stars change their positions each night
   **b.** the earth is turning on its axis
   **c.** the planets are moving around the sun
4. Observations of Mars have found signs of
   **a.** erosion   **b.** life   **c.** oceans

## NOW TRY THESE

1. What are the names of the nine planets?
2. Place the planets in order by size, from smallest to largest.
3. How are the surfaces of Mercury, Mars, and the moon similar?
4. Why are scientists puzzled by the canyons on Mars?

# What do we know about the outer planets?

Jupiter as photographed through a telescope. Notice the Great Red Spot.

**Far out.** Jupiter, Saturn, Uranus (yuh-RAY-nus), Neptune (NEP-choon), and Pluto (PLOO-toh) are the outer planets. They are very far from the sun. The only outer planets that can be seen without a telescope are the giants, Jupiter and Saturn.

▶ Which are the outer planets?

**Biggest of all.** Jupiter is the largest planet. It has a diameter of 143 000 kilometers. The earth's diameter is less than 13 000 kilometers. Jupiter has 125 times the surface area of earth. Jupiter is made of very light material. Its density is only ¼ that of the earth. Jupiter's surface has not been seen. It is completely covered by clouds. Look at the photo of Jupiter. The clouds are arranged in bands. Notice the large oval spot. It is called the "Great Red Spot." The spot slowly changes its position. But it doesn't go away. Astronomers think it may be a huge, spinning mass of clouds, like a hurricane on the earth.

Jupiter has 13 known satellites. Four of them are as large as or larger than the earth's moon. These four satellites were first seen by Galileo in 1610. If you can find Jupiter in the sky, look at it with binoculars or a small telescope. One, two, three, or four bright objects in a row may be seen near the planet. These are Jupiter's satellites.

▶ Why can't Jupiter's surface be seen?

fourth moon

Jupiter with four of its moons.

**A ringed planet.** Saturn is the second largest planet. It is like Jupiter in many ways. Its density is low. It is covered with clouds. Saturn has 10 satellites. There is one big difference between Saturn and Jupiter. There is a set of giant rings around Saturn. The rings are made of very small particles that seem to be ice.

▶ How is Saturn different from Jupiter?

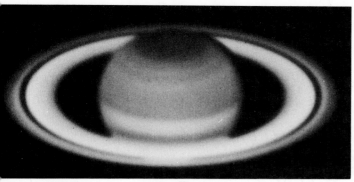
Saturn

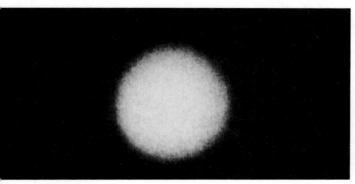
Uranus

**The three most distant planets.** Uranus, Neptune, and Pluto circle the sun in orbits beyond Saturn. These planets can be seen only with a telescope. Uranus and Neptune are very much alike. They are both about 50 000 kilometers in diameter. Both have low densities. They have atmospheres like those of Jupiter and Saturn. Uranus has rings like those around Saturn. Pluto was the last planet to be discovered. It is much smaller than the other outer planets. It is so far from the sun that it is always dark on Pluto. To a person on Pluto, the sun would look like just a bright star.

▶ Which is the smallest of the outer planets?

## WHAT YOU LEARNED

1. The outer planets are Jupiter, Saturn, Uranus, Neptune, and Pluto.
2. The largest planet is Jupiter.
3. Jupiter, Saturn, Neptune, and Uranus have low densities.
4. Saturn and Uranus have rings.

## ANSWER THESE

*Use the correct words to fill in the blank spaces in the paragraph.*

The largest planet in the solar system is _____. The second largest is _____. These two planets together with _____, _____, and _____ are called the _____ planets. The surfaces of Jupiter and Saturn have not been seen because they are covered by _____. The clouds of Jupiter are arranged into _____. A strange feature of Jupiter is its large _____ _____. An unusual feature of Saturn and Uranus is their _____. All the outer planets except Pluto have low _____. The sun seen from Pluto would look like just another _____.

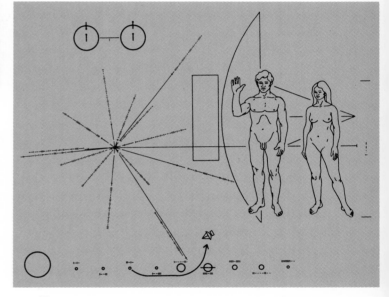
The message carried to outer space by the Pioneer X spacecraft.

## FINDING OUT MORE

The first spacecraft to leave the solar system was Pioneer X. It was launched by the United States late in 1972. Its mission was to fly by Jupiter and then to leave the solar system. Pioneer X carries a message. Perhaps some day it will be found by other intelligent life. This message is a drawing engraved on a metal plate on the surface of the ship. It shows a man and a woman and compares their size to that of the spacecraft. It also shows where the spacecraft came from.

# What else do we know about the solar system?

Halley's comet

**Our sun's complete family.** The sun and all the objects that orbit it make up the solar system. The nine planets and their satellites are the main members of the solar system. But there are other members. Between Mars and Jupiter a large group of rocks circle the sun. They are called asteroids (AST-uh-royds). Asteroids are not round like the planets. They are shaped more like chunks of broken rocks. Many astronomers think that the asteroids are pieces of a planet that was once between Mars and Jupiter. Asteroids are much smaller than planets. The largest is called Ceres (SEER-eez). It is about 775 kilometers in diameter. Most asteroids are smaller than 10 kilometers in diameter.

▶ **What are the asteroids?**

**Heads or tails?** Bright objects with glowing tails may sometimes be seen in the sky. They are called comets (KOM-ets). Like planets and asteroids, comets are members of the solar system. They travel around the sun. The orbits of the planets are nearly circles. The orbits of most comets are long and narrow. Many comets travel out beyond the orbit of Pluto.

Comets are made of frozen gases and rocks. As the comet comes near the sun, the frozen gases are heated. They change to a vapor and begin to glow. This is the comet's head. Part of the glowing gas is pushed away from the sun. This becomes the tail of the comet. A comet's tail always points away from the sun. Comets do not contain very much matter. On May 21, 1910, the earth passed right through the tail of Halley's Comet. There was no effect on the earth. Halley's Comet will be visible from the earth again in 1986.

▶ **How is the orbit of a comet different from that of a planet?**

**Catch a falling star.** On a clear, dark night you may see as many as ten "falling stars" each hour. They are not really falling stars. They are meteors (MEE-tee-ors). Most meteors are bits of rock smaller than a grain of sand. As meteors fall into the earth's atmosphere, friction heats them. They glow brightly and burn up. Meteors are members of the solar system. Some astronomers think that they are asteroids caught by the earth's gravity. Others think that they are the remains of comets. Millions of tiny meteors hit our atmosphere each day. Some of these meteors are large enough to reach the earth's surface. Meteors that strike the earth are called meteorites (MEE-tee-or-ites). Meteorites are on display at science museums all over the world. Meteorites may make a crater

**The Willamette Meteorite.** This 12 700-kilogram mass fell in the state of Oregon. It is the fourth largest meteorite found on earth.

where they land. Canyon Diablo, in Arizona, was created when a large meteorite struck the earth thousands of years ago.

▶ **What is the difference between a meteor and a meteorite?**

## WHAT YOU LEARNED

1. Asteroids may be the remains of a broken planet.
2. Comets have long narrow orbits.
3. The tail of a comet always points away from the sun.
4. Meteors are called falling stars because they glow brightly as they pass through the atmosphere.

## ANSWER THESE

Tell whether each statement is true or false. If it is false, tell why it is false.

1. The sun and its nine planets make up the solar system.
2. Asteroids are rocks from outer space passing through the solar system.
3. A comet's tail appears only when it gets near the sun.
4. The earth might be destroyed if it passed through a comet's tail.
5. "Falling stars" are bits of rock that become very hot as they pass through the atmosphere.

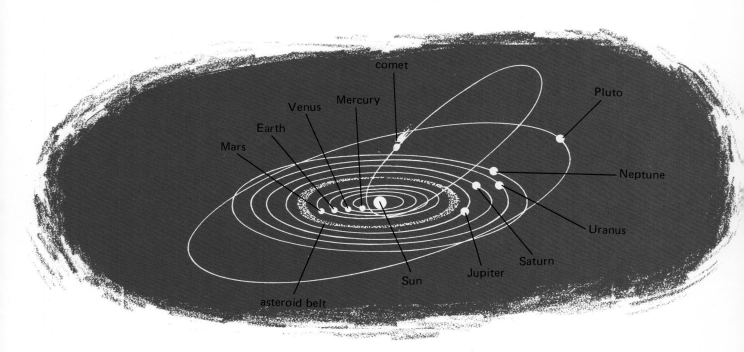

## SCIENCE WORDS

**asteroids** (AST-uh-royds)
  broken chunks of rock that orbit the sun
**Ceres** (SEER-eez)
  the largest asteroid
**comet** (KOM-et)
  a mass of rocks and gases that orbits the sun
**meteor** (MEE-tee-or)
  a rock that enters the earth's atmosphere
**meteorite** (MEE-tee-or-ite)
  a meteor that hits the earth's surface

## NOW TRY THESE

1. Name the parts of the solar system.
2. How are comets different from asteroids?
3. What is a meteorite?

## FINDING OUT MORE

The orbits of the planets are all nearly in the same flat disc around the sun. This disc is called the plane of the ecliptic (uh-KLIP-tik). The orbits of asteroids, comets, and meteors are tilted at many different angles. They are not in the plane of the ecliptic.

*Do the following questions on a separate sheet of paper.*

**Modified True/False**     *Write down each of the following statements, leaving a blank line between each line you write. Before the number for each statement, write T if the statement is true and F if the statement is fale. For the false statements, cross out the word written in capital letters and write above it a word that will make the statement true.*

1. Too much sun can be GOOD for you.
2. Gravity of the moon is only ONE-SIXTH as strong as gravity on the earth.
3. The ROTATION of the moon takes 27 and one-third days.
4. When the entire moon is bright, we call it a NEW moon.
5. The UMBRA is the dark part of a shadow.
6. The sun's temperature is 6000°C at the CENTER.
7. The PHOTOSPHERE is the innermost layer of the sun's atmosphere.
8. The CORONA is the outermost layer of the sun's atmosphere.
9. The planet with the largest rings is URANUS.
10. Bright objects with glowing tails are called PLANETS.

**Multiple Choice**     *Write the letter of the choice that best completes the statement or answers the question.*

1. The earth's orbital velocity is greatest at
   a. aphelion
   b. perihelion
   c. the vernal equinox
2. The earth rotates fastest at
   a. the North Pole
   b. the equator
   c. the Prime Meridian
3. If the earth's axis were not tilted,
   a. the earth would not spin
   b. time would stand still
   c. day and night would be equal
4. The earth is closest to the sun in
   a. January
   b. July
   c. August

5. A leap year has
   a. 365 days
   b. 364 days
   c. 366 days
6. Each time zone is
   a. 15° wide
   b. 30° wide
   c. 45° wide
7. A tide table shows
   a. 2 high and 1 low tide per day
   b. 2 high and 2 low tides per day
   c. 1 high and 2 low tides per day
8. The effect of the moon's pull on the earth's tides is
   a. less than that of the sun
   b. equal to that of the sun
   c. greater than that of the sun

# UNIT 16

# Motion in the Solar System

## Unit Lessons

1. What is inertia?
2. Why do the planets circle the sun?
3. What is the shape of the earth's orbit?
4. How do we know that the earth turns?
5. Why do we have day and night?
6. Why do the seasons change?
7. How do we measure time?
8. What are time zones?
9. What causes tides?
10. What causes the tides to change?
11. What makes a rocket move?
12. How can rockets travel in space?
13. How is space being explored?

## Goals and Objectives

After completing this unit, you should be able to:

- understand how gravity and inertia keep the earth in orbit.
- explain how a pendulum demonstrates the rotation of the earth.
- explain how the tilt of the earth's axis creates our seasons.
- understand how time is measured by the motions of earth.
- explain how gravity and the earth's motion affect the tides.
- describe how rockets can escape the earth's gravity.
- understand how the frontier of space is starting to be explored.

# What is inertia?

**If it's not moving, it's resting.** Place a ball on the floor. Would you expect it to move by itself? The ball is at rest. Any object at rest will remain at rest if it is left alone. It will move only if some force acts on it. Kick the ball. Your foot supplies a force. The force makes the ball move.

▶ **How can an object at rest be made to move?**

**Rolling along.** Have you ever coasted on a bike? The bike continues to roll for a while after you stop pedaling. You supplied a force that started the bike moving. The bike keeps moving even after you stop pedaling. But it won't keep moving forever. Sooner or later, the bike will stop. Friction (FRIC-shun) is the force that stops it.

A force was needed to start the bike. Another force is needed to stop the bike. If there were no friction, the bike would never stop moving. Things that are at rest won't move until a force starts them. Things that are in motion keep moving until a force stops them. Forces start and stop motion.

▶ **What is needed to stop something that is moving?**

**Make me move, make me stop.** Objects do not move by themselves. Objects do not stop moving by themselves. All objects resist changes in motion. This property of objects is called <u>inertia</u> (in-ER-shuh). Have you ever seen a magician pull a tablecloth out from under some dishes? Inertia makes this possible. The pull on the tablecloth makes it move. The dishes have inertia. They resist the motion of the tablecloth. They stay where they are. (It takes practice to do this trick. The friction of the tablecloth does make the dishes move a little. You should not try it with dishes that may break!)

▶ **What property of objects makes them resist changes in motion?**

324

**Keep moving.** All objects have inertia. Small objects such as coins have inertia. Large objects like the sun, moon, and earth have inertia. The earth moves around the sun. It keeps moving because there are no forces acting on it to stop its motion. Moving bodies in space keep moving.

▶ What kinds of objects have inertia?

## WHAT YOU LEARNED

1. Objects at rest remain at rest until a force moves them.
2. Objects in motion keep moving until a force stops them.
3. Friction is a force that stops motion.
4. Objects resist changes in motion because of their inertia.

## SCIENCE WORDS

**friction** (FRIC-shun)
   a force that stops motion
**inertia** (in-ER-shuh)
   the property of objects that makes them resist changes in motion

## ANSWER THESE

1. In order to move an object, you need
   **a.** gravity
   **b.** a force
   **c.** wheels

2. If they are left alone, objects at rest will
   **a.** move
   **b.** stay at rest
   **c.** fall
3. Objects in motion resist being stopped because of
   **a.** space
   **b.** inertia
   **c.** friction

## NOW TRY THESE

Solve the puzzles to find the science words.

**1.** ◯ − r g + ◯ − a h + ◯ − p n o

**2. 4 − u +** 🎲 **− d i**

## DO THIS AT HOME

Balance an index card on your finger as shown in the picture. Place a coin on the card, right over the tip of your finger. Flick the card away quickly with your other hand. Practice doing this several times. Can you get the coin to remain in place while the card shoots out from under it? What makes this trick work?

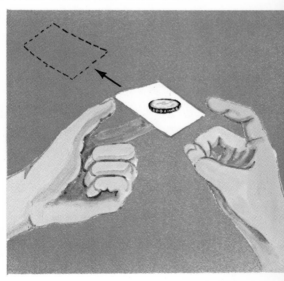

325

# Why do the planets circle the sun?

**Play ball.** It's a long fly ball to center field. The outfielder waits under it. Down comes the ball. The outfielder makes the catch and the batter is out. A ball hit high into the air soon falls to the ground. Gravity (GRAV-uh-tee) is the force that pulls it down. Gravity pulls all objects toward the earth.

▶ **What force pulls a ball down to the ground?**

**You always throw a curve.** Throw a ball. It moves forward. At the same time, gravity is pulling it toward the earth. The ball has two motions: a forward motion and a downward motion. The ball takes a curved path.

▶ **What are the two motions of a ball that you throw?**

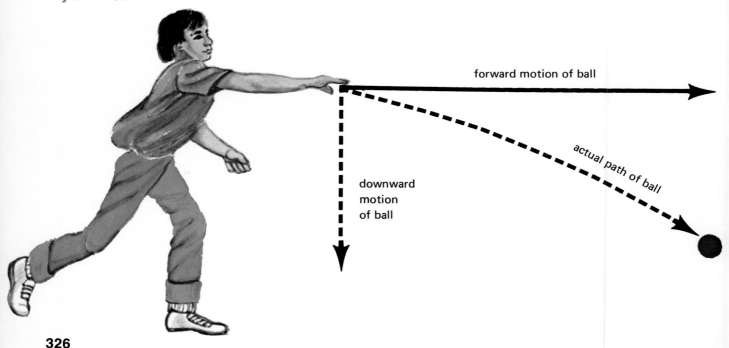

forward motion of ball

downward motion of ball

actual path of ball

**Spinning a key.** Tie a key to a string. Make sure you have a clear space around you. Then swing the key around your head. You can feel a pull in the string. The key has inertia. The key tends to fly away in a straight line. The pull of the string keeps the key from flying away. The pull of the string makes the key move in a curved path around your head.

▶ **What keeps the key moving in a curved path?**

**Everything's got pull.** The earth is not the only thing that pulls on other objects. Every object in the universe pulls on every other object. The pull that objects have on each other is called <u>gravitational attraction</u> (grav-uh-TAY-shun-ul uh-TRAC-shun). There is gravitational attraction between all objects in the universe. There is a gravitational attraction between the sun and each of the planets. Gravitational attraction pulls the planets toward the sun as they move through space. Gravitational attraction keeps the planets in their orbits around the sun, instead of flying off into space.

▶ **What keeps the planets in their orbits around the sun?**

**WHAT YOU LEARNED**

1. Gravity pulls all objects toward the earth.
2. Gravitational attraction exists between all objects in the universe.

3. Gravitational attraction keeps the planets in orbit around the sun.

**SCIENCE WORDS**

**gravity** (GRAV-uh-tee)
 a force that pulls all objects toward the earth
**gravitational attraction** (grav-uh-TAY-shun-ul uh-TRAC-shun)
 a force that exists between all objects in the universe

**ANSWER THESE**

1. A glass that you drop falls to the floor because of
   **a.** inertia
   **b.** gravity
   **c.** air pressure
2. The attraction between the earth and the moon is called
   **a.** inertial attraction
   **b.** forceful attraction
   **c.** gravitational attraction
3. The planets would move away into space if it were not for the sun's
   **a.** temperature
   **b.** gravitational attraction
   **c.** inertia

**NOW TRY THESE**

1. How does gravity cause a river to flow?
2. Why would the earth have no atmosphere if there were no gravity?

**WHAT'S HAPPENING**

Stamp collectors know about space travel. Many stamps have been printed that show man's exploration and conquest of space. Many countries have honored astronauts by putting their pictures on stamps. The first men to set foot on the moon canceled a stamp there to mark the event. You may wish to start a collection of space stamps. Your local Post Office can help you get started.

# What is the shape of the earth's orbit?

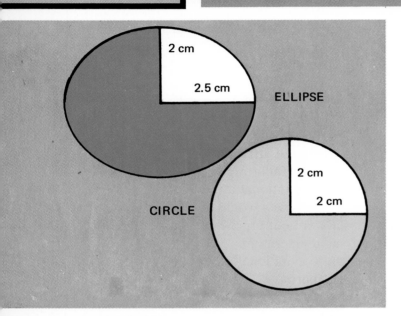

2 cm
2.5 cm
ELLIPSE

2 cm
2 cm
CIRCLE

**Do we always go around in circles?** A circle is round. All lines drawn from the center of a circle to the edge of the circle are the same length. An <u>ellipse</u> (uh-LIPS) has an oval shape. Lines drawn from the center to different parts of an ellipse have different lengths.

▶ What is the shape of an ellipse?

**What path does the earth take?** The earth travels around the sun in an <u>elliptical</u> (uh-LIP-tuh-cul) <u>orbit</u>. The earth is not the same distance from the sun at all times. In January, the earth is about 147 million kilometers from the sun. In July, the earth is about 152 million kilometers from the sun. <u>Perihelion</u> (per-uh-HEEL-yun) is the point at which the earth is closest to the sun. <u>Aphelion</u> (af-FEEL-yun) is the point at which the earth is farthest away from the sun. Perihelion occurs in January. Aphelion occurs in July.

▶ What is the shape of the earth's orbit?

**The closer they get, the faster they move.** As objects move closer to each other, the gravitational force between them increases. As the earth gets closer to the sun, there is a greater attraction between them. This causes the earth to move faster. The speeding up occurs at perihelion. At

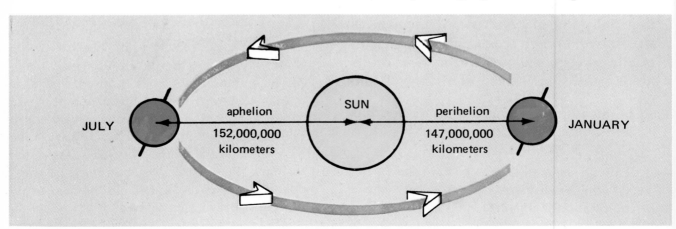

JULY
aphelion
152,000,000 kilometers
SUN
perihelion
147,000,000 kilometers
JANUARY

aphelion, the earth is farther away from the sun. The gravitational force is smaller. The earth moves more slowly.

▶ **When does the earth move faster in its orbit?**

## What are the orbits of the other planets?

All of the planets travel in elliptical orbits around the sun. The planets move fastest at perihelion. They move slowest at aphelion. The speed at which a planet travels along its orbit is called its orbital velocity (OR-buh-tul vuh-LOS-uh-tee). The closer a planet is to the sun, the greater its orbital velocity. Planets travel at different speeds at different parts of their orbits.

▶ **When do planets move fastest?**

### SCIENCE WORDS

**ellipse** (uh-LIPS)
  an oval shape
**elliptical** (uh-LIP-tuh-cul) **orbit**
  an oval-shaped path
**perihelion** (per-uh-HEEL-yun)
  the point in an orbit at which a planet is closest to the sun
**aphelion** (af-FEEL-yun)
  the point in an orbit at which a planet is farthest from the sun
**orbital velocity** (OR-buh-tul vuh-LOS-uh-tee)
  the speed at which a planet travels along its orbit

### WHAT YOU LEARNED

1. The planets travel around the sun in elliptical orbits.
2. Perihelion is the point in an orbit at which a planet is closest to the sun.
3. Aphelion is the point in an orbit at which a planet is farthest from the sun.
4. The closer a planet is to the sun, the greater its orbital velocity.

### ANSWER THESE

1. The planets travel around the sun in orbits that are (circular/elliptical).
2. The earth is closest to the sun at (aphelion/perihelion).
3. At perihelion the gravitational force between the sun and the planets (increases/decreases).
4. The earth's orbital velocity is greatest in the month of _____.
5. The earth's aphelion occurs during the month of _____.

### FINDING OUT MORE

The planets are different distances from the sun. They travel around the sun at different velocities. Those closest to the sun travel fastest. Those farthest away from the sun travel slowest. The chart shows how far the planets are from the sun, and how fast they move around it. The chart also shows how many of our earth years it takes for each planet to make one complete trip around the sun.

| Planet | Average distance from the sun | Orbital velocity | Time it takes to go around the sun (one revolution) |
|---|---|---|---|
| Mercury | 58 million km | 47.8 km per second | .24 year |
| Venus | 108 million km | 33.9 km per second | .62 year |
| Earth | 150 million km | 29.7 km per second | 1.00 year |
| Mars | 228 million km | 24.1 km per second | 1.88 years |
| Jupiter | 779 million km | 13.7 km per second | 11.86 years |
| Saturn | 1,430 million km | 9.6 km per second | 29.46 years |
| Uranus | 2,900 million km | 6.8 km per second | 84.01 years |
| Neptune | 4,500 million km | 5.5 km per second | 164.80 years |
| Pluto | 5,950 million km | 4.8 km per second | 248.40 years |

# How do we know that the earth turns?

**Life on a merry-go-round.** You spend your life on a merry-go-round. It is called the earth. The earth rotates around its axis once a day. The earth's rotation causes all places on earth to move in circles around the earth's axis. Places on the equator move fastest. Places near the poles move slowly. In the United States, we are carried around the earth's axis at a speed of about 1250 kilometers per hour.

▶ Why do places on the earth move in circles around the earth's axis?

**How do we know we are rotating?** The photograph is a time exposure of stars above the North Pole. In an ordinary photograph, stars look like tiny dots. In this picture, the stars have made circular paths. When a time exposure is taken, the camera shutter is left open for some time. The earth turned while the camera shutter was open. This caused the camera to turn, also. The circular paths in the picture are called <u>star trails</u>. The trails are circular because the earth rotated beneath the stars.

▶ Why are the star trails circular?

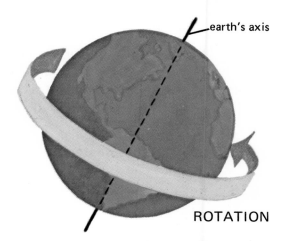
ROTATION
earth's axis

This time exposure photo shows the trails of stars located above the North Pole.

**Blowin' in the wind.** Winds blow from region to region on the earth. The air does not move in a straight line. The winds curve to one side. They curve because of the earth's rotation. Winds help cause ocean currents. Ocean currents also curve. They curve clockwise in the Northern Hemisphere, and counterclockwise in the Southern Hemisphere. The currents curve because of the earth's rotation.

▶ What causes winds to curve as they move from region to region?

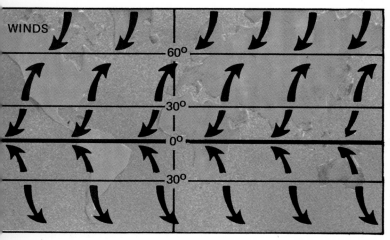
WINDS
60°
30°
0°
30°

**Watch the swinging ball.** Attach a heavy weight to a string. Hang the string on a stand. Let the weight swing back and forth. You have made a simple <u>pendulum</u> (PEN-dyuh-lum). A pendulum can be used to show that the earth rotates. The picture shows a large pendulum at the Smithsonian Institution in Washington, D.C. This pendulum appears to be constantly changing its direction of swing. The pendulum is not really changing its direction. The earth is rotating beneath the pendulum. That is what makes the pendulum seem to change direction.

▶ Why does a pendulum on the earth seem to change its direction of swing?

## WHAT YOU LEARNED

1. The rotation of the earth makes all places on earth move in circles.
2. The rotation of the earth makes stars appear to move in circular paths.
3. The rotation of the earth causes winds and ocean currents to curve.
4. The rotation of the earth makes a pendulum appear to change the direction of its swing.

## SCIENCE WORDS

**star trails**
 lines on photographs of the stars that are caused by the motion of the earth when a time exposure is made

**pendulum** (PEN-dyuh-lum)
 a weight on a string that swings back and forth

On the floor under this pendulum, there are many little pegs in a circle. The pendulum knocks another peg down every few minutes as the earth turns.

## ANSWER THESE

1. The earth rotates on its
 a. top
 b. axis
 c. side
2. Star trails of stars above the North Pole are
 a. square
 b. straight
 c. circular
3. In the Northern Hemisphere, ocean currents flow
 a. straight
 b. clockwise
 c. counterclockwise
4. A pendulum can show that
 a. the earth is round
 b. the earth moves around the sun
 c. the earth rotates on its axis

## NOW TRY THESE

Unscramble the words in capital letters.
1. The earth turns on its ISAX.
2. A DULUMNEP swings back and forth.
3. Winds VURCE because of the earth's rotation.
4. Winds help cause NEACO STENRUCR.

## FINDING OUT MORE

**A little wider around the center.** The earth is a sphere, but it is not a perfect sphere. The equatorial diameter is larger than the polar diameter. The distance around the equator is 40,076 kilometers. The distance around the poles is 40,008 kilometers. The poles are a little flattened. This difference is due to the rotation of the earth.

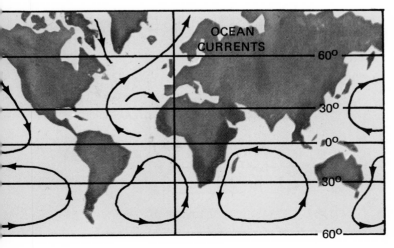

OCEAN CURRENTS

60°

30°

0°

30°

60°

# Why do we have day and night?

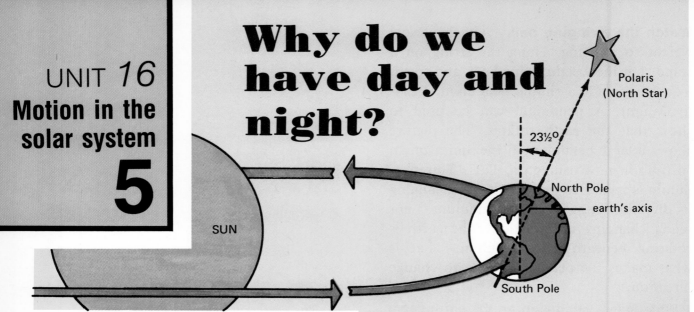

Polaris (North Star)

23½°

North Pole

earth's axis

South Pole

SUN

**Day and night.** The earth's rotation causes the change from day to night and back to day again. The side of the earth that faces the sun has daylight. The side that faces away from the sun has night. As the earth turns, new parts of the earth are made light or dark. The daylight side of the earth moves into darkness. The night side moves into the sunlight. The earth's rotation causes day and night.

▶ **What causes day and night?**

**Tilt!** The earth turns on its axis. The axis of the earth does not point straight up. The axis is tilted at an angle of 23½°. The axis is always tilted in the same direction. One end of the axis is called the North Pole. The other end is called the South Pole. The North Pole points toward the star Polaris. Polaris is also called the North Star.

▶ **Which star does the earth's North Pole point toward?**

**What a difference a day makes.** Are days and nights the same length? During summer, the days are longer than the nights. In winter, the nights are longer than the days. If the earth's axis were not tilted, daytime and nighttime would be equal all year. Diagram 1 shows what that would be like. All of the lines in diagram 1 have equal amounts of daytime and nighttime. Because the earth's axis is tilted, days and nights are not always the same length. Diagram 2 shows the earth's tilt. Only line C has equal amounts of daytime and nighttime. Line B has a longer daytime part. It has longer days than nights. Line D has a longer nighttime part. It has longer nights than days. Line A is all in daylight. Line E is all in darkness. Days and nights have different lengths because of the earth's tilt.

▶ **Why do days and nights have different lengths?**

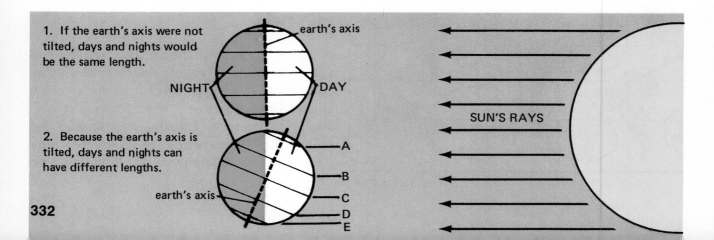

1. If the earth's axis were not tilted, days and nights would be the same length.

earth's axis

NIGHT    DAY

2. Because the earth's axis is tilted, days and nights can have different lengths.

earth's axis

A
B
C
D
E

SUN'S RAYS

**Sunrise and sunset.** The earth rotates from west to east. This makes the sun appear to rise in the east and go down in the west. As the earth turns, the sun seems to move across the sky. The sun seems to move from east to west. This is because the earth is turning from west to east.

▶ **What is the direction of the earth's rotation?**

## WHAT YOU LEARNED

1. The earth's rotation causes day and night.
2. The North Pole of the earth points to the star Polaris (North Star).
3. Days and nights are not the same length because the earth's axis is tilted.
4. The sun rises in the east and sets in the west because of the earth's rotation.

## ANSWER THESE

1. The side of the earth facing the sun has
   a. daytime
   b. nighttime
   c. midnight
2. The earth's axis is tilted
   a. 15°
   b. 23½°
   c. 90°
3. During the summer, the days are
   a. shorter than the nights
   b. longer than the nights
   c. the same length as the nights
4. The name of the North Star is
   a. Sirius
   b. Rigel
   c. Polaris
5. The sun rises in the
   a. east
   b. north
   c. west

## NOW TRY THIS

Solve the puzzle to find what the earth turns around.

## FINDING OUT MORE

Alaska is sometimes called the land of the midnight sun. In summer, the sun shines day and night. Look back at the diagram showing the tilted earth. Alaska lies along line A in the diagram. Line A is all in daylight. Alaska has only daylight during the summer months. During the winter months, the sun does not appear at all in Alaska. There is only nighttime in Alaska during the winter.

10:45 P.M.   11:00 P.M.   11:15 P.M.   11:30 P.M.   11:45 P.M.   12:00 P.M. (midnight)   12:15 A.M.   12:30 A.M.   12:45 A.M.

This is a kind of time exposure of the sun taken in the northern part of Canada. The camera was snapped every 15 minutes between 10:30 P.M. and 1:00 A.M. on a summer night. You can see how the sun came down close to the horizon, but then climbed up into the sky again. In the Far North, the sun does not set in the summer, even at midnight.

# Why do the seasons change?

**Near and far.** We are closest to the sun in January. Yet at this time we have our winter. In July we are farthest from the sun. Yet this is when we have our summer. During the year there are differences in the distance between the earth and the sun. But these differences have nothing to do with the change in seasons. The seasons do not depend on our distance from the sun.

▶ **During which season are we closest to the sun?**

**Shine some light on the subject.** Hold a flashlight over a piece of lined paper. Shine the flashlight straight down on the paper, as shown in the drawing. Count how many lines are lighted by the flashlight. Then tilt the flashlight a little, making sure you keep it at the same height. Again count the number of lines on the paper that are lighted. More lines are lighted when the light shines down at a slant. The light spreads out more. Direct rays of light cover a smaller area than slanted rays. The direct rays appear brighter than the slanted rays. The light energy is not spread out as much.

▶ **Why do direct rays of light appear brighter than slanted rays?**

DIRECT RAYS

SLANTED RAYS

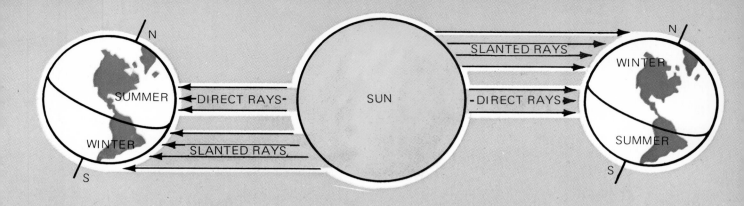

**What's your slant on the seasons?** The earth's axis is tilted. Parts of the earth get the direct rays of the sun. Direct rays heat best. These parts of the earth have summer. Other parts of the earth get the sun's rays at a slant. The slanted rays spread out the heat. These parts of the earth have winter. As the earth moves around the sun, the seasons change. Summer and winter come to different places.

▶ **What season is it in the parts of the earth that get direct rays of the sun?**

**Day by day.** In the summer, we get the direct rays of the sun. The days are also longer in summer. During longer days, the earth gets more heat from the sun. During the winter, the days are shorter. We get less heat from the sun. With less heat, the days are colder. Both the angle of the sun's rays and the length of day cause the differences in the seasons.

▶ **What two things cause the differences in the seasons?**

## WHAT YOU LEARNED

1. Direct rays of the sun heat better than slanted rays.
2. As the earth moves around the sun, the angle of the sun's rays changes.
3. As the earth moves around the sun, the seasons change.
4. Both the angle of the sun's rays and the length of day cause the differences in the seasons.

## ANSWER THESE

1. The earth's changing distance from the sun
   a. causes the seasons to change
   b. keeps the seasons from changing
   c. does not affect the seasons
2. Compared to direct rays, slanted rays of light
   a. cover a greater area
   b. cover a smaller area
   c. are brighter
3. The angle of the sun's rays changes during the year because of the tilt of the axis of the
   a. sun
   b. earth
   c. moon
4. Changes in the length of day are caused by the
   a. sun's rays
   b. earth's tilt
   c. phases of the moon
5. The differences in the seasons are caused
   a. only by the angle of the sun's rays
   b. only by the length of day
   c. by both

## WHAT'S HAPPENING

Look once again at the diagram at the top of the page. Notice that when the Northern Hemisphere gets the slanted rays of the sun, it has winter. At that time, the Southern Hemisphere gets the direct rays of the sun. It has summer. When summer comes to the Northern Hemisphere, it is winter in the Southern Hemisphere. The Northern and Southern Hemispheres have opposite seasons. What kind of clothing would you take along on a trip to South America in July?

# How do we measure time?

**What time is it?** Look at a clock to see the time. Then close your eyes. Open your eyes again when you think two minutes have passed. Most people can't tell time without a clock. Were you able to? Hours, minutes, and seconds are measurements of time. Days, months, and years are also measurements of time. But what are time measurements based on? Time is measured by the movements of the earth.

▶ **How is time measured?**

**Yesterday, today, and tomorrow.** One day is measured by the rotation of the earth. You can measure one rotation of the earth. Put a sheet of paper in sunlight. Tape it down so it cannot move. Use some clay to stand a pencil up on the paper. Trace the shadow cast by the pencil. Write down the exact time. Leave everything in place.

As the sun moves across the sky, the shadow moves across the paper. The next day, the shadow appears again. It moves across the paper. When the shadow lines up with the line you drew, note the time again. The earth has made one complete rotation. This is called one solar day. The solar day is divided into 24 equal parts called hours. Each hour is divided into 60 minutes. Each minute is divided into 60 seconds.

▶ **What motion of the earth measures a solar day?**

**The year.** A year is measured by the revolution of the earth around the sun. It takes the earth 365¼ days to make one revolution. But our year by the calendar has only 365 days. The extra quarter of a day in each revolution is carried over from year to year. Every four years, an extra day is added in February . This extra day gives us our leap year. A leap year has 366 days. The seasons of the year change as the earth revolves around the sun. Different seasons begin and end as the earth reaches certain places in its orbit. Leap years help keep the seasons in the same months of the year.

▶ **What motion of the earth measures a year?**

**Many moons ago.** Long ago, people used the moon to measure time. The time between full moons was called one moon. This time was about 29½ days. Our months are about 30 days long. They were once based on the phases of the moon. Some people still use the moon to measure time. The Hebrew and Chinese calendars are based on the phases of the moon.

▶ **Which people use the phases of the moon to measure time?**

## WHAT YOU LEARNED

1. Time is measured by the movements of the earth.
2. A day is measured by the earth's rotation.
3. A year is measured by the earth's revolution around the sun.
4. Seasons depend on where the earth is in its orbit around the sun.
5. Months were once based on the phases of the moon.

## SCIENCE WORDS

**solar day**
    the time it takes for the sun to appear at the same place twice in a row

**leap year**
    a year that has 366 days, instead of 365

## ANSWER THESE

1. One revolution of the earth measures a
    **a.** year
    **b.** month
    **c.** day
2. The number of days in a year is
    **a.** 24
    **b.** 365¼
    **c.** 29½
3. The earth's place in its orbit around the sun determines
    **a.** seasons
    **b.** months
    **c.** days
4. The month was once based on the motions of the
    **a.** sun
    **b.** moon
    **c.** stars

## NOW TRY THIS

The three faces represent different measurements of time. The words are hidden in the faces. See if you can find which unit of time each face represents.

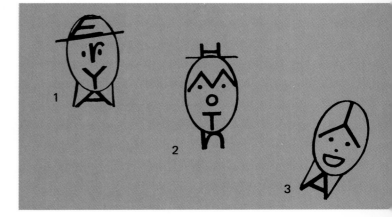

## FINDING OUT MORE

All the planets rotate. On each planet, one complete rotation equals one day for that planet. The chart shows how many earth days or hours it takes each planet to make one complete rotation. Which planet has the longest day?

| PLANET | ROTATION (measured in hours and days on earth) | |
| --- | --- | --- |
| Mercury | 59 | days |
| Venus | 243 | days |
| Earth | 24 | hours |
| Mars | 24.6 | hours |
| Jupiter | 9.9 | hours |
| Saturn | 10.3 | hours |
| Uranus | 10.7 | hours |
| Neptune | 15 | hours |
| Pluto | 6.4 | days |

# What are time zones?

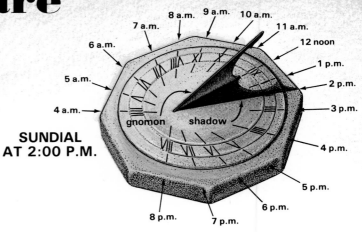

SUNDIAL
AT 2:00 P.M.

**The sundial.** A sundial has two parts. One part is the face that lies flat and has numbers marked on it. The flat face is called the plane. The other part is the pointer that sits on the flat face. This pointer is called the gnomon (NOH-mun). The shadow of the pointer moves across the face of a sundial as the position of the sun in the sky changes. The shadow of the pointer is shortest when the sun is highest overhead. When the shadow is shortest, the time is called solar noon. All points on the line that runs directly north and south of the sundial are on the same meridian. All these points will have solar noon at the same time.

▶ **What happens to the shadow of the pointer on a sundial as time passes?**

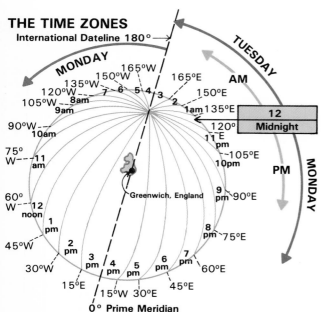

**THE TIME ZONES**

The lines marking the 24 time zones run along meridians that are 15° apart.

**Neighboring town, different times.** When it is solar noon where you are, the solar time will be different at all places to your east or west. At a place 20 kilometers to the east, the sun would have been directly overhead about a minute earlier. Solar noon would have already passed there. The solar time would be about 12:01 p.m., a minute later than your time. At a place 20 kilometers to the west, the sun would have not quite gotten to its position directly overhead. Solar noon would not have come yet. The time there would be about 11:59 a.m. Suppose solar time were used to tell time. Then all neighboring towns only short distances apart in an east-west direction would have different times. When it was solar noon in Philadelphia, it would be 12:04 p.m. in New York and 12:17 p.m. in Boston.

▶ **When it is solar noon at one place, at what places would the solar time be different?**

**Time zones.** To avoid confusion, railroads in 1883 started using standard time. The earth was divided into 24 regions, each 15° of longitude wide. Each of the regions became a time zone. All places within a time zone have the same time. The earth is divided into 24 time zones.

All of the states in the United States except Hawaii and Alaska are in one of four time zones. Only Alaska and Hawaii are not in one of these zones. The four zones are Eastern,

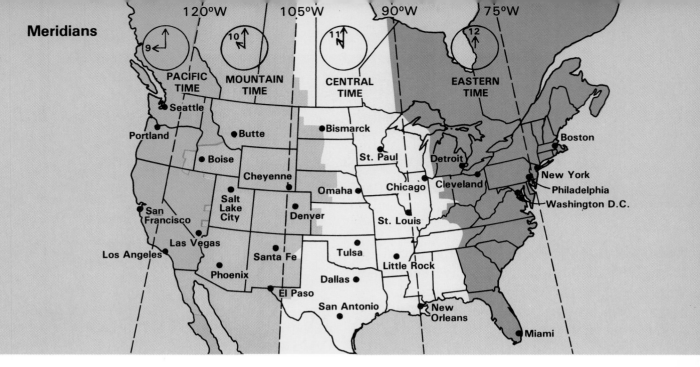

**Meridians**

Central, Mountain, and Pacific. Look at the map and note that each zone is 15° wide. As you move west, the time in each zone is one hour earlier. When it is noon in New York, it is 11:00 a.m. in Chicago. Note that time zones do not have completely straight boundaries. This was done to keep whole states or large neighboring cities in the same time zone.

▶ How many time zones are there in the 48 states that touch one another?

## WHAT YOU LEARNED

1. When the shadow of a sundial's pointer is shortest, the time is called solar noon.
2. The solar time is different in neighboring places in an east-west direction.
3. The earth is divided into 24 time zones, each 15° of longitude wide.
4. All of the states in the U.S. (except Hawaii and Alaska) fall into one of four time zones — Eastern, Central, Mountain, and Pacific.

## SCIENCE WORDS

**gnomon** (NOH-mun)
the pointer of a sundial

**solar noon**
when the shadow of a sundial's pointer is shortest, with the sun highest overhead

**time zone**
a region of the earth where all the places in it have the same time

**plane**
the flat face on a sundial

## ANSWER THESE

1. The shadow of a sundial's pointer is shortest when
   a. the sun is highest overhead
   b. the sun is directly to the east
   c. the sun is directly to the west
2. All the points on a meridian have solar noon
   a. at different times
   b. at the same time
   c. in the evening
3. If it is solar noon where you are, solar noon at a place 20 km to the west
   a. would not have come yet
   b. would already have passed
   c. would be occurring at the same time

## NOW TRY THESE

Use the map of the United States to answer the following.

1. In what time zones are the following cities?
   a. New York    b. San Francisco    c. Detroit
   d. Dallas      e. Boston           f. Denver
2. When it is 8:00 p.m. in Philadelphia, what time is it in
   a. San Antonio        c. Cleveland
   b. Santa Fe           d. Miami

**339**

# What causes tides?

**What are tides?** The level of the ocean rises and falls throughout the day. People who live near the ocean can watch this happen at a beach. During one part of the day, the ocean water will rise and cover the beach. Later, the water level will fall, and the beach will be uncovered again. These changes in ocean level are called <u>tides</u>. The time of high water level is called high tide. The time of low water level is called low tide. Newspapers in cities near the ocean often print a tide table. The tide table tells when high tide and low tide will occur each day. This table is very useful to fishermen and sailors.

▶ **What are tides?**

**Changing tides.** A tide table shows two high tides and two low tides each day. The tides change about every 6 hours and 15 minutes. Water floods the beach slowly until high tide is reached. The incoming tide is called <u>flood tide</u>. Then the water flows off the beach until low tide is reached. The outgoing tide is called <u>ebb tide</u>. The water level changes because of the tides.

▶ **How often do the tides change?**

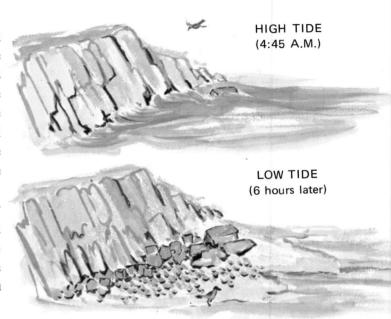

HIGH TIDE
(4:45 A.M.)

LOW TIDE
(6 hours later)

**Reaching for the moon.** One cause of tides is the pull of the moon's gravity. Look at the diagram on the following page. The moon pulls everything on the earth toward itself. This pull causes the water in the oceans to flow toward the moon. The water piles up around point A, directly below the moon. There is a high tide at point A.

▶ **What causes a high tide on the earth directly below the moon?**

**The tide on the other side.** Look at the diagram again. You will see a high tide at point C. This is on the side of the earth away from the moon. There is a high tide at point A, facing the moon. There is another high tide at point C, away from the moon.

▶ **Where do the two high tides occur on the earth?**

**Tides around the clock.** Look at the diagram of the tides. There are two high tides, at points A and C. Halfway between A and C there are two low tides, at points B and D. The earth turns on its axis once in 24 hours. As it turns, the tides change at every place on the earth. Suppose you are on the beach at point A. It will be high tide where you are. For somebody at point B, it is low tide. Six hours later, the earth will carry you around to point B. The high tide stays where it is at point A, under the moon. Where you are, at point B, it is now low tide. Six hours later, you will be at point C, and the tide will be high again. Six hours after that, you will be at point D, and the tide will be low again. In the course of one day, each place on the earth has two high tides and two low tides. The earth's rotation causes the tides to rise and fall twice each day.

▶ **What motion of the earth causes the tides to rise and fall twice each day?**

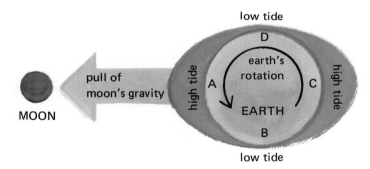

## WHAT YOU LEARNED

1. The daily changes in the level of the earth's waters are called tides.
2. The pull of the moon's gravity is one cause of tides.
3. High tides occur on opposite sides of the earth at the same time.
4. As the earth turns, the tides rise and fall twice each day at each place on the earth.

## SCIENCE WORDS

**tides**
    the daily changes in the level of the earth's waters
**flood tide**
    the incoming or rising tide
**ebb tide**
    the outgoing or falling tide

## ANSWER THESE

1. Each day, we have high tides
    a. once
    b. twice
    c. four times
2. Some tides are caused by
    a. winds
    b. rain
    c. the moon's gravity
3. When the moon is directly overhead, there is
    a. high tide
    b. low tide
    c. no tide

---

### NOW TRY THIS

**Across**
2. Incoming tide
4. About every 6 hours and 15 minutes, the tides _____.
6. A good place to see the changes of tides

**Down**
1. Object in space causing tides
3. Force that causes tides
5. Outgoing tide

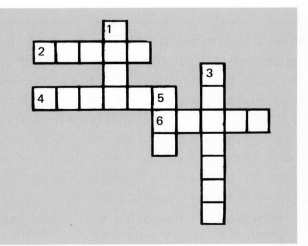

UNIT 16
**Motion in the solar system**
**10**

# What causes the tides to change?

**Newton again?** It was Isaac Newton who first explained the law of gravitation. Newton said that every object in the universe attracts every other object. He pointed out that this attraction depends partly on the distance between the objects. If the objects are close together, there is a greater attraction between them. If the objects are farther apart, the attraction is smaller.

▶ How does distance affect the attraction between two objects?

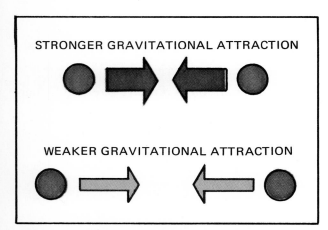

**Who's got more pull?** The sun and the moon both attract the earth. The moon is the main cause of tides on earth. The sun also affects our tides, but not as much as the moon. The moon is 380 000 kilometers away. The sun is 150 000 000 kilometers away. Because of the sun's greater distance from the earth, its pull on the earth's waters is weaker than the moon's.

▶ Why doesn't the sun's pull affect the earth's tides as much as the moon's pull?

**All lined up.** Twice a month, the earth, sun, and moon line up. This occurs during the new moon and during the full moon. At these times, the gravitational force of the sun is added to the gravitational force of the moon. When these forces combine, high tides are higher than usual. Low tides are lower than usual. These are called spring tides.

▶ What happens during spring tides?

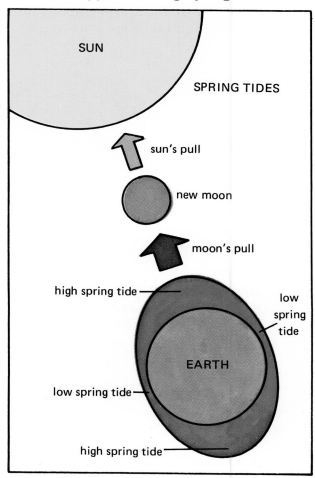

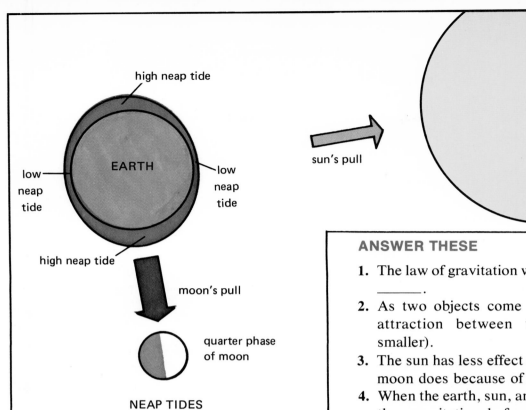

**NEAP TIDES**

**Two-way pull.** During the moon's first and last quarter phases, the sun and the moon are at right angles to the earth. Their pulls on the earth's water act against each other. High tides are not as high as usual. Low tides are not as low as usual. These are called <u>neap</u> (NEEP) <u>tides</u>.

▶ **What happens during neap tides?**

## WHAT YOU LEARNED

1. The sun and the moon both affect the earth's tides.
2. Spring tides occur when the pulls of the sun and the moon are combined.
3. Neap tides occur when the pulls of the sun and the moon act against each other.

## SCIENCE WORDS

**spring tides**
    extra high tides and extra low tides

**neap (NEEP) tides**
    tides that are not as high or as low as usual

## ANSWER THESE

1. The law of gravitation was first explained by _____ .
2. As two objects come closer together, the attraction between them gets (larger/ smaller).
3. The sun has less effect on our tides than the moon does because of the sun's _____ .
4. When the earth, sun, and moon are lined up, the gravitational forces on the earth's waters (increase/decrease).
5. During spring tides, high tide is (higher/ lower) than usual.
6. When the sun and moon are at right angles to the earth, the gravitational forces on the earth's waters (increase/decrease). This is called _____ tide.
7. During neap tides, high tide is (higher/ lower) than usual.
8. Spring tides occur (once/twice) a month during the new and full moon.

## NOW TRY THESE

Tell whether each of the following statements has to do with spring tides, neap tides, or both.

1. Occur during the full moon phase.
2. Smaller difference than usual between low and high tides.
3. High tide is very high.
4. Low tide is very low.
5. Occur during the last quarter phase of the moon.
6. High tide is lower than usual.
7. Occur during the new moon phase.
8. Occur twice a month.
9. Occur during the first quarter phase of the moon.
10. Low tide is higher than usual.

**343**

# What makes a rocket move?

**An old Chinese invention.** You may have watched a space launch on television. Satellites are placed in orbit by rocket engines. Rockets were invented by the Chinese over 800 years ago. They were used by the ancient Chinese to launch fireworks and weapons.

▶ What were rockets first used for?

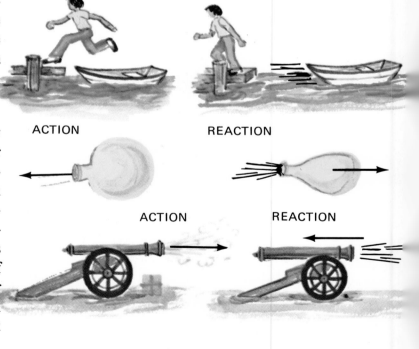

For every action, there is an equal reaction in the opposite direction.

**Where's the action?** To understand how a rocket moves, we can look at some other examples of movement. Each of the drawings shows an action and a reaction. Each time an action takes place, there is a reaction. The reaction is in the opposite direction to the action. It has the same force as the action. Isaac Newton stated the law of action and reaction. The law says that for every action, there is an equal reaction in the opposite direction. It is this law that explains how a rocket moves.

▶ What is the law of action and reaction?

344

**How does a rocket engine work?** Fuel is burned inside a rocket. It may be solid or liquid fuel. As the fuel burns, hot gases begin to expand. They create pressure inside the rocket. The hot gases are forced out of the rear of the rocket. This is the action. The rocket speeds off in the opposite direction. This is the reaction.

▶ **How is pressure created inside a rocket?**

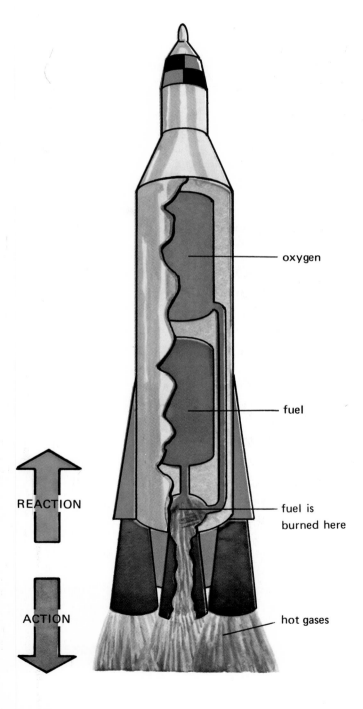

REACTION

ACTION

oxygen

fuel

fuel is burned here

hot gases

**There is no air in outer space.** Rockets need oxygen to burn fuel. There is no air in space to supply oxygen to a rocket. Rockets must carry their own oxygen. This oxygen enables a rocket to burn fuel in space.

▶ **Why do rockets have to carry their own oxygen?**

### WHAT YOU LEARNED

1. For every action, there is an equal reaction in the opposite direction.
2. The law of action and reaction explains how rockets move.
3. Rockets must carry their own supply of oxygen in space.

### ANSWER THESE

1. The first rockets were used by the
   a. Russians
   b. Americans
   c. Chinese
2. The law of action and reaction was first stated by
   a. Newton
   b. Galileo
   c. Confucius
3. Action and reaction are
   a. not related
   b. in opposite directions
   c. in the same direction
4. Rockets carry
   a. only fuel
   b. only oxygen
   c. both fuel and oxygen

### WHAT'S HAPPENING

Many schools and towns have rocket clubs. Club members learn how to make and launch rockets. The rockets are launched in safe areas set aside by the community. Adults help to launch the rockets safely. Some of the rockets carry cameras, radios, or other instruments for doing experiments. If you are interested in rockets, you might like to find out if there is a rocket club in your town.

# How can rockets travel into space?

**Down to earth.** Toss a coin into the air. The earth's gravity pulls it down again. Toss the coin harder. When you use more force, the coin moves faster. It moves higher. The greater the force on an object, the faster it moves. The faster it moves, the higher it can go.

▶ **What happens to an object's speed when there is more force on it?**

**Getting away from it all.** The force that pushes a rocket forward is called thrust. The greater the thrust, the faster and higher the rocket will go. A rocket can get started into space if it has a speed of about 40 250 kilometers per hour. Once a rocket is moving at this speed, it can escape the earth's gravity. The speed of 40 250 kilometers per hour is known as the escape velocity for a rocket on the earth.

▶ **What is the escape velocity for a rocket on the earth?**

**The multistage rocket.** A great deal of thrust is needed to reach escape velocity. This thrust can be produced only by large rockets with large amounts of fuel. Such rockets are very heavy. A multistage (MUL-tee-stayj) rocket is a heavy rocket that becomes lighter as it goes along.

The multistage rocket is actually several rocket engines fitted one on top of another. The largest engine is at the bottom. It supplies most of the thrust. This engine is fired first to lift the rocket from the ground. When its fuel is used up, the engine drops

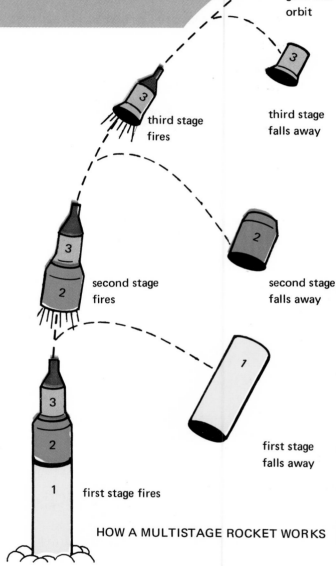

spaceship goes into orbit

third stage fires

third stage falls away

second stage fires

second stage falls away

first stage fires

first stage falls away

HOW A MULTISTAGE ROCKET WORKS

away from the rocket ship. This makes the ship lighter. Then the second engine is fired until it also uses up its fuel and drops off. Each engine thrusts the rocket ship forward and then falls away. The rocket gets lighter as its fuel is used up.

▶ **What happens to a multistage rocket as its fuel gets used up?**

**Blast off!** A rocket moves away from earth. As it moves farther away, the pull of the earth's gravity on it becomes weaker. The rocket uses little fuel out in space. There is nothing in space to slow down its motion. The rocket keeps moving because of its inertia. Fuel is needed in space only to change the rocket's speed or direction.

▶ **What is fuel needed for in space?**

## WHAT YOU LEARNED

1. The greater the force on a rocket, the faster and higher it goes.
2. If a rocket is given enough speed, it will escape from the earth's gravity.
3. Multistage rockets are used to escape the earth's gravity.
4. A rocket keeps moving in space because of its inertia.

## SCIENCE WORDS

**thrust**
   the forward force on a rocket
**escape velocity**
   the starting speed needed by a rocket to escape the earth's gravity (40 250 kilometers per hour)
**multistage** (MUL-tee-stayj) **rocket**
   a rocket with many stages

## ANSWER THESE

1. As the force on an object is increased, its speed
   a. increases
   b. decreases
   c. remains the same
2. For a rocket to travel into space, it must
   a. have wings
   b. be very light
   c. travel at the escape velocity
3. The force needed to move a rocket forward is called
   a. thrust
   b. escape velocity
   c. drag

4. The engines in a multistage rocket drop off in order to make the rocket
   a. cheaper
   b. less noisy
   c. lighter

## NOW TRY THIS

Copy the crossword puzzle onto a separate sheet of paper. Then fill in the correct words.

**Across**
2. Type of rocket
4. Ship that goes into space
6. Causes objects to fall to the earth

**Down**
1. 40 250 kilometers per hour is escape _____.
3. Keeps a rocket moving in space
5. Force that moves a rocket forward

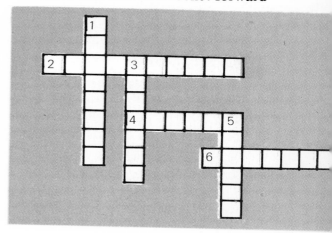

## PEOPLE IN SCIENCE

**Marguerite S. Chang**

Dr. Chang was educated in mainland China and in the United States. She has done research on rocket fuels. Among her accomplishments are several inventions. She has received a number of special awards for her achievements. In 1973 the Federal Woman's Award was presented to her for outstanding government service.

347

# How is space being explored?

The Apollo command module

**People in space.** Space can be explored by manned space ships. An example of manned exploration of space was the Apollo flights. Six of the Apollo flights landed safely on the moon. All of the astronauts on these flights returned safely to earth. Since Apollo, many unmanned space ships have been launched. These are called unmanned space probes, or just space probes. Many kinds of space exploration are best done with a space probe. The probes sent to Venus are examples. Some probes sent to Venus went down through its atmosphere. They were all destroyed by the high temperatures on the planet's surface. But they sent back important information before their destruction. We are not yet able to keep an astronaut alive on the surface of Venus. Another reason for unmanned exploration is that no supplies for astronauts need be carried. Probes can be made smaller than manned spaceships. Finally, space probes need only go on one-way trips. Manned space ships must be able to return to earth.

▶ How is Venus being explored?

**What is a space station?** So far, almost all the ships used in space have been used only once. They have either remained in space, remained on other planets, or have burned on re-entering the earth's atmosphere. This is very wasteful and expensive. The space station Skylab was built to help solve this problem. Skylab was an artificial satellite about the size of a small house. It was placed into orbit around the earth in May, 1973. Skylab stayed in orbit while different teams of astronauts visited it. It was the first space station. Astronauts in Skylab were able to stay in space for long periods of time. In November, 1973, a team of three astronauts lived in Skylab for 85 days. They were able to perform many experiments. The Skylab missions showed that people could live and work in space for long times and remain healthy.

▶ What was the first space station?

The Skylab spacecraft

**Space stations of the future.** Space shuttles are now being built. A space shuttle is a manned ship that is able to go into earth orbit and return to earth to be used again. Using the space shuttles to carry parts, large space stations may be built. Men and women will work and live in these stations. At these cities in the sky, spaceships large enough to explore the entire solar system may be built. These ships, too large to land on the earth, will cruise to the planets and return to the space station. Men and women from the space cruisers and the space station will use the space shuttle to return to earth. Perhaps some day people will be able to take cruises in space just as they take cruises on the earth now.

▶ **How might space stations be used in the future?**

An artist's idea of what a space station will look like

## WHAT YOU LEARNED

1. Space is being explored by both manned ships and unmanned probes.
2. Skylab proved that people could live and work in space for long periods of time.
3. Reusable space shuttles are being made.
4. Large space stations could be the starting place for future expeditions into space.

Space shuttles similar to the one shown here lifting off may be used to carry "commuters" between earth and space stations on a regular basis in the near future.

## ANSWER THESE

1. The Apollo flights were
   a. test flights for large gliders
   b. space stations built during the 1960's
   c. a program of manned exploration of the moon
2. One reason for the use of unmanned probes is that
   a. they can go to places where an astronaut could not go
   b. people cannot live for long periods of time in space
   c. there are not enough astronauts
3. Skylab was a
   a. space probe  b. space station
   c. Martian lander
4. The space shuttle is
   a. able to return to earth and be reused
   b. used to explore the dark side of the moon
   c. used to live in space for long periods of time

# UNIT 16 Review

*Do the following questions on a separate sheet of paper.*

**Matching**     *Write down each of the statements in Column I, leaving one line of space after each statement. On the blank line following each statement, write the word or phrase from Column II that is described by that statement.*

| Column I | Column II |
|---|---|
| 1. A force that stops motion. | ebb tides |
| 2. An oval shape. | thrust |
| 3. Turning around an axis. | neap tides |
| 4. A year that has 366 days. | ellipse |
| 5. When the sun is highest overhead. | flood tides |
| 6. The outgoing or falling tides. | friction |
| 7. The incoming or rising tides. | spring tides |
| 8. Extra high and extra low tides. | solar noon |
| 9. The forward force on a rocket. | leap year |
| 10. Tides that aren't as high or low as usual. | rotation |

*Do the following questions on a separate sheet of paper.*

**Multiple Choice**     *Write the letter of the choice that best completes the statement or answers the question.*

1. The moon has no
   a. atmosphere
   b. craters
   c. gravity

2. Only one side of the moon
   a. has craters
   b. is made of rock
   c. faces the earth

3. During the new moon phase,
   a. the moon appears ''full''
   b. we cannot see the moon
   c. we can see half the moon

4. Umbra and penumbra are scientific words for
   a. light
   b. phases of the moon
   c. regions of a shadow

5. The sun is made up mostly of
   a. hydrogen and helium
   b. hydrogen and oxygen
   c. hydrogen and nitrogen

6. Scientists have found evidence on Mars of
   a. complex life
   b. dried up rivers
   c. dead forests

7. The planet with the largest number of natural satellites is
   a. Jupiter
   b. Venus
   c. Earth

8. Most asteroids have an orbit between
   a. Venus and Mercury
   b. Neptune and Uranus
   c. Mars and Jupiter

# Jobs and Careers

# Related to Earth Science

Many jobs make use of an understanding of earth science. If you enjoy earth science, you might want to consider getting such a job. The astronomer, meteorologist, geologist, conservationist, and earth science teacher are all people whose understanding of earth science helps them in their work.

Read about the careers on the following pages. Think about your own likes and dislikes. Which of these jobs would be right for you?

Dr. Frank Field, a popular TV weather man.

A storm warning received in time could have helped this family prepare for being snowbound.

A meteorologist recording air temperatures.

# Meteorologist

A meteorologist is a weather forecaster. Today, the forecasting of the weather makes use of advanced scientific instruments, including satellites and computers. It calls for gathering facts about the atmosphere at hundreds of different places and at many altitudes.

Some meteorologists are experienced in putting all the facts together and making charts that help predict the weather. Forecasts may be made for tomorrow's weather, or they may be made for periods of a week or more ahead.

Weather forecasting is still not an exact science. Forecasts are often incorrect. Many meteorologists study the science of the atmosphere to find out what causes the weather. They are looking for theories that can be used to make forecasting more accurate.

Meteorologists are employed by many organizations besides the National Weather Service. Airlines and airports need meteorologists to check constantly on the local weather prospects. Pilots need to know such things as wind speed and direction, cloud conditions, and visibility during take-offs and landings.

Weather is of course very important to farmers and to others living in the country. Groups of farmers often hire their own meteorologists to have forecasts for their particular regions. Even the operators of ski resorts and other recreational businesses employ meteorologists to help them plan ahead.

Perhaps the most glamorous of the meteorologist's jobs is being a TV weather reporter. Some of them have millions of loyal viewers.

Preparing a detailed weather map from weather station reports.

Computers and TV screens help this meteorologist make quick and accurate weather forecasts.

# Geologist

A scientist who studies the earth is called a geologist. There are many types of geologists.

Mineralogists are geologists who study rocks and the minerals that make up rocks.

Paleontologists study fossils. Fossils tell much about what the earth was like at various times in the past.

Oceanographers study the oceans. They study the minerals dissolved in ocean water. They want to know about ocean currents, and the temperature of the water. They study the plants and animals living in the oceans. The oceans may someday be an important source of our food.

Petroleum geologists are experts in knowing where to look for gas and oil. From different kinds of observations, they are able to tell what places within the earth are most likely to contain these fuels.

Geomorphologists study features on the earth's surface and what causes these features to change. They study, for example, how mountains are formed in one area and worn away in another.

Geologists usually attend four years of college, and many study three or four years beyond college.

Jack Horner (sitting), a Princeton University paleontologist, found these fossil bones of a baby duckbill dinosaur near his family home in Montana. The other man is William Seldon, curator of Rutgers Geology Museum.

Dr. Lucky M. Force, measuring the tilt of a tree at Mt. Vernon, Virginia. The tilt of the tree was caused by movement of the earth.

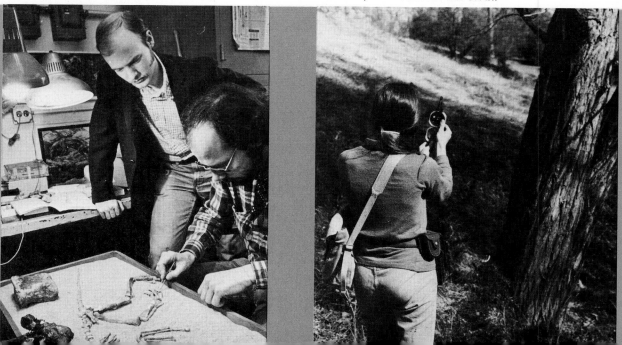

E.J. Dwornik, a geologist who works for the government, using an electron microscope. Electron microscopes help geologists study minerals.

Dr. Louis Leakey, a paleontologist who found human skulls in Africa.

Oceanographers on a research ship taking sea water samples. Many important minerals can be found in sea water.

355

# Conservationist

Conservationists are concerned with keeping the environment safe and healthy. They are also concerned with seeing that natural resources are used wisely.

Foresters are conservationists who manage woodlands. They protect trees from fire, disease, and insects. Many foresters work for the Forest Service of the federal government or a state government. Some work for a private industry, such as a company that makes paper from trees.

Soil scientists are conservationists who are experts on the subject of soils. These scientists tell farmers how to make their land better for growing crops and how to keep their land fertile. Soil scientists are also concerned with protecting land from erosion and protecting water from pollution.

Some conservationists are concerned with plants and animals. They study why certain kinds of plants and animals increase in numbers while others die out. These scientists try to save valuable kinds of plants and animals. They also try to limit the number of some kinds of plants and animals that are harmful to an environment. Too many mice, for example, may completely destroy grain crops. This kind of conservation is called wildlife management.

Conservationists generally receive training in colleges in conservation and related subjects.

A student from Washington, D. C., removing a core of wood from a tree. Much can be learned from tree cores about floods that took place in the past.

A park ranger.

# Earth Science Teacher

Science touches every part of our daily lives. The discoveries of scientists create new materials and new ways of doing things. We, and the world we live in, are constantly being affected and changed by science. In such a time, science teaching is very important and very challenging. There is always a need for good science teachers.

More and more schools are giving courses in earth science. These courses are often taught in grades 7 to 9, but may be taught in later years. Some high schools are also offering courses in astronomy, geology, and oceanography. Teachers are needed for all these courses.

Science teachers have to do much more than stand in front of a class and talk or ask questions. They must be able to perform scientific demonstrations, direct a class laboratory, handle living things, and conduct field trips. Science teachers work in an exciting world. They often make students excited about science, too.

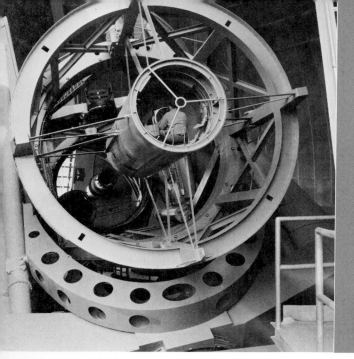

The large 200-inch telescope at the Hale Observatories. The person at the center is focusing the telescope.

Dr. Nancy G. Roman, an astronomer who works for NASA, the National Aeronautics and Space Administration. Electronic instruments, such as those she is using, are important tools for astronomers.

# Astronomer

Astronomers study planets and stars and other objects in deep space. They are interested in how the earth is related to the rest of the universe.

Some astronomers are hired to do research by the government or by a college or university. These astronomers use telescopes and electronic instruments to make observations. They study their observations to see if the observations fit a pattern. Observing the sky often means long hours of work at night and still more time working on the data produced by the observations.

While some astronomers do research, others teach astronomy to college students. Some teachers do research, too.

Still other astronomers are hired by planetariums to present astronomy programs to the public.

If you want to become an astronomer, you must have a good understanding of mathematics and physics. After college, most astronomy students spend three or four more years of study at a graduate school.

# GLOSSARY OF SCIENCE WORDS

On the following pages are the meanings of all the important science words in this book. At the end of each meaning, there are two numbers. These numbers tell you the lesson where you can find out more about the word. The first number is the Unit Number. The second number is the lesson number in that unit.

For example, look at the meaning of the first word in the glossary, **abrasion**. The numbers 5-1 tell you that you can find out more about the meaning of "abrasion" by reading lesson 1 in Unit 5.

## A

**abrasion** (uh-BRAY-zhun): The wearing away of rocks by rubbing and hitting. (5-1)

**absolute** (AB-suh-loot) **humidity:** The actual amount of water vapor in the air. (11-2)

**absolute magnitude** (AB-suh-loot MAG-nuh-tood): The amount of light a star really gives off. (14-2) (14-2)

**absorb** (ab-SORB): Take in. (8-1)

**abyssal** (uh-BIS-ul) **zone:** The deepest zone in the ocean. (9-8)

**acidic** (uh-SED-ik) **soil:** A sour soil; one lacking the elements that make a soil basic. (4-10)

**adapt** (a-DAPT): Change in order to adjust to changes in the environment. (7-4)

**air currents** (CUR-rents): Up-and-down movements of air. (10-13)

**air mass:** A large volume of air that covers a region. (11-9)

**algae** (Al-gee): Microscopic green plants. (12-5)

**amber:** Hardened pine sap. (7-3)

**anemometer** (an-uh-MOM-uh-ter): An instrument used to measure wind speed. (10-16)

**aneroid** (AN-uh-royd) **barometer:** An instrument that measures air pressure, but uses no liquid. (10-10)

**antarctica** (ant-ARK-tih-kuh): The region surrounding the South Pole, now covered by a continental glacier. (5-6)

**antenna** (an-TEN-uh): A tool used to receive radio waves. (13-2)

**anticline** (AN-tih-kline): Upward fold of rock layers. (6-6)

**anti-pollution device** (duh-VISE): Something that helps to stop pollution. (12-6)

**aphelion** (uh-FEEL-yun): The point in an orbit at which a planet is farthest from the sun. (16-3)

**aqueduct** (AK-wuh-duct): A means of sending water from one place to another. (12-5)

**arid** (A-rid) **climate:** A climate in which plants get much less rainful than they need. (11-14)

**asteroids** (AST-uh-royds): Broken chunks of rock that orbit the sun. (15-12)

**astronomer** (uh-STRON-uh-mer): A person who studies astronomy. (13-2)

**astronomical** (as-truh-NOM-ih-cul) **unit:** A unit of distance that astronomers use; it is about 150 million kilometers. (13-6)

**astronomy** (uh-STRON-uh-mee): The study of the stars and other heavenly bodies. (13-1)

**atmosphere** (AT-muh-sfeer): The air around the earth. (1-2)

**axis** (AK-sis): An imaginary line around which something spins. (15-3)

## B

**bacteria** (bac-TEER-ee-uh): Tiny organisms found in soil, water, and air. (10-2)

**banks:** The sides of a river. (5-2)

**basic** (BAYS-ik) **soil:** A sweet soil; one having a great deal of the elements calcium, magnesium, sodium, or potassium. (4-10)

**bathyal** (BATH-ee-ul) **zone:** The ocean region below the neretic zone. (9-8)

**bathyscaphe** (BATH-ih-skaf): A special boat that can dive very deep and withstand large amounts of pressure. (9-1)

**beach:** Shoreline covered by weathered rock material. (5-10)

**bed:** The bottom of a river. (5-2)

**bedrock:** The solid rock that lies under the soil. (4-5)

**benthic** (BEN-thik) **division:** The entire ocean floor. (9-8)

**benthos** (BEN-thos): Plants and animals that live on the ocean floor. (9-7)

**binary star:** Two stars that move around each other. (14-4)

**black dwarf:** A small, cold, dark body formed when a star uses up all its energy (14-3)

**black hole:** A star whose matter fell inward into a very small space. (14-4)

**breaker** (BRAY-ker): Tumbling water formed when a wave breaks. (5-8)

**breeze:** A light wind. (10-15)

**capacity** (kuh-PASS-uh-tee): The amount of material something can hold. (11-2)

**carat** (KAR-ut): A unit of mass for gems, equal to 0.2 grams. (2-11)

**carbonation** (car-buh-NAY-shun): The chemical reaction between carbonic acid and other substances. (4-3)

**cast:** A mold that has filled up with minerals. (7-2)

**centimeter** (SEN-tih-mee-ter): 1/100 of a meter. (Page 5)

**ceres** (SEER-eez): The largest asteroid. (15-12)

**chemical change:** A change in which one or more new substances are produced. (4-3)

**chemical formula** (FOR-myoo-luh): A kind of shorthand scientists use to give information about chemicals. (2-4)

**chemical symbol** (SIM-bul): A kind of shorthand used to write the names of chemical elements. (2-2)

**chemical** (KEM-ih-kuh) **weathering:** Weathering in which chemical change takes place. (4-2)

**chromosphere** (KROH-muh-sfere): The weak, red layer of the sun's atmosphere next to the photosphere. (15-9)

**cinders** (SIN-ders): Solid pieces of lava that are thrown out of a volcano. (6-5)

**cirrus** (SIR-us) **clouds:** Light and feathery clouds. (11-7)

**classification** (CLASS-i-fi-CAY-shun): Grouping things together that are alike in some way. (3-1)

**cleavage** (CLEE-vidge): The splitting of a mineral along a flat surface. (2-7)

**climate** (KLY-mut): The average weather of an area during the year. (11-13)

**coarse** (CORS) **soils:** Soils made up of large particles. (4-6)

**combined nitrogen:** Nitrogen combined chemically with other elements. (4-11)

**comet** (KOM-et): A mass of rocks and gases that orbits the sun. (15-12)

**compound** (KOM-pound): A substance made up of two or more elements. (2-3)

**concave** (CON-cave) **mirror:** A mirror that is curved inward. (13-4)

**condensation** (con-den-SAY-shun): Changing from a gas to a liquid (11-5)

**conduction** (con-DUCK-shun): A method of moving heat by contact. (10-5)

**conglomerate** (con-GLOM-er-it): Sedimentary rock made of pebbles and gravel. (3-6)

**conservation** (kon-ser-VAY-shun): Using as little of natural resources as possible in order to make them last longer. (12-1)

**constellation** (con-stuh-LAY-shun): A group of stars that forms a pattern in the sky. (13-7)

**continental** (kon-tuh-NEN-til) **glacier:** A sheet of ice large enough to cover a large part of a continent. (5-6)

**continental** (kon-tuh-NEN-til) **shelf:** The edge of the continent that slopes gently under the ocean water. (9-4)

**continental slope:** Having a slope steeper than the continental shelf, the continental slope connects the continental shelf with the ocean basin. (9-4)

**continents** (KON-tuh-nents): Very large areas of land. (6-8)

**contour interval** (CON-toor IN-ter-vul): The difference in elevation between two neighboring contour lines. (1-9)

**contour** (CON-toor) **line:** A line on a map showing points having the same elevation. (1-8)

**convection** (kon-VEK-shun) **cell:** A convection current that flows around in a loop. (6-9)

**convection** (kon-VEK-shun) **current:** The movement of material within a fluid caused by uneven temperature. (6-9) The upward movement of warm air and downward movement of cool air. (10-6)

**convex** (CON-vex) **lens:** A lens that is thicker in the middle than at the edges. (13-3)

**coquina** (coh-KEE-nuh): Sedimentary rock formed from sea shells that are cemented together. (3-5)

**core:** The center part of the earth. (1-3)

**corona:** The layer of the sun's atmosphere farthest from the sun. (15-9)

**corundum** (kuh-RUN-dum): A mineral composed of aluminum oxide. (2-11)

**cosmic** (KAHZ-mik) **rays:** Streams of particles found in atoms, which are released from solar flares. (15-8)

**crater** (CRAY-ter): A hole at the top of a volcano. (6-5) A bowl-shaped hole. (15-2)

**crescent** (CRESS-ent) **phase:** A phase of the moon in which we see less than half of the moon's face. (15-4)

**crest:** The top of a wave. (5-8)

**crust:** The thin outside layer of the earth. (1-3)

**crustal** (KRUS-tul) **plates:** The large pieces of the earth's crust. (6-9)

**crystal** (CRISS-tul): A piece of a mineral with a definite shape. (2-9)

**cumulus** (KYU-myu-lus) **clouds:** Big and puffy clouds. (11-7)

## D

**delta** (dell-tuh): A mud deposit found at the mouths of some rivers. (5-3)

**dense:** Heavy for its size. (p. 7)

**density** (DEN-suh-tee): A number describing how dense a material is. (p. 7) The mass of an object divided by its volume. (2-7)

**density currents:** Currents of water that move up and down in the ocean. (9-6)

**deposition** (dep-uh-ZISH-un): The settling of rock material where the water in a river is slowing down. (5-3)

**desert** (DEZ-ert): A very dry region. (5-7)

**desert soil:** Soil in a dry region rich in minerals but lacking humus. (4-8)

**dew:** Water that condenses on cold surfaces. (11-5)

**dew point:** Temperature at which water vapor condenses. (11-5)

**diatoms** (DY-uh-tums): Plant plankton. (9-7)

**dike:** Magma that cuts across layers of rock in the earth's crust. (6-4)

**dilute** (duh-LUTE): To make a solution weaker. (9-3)

**distorted** (dis-TORT-ed): Not showing correct distance, shape, or direction. (1-4)

**distributaries** (dih-STRIB-yoo-ter-eez): Smaller rivers that flow out of another river. (5-4)

**domed** (DOHMD) **mountain:** A mountain formed by magma pushing up the crust to form a dome shape. (6-4)

## E

**earthquake:** Sudden, strong movements in the earth's crust. (6-1)

**ebb tide:** The outgoing or falling tide. (16-9)

**echo** (EK-oh): A sound that bounces off an object. (7-1)

**echo sounder:** An instrument that uses echoes to measure ocean depths. (9-1)

**eclipse** (uh-CLIPS): What happens when one body in space blocks the sun's light from reaching another body. (15-5)

**eclipsing** (ih-KLIP-sing) **binary star:** A binary star having one star that blocks the light of the other. (14-4)

**element** (EL-uh-ment): A substance of the simplest type. (2-1)

**elevation** (el-uh-VAY-shun): The distance of a point above or below sea level. (1-8)

**ellipse** (uh-LIPS): An oval shape. (16-3)

**elliptical** (ih-LIP-tih-kul) **galaxy:** A small group of stars shaped like a round or flattened ball. (14-5)

**elliptical** (uh-LIP-tuh-cul) **orbit:** An oval-shaped path. (16-3)

**environment** (en-VY-run-ment): Everything around you. (9-8)

**epicenter** (EP-ih-sen-ter): Place on the surface of the earth directly above the focus. (6-2)

**epochs** (EP-uks): Still smaller intervals of time that recent periods of the geologic time scale are divided into. (7-5)

**eras** (ER-uhs): Five periods of time that the geologic time scale is divided into. (7-5)

**erosion** (eh-ROH-zhun): The breaking up and carrying away of materials in the earth's crust. (5-1)

**erratic** (uh-RAT-ik): A rock carried a large distance by a glacier. (5-6)

**escape velocity:** The starting speed needed by a rocket to escape the earth's gravity (40,250 kilometers per hour). (16-12)

**evaporation** (eh-vap-uh-RAY-shun): The changing of a liquid to a gas without boiling (8-1)

**explosive** (eck-SPLO-siv) **volcano:** A volcano that shoots up through the surface with great force. (6-5)

**extinct** (eck-STINCT): Something that once lived on the earth but is no longer found alive. (7-3)

**eyepiece lens:** A lens that acts like a magnifying glass. (13-3)

## F

**fault** (FAWLT): A break in the crust of the earth. (6-1)

**faulting** (FAWL-ting): Movement in the earth's crust so that one part of the ground slides past another part. (6-1)

**fault plateau:** A plateau formed when land on one side of a fault is raised up. (6-7)

**fertilizer** (FURT-uh-lie-zer): A chemical used to help plants grow. (12-5)

**fine soils:** Soils made up of small particles. (4-6)

**fissure** (FISH-er): A crack in the earth's crust. (6-5)

**flood plain:** An area alongside a river where soil is deposited during flooding. (5-4)

**flood tide:** The incoming or rising tide. (16-9)

**foam** (FOHM): Bubbles formed on a liquid. (5-8)

**focus** (FOH-kus): The place within the crust of the earth where an earthquake starts. (6-2) A point where light rays are brought together. (13-3)

**folded:** Bent and pushed upward. (6-1)

**forest soil:** Soil with a thin topsoil but in a climate wet enough to support the growth of trees. (4-8)

**fossil** (FOSS-il): Anything left behind by prehistoric life. (7-2)

**fossil fuel:** A fuel that is formed from the remains of living things. (7-6)

**fracture** (FRAC-choor): The way a mineral breaks along uneven surfaces. (2-8)

**free nitrogen:** Nitrogen that is not combined with other elements. (4-11)

**friction** (FRIC-shun): A force that stops motion. (16-1)

**front:** Surface between two air masses. (11-10)

**frost:** Ice that forms by condensation below the freezing point. (11-5)

**frost action:** Mechanical weathering caused by the freezing and melting of water. (4-2)

**fuel** (FEWL): A material that gives off heat when it is burned. (17-6)

**fuse** (FYOOZ): Combine. (15-7)

### G

**galaxy** (GAL-uhk-see): A group of many stars. (14-5)

**gem** (JEM): A cut or shaped gemstone. (2-11)

**gemstones** (JEM-stones): Minerals that show some form of beauty. (2-11)

**geologic** (jee-uh-LOJ-ik) **time scale:** A history of the earth based on observations of rocks and fossils. (7-5)

**geothermal** (jee-oh-THER-mill) **energy:** Heat within the crust of the earth. (12-3)

**geyser** (GUY-ser): The shooting out of the ground of boiling water and steam produced by geothermal energy. (12-3)

**giant stars:** Very bright, large stars that are fairly cool. (14-2)

**gibbous** (GIB-bus) **phase:** A phase of the moon in which we see more than half of the moon's face. (15-4)

**glacier** (GLAY-sher): A moving river of ice and snow. (5-5)

**gneiss** (NICE): A metamorphic rock with bands of minerals. (3-8)

**gnomon** (NOH-mun): The pointer of a sundial. (16-8)

**gram:** A unit of mass in the metric system. (Page 3)

**grassland soil:** Soil with rich topsoil and enough rainfall to support the growth of many kinds of plants. (4-8)

**gravitational attraction** (grav-uh-TAY-shun-al uh-TRAC-shun): A force that exists between all objects in the universe. (16-2)

**gravity** (GRAV-uh-tee): A force that pulls all objects toward the earth. (16-2)

**ground water:** Water that sinks into the crust of the earth and collects there. (8-3)

**gully** (GUL-ee): A deep groove in the ground. (5-12)

**guyot** (GEE-oh): A seamount with a flat top. (9-4)

### H

**H-R diagram:** A chart that describes the colors of the stars and the amount of light they give off. (14-2)

**hard water:** Water that contains calcium or magnesium salts. (8-5)

**hemisphere** (HEM-uh-sfeer): One half of a globe or sphere. (1-5)

**horizontal** (hor-uh-ZONT-ul) **movement:** Moving across the surface of the earth. (10-13)

**humid** (HYOO-mid) **climate:** A climate in which plants get more rainfall than they need. (11-14)

**humidity** (hyoo-MID-uh-tee): Amount of water vapor in the air. (11-2)

**humus** (HYOO-mus): Material formed from the decaying remains of animals and plants. (4-5)

**hydration** (high-DRAY-shun): The chemical reaction between water and other substances. (4-3)

**hydroelectric** (HY-droh-ih-LEK-trik) **plant:** A place where moving water is used to produce electricity. (12-2)

**hydrogen** (HY-druh-jen): The element that combines with oxygen to make water. (2-1)

**hydrologist** (hy-DRAHL-uh-jist): A scientist who studies the water on the earth. (8-4)

**hydrology** (hy-DRAHL-ul-jee): The study of water on the earth. (8-4)

**hydrosphere** (HY-dro-sfeer): The part of the earth's surface covered by water. (1-2)

**hypothesis** (hy-POTH-uh-sis): A guess based on accurate observations. (1-1)

### I

**identify** (eye-DEN-ti-fy): Tell what something is. (2-6)

**igneous** (IG-nee-us) **rocks:** Rocks formed from the cooling of hot, melted materials. (3-1)

**immature** (im-uh-TYOOR) **soil:** Younger soils lacking a subsoil. (4-7)

**impression:** A shape left in something by an object. (7-2)

**inertia** (in-ER-shuh): The property of objects that makes them resist changes in motion. (16-1)

**instrument** (IN-struh-ment): Something that helps our senses make accurate observations. (1-1)

**ion** (EYE-on): A charged particle. (10-3)

**ionosphere** (eye-ON-uh-sfeer): An upper level of the atmosphere that has ions and reflects radio waves. (10-3)

**irregular** (ih-REG-yoo-ler) **galazy:** A small group of stars with no definite shape. (14-5)

**isobar** (EYE-suh-bar): Line drawn on a weather map connecting points of equal air pressure. (11-12)

**K**

**kilogram** (KILL-uh-gram): 1000 grams. (Page 3)

**kilometer** (KILL-uh-mee-ter): 1000 meters. (Page 5)

**kinetic** (ki-NET-ik) **energy:** The energy of motion. (12-2)

**L**

**lagoon** (luh-GOON): Water between an offshore bar and the mainland. (5-10)

**latitude** (LAT-uh-tood): The number of degrees by which a place on earth is north or south of the equator. (1-6)

**lava** (LAH-vuh): Magma that comes through the earth's surface. (3-2)

**leaching** (LEECH-ing): The movement of minerals downward away from the topsoil. (4-8)

**leap year:** A year that has 366 days, instead of 365. (16-7)

**leeward** (LEE-werd) **side:** The side of a mountain or hill away from the wind. (5-7)

**light-year:** The distance light can travel in one year; one light-year equals about 10 trillion kilometers. (13-6)

**limestone** (LIME-stone): A sedimentary rock made of calcite. (3-4)

**liter** (LEE-ter): 1000 cubic centimeters. (Page 5)

**lithosphere** (LITH-o-sfeer): The solid part of the earth. (1-2)

**longshore current:** Flow of water parallel to the shoreline. (5-10)

**longitude** (LON-jih-tood): The number of degrees by which a place on earth is east or west of the prime meridian. (1-6)

**lunar** (LOO-ner) **eclipse:** An eclipse of the moon. (15-5)

**luster** (LUSS-ter): The amount of shininess of a mineral or object. (2-6)

**M**

**magma** (MAG-muh): Melted rocks and minerals inside the earth. (3-2)

**magnetite** (MAG-nuh-tite): A mineral that is attracted to a magnet. (2-9)

**magnitude** (MAG-nih-tood): A measure of the brightness a star appears to have. (14-1)

**main sequence** (SEE-kwens) **stars:** Most of the stars we see, which fall along one line in an H-R diagram. (14-2)

**mammals** (MAM-uls): A group of animals to which humans, whales, seals, and porpoises belong. (9-7)

**mammoth** (MAM-uth): An ancient woolly elephant. (7-3)

**mantle** (MAN-tull): The thick layer of the earth just under the crust. (1-3)

**manure** (muh-NYOOR): Waste from animals. (4-9)

**map projection** (pruh-JEK-shun): Flat map made with the help of a globe. (1-5)

**map scale:** A map feature that tells how map distances compare to real distances on earth. (1-7)

**map symbols** (SIM-buls): Simple drawings used on a map to represent real objects. (1-7)

**marine** (muh-REEN): Living in the ocean. (9-7)

**maritime** (MAR-uh-timne): Having to do with the sea. (11-9)

**matter:** Anything that takes up space and has mass. (8-1)

**mature** (muh-TYOOR) **soil:** Older soils having all three horizons. (4-7)

**meanders** (mee-AN-ders): Curved loops in a river. (5-4)

**mechanical** (muh-KAN-ih-kul) **weathering:** Weathering in which chemical change does not take place. (4-2)

**mercury barometer** (buh-ROM-uh-ter): An instrument that uses a column of mercury to measure air pressure. (10-10)

**meridians** (muh-RID-ee-uns): Imaginary lines running from the North Pole to the South Pole. (1-6)

**metamorphic** (met-uh-MOR-fic) **rocks:** Rocks formed when other rocks are put under great heat and pressure. (3-1) Rocks formed by changes in other rocks. (3-7)

**meteor** (MEE-tee-or): A rock that enters the earth's atmosphere. (15-12)

**meteorite** (MEE-tee-or-ite): A meteor that hits the earth's surface. (15-12)

**meteorologist** (meet-ee-uh-ROL-uh-jist): A weather scientist. (11-11)

**meter** (MEE-ter): The unit of length in the metric system. (Page 5)

**metric system** (MEH-trick SIS-tem): The units of measurement used by scientists. (Paged 3)

**Mid-Atlantic Ridge:** A large underwater mountain range running down the middle of the Atlantic Ocean. (6-10)

**middle-latitude:** Between the low latitudes near the equator and the high latitudes near the poles. (11-14)

**Milky Way galaxy:** A spiral galaxy containing the moon, the sun and all its planets, and all the stars we can see with the unaided eye. (14-6)

**millimeter** (MILL-ih-mee-ter): 1/1000 of a meter. (Page 5)

**mineral** (MIN-uh-rul): A material found in the crust of the earth. (2-5)

**mixed layer:** A layer of water in the ocean next to the surface where the water is well mixed. (9-2)

**Mizar** (MY-zar): The binary star in the handle of the Big Dipper. (14-4)

**model** (MOD-ul): Something that represents the real thing (1-4)

**mold:** A hardened impression left by an object. (7-2)

**molten** (MOLE-ten): Melted. (3-2)

**monsoon** (mon-SOON): Wind that changes direction with the seasons. (10-15)

**moraine** (mor-AIN): A long hill made of loose material carried and then left by a glacier. (5-5)

**mountain:** Mound of land whose elevation is at least 600 meters higher than the surrounding land. (6-6)

**mouth:** The place where a river ends. (5-2)

**multistage** (MUL-tee-stayj) **rocket:** A rocket with many stages. (16-12)

### N

**natural gas:** A gas found in the earth's crust. (7-6)

**natural resources:** Materials from the earth that are needed for life. (12-1)

**navigator** (NAV-ih-gate-er): A person who is trained to guide a ship or airplane from one place to another. (13-1)

**neap** (NEEP) **tides:** Tides that are not as high or as low as usual. (16-10)

**nebula** (NEB-yoo-luh): A large cloud of gas and dust that reflects light. (14-5)

**nekton** (NEK-ton): Free-swimming sea animals. (9-7)

**neritic** (nuh-RIT-ik) **zone:** The ocean region from the shore to the end of the continental shelf. (9-8)

**neutral** (NOO-trul) **soil:** A soil that is neither acidic nor basic. (4-10)

**neutrons** (NEW-trons): Density packed particles that make up pulsars. (14-4)

**nitrogen-fixing bacteria:** Bacteria that are able to change free nitrogen to combined nitrogen. (4-11)

**nova** (NOH-vuh): A very bright star formed when a red giant explodes off its outer layer. (14-3)

**nuclear energy:** Energy from the splitting of atoms. (12-3)

**nuclear** (NOO-clee-er) **reaction:** A reaction in which the nuclei of atoms change. (15-7)

**nucleus** (NEW-klee-us): The center of the Milky Way galaxy, made up of about 80 billion stars. (14-6)

### O

**objective** (ob-JEC-tiv) **lens:** A lens that collects light and brings it to a focus. (13-3)

**observation** (ob-zer-VAY-shun): A fact about our surroundings obtained by using our senses. (1-1)

**ocean currents** (KUR-ents): Rivers of water flowing through the ocean. (9-6)

**ocean trench:** A deep ditch in the ocean. (6-10)

**ocean-floor spreading:** The widening of an ocean. (6-10)

**oceanographer** (oh-shun-OG-ruh-fur): A scientist who studies the oceans. (9-1)

**offshore bar** (barrier beach): Deposit of sand sticking out of the water and running parallel to the shoreline. (5-10)

**ooze:** Ocean basin sediments formed from the shells and skeletons of microscopic life. (9-5)

**orbital velocity** (OR-buh-tul vuh-LOS-uh-tee): The speed at which a planet travels along its orbit. (16-3)

**ore** (OR): A mineral that has a large amount of metal in it. (2-10)

**organic** (or-GAN-ik) **fertilizers:** Fertilizers from the decay of dead animal and plant life. (4-9)

**organic** (or-GAN-ik) **material:** The material making up things that are now alive or were once alive. (4-5)

**organism** (OR-gun-ism): A living thing. (9-7)

**oxbow lake:** A lake formed from what was once a section of a meandering river. (5-4)

**oxidation** (ok-suh-DAY-shun): The chemical reaction between oxygen and other substances. (4-3)

**oxygen** (OK-sih-jen): The element that combines with hydrogen to make water. (2-1)

**ozone** (OH-zone): A form of oxygen in the air that stops ultraviolet light rays. (10-3)

## P

**parallels** (PAR-uh-lels): Imaginary lines running horizontally around the earth. (1-6)

**parent material:** The pieces of rock that break away from bedrock. (4-5)

**partial** (PAR-shul) **solar eclipse:** An eclipse of the sun in which only part of the sun's face is darkened. (15-6)

**particle** (PAR-tih-kul): A small piece of a solid material. (3-4)

**pelagic** (puh-LAJ-ik) **division:** The waters of the ocean. (9-8)

**pendulum** (PEN-dyuh-lum): A weight on a string that swings back and forth. (16-4)

**penumbra** (peh-NUM-bruh): The lighter shadow around an umbra. (15-5)

**perihelion** (per-uh-HEEL-yun): The point in an orbit at which a planet is closest to the sun. (16-3)

**periods:** Smaller intervals of time that some eras of the geologic time scale are divided into. (7-5)

**pesticide** (PES-tuh-side): A chemical used to destroy pests, such as rats, mice, and harmful insects. (12-5) Chemicals that kill insects and weeds. (12-6)

**petroleum** (puh-TRO-lee-um): A liquid fossil fuel; crude oil. (7-6)

**phase:** A state that matter can exist in. (8-1)

**phases:** (FAY-ziz): Changes we see in the moon's shape. (15-4)

**photosphere** (FOH-tuh-sfere): The innermost layer of the sun's atmosphere. (15-8)

**photosynthesis** (foh-toh-SIN-thuh-sis): The use of sunlight by plants to make food. (15-1)

**physical** (FIX-uh-kul) **change:** A change that does not change the properties of a substance. (4-1)

**physical properties** (FIZ-uh-kul PROP-er-teez): Facts about an object that help identify it. (2-6)

**plain:** Large, flat area whose elevation differs little from that of the surrounding area. (6-7)

**planet** (PLAN-et): A large body that moves around the sun. (15-10)

**plankton** (PLANK-tun): Tiny floating marine organisms. (9-7)

**plateau** (pla-TOH): Large, flat area whose elevation on at least one side is sharply higher than that of the surrounding area. (6-7)

**polar** (POH-ler): Having to do with the areas around the North and South Poles. (11-9)

**pollutant** (puh-LOOT-ent): Material that makes the environment dirty. (12-4)

**pores:** Tiny openings or cracks in rocks or soil that water and air can get into. (8-3)

**potential** (puh-TEN-shul) **energy:** Stored energy. (12-2)

**precipitation** (pruh-sip-uh-TAY-shun): Falling of water or ice formed by condensation. (11-6)

**prehistoric** (PREE-his-TAHR-ic): Before the written history of people on earth. (7-2)

**preserve** (pre-ZERVE): Keep something as it is. (7-3)

**pressure** (PRESH-ur): A pressing force. (3-7)

**prominence** (PROM-uh-nuns): A flamelike cloud of gas that shoots up from the chromosphere. (15-9)

**promontory** (PRAHM-un-tor-ee): A section of hard rock that sticks out into the ocean. (5-9)

**properties** (PROP-er-teez): Facts about a substance that help to describe it. (2-3)

**psychrometer** (sy-CROM-uh-ter): An instrument used to find relative humidity. (11-4)

**pulsar** (PUHL-sohr): A small star that gives off little light but sends out radio waves. (14-4)

**pulsating** (PUHL-sayt-ing) **star**, or **cepheid** (SEEF-ee-id): A variable star that changes in size and brightness in a regular manner. (14-4)

## Q

**quartz** (KWORTZ): A mineral made of silicon dioxide. (2-5)

**quasar** (KWAY-sahr): A large group of faraway stars that send out energy in the form of radio waves and light. (14-4)

**quiet volcano:** A volcano formed when lava flows freely through the surface. (6-5)

## R

**radiant** (RAY-dee-unt) **energy:** Energy that can travel through empty space. (10-4)

**radiation** (RAY-dee-AY-shun): Giving off radiant energy. (10-4)

**red giant** (supergiant): The form a main sequence star takes for a short time after its hydrogen is used up. (14-3)

**reflecting** (rih-FLEC-ting) **telescope:** A telescope that uses a mirror to collect light. (13-4)

**refract** (ree-FRACT): To bend. (13-3)

**refracting** (ree-FRACT-ing) **telescope:** A telescope that uses only lenses. (13-3)

**region** (REE-jun): A place or area. (5-7)

**relative** (REL-uh-tiv) **humidity:** The amount of moisture in the air compared to its capacity. (11-3)

**renewable** (ree-NEW-uh-bull) **resources:** Natural resources that cannot be replaced after they are used. (12-1)

**reservoir** (REZ-er-vwarh): A large body of water used to supply drinking water. (12-5)

**residual** (rih-ZIJ-oo-ul) **soil:** A soil made up of material from the bedrock below it. (4-6)

**revolution** (reh-vuh-LOO-shun): The motion of a body traveling around another body. (15-3)

**revolve** (rih-VOLV): Move around another body. (15-3)

**Richter** (RIK-ter) **Scale:** Scale that measures how large an earthquake is. (6-3)

**ridges:** Ranges of mountains on the ocean basin. (9-4)

**rotate** (ROH-tate): Spin like a top. (10-14) Spin around an axis. (15-3)

**rotation** (roh-TAY-shun): Spinning around an axis. (15-3)

**ruby** (ROO-bee): A deep red corundum gemstone. (2-11)

**runoff** (RUN-off): Water that runs over the ground. (5-1)

### S

**saber-toothed-tiger:** An extinct animal. (7-3)

**salinity** (suh-LIN-uh-tee): The amount of salt and other dissolved minerals in ocean water. (9-3)

**sandbar:** A long underwater deposit of sand parallel to the shoreline. (5-10)

**sandstone** (SAND-stone): Sedimentary rock made of sand. (3-6)

**sapphire** (SAF-ire): A blue corundum gemstone. (2-11)

**satellite** (SAT-uh-lite): A body that moves around a larger one in space. (13-1)

**saturated** (SACH-uh-ray-tid): Filled up. (8-3) (11-3)

**schist** (SHIST): A metamorphic rock showing minerals flattened into bands or layers. (3-8)

**sea arch:** Arch formed when waves cut through a promontory. (5-9)

**sea cliffs:** Steep-faced rocks on a shoreline. (5-9)

**sea level:** The average level of water in the oceans. (1-8)

**seamount** (SEE-mount): A mountain peak that rises from the ocean floor but does not show above the ocean surface. (9-4)

**seaweed:** A kind of sea plant. (9-7)

**sediment** (SED-uh-ment): Soil and other matter that has settled to the bottom of a river. (5-4)

**sedimentary** (sed-uh-MEN-tuh-ree) **rocks:** Rocks formed by the cementing of materials together. (3-1)

**seismogram** (SIZE-muh-gram): Sheet of paper showing the wavy lines drawn by a seismograph. (6-3)

**seismograph** (SIZE-mo-graf): An instrument that measures movements in the earth's crust. (6-1)

**seismologists** (size-MAHL-uh-gists): Scientists who study earthquakes. (6-3)

**semiarid** (SEM-ee-A-rid) **climate:** A climate in which plants get less rainfall than they need. (11-14)

**sewage treatment plant:** A place where raw sewage is changed into less harmful substances. (12-6)

**shale:** Sedimentary rock made of mud and clay. (3-6)

**shallow** (SHAL-oh): Not deep. (5-8)

**shoreline features:** The different shapes of a shoreline produced by wave action. (5-9)

**sill:** Magma that flows in between the layers of rock in the earth's crust. (6-4)

**slate:** A metamorphic rock that is made from shale and that breaks in flat sheets. (3-8)

**smog:** A mixture of smoke, fog, and chemicals. (12-4)

**soil horizons** (hor-EYE-zunz): The different layers of soil. (4-7)

**soil profile** (PRO-file): A side view of the layers making up a soil. (4-7)

**solar cells:** Devices that change sunlight into electricity. (12-3)

**solar day:** The time it takes for the sun to appear at the same place twice in a row. (16-7)

**solar energy:** Energy from sunlight. (12-3)

**solar flare:** The release of energy from the outer part of the sun's atmosphere above a sunspot group. (15-8)

**solar noon:** When the shadow of a sundial's pointer is shortest, with the sun highest overhead. (16-8)

**source** (SORSS): A river's head or place where the river starts. (5-2)

**space probe:** An unmanned device sent close to the planets to make observations. (15-10)

**spectroscope** (SPEC-truh-scope): A tool used to break up light so it can be studied. (13-2)

**sphere** (SFEER): A ball or globe. (1-2)

**spiral** (SPY-rul) **galaxy:** A group of stars that is shaped like a pancake with arms branching out from the center. (14-5)

**splash zone:** The area where the waves crash into the shore. (9-8)

**spring tides:** Extra high tides and extra low tides. (16-10)

**stack:** Tiny rock island formed when the top of a sea arch falls into the sea. (5-9)

**star trails:** Lines on photographs of the stars that are caused by the motion of the earth when a time exposure is made. (16-4)

**station model:** A record of weather information at a weather station. (11-11)

**stationary** (STAY-shun-er-ee): Not moving. (11-10)

**stationary front:** Front that does not move. (11-10)

**stratosphere** (STRAT-uh-sfeer): The second layer of the atmosphere, where the temperature does not change much and where there is much ozone. (10-3)

**stratus** (STRAT-us) **clouds:** Clouds that form a sheet across the sky. (11-7)

**streak** (STREEK): The powder a mineral leaves when it is rubbed. (2-7)

**subhumid** (SUB-hyoo-mid) **climate:** A climate in which plants get just enough rainfall. (11-14)

**subscripts** (SUB-SKRIPTS): Numbers appearing slightly below the line in chemical formulas. (2-4)

**subsoil:** Name given to horizon B, the layer below the topsoil. (4-7)

**sunspot:** A dark, cooler area of the sun's surface that appears to move. (15-8)

**sunspot group:** Several sunspots in an area formed by the break-up of one sunspot. (15-8)

**supergiants:** Very large stars. (14-2)

**supernova** (SUE-per-NOH-vuh): A star of very great brightness formed when a red giant blows up with very great force. (14-3)

**surf:** The foamy water made from breakers. (5-8)

**swamp:** An area of shallow water where a lot of plant life grows. (7-6)

**syncline** (SIN-kline): Downward fold of rock layers. (6-6)

T

**telescope** (TEL-uh-scope): A tool used to study distant objects. (13-2)

**terminal** (TURM-i-nul) **moraine:** A long hill of loose material formed at the front end of a glacier. (5-5)

**texture** (TEKS-cher): The size of the crystals in a rock. (3-3) The size of particles making up a soil. (4-6)

**theory of continental** (kon-tuh-NEN-tul) **drift:** A theory that states that the continents have been moving and still are moving. (6-8)

**theory of plate tectonics** (tek-TON-iks): A theory that states that the earth's crust is cracked to form about 20 large pieces. (6-9)

**thermocline** (THER-muh-kline): A layer of water in the ocean below the mixed layer where the water temperature drops sharply with depth. (9-2)

**thermonuclear fusion** (ther-moh-NOO-clee-er FYOO-zhun): A reaction in which the nuclei of atoms combine. (15-7)

**thrust:** The forward force on a rocket. (16-12)

**tidal energy:** Energy of the moving water of the tides. (12-3)

**tides:** The daily changes in the level of the earth's waters. (16-9)

**topographic** (top-uh-GRAF-ik) **map:** A land map that uses contour lines to show elevations. (1-9)

**topsoil:** Name given to horizon A, the top layer. (4-7)

**total solar** (SOH-ler) **eclipse:** An eclipse of the sun in which the sun's entire face is darkened. (15-6)

**transmit** (trans-MIT): Allow to pass through. (10-4)

**transpiration** (trans-puh-RAY-shun): The process by which plants give off water vapor to the atmosphere. (11-1)

**transported** (trans-POR-tid) **soil:** A soil made of material that did not come from the bedrock below it. (4-6)

**transverse** (trans-VURS) **wave:** A wave causing the particles of matter the wave passes through to move from side to side as the wave moves forward. (6-2)

**tremor** (TREM-er): A slight shaking of the earth's crust. (6-1)

**trenches:** Very deep canyons in the ocean basin. (9-4)

**tributaries** (TRIB-yoo-ter-eez): Smaller rivers that flow into a larger river. (5-4)

**trilobites** (TRY-lo-bites): Animals that lived in the oceans about 600 million years ago. (7-5)

**tropical** (TROP-uh-kul): Having to do with the warm regions near the equator. (11-9, 11-14)

**tropics** (TROP-iks): Region near the equator where it is hot and damp. (6-8)

**tropopause** (TROPE-uh-pawz): The top of the troposphere, where the troposphere ends. (10-3)

**troposphere** (TROPE-uh-sfeer): The lowerst layer of the atmosphere, where weather occurs. (10-3)

**trough** (TROFF): The bottom of a wave. (5-8)

**tundra** (TUN-druh): Soil in a cold climate with thin A and B horizons. (4-8)

U

**umbra** (UM-bruh): The dark part of a shawdow. (15-5)

**undertow:** Backward flow of water after a wave splashes on the shore. (5-10)

**unit** (YOU-nit): An amount that is used to measure things. (Page 3)

**universal** (you-nuh-VER-sul): Worldwide, throughout the world. (2-2)

**uranium** (you-RAY-nee-um): A radioactive element found in many igneous rocks. (7-5)

## V

**variable** (VAIR-ee-uh-bul) **star:** A star that shows a large change in brightness. (14-4)

**volcanic** (vol-CAN-ic) **cone:** A mountain built up around the opening of a volcano. (6-5)

**volcano** (vol-CAY-no): An opening in the earth's crust from which lava comes out. (6-5)

**volcanism** (VOL-ca-nism): Movement of molten rock on or inside the earth's crust. (6-4)

## W

**water cycle** (SY-cul): The movement of water into and out of the atmosphere. (5-1)

**water table:** The top level of saturated rock in the ground. (8-3)

**water vapor** (VAY-per): Molecules of water in the air. (10-11)

**wave-cut terrace** (TER-is): A flat section of rock remaining when the rock above was worn away by wave action. (5-9)

**weathering:** The breaking down and wearing away of rocks. (4-2)

**weather vane:** Instrument used to measure wind direction. (10-16)

**weathering** (WETH-uh-ring): The breaking down of materials in the crust of the earth. (4-2)

**white dwarfs:** Hot, very small stars. (14-2)

**winds:** Horizontal movements of air. (10-13)

**windward** (WIND-werd) **side:** The side of a mountain or hill facing the wind. (5-7)

# INDEX

## A

**abbreviating units**, 5
**absolute humidity**, 227
**abrasion**, of rocks, 97
**acid test**, for calcite, 47, 63
**acidic soils**, 88
**action**, and reaction, 344-345
**Adirondack Mountains**, 128
**aeration**, and water treatment, 169
**Agassiz**, Louis, 107
**age**, of Earth, 144
**air**, 190-193
**air conditioning**, 229
**air currents**, 214
**air masses**, 240-243
**air pollution**, 260, 265
**air pressure**, 204-213
    amount of, 206-207
    and altitude, 209
    and regions of the earth, 212-213
    and station models, 245
    and temperature, 210
    and water vapor, 211
    changes in, 210-211
    direction of, 204-205
**algae**, and pollution, 263
**altimeter**, 209
**altitude**
    and air pressure, 209
    and climate, 248
**amber**, fossils in, 149
**amplifiers**, 10
**Anchorage**, Alaska,
    earthquake at, 122
**anemometer**, 220
**aneroid barometer**, 208
**animals**
    extinct, 148, 150
    ocean, 184
    prehistoric, 146
**Antarctica**, 106
**antenna**, 270
**aphelion**, 328
**Apollo space flights**, 348
**aquarium**, 185
**aqueducts**, 262
**Archimedes**, 43
**area**, 2-5
**arid climates**, 250
**Arizona**, 321
**asbestos**, fracture of, 44
**asteroids**, 320
**astronomer**, 270
**astronomical unit**, 278

**astronomy**, 268-281
**Atlantic Ocean**, 140
**atmosphere**, 13, 190-195
    heating of, 198-201
**axis**, 302
    of earth, 330, 232

## B

**bacteria**, 92, 193
**balloons**, weather, 220
**barometers**, 208-209
**basic soils**, 88
**basins of the oceans**, 178, 180
**bathyscaphe**, 172
**bauxite**, 48
**beach**, formation of, 111
**bedrock**, 80, 82
**Betelgeuse**, 281
**bicarbonates**, 167
**Big Dipper**, 280
**bodies of water**, and climate, 248
**bottle**, found in the ocean, 182
**breakers**, 111
**Bromery**, Randolph, 145
**bromthymol blue**, 89
**burning**, 192

## C

**calcite**, 40, 41, 48
    and shells, 62
    test for, 47
**calcium carbonate**, 62
**canals**, on Mars, 281
**Canyon Diablo**, 321
**canyons**, 100
**carats**, 50-51
**carbon**, 30
    and charcoal, 154
    and dating of remains of life, 144
**carbon dioxide**, 193
    and pollution, 261
    and weathering, 75
    on Venus, 316
**carbonates**, 167
**Cassiopeia**, 280
**cast**, a kind of fossil, 147
**caves**, limestone, 65
**cell**, convection, 138
**centimeter**, 4-5
**Central Park**, 106
**Ceres**, 320
**chalk cliffs**, 63
**Chang**, Marguerite S., 347
**changes**, in rocks, 66-69, 74-77
**charcoal**, 154
**chasms**, 100

**chemical changes**, 72-73, 298
    in rocks, 66
**chemical formulas**, 36
**chemical symbols**, 32
**chemical weathering**, 77
**chemicals**
    and weather pollution, 262
    in the soil, 88
**chlorination**,
    and water treatment, 169
**cinders**, 130
**cirrus clouds**, 236
**classification**, 54
**classifying climates**, 250
**classifying rocks**, 54
**clay**, 83
**cleavage**, of mineral, 44
**climates**, 248-251
    kinds of, 250
**clouds**
    formation of, 234
    kinds of, 236-237
**coagulation**,
    and water treatment, 168
**coal**, formation of, 154
**cold front**, 242, 246
**color**
    of a mineral, 40
    on maps, 23, 27
**combined nitrogen**, 92
**comets**, 320
**compacting soils**, 83
**compounds**, chemical, 30-31
**concave mirror**, 274
**concrete**, 60
**condensation**, 232
**conduction**, 198
**conglomerate**, 64
**conservation**, of soil, 97, 109
**constellations**, 280-281
**continental air masses**, 240-241
**continental drift**, 136
**continental glacier**, 106
**continental shelf**, 178, 180
**continental slope**, 178, 180
**continents**, 136
**contour intervals**, 26
**contour lines**, 24
**contour map**, 25
**contour plowing**, 25
**convection**, 200-201
**convection cell**, 138
**convection currents**, 138
**convex lens**, 272
**coquina**, 62
**coral**, 67
**core**, of earth, 15

## H

**hail**, 235
**halite**, 46, 61
**Halley's Comet**, 320
**hard water**, 166
**hardness**, of a mineral, 41
**Hawaiian Islands**, 130, 179
**heads of early people**, 151
**heat**
    and chemical changes
    in rocks, 68
    and the earth, 196-201
**helium**, in sun, 311
**hematite**, 42, 48
**hemisphere**, 18
**hemispheres**, Magdeburg, 207
**high-pressure regions**, 216
**highs**, 246
**horse**, changes in, 150
**human fossils**, 149
**humid climates**, 250
**humidity**, 226
**humus**, 81, 93
**hurricanes**, 111
**hydrogen**, 30
**hydrosphere**, 12
**hygrometer**, 227
**hypothesis**, 11

## I

**ice**
    and glaciers, 104
    and preservation of fossils, 148
**ice age**, 106-107
**ice sheet**, 106
**icebergs**, 105, 180
**identification**
    of minerals, 40, 116
    of rocks, 58, 64, 68-69
**igneous rocks**, 54, 57, 58, 129
**image**, in telescope, 272
**impressions**, fossil, 147
**inertia**, 324-325
**inner core**, of earth, 15
**inner planets**, 316-317
**insect fossils**, 149
**instruments**
    aids to observation, 10
    for studying oceans, 173
**intelligent life in space**, 349
**International Bureau of Weights
    and Measures**, 3
**interval**, contour, 26
**ionosphere**, 194-195
**ions**, 195
**isobars**, 246

## J

**jet streams**, 215
**jetties**, 111
**jewels**, in watches, 51
**jigsaw puzzle**, 136-137
**Jupiter**, 316-318

## K

**kilogram**, 3

## L

**lakes**, glacial, 106
**land**, 13
    heating and cooling of, 202-203
**land breezes**, 218
**land shapes and
    running water**, 100-101
**latitude**, 20
    and climate, 248
**lava**, 54, 57, 128, 130
**layers**
    in sedimentary rocks, 122
    of the atmosphere, 194-195
**leaching**, 88
**Leakey**, Dr. Louis, 149
**Leakey**, Mary Nicol, 149
**leap year**, 336
**leeward side**, 109
**leeward side of mountains**, 249
**length**, 2-5
**life**
    found in the soil, 92-93
    history of, 151, 153
    in the oceans, 184
**light**, speed of, 278
**light-year**, 278
**limestone**, 61, 62, 64, 67, 69
**limestone caves**, 64
**liquids**, volume of, 5
**liter**, 5
**lithosphere**, 13
**Little Dipper**, 280
**loam**, 83
**local winds**, 218-219
**lodestone**, 46
**longitude**, 20-21
**long-wave radiation**, 199
**lows**, 246
**low-pressure regions**, 216
**lunar eclipses**, 306-307
**luster**, 40

## M

**Magdeburg Hemispheres**, 207
**magma**, 56, 66, 128-129, 140
**magnetic stripes**, 179
**magnetism**, and minerals, 46

**magnetite**, 46
**magnets**, natural, 46
**magnitude**, of stars, 284
**mammals**, ocean, 185
**mammoth**, 148
**man**, early, 151
**mantle**, 14
**map projections**, 18
**map scale**, 16, 22
**map symbols**, 23
**maps**, 16-27
    color on, 23, 27
    contour, 25
    topographic, 26
    weather, 246-247
**marble**, 67-69
**marine life**, 184
**maritime air masses**, 240
**Mars**, 316-317
**mass**, 2-3, 43
**meandering rivers**, 100
**measuring**, 2-5
**Mercury**, 316-317
**mercury**, and pollution, 284
**mercury barometer**, 208
**meridians**, 20
**message on Pioneer X**, 319
**metamorphic rocks** 54, 66, 68-69
**meteorologists**, 244
**meteorites**, 180, 320
**meteors**, 320
**metric system**, 2-5
**mica**, 44, 48, 58
**Mid-Atlantic Ridge**, 140
**middle-latitude climate**, 250
**millibars**, 245
**millimeter**, 4-5
**Milky Way Galaxy**, 349
**minerals**, 38-51
    identification of, 40-47
    in the ocean, 116-117
    uses of, 48-49
**mirrors**, in telescopes, 274-275
**model**, 16
**molds**, fossil, 147
**molecules**, and air pressure, 206
**monsoons**, 218
**month**, 337
**moon**, 300-307
    and tides, 340-343
    and time, 337
    eclipses of, 306-307
    first landing on, 300
    motions of, 302-303
    phases of, 304-305
    size of, 300
    surface of, 272, 300

PHOTOGRAPH CREDITS

Photographs on the following pages by George A. Bakacs:
    167, 190, 196, 224, 230, 232, 262 (top), 263, 299, 306

Photographs on the following pages by Edward M. Steele:
    6, 34, 35, 58 (top and bottom), 74 (top and bottom), 75, 76, 77, **79, 84, 106 (top)**,
    151, 158, 236 (bottom left), 254, 255 (bottom), 257 (bottom), 258 (bottom), 259,
    264 (bottom), 265, 320 (bottom)

Photographs on the following pages by Dennis DiCicco/Peter Arnold Inc.
    286, 292 (top, bottom), 293, 294, 295, 312 (top, bottom), 313